# INSTRUCTOR'S SOLUTIONS MANUAL

## INTRODUCTION TO QUANTUM MECHANICS

### SECOND EDITION

# DAVID J. GRIFFITHS

*Reed College*

PEARSON
Prentice Hall

Upper Saddle River, NJ 07458

Associate Editor: Christian Botting
Senior Editor: Erik Fahlgren
Editor-in-Chief, Science: John Challice
name_9 Vice President of Production & Manufacturing: David W. Riccardi
Executive Managing Editor: Kathleen Schiaparelli
Assistant Managing Editor: Becca Richter
Production Editor: Dana Dunn
Supplement Cover Manager: Paul Gourhan
Supplement Cover Designer: Joanne Alexandris
Manufacturing Buyer: Ilene Kahn

© 2005 Pearson Education, Inc.
Pearson Prentice Hall
Pearson Education, Inc.
Upper Saddle River, NJ 07458

The author and publisher of this book have used their best efforts in preparing this book. These efforts include the development, research, and testing of the theories and programs to determine their effectiveness. The author and publisher make no warranty of any kind, expressed or implied, with regard to these programs or the documentation contained in this book. The author and publisher shall not be liable in any event for incidental or consequential damages in connection with, or arising out of, the furnishing, performance, or use of these programs.

Printed in the United States of America

10  9  8  7  6  5  4  3  2  1

ISBN 0-13-111893-5

Pearson Education Ltd., *London*
Pearson Education Australia Pty. Ltd., *Sydney*
Pearson Education Singapore, Pte. Ltd.
Pearson Education North Asia Ltd., *Hong Kong*
Pearson Education Canada, Inc., *Toronto*
Pearson Educación de Mexico, S.A. de C.V.
Pearson Education—Japan, *Tokyo*
Pearson Education Malaysia, Pte. Ltd.

# Contents

# Preface

These are my own solutions to the problems in *Introduction to Quantum Mechanics, 2nd ed.* I have made every effort to insure that they are clear and correct, but errors are bound to occur, and for this I apologize in advance. I would like to thank the many people who pointed out mistakes in the solution manual for the first edition, and encourage anyone who finds defects in this one to alert me (griffith@reed.edu). I'll maintain a list of errata on my web page (http://academic.reed.edu/physics/faculty/griffiths.html), and incorporate corrections in the manual itself from time to time. I also thank my students at Reed and at Smith for many useful suggestions, and above all Neelaksh Sadhoo, who did most of the typesetting.

At the end of the manual there is a grid that correlates the problem numbers in the second edition with those in the first edition.

David Griffiths

# Chapter 1

# The Wave Function

## Problem 1.1

**(a)**

$$\langle j \rangle^2 = 21^2 = \boxed{441.}$$

$$\langle j^2 \rangle = \frac{1}{N} \sum j^2 N(j) = \frac{1}{14} \left[ (14^2) + (15^2) + 3(16^2) + 2(22^2) + 2(24^2) + 5(25^2) \right]$$

$$= \frac{1}{14} (196 + 225 + 768 + 968 + 1152 + 3125) = \frac{6434}{14} = \boxed{459.571.}$$

**(b)**

| $j$ | $\Delta j = j - \langle j \rangle$ |
|-----|-----|
| 14 | $14 - 21 = -7$ |
| 15 | $15 - 21 = -6$ |
| 16 | $16 - 21 = -5$ |
| 22 | $22 - 21 = 1$ |
| 24 | $24 - 21 = 3$ |
| 25 | $25 - 21 = 4$ |

$$\sigma^2 = \frac{1}{N} \sum (\Delta j)^2 N(j) = \frac{1}{14} \left[ (-7)^2 + (-6)^2 + (-5)^2 \cdot 3 + (1)^2 \cdot 2 + (3)^2 \cdot 2 + (4)^2 \cdot 5 \right]$$

$$= \frac{1}{14} (49 + 36 + 75 + 2 + 18 + 80) = \frac{260}{14} = \boxed{18.571.}$$

$$\sigma = \sqrt{18.571} = \boxed{4.309.}$$

**(c)**

$$\langle j^2 \rangle - \langle j \rangle^2 = 459.571 - 441 = 18.571. \quad \text{[Agrees with (b).]}$$

## Problem 1.2

(a)

$$\langle x^2 \rangle = \int_0^h x^2 \frac{1}{2\sqrt{hx}} dx = \frac{1}{2\sqrt{h}} \left( \frac{2}{5} x^{5/2} \right) \Big|_0^h = \frac{h^2}{5}.$$

$$\sigma^2 = \langle x^2 \rangle - \langle x \rangle^2 = \frac{h^2}{5} - \left( \frac{h}{3} \right)^2 = \frac{4}{45} h^2 \;\Rightarrow\; \sigma = \boxed{\frac{2h}{3\sqrt{5}} = 0.2981h.}$$

(b)

$$P = 1 - \int_{x_-}^{x_+} \frac{1}{2\sqrt{hx}} dx = 1 - \frac{1}{2\sqrt{h}} (2\sqrt{x}) \Big|_{x_-}^{x_+} = 1 - \frac{1}{\sqrt{h}} \left( \sqrt{x_+} - \sqrt{x_-} \right).$$

$$x_+ \equiv \langle x \rangle + \sigma = 0.3333h + 0.2981h = 0.6315h; \quad x_- \equiv \langle x \rangle - \sigma = 0.3333h - 0.2981h = 0.0352h.$$

$$P = 1 - \sqrt{0.6315} + \sqrt{0.0352} = \boxed{0.393.}$$

## Problem 1.3

(a)

$$1 = \int_{-\infty}^{\infty} A e^{-\lambda(x-a)^2} dx. \quad \text{Let } u \equiv x - a, \, du = dx, \, u : -\infty \to \infty.$$

$$1 = A \int_{-\infty}^{\infty} e^{-\lambda u^2} du = A\sqrt{\frac{\pi}{\lambda}} \;\Rightarrow\; \boxed{A = \sqrt{\frac{\lambda}{\pi}}.}$$

(b)

$$\langle x \rangle = A \int_{-\infty}^{\infty} x e^{-\lambda(x-a)^2} dx = A \int_{-\infty}^{\infty} (u+a) e^{-\lambda u^2} du$$

$$= A \left[ \int_{-\infty}^{\infty} u e^{-\lambda u^2} du + a \int_{-\infty}^{\infty} e^{-\lambda u^2} du \right] = A \left( 0 + a\sqrt{\frac{\pi}{\lambda}} \right) = \boxed{a.}$$

$$\langle x^2 \rangle = A \int_{-\infty}^{\infty} x^2 e^{-\lambda(x-a)^2} dx$$

$$= A \left\{ \int_{-\infty}^{\infty} u^2 e^{-\lambda u^2} du + 2a \int_{-\infty}^{\infty} u e^{-\lambda u^2} du + a^2 \int_{-\infty}^{\infty} e^{-\lambda u^2} du \right\}$$

$$= A \left[ \frac{1}{2\lambda} \sqrt{\frac{\pi}{\lambda}} + 0 + a^2 \sqrt{\frac{\pi}{\lambda}} \right] = \boxed{a^2 + \frac{1}{2\lambda}.}$$

$$\sigma^2 = \langle x^2 \rangle - \langle x \rangle^2 = a^2 + \frac{1}{2\lambda} - a^2 = \frac{1}{2\lambda}; \quad \boxed{\sigma = \frac{1}{\sqrt{2\lambda}}.}$$

**(c)**

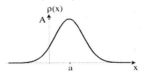

---

## Problem 1.4

**(a)**

$$1 = \frac{|A|^2}{a^2}\int_0^a x^2 dx + \frac{|A|^2}{(b-a)^2}\int_a^b (b-x)^2 dx = |A|^2 \left\{ \frac{1}{a^2}\left(\frac{x^3}{3}\right)\Big|_0^a + \frac{1}{(b-a)^2}\left(-\frac{(b-x)^3}{3}\right)\Big|_a^b \right\}$$

$$= |A|^2\left[\frac{a}{3} + \frac{b-a}{3}\right] = |A|^2\frac{b}{3} \quad \Rightarrow \quad \boxed{A = \sqrt{\frac{3}{b}}.}$$

**(b)**

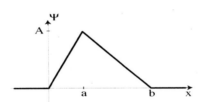

**(c)** At $\boxed{x = a.}$

**(d)**

$$P = \int_0^a |\Psi|^2 dx = \frac{|A|^2}{a^2}\int_0^a x^2 dx = |A|^2\frac{a}{3} = \boxed{\frac{a}{b}.} \begin{cases} P = 1 & \text{if } b = a, \checkmark \\ P = 1/2 & \text{if } b = 2a. \checkmark \end{cases}$$

**(e)**

$$\langle x \rangle = \int x|\Psi|^2 dx = |A|^2\left\{ \frac{1}{a^2}\int_0^a x^3 dx + \frac{1}{(b-a)^2}\int_a^b x(b-x)^2 dx \right\}$$

$$= \frac{3}{b}\left\{ \frac{1}{a^2}\left(\frac{x^4}{4}\right)\Big|_0^a + \frac{1}{(b-a)^2}\left(b^2\frac{x^2}{2} - 2b\frac{x^3}{3} + \frac{x^4}{4}\right)\Big|_a^b \right\}$$

$$= \frac{3}{4b(b-a)^2}\left[ a^2(b-a)^2 + 2b^4 - 8b^4/3 + b^4 - 2a^2b^2 + 8a^3b/3 - a^4 \right]$$

$$= \frac{3}{4b(b-a)^2}\left( \frac{b^4}{3} - a^2b^2 + \frac{2}{3}a^3b \right) = \frac{1}{4(b-a)^2}(b^3 - 3a^2b + 2a^3) = \boxed{\frac{2a+b}{4}.}$$

---

## Problem 1.5

(a)

$$1 = \int |\Psi|^2 dx = 2|A|^2 \int_0^\infty e^{-2\lambda x} dx = 2|A|^2 \left( \frac{e^{-2\lambda x}}{-2\lambda} \right)\Big|_0^\infty = \frac{|A|^2}{\lambda}; \quad \boxed{A = \sqrt{\lambda}.}$$

(b)

$$\langle x \rangle = \int x|\Psi|^2 dx = |A|^2 \int_{-\infty}^\infty x e^{-2\lambda|x|} dx = \boxed{0.} \qquad \text{[Odd integrand.]}$$

$$\langle x^2 \rangle = 2|A|^2 \int_0^\infty x^2 e^{-2\lambda x} dx = 2\lambda \left[ \frac{2}{(2\lambda)^3} \right] = \boxed{\frac{1}{2\lambda^2}.}$$

(c)

$$\sigma^2 = \langle x^2 \rangle - \langle x \rangle^2 = \frac{1}{2\lambda^2}; \qquad \boxed{\sigma = \frac{1}{\sqrt{2}\lambda}.} \qquad |\Psi(\pm\sigma)|^2 = |A|^2 e^{-2\lambda\sigma} = \lambda e^{-2\lambda/\sqrt{2}\lambda} = \lambda e^{-\sqrt{2}} = 0.2431\lambda.$$

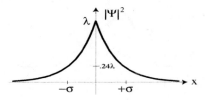

*Probability outside*:

$$2 \int_\sigma^\infty |\Psi|^2 dx = 2|A|^2 \int_\sigma^\infty e^{-2\lambda x} dx = 2\lambda \left( \frac{e^{-2\lambda x}}{-2\lambda} \right)\Big|_\sigma^\infty = e^{-2\lambda\sigma} = \boxed{e^{-\sqrt{2}} = 0.2431.}$$

## Problem 1.6

For integration by parts, the differentiation has to be with respect to the *integration* variable – in this case the differentiation is with respect to $t$, but the integration variable is $x$. It's true that

$$\frac{\partial}{\partial t}(x|\Psi|^2) = \frac{\partial x}{\partial t}|\Psi|^2 + x\frac{\partial}{\partial t}|\Psi|^2 = x\frac{\partial}{\partial t}|\Psi|^2,$$

but this does *not* allow us to perform the integration:

$$\int_a^b x\frac{\partial}{\partial t}|\Psi|^2 dx = \int_a^b \frac{\partial}{\partial t}(x|\Psi|^2)dx \neq (x|\Psi|^2)\Big|_a^b.$$

## Problem 1.7

From Eq. 1.33, $\frac{d\langle p \rangle}{dt} = -i\hbar \int \frac{\partial}{\partial t}\left(\Psi^* \frac{\partial \Psi}{\partial x}\right) dx$. But, noting that $\frac{\partial^2 \Psi}{\partial x \partial t} = \frac{\partial^2 \Psi}{\partial t \partial x}$ and using Eqs. 1.23-1.24:

$$\frac{\partial}{\partial t}\left(\Psi^* \frac{\partial \Psi}{\partial x}\right) = \frac{\partial \Psi^*}{\partial t}\frac{\partial \Psi}{\partial x} + \Psi^* \frac{\partial}{\partial x}\left(\frac{\partial \Psi}{\partial t}\right) = \left[-\frac{i\hbar}{2m}\frac{\partial^2 \Psi^*}{\partial x^2} + \frac{i}{\hbar}V\Psi^*\right]\frac{\partial \Psi}{\partial x} + \Psi^* \frac{\partial}{\partial x}\left[\frac{i\hbar}{2m}\frac{\partial^2 \Psi}{\partial x^2} - \frac{i}{\hbar}V\Psi\right]$$

$$= \frac{i\hbar}{2m}\left[\Psi^* \frac{\partial^3 \Psi}{\partial x^3} - \frac{\partial^2 \Psi^*}{\partial x^2}\frac{\partial \Psi}{\partial x}\right] + \frac{i}{\hbar}\left[V\Psi^*\frac{\partial \Psi}{\partial x} - \Psi^*\frac{\partial}{\partial x}(V\Psi)\right]$$

The first term integrates to zero, using integration by parts twice, and the second term can be simplified to $V\Psi^*\frac{\partial \Psi}{\partial x} - \Psi^* V \frac{\partial \Psi}{\partial x} - \Psi^* \frac{\partial V}{\partial x}\Psi = -|\Psi|^2 \frac{\partial V}{\partial x}$. So

$$\frac{d\langle p \rangle}{dt} = -i\hbar\left(\frac{i}{\hbar}\right)\int -|\Psi|^2 \frac{\partial V}{\partial x} dx = \langle -\frac{\partial V}{\partial x}\rangle. \qquad \text{QED}$$

---

## Problem 1.8

Suppose $\Psi$ satisfies the Schrödinger equation *without* $V_0$: $i\hbar\frac{\partial \Psi}{\partial t} = -\frac{\hbar^2}{2m}\frac{\partial^2 \Psi}{\partial x^2} + V\Psi$. We want to find the solution $\Psi_0$ with $V_0$: $i\hbar\frac{\partial \Psi_0}{\partial t} = -\frac{\hbar^2}{2m}\frac{\partial^2 \Psi_0}{\partial x^2} + (V + V_0)\Psi_0$.

*Claim:* $\Psi_0 = \Psi e^{-iV_0 t/\hbar}$.

*Proof:* $i\hbar\frac{\partial \Psi_0}{\partial t} = i\hbar\frac{\partial \Psi}{\partial t}e^{-iV_0 t/\hbar} + i\hbar\Psi\left(-\frac{iV_0}{\hbar}\right)e^{-iV_0 t/\hbar} = \left[-\frac{\hbar^2}{2m}\frac{\partial^2 \Psi}{\partial x^2} + V\Psi\right]e^{-iV_0 t/\hbar} + V_0\Psi e^{-iV_0 t/\hbar}$

$$= -\frac{\hbar^2}{2m}\frac{\partial^2 \Psi_0}{\partial x^2} + (V + V_0)\Psi_0. \qquad \text{QED}$$

This has *no* effect on the expectation value of a dynamical variable, since the extra phase factor, being independent of $x$, cancels out in Eq. 1.36.

---

## Problem 1.9

(a)

$$1 = 2|A|^2 \int_0^\infty e^{-2amx^2/\hbar}dx = 2|A|^2 \frac{1}{2}\sqrt{\frac{\pi}{(2am/\hbar)}} = |A|^2\sqrt{\frac{\pi\hbar}{2am}}; \qquad \boxed{A = \left(\frac{2am}{\pi\hbar}\right)^{1/4}.}$$

(b)

$$\frac{\partial \Psi}{\partial t} = -ia\Psi; \qquad \frac{\partial \Psi}{\partial x} = -\frac{2amx}{\hbar}\Psi; \qquad \frac{\partial^2 \Psi}{\partial x^2} = -\frac{2am}{\hbar}\left(\Psi + x\frac{\partial \Psi}{\partial x}\right) = -\frac{2am}{\hbar}\left(1 - \frac{2amx^2}{\hbar}\right)\Psi.$$

Plug these into the Schrödinger equation, $i\hbar\frac{\partial \Psi}{\partial t} = -\frac{\hbar^2}{2m}\frac{\partial^2 \Psi}{\partial x^2} + V\Psi$:

$$V\Psi = i\hbar(-ia)\Psi + \frac{\hbar^2}{2m}\left(-\frac{2am}{\hbar}\right)\left(1 - \frac{2amx^2}{\hbar}\right)\Psi$$

$$= \left[\hbar a - \hbar a\left(1 - \frac{2amx^2}{\hbar}\right)\right]\Psi = 2a^2mx^2\Psi, \quad \text{so} \quad \boxed{V(x) = 2ma^2x^2.}$$

**(c)**

$$\langle x \rangle = \int_{-\infty}^{\infty} x |\Psi|^2 dx = \boxed{0.} \qquad \text{[Odd integrand.]}$$

$$\langle x^2 \rangle = 2|A|^2 \int_0^{\infty} x^2 e^{-2amx^2/\hbar} dx = 2|A|^2 \frac{1}{2^2(2am/\hbar)} \sqrt{\frac{\pi \hbar}{2am}} = \boxed{\frac{\hbar}{4am}.}$$

$$\langle p \rangle = m \frac{d \langle x \rangle}{dt} = \boxed{0.}$$

$$\langle p^2 \rangle = \int \Psi^* \left( \frac{\hbar}{i} \frac{\partial}{\partial x} \right)^2 \Psi dx = -\hbar^2 \int \Psi^* \frac{\partial^2 \Psi}{\partial x^2} dx$$

$$= -\hbar^2 \int \Psi^* \left[ -\frac{2am}{\hbar} \left( 1 - \frac{2amx^2}{\hbar} \right) \Psi \right] dx = 2am\hbar \left\{ \int |\Psi|^2 dx - \frac{2am}{\hbar} \int x^2 |\Psi|^2 dx \right\}$$

$$= 2am\hbar \left( 1 - \frac{2am}{\hbar} \langle x^2 \rangle \right) = 2am\hbar \left( 1 - \frac{2am}{\hbar} \frac{\hbar}{4am} \right) = 2am\hbar \left( \frac{1}{2} \right) = \boxed{am\hbar.}$$

**(d)**

$$\sigma_x^2 = \langle x^2 \rangle - \langle x \rangle^2 = \frac{\hbar}{4am} \implies \boxed{\sigma_x = \sqrt{\frac{\hbar}{4am}}}; \quad \sigma_p^2 = \langle p^2 \rangle - \langle p \rangle^2 = am\hbar \implies \boxed{\sigma_p = \sqrt{am\hbar}.}$$

$$\sigma_x \sigma_p = \sqrt{\frac{\hbar}{4am}} \sqrt{am\hbar} = \frac{\hbar}{2}. \text{ This } is \text{ (just barely) consistent with the uncertainty principle.}$$

---

## Problem 1.10

From Math Tables: $\pi = 3.141592653589793238462643 \cdots$

**(a)**

| | | | | |
|---|---|---|---|---|
| $P(0) = 0$ | $P(1) = 2/25$ | $P(2) = 3/25$ | $P(3) = 5/25$ | $P(4) = 3/25$ |
| $P(5) = 3/25$ | $P(6) = 3/25$ | $P(7) = 1/25$ | $P(8) = 2/25$ | $P(9) = 3/25$ |

In general, $P(j) = \frac{N(j)}{N}$.

**(b)** *Most probable:* $\boxed{3.}$  *Median:* 13 are $\leq 4$, 12 are $\geq 5$, so median is $\boxed{4.}$

*Average:* $\langle j \rangle = \frac{1}{25}[0 \cdot 0 + 1 \cdot 2 + 2 \cdot 3 + 3 \cdot 5 + 4 \cdot 3 + 5 \cdot 3 + 6 \cdot 3 + 7 \cdot 1 + 8 \cdot 2 + 9 \cdot 3]$

$= \frac{1}{25}[0 + 2 + 6 + 15 + 12 + 15 + 18 + 7 + 16 + 27] = \frac{118}{25} = \boxed{4.72.}$

**(c)** $\langle j^2 \rangle = \frac{1}{25}[0 + 1^2 \cdot 2 + 2^2 \cdot 3 + 3^2 \cdot 5 + 4^2 \cdot 3 + 5^2 \cdot 3 + 6^2 \cdot 3 + 7^2 \cdot 1 + 8^2 \cdot 2 + 9^2 \cdot 3]$

$= \frac{1}{25}[0 + 2 + 12 + 45 + 48 + 75 + 108 + 49 + 128 + 243] = \frac{710}{25} = \boxed{28.4.}$

$\sigma^2 = \langle j^2 \rangle - \langle j \rangle^2 = 28.4 - 4.72^2 = 28.4 - 22.2784 = 6.1216; \quad \sigma = \sqrt{6.1216} = \boxed{2.474.}$

---

## Problem 1.11

(a) Constant for $0 \leq \theta \leq \pi$, otherwise zero. In view of Eq. 1.16, the constant is $1/\pi$.

$$\rho(\theta) = \begin{cases} 1/\pi, & \text{if } 0 \leq \theta \leq \pi, \\ 0, & \text{otherwise.} \end{cases}$$

(b)

$$\langle \theta \rangle = \int \theta \rho(\theta)\, d\theta = \frac{1}{\pi} \int_0^\pi \theta\, d\theta = \frac{1}{\pi} \left( \frac{\theta^2}{2} \right) \Big|_0^\pi = \boxed{\frac{\pi}{2}} \quad \text{[of course]}.$$

$$\langle \theta^2 \rangle = \frac{1}{\pi} \int_0^\pi \theta^2\, d\theta = \frac{1}{\pi} \left( \frac{\theta^3}{3} \right) \Big|_0^\pi = \boxed{\frac{\pi^2}{3}}.$$

$$\sigma^2 = \langle \theta^2 \rangle - \langle \theta \rangle^2 = \frac{\pi^2}{3} - \frac{\pi^2}{4} = \frac{\pi^2}{12}; \quad \boxed{\sigma = \frac{\pi}{2\sqrt{3}}}.$$

(c)

$$\langle \sin\theta \rangle = \frac{1}{\pi} \int_0^\pi \sin\theta\, d\theta = \frac{1}{\pi} \left( -\cos\theta \right)\big|_0^\pi = \frac{1}{\pi}(1 - (-1)) = \boxed{\frac{2}{\pi}}.$$

$$\langle \cos\theta \rangle = \frac{1}{\pi} \int_0^\pi \cos\theta\, d\theta = \frac{1}{\pi} \left( \sin\theta \right)\big|_0^\pi = \boxed{0.}$$

$$\langle \cos^2\theta \rangle = \frac{1}{\pi} \int_0^\pi \cos^2\theta\, d\theta = \frac{1}{\pi} \int_0^\pi (1/2) d\theta = \boxed{\frac{1}{2}.}$$

[Because $\sin^2\theta + \cos^2\theta = 1$, and the integrals of $\sin^2$ and $\cos^2$ are equal (over suitable intervals), one can replace them by 1/2 in such cases.]

## Problem 1.12

(a) $x = r\cos\theta \Rightarrow dx = -r\sin\theta\, d\theta$. The probability that the needle lies in range $d\theta$ is $\rho(\theta)d\theta = \frac{1}{\pi}d\theta$, so the probability that it's in the range $dx$ is

$$\rho(x)dx = \frac{1}{\pi} \frac{dx}{r\sin\theta} = \frac{1}{\pi} \frac{dx}{r\sqrt{1 - (x/r)^2}} = \frac{dx}{\pi\sqrt{r^2 - x^2}}.$$

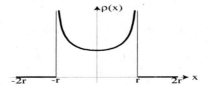

$$\therefore \boxed{\rho(x) = \begin{cases} \frac{1}{\pi\sqrt{r^2-x^2}}, & \text{if } -r < x < r, \\ 0, & \text{otherwise.} \end{cases}}$$
   [*Note:* We want the *magnitude* of $dx$ here.]

Total: $\int_{-r}^{r} \frac{1}{\pi\sqrt{r^2-x^2}}dx = \frac{2}{\pi}\int_0^r \frac{1}{\sqrt{r^2-x^2}}dx = \frac{2}{\pi}\sin^{-1}\frac{x}{r}\Big|_0^r = \frac{2}{\pi}\sin^{-1}(1) = \frac{2}{\pi}\cdot\frac{\pi}{2} = 1.\checkmark$

**(b)**

$$\langle x \rangle = \frac{1}{\pi}\int_{-r}^{r} x\frac{1}{\sqrt{r^2-x^2}}dx = \boxed{0} \quad \text{[odd integrand, even interval]}.$$

$$\langle x^2 \rangle = \frac{2}{\pi}\int_0^r \frac{x^2}{\sqrt{r^2-x^2}}dx = \frac{2}{\pi}\left[-\frac{x}{2}\sqrt{r^2-x^2} + \frac{r^2}{2}\sin^{-1}\left(\frac{x}{r}\right)\right]\Big|_0^r = \frac{2}{\pi}\frac{r^2}{2}\sin^{-1}(1) = \boxed{\frac{r^2}{2}}.$$

$$\sigma^2 = \langle x^2 \rangle - \langle x \rangle^2 = r^2/2 \implies \boxed{\sigma = r/\sqrt{2}.}$$

To get $\langle x \rangle$ and $\langle x^2 \rangle$ from Problem 1.11(c), use $x = r\cos\theta$, so $\langle x \rangle = r\langle\cos\theta\rangle = 0$, $\langle x^2 \rangle = r^2\langle\cos^2\theta\rangle = r^2/2$.

---

## Problem 1.13

Suppose the eye end lands a distance $y$ up from a line ($0 \le y < l$), and let $x$ be the projection along that same direction ($-l \le x < l$). The needle crosses the line above if $y + x \ge l$ (i.e. $x \ge l - y$), and it crosses the line below if $y + x < 0$ (i.e. $x < -y$). So for a given value of $y$, the probability of crossing (using Problem 1.12) is

$$P(y) = \int_{-l}^{-y} \rho(x)dx + \int_{l-y}^{l} \rho(x)dx = \frac{1}{\pi}\left\{\int_{-l}^{-y}\frac{1}{\sqrt{l^2-x^2}}dx + \int_{l-y}^{l}\frac{1}{\sqrt{l^2-x^2}}dx\right\}$$

$$= \frac{1}{\pi}\left\{\sin^{-1}\left(\frac{x}{l}\right)\Big|_{-l}^{-y} + \sin^{-1}\left(\frac{x}{l}\right)\Big|_{l-y}^{l}\right\} = \frac{1}{\pi}\left[-\sin^{-1}(y/l) + 2\sin^{-1}(1) - \sin^{-1}(1-y/l)\right]$$

$$= 1 - \frac{\sin^{-1}(y/l)}{\pi} - \frac{\sin^{-1}(1-y/l)}{\pi}.$$

Now, all values of $y$ are equally likely, so $\rho(y) = 1/l$, and hence the probability of crossing is

$$P = \frac{1}{\pi l}\int_0^l \left[\pi - \sin^{-1}\left(\frac{y}{l}\right) - \sin^{-1}\left(\frac{l-y}{l}\right)\right]dy = \frac{1}{\pi l}\int_0^l \left[\pi - 2\sin^{-1}(y/l)\right]dy$$

$$= \frac{1}{\pi l}\left[\pi l - 2\left(y\sin^{-1}(y/l) + l\sqrt{1-(y/l)^2}\right)\Big|_0^l\right] = 1 - \frac{2}{\pi l}[l\sin^{-1}(1) - l] = 1 - 1 + \frac{2}{\pi} = \boxed{\frac{2}{\pi}.}$$

---

## Problem 1.14

**(a)** $P_{ab}(t) = \int_a^b |\Psi(x,t)^2 dx$,    so $\frac{dP_{ab}}{dt} = \int_a^b \frac{\partial}{\partial t}|\Psi|^2 dx$. But (Eq. 1.25):

$$\frac{\partial |\Psi|^2}{\partial t} = \frac{\partial}{\partial x}\left[\frac{i\hbar}{2m}\left(\Psi^* \frac{\partial \Psi}{\partial x} - \frac{\partial \Psi^*}{\partial x}\Psi\right)\right] = -\frac{\partial}{\partial t}J(x,t).$$

$$\therefore \frac{dP_{ab}}{dt} = -\int_a^b \frac{\partial}{\partial x}J(x,t)dx = -\left[J(x,t)\right]\big|_a^b = J(a,t) - J(b,t). \qquad \text{QED}$$

Probability is dimensionless, so $J$ has the dimensions 1/time, and units $\boxed{\text{seconds}^{-1}.}$

**(b)** Here $\Psi(x,t) = f(x)e^{-iat}$, where $f(x) \equiv Ae^{-amx^2/\hbar}$, so $\Psi\frac{\partial \Psi^*}{\partial x} = fe^{-iat}\frac{df}{dx}e^{iat} = f\frac{df}{dx}$,

and $\Psi^*\frac{\partial \Psi}{\partial x} = f\frac{df}{dx}$ too, so $\boxed{J(x,t) = 0.}$

## Problem 1.15

**(a)** Eq. 1.24 now reads $\frac{\partial \Psi^*}{\partial t} = -\frac{i\hbar}{2m}\frac{\partial^2 \Psi^*}{\partial x^2} + \frac{i}{\hbar}V^*\Psi^*$, and Eq. 1.25 picks up an extra term:

$$\frac{\partial}{\partial t}|\Psi|^2 = \cdots + \frac{i}{\hbar}|\Psi|^2(V^* - V) = \cdots + \frac{i}{\hbar}|\Psi|^2(V_0 + i\Gamma - V_0 + i\Gamma) = \cdots - \frac{2\Gamma}{\hbar}|\Psi|^2,$$

and Eq. 1.27 becomes $\frac{dP}{dt} = -\frac{2\Gamma}{\hbar}\int_{-\infty}^{\infty}|\Psi|^2 dx = -\frac{2\Gamma}{\hbar}P.$     QED

**(b)**

$$\frac{dP}{P} = -\frac{2\Gamma}{\hbar}dt \implies \ln P = -\frac{2\Gamma}{\hbar}t + \text{constant} \implies \boxed{P(t) = P(0)e^{-2\Gamma t/\hbar},} \text{ so } \boxed{\tau = \frac{\hbar}{2\Gamma}.}$$

## Problem 1.16

Use Eqs. [1.23] and [1.24], and integration by parts:

$$\frac{d}{dt}\int_{-\infty}^{\infty} \Psi_1^* \Psi_2 \, dx = \int_{-\infty}^{\infty} \frac{\partial}{\partial t}\left(\Psi_1^* \Psi_2\right) dx = \int_{-\infty}^{\infty} \left(\frac{\partial \Psi_1^*}{\partial t}\Psi_2 + \Psi_1^* \frac{\partial \Psi_2}{\partial t}\right) dx$$

$$= \int_{-\infty}^{\infty} \left[\left(\frac{-i\hbar}{2m}\frac{\partial^2 \Psi_1^*}{\partial x^2} + \frac{i}{\hbar}V\Psi_1^*\right)\Psi_2 + \Psi_1^*\left(\frac{i\hbar}{2m}\frac{\partial^2 \Psi_2}{\partial x^2} - \frac{i}{\hbar}V\Psi_2\right)\right] dx$$

$$= -\frac{i\hbar}{2m}\int_{-\infty}^{\infty}\left(\frac{\partial^2 \Psi_1^*}{\partial x^2}\Psi_2 - \Psi_1^*\frac{\partial^2 \Psi_2}{\partial x^2}\right) dx$$

$$= -\frac{i\hbar}{2m}\left[\frac{\partial \Psi_1^*}{\partial x}\Psi_2\bigg|_{-\infty}^{\infty} - \int_{-\infty}^{\infty}\frac{\partial \Psi_1^*}{\partial x}\frac{\partial \Psi_2}{\partial x} dx - \Psi_1^*\frac{\partial \Psi_2}{\partial x}\bigg|_{-\infty}^{\infty} + \int_{-\infty}^{\infty}\frac{\partial \Psi_1^*}{\partial x}\frac{\partial \Psi_2}{\partial x} dx\right] = 0. \text{ QED}$$

## Problem 1.17

(a)

$$1 = |A|^2 \int_{-a}^{a} \left(a^2 - x^2\right)^2 dx = 2|A|^2 \int_{0}^{a} \left(a^4 - 2a^2x^2 + x^4\right) dx = 2|A|^2 \left[a^4 x - 2a^2 \frac{x^3}{3} + \frac{x^5}{5}\right]\Big|_0^a$$

$$= 2|A|^2 a^5 \left(1 - \frac{2}{3} + \frac{1}{5}\right) = \frac{16}{15} a^5 |A|^2, \text{ so } \boxed{A = \sqrt{\frac{15}{16a^5}}.}$$

(b)

$$\langle x \rangle = \int_{-a}^{a} x |\Psi|^2 \, dx = \boxed{0.} \quad \text{(Odd integrand.)}$$

(c)

$$\langle p \rangle = \frac{\hbar}{i} A^2 \int_{-a}^{a} \left(a^2 - x^2\right) \underbrace{\frac{d}{dx}\left(a^2 - x^2\right)}_{-2x} \, dx = \boxed{0.} \quad \text{(Odd integrand.)}$$

Since we only know $\langle x \rangle$ at $t = 0$ we cannot calculate $d\langle x \rangle / dt$ directly.

(d)

$$\langle x^2 \rangle = A^2 \int_{-a}^{a} x^2 \left(a^2 - x^2\right)^2 dx = 2A^2 \int_{0}^{a} \left(a^4 x^2 - 2a^2 x^4 + x^6\right) dx$$

$$= 2 \frac{15}{16a^5} \left[a^4 \frac{x^3}{3} - 2a^2 \frac{x^5}{5} + \frac{x^7}{7}\right]\Big|_0^a = \frac{15}{8a^5}\left(a^7\right)\left(\frac{1}{3} - \frac{2}{5} + \frac{1}{7}\right)$$

$$= \frac{15a^2}{8}\left(\frac{35 - 42 + 15}{3 \cdot 5 \cdot 7}\right) = \frac{a^2}{8} \cdot \frac{8}{7} = \boxed{\frac{a^2}{7}.}$$

(e)

$$\langle p^2 \rangle = -A^2 \hbar^2 \int_{-a}^{a} \left(a^2 - x^2\right) \underbrace{\frac{d^2}{dx^2}\left(a^2 - x^2\right)}_{-2} \, dx = 2A^2 \hbar^2 2 \int_{0}^{a} \left(a^2 - x^2\right) dx$$

$$= 4 \cdot \frac{15}{16a^5} \hbar^2 \left(a^2 x - \frac{x^3}{3}\right)\Big|_0^a = \frac{15\hbar^2}{4a^5}\left(a^3 - \frac{a^3}{3}\right) = \frac{15\hbar^2}{4a^2} \cdot \frac{2}{3} = \boxed{\frac{5}{2}\frac{\hbar^2}{a^2}.}$$

(f)

$$\sigma_x = \sqrt{\langle x^2 \rangle - \langle x \rangle^2} = \sqrt{\frac{1}{7}a^2} = \boxed{\frac{a}{\sqrt{7}}.}$$

(g)

$$\sigma_p = \sqrt{\langle p^2 \rangle - \langle p \rangle^2} = \sqrt{\frac{5}{2}\frac{\hbar^2}{a^2}} = \boxed{\sqrt{\frac{5}{2}}\frac{\hbar}{a}.}$$

**(h)**

$$\sigma_x \sigma_p = \frac{a}{\sqrt{7}} \cdot \sqrt{\frac{5}{2}\frac{\hbar}{a}} = \sqrt{\frac{5}{14}}\hbar = \sqrt{\frac{10}{7}}\frac{\hbar}{2} > \frac{\hbar}{2}. \checkmark$$

## Problem 1.18

$$\frac{h}{\sqrt{3mk_BT}} > d \;\Rightarrow\; T < \frac{h^2}{3mk_Bd^2}.$$

**(a)** Electrons ($m = 9.1 \times 10^{-31}$ kg):

$$T < \frac{(6.6 \times 10^{-34})^2}{3(9.1 \times 10^{-31})(1.4 \times 10^{-23})(3 \times 10^{-10})^2} = \boxed{1.3 \times 10^5 \text{ K.}}$$

Sodium nuclei ($m = 23m_p = 23(1.7 \times 10^{-27}) = 3.9 \times 10^{-26}$ kg):

$$T < \frac{(6.6 \times 10^{-34})^2}{3(3.9 \times 10^{-26})(1.4 \times 10^{-23})(3 \times 10^{-10})^2} = \boxed{3.0 \text{ K.}}$$

**(b)** $PV = Nk_BT$; volume occupied by one molecule ($N = 1$, $V = d^3$) $\Rightarrow d = (k_BT/P)^{1/3}$.

$$T < \frac{h^2}{2mk_B}\left(\frac{P}{k_BT}\right)^{2/3} \;\Rightarrow\; T^{5/3} < \frac{h^2}{3m}\frac{P^{2/3}}{k_B^{5/3}} \;\Rightarrow\; T < \frac{1}{k_B}\left(\frac{h^2}{3m}\right)^{3/5}P^{2/5}.$$

For helium ($m = 4m_p = 6.8 \times 10^{-27}$ kg) at 1 atm $= 1.0 \times 10^5$ N/m$^2$:

$$T < \frac{1}{(1.4 \times 10^{-23})}\left(\frac{(6.6 \times 10^{-34})^2}{3(6.8 \times 10^{-27})}\right)^{3/5}(1.0 \times 10^5)^{2/5} = \boxed{2.8 \text{ K.}}$$

For hydrogen ($m = 2m_p = 3.4 \times 10^{-27}$ kg) with $d = 0.01$ m:

$$T < \frac{(6.6 \times 10^{-34})^2}{3(3.4 \times 10^{-27})(1.4 \times 10^{-23})(10^{-2})^2} = \boxed{3.1 \times 10^{-14} \text{ K.}}$$

At 3 K it is definitely in the classical regime.

# Chapter 2

# Time-Independent Schrödinger Equation

## Problem 2.1

**(a)**

$$\Psi(x,t) = \psi(x)e^{-i(E_0+i\Gamma)t/\hbar} = \psi(x)e^{\Gamma t/\hbar}e^{-iE_0 t/\hbar} \Longrightarrow |\Psi|^2 = |\psi|^2 e^{2\Gamma t/\hbar}.$$

$$\int_{-\infty}^{\infty} |\Psi(x,t)|^2 dx = e^{2\Gamma t/\hbar}\int_{-\infty}^{\infty} |\psi|^2 dx.$$

The second term is independent of $t$, so if the product is to be 1 for all time, the first term ($e^{2\Gamma t/\hbar}$) must also be constant, and hence $\Gamma = 0$.     QED

**(b)** If $\psi$ satisfies Eq. 2.5, $-\frac{\hbar^2}{2m}\frac{\partial^2\psi}{dx^2} + V\psi = E\psi$, then (taking the complex conjugate and noting that $V$ and $E$ are real): $-\frac{\hbar^2}{2m}\frac{\partial^2\psi^*}{dx^2} + V\psi^* = E\psi^*$, so $\psi^*$ *also* satisfies Eq. 2.5. Now, if $\psi_1$ and $\psi_2$ satisfy Eq. 2.5, so too does any linear combination of them ($\psi_3 \equiv c_1\psi_1 + c_2\psi_2$):

$$-\frac{\hbar^2}{2m}\frac{\partial^2\psi_3}{dx^2} + V\psi_3 = -\frac{\hbar^2}{2m}\left(c_1\frac{\partial^2\psi_1}{dx^2} + c_2\frac{\partial^2\psi_2}{\partial x^2}\right) + V(c_1\psi_1 + c_2\psi_2)$$

$$= c_1\left[-\frac{\hbar^2}{2m}\frac{d^2\psi_1}{dx^2} + V\psi_1\right] + c_2\left[-\frac{\hbar^2}{2m}\frac{d^2\psi_2}{dx^2} + V\psi_2\right]$$

$$= c_1(E\psi_1) + c_2(E\psi_2) = E(c_1\psi_1 + c_2\psi_2) = E\psi_3.$$

Thus, $(\psi + \psi^*)$ and $i(\psi - \psi^*)$ – both of which are *real* – satisfy Eq. 2.5. *Conclusion:* From any complex solution, we can always construct two *real* solutions (of course, if $\psi$ is already real, the second one will be zero). In particular, since $\psi = \frac{1}{2}[(\psi + \psi^*) - i(i(\psi - \psi^*))]$, $\psi$ can be expressed as a linear combination of two real solutions.     QED

**(c)** If $\psi(x)$ satisfies Eq. 2.5, then, changing variables $x \rightarrow -x$ and noting that $\partial^2/\partial(-x)^2 = \partial^2/\partial x^2$,

$$-\frac{\hbar^2}{2m}\frac{\partial^2\psi(-x)}{dx^2} + V(-x)\psi(-x) = E\psi(-x);$$

so if $V(-x) = V(x)$ then $\psi(-x)$ *also* satisfies Eq. 2.5. It follows that $\psi_+(x) \equiv \psi(x) + \psi(-x)$ (which is *even*: $\psi_+(-x) = \psi_+(x)$) and $\psi_-(x) \equiv \psi(x) - \psi(-x)$ (which is *odd*: $\psi_-(-x) = -\psi_-(x)$) both satisfy Eq.

2.5. But $\psi(x) = \frac{1}{2}(\psi_+(x) + \psi_-(x))$, so any solution can be expressed as a linear combination of even and odd solutions. QED

## Problem 2.2

Given $\frac{d^2\psi}{dx^2} = \frac{2m}{\hbar^2}[V(x) - E]\psi$, if $E < V_{\min}$, then $\psi''$ and $\psi$ always have the same sign: If $\psi$ is positive(negative), then $\psi''$ is also positive(negative). This means that $\psi$ always curves away from the axis (see Figure). However, it has got to go to zero as $x \to -\infty$ (else it would not be normalizable). At some point it's got to *depart* from zero (if it *doesn't*, it's going to be identically zero *everywhere*), in (say) the positive direction. At this point its slope is positive, and *increasing*, so $\psi$ gets bigger and bigger as $x$ increases. It can't ever "turn over" and head back toward the axis, because that would requuire a negative second derivative—it always has to bend away from the axis. By the same token, if it starts out heading negative, it just runs more and more negative. In neither case is there any way for it to come back to zero, as it must (at $x \to \infty$) in order to be normalizable. QED

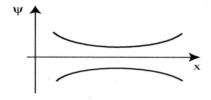

## Problem 2.3

Equation 2.20 says $\frac{d^2\psi}{dx^2} = -\frac{2mE}{\hbar^2}\psi$; Eq. 2.23 says $\psi(0) = \psi(a) = 0$. If $E = 0$, $d^2\psi/dx^2 = 0$, so $\psi(x) = A + Bx$; $\psi(0) = A = 0 \Rightarrow \psi = Bx$; $\psi(a) = Ba = 0 \Rightarrow B = 0$, so $\psi = 0$. If $E < 0$, $d^2\psi/dx^2 = \kappa^2\psi$, with $\kappa \equiv \sqrt{-2mE}/\hbar$ real, so $\psi(x) = Ae^{\kappa x} + Be^{-\kappa x}$. This time $\psi(0) = A + B = 0 \Rightarrow B = -A$, so $\psi = A(e^{\kappa x} - e^{-\kappa x})$, while $\psi(a) = A\left(e^{\kappa a} - e^{i\kappa a}\right) = 0 \Rightarrow$ either $A = 0$, so $\psi = 0$, or else $e^{\kappa a} = e^{-\kappa a}$, so $e^{2\kappa a} = 1$, so $2\kappa a = \ln(1) = 0$, so $\kappa = 0$, and again $\psi = 0$. In all cases, then, the boundary conditions force $\psi = 0$, which is unacceptable (non-normalizable).

## Problem 2.4

$$\langle x \rangle = \int x|\psi|^2 dx = \frac{2}{a}\int_0^a x\sin^2\left(\frac{n\pi}{a}x\right)dx. \qquad \text{Let } y \equiv \frac{n\pi}{a}x, \text{ so } dx = \frac{a}{n\pi}dy; \quad y : 0 \to n\pi.$$

$$= \frac{2}{a}\left(\frac{a}{n\pi}\right)^2\int_0^{n\pi} y\sin^2 y\, dy = \frac{2a}{n^2\pi^2}\left[\frac{y^2}{4} - \frac{y\sin 2y}{4} - \frac{\cos 2y}{8}\right]\Bigg|_0^{n\pi}$$

$$= \frac{2a}{n^2\pi^2}\left[\frac{n^2\pi^2}{4} - \frac{\cos 2n\pi}{8} + \frac{1}{8}\right] = \boxed{\frac{a}{2}.} \quad \text{(Independent of } n\text{.)}$$

$$\langle x^2 \rangle = \frac{2}{a} \int_0^a x^2 \sin^2\left(\frac{n\pi}{a}x\right) dx = \frac{2}{a}\left(\frac{a}{n\pi}\right)^3 \int_0^{n\pi} y^2 \sin^2 y \, dy$$

$$= \frac{2a^2}{(n\pi)^3}\left[\frac{y^3}{6} - \left(\frac{y^3}{4} - \frac{1}{8}\right)\sin 2y - \frac{y\cos 2y}{4}\right]_0^{n\pi}$$

$$= \frac{2a^2}{(n\pi)^3}\left[\frac{(n\pi)^3}{6} - \frac{n\pi\cos(2n\pi)}{4}\right] = \boxed{a^2\left[\frac{1}{3} - \frac{1}{2(n\pi)^2}\right]}.$$

$$\langle p \rangle = m\frac{d\langle x\rangle}{dt} = \boxed{0.} \quad (Note: \text{Eq. 1.33 is much faster than Eq. 1.35.})$$

$$\langle p^2 \rangle = \int \psi_n^* \left(\frac{\hbar}{i}\frac{d}{dx}\right)^2 \psi_n \, dx = -\hbar^2 \int \psi_n^* \left(\frac{d^2\psi_n}{dx^2}\right) dx$$

$$= (-\hbar^2)\left(-\frac{2mE_n}{\hbar^2}\right)\int \psi_n^*\psi_n \, dx = 2mE_n = \boxed{\left(\frac{n\pi\hbar}{a}\right)^2}.$$

$$\sigma_x^2 = \langle x^2\rangle - \langle x\rangle^2 = a^2\left(\frac{1}{3} - \frac{1}{2(n\pi)^2} - \frac{1}{4}\right) = \frac{a^2}{4}\left(\frac{1}{3} - \frac{2}{(n\pi)^2}\right); \quad \boxed{\sigma_x = \frac{a}{2}\sqrt{\frac{1}{3} - \frac{2}{(n\pi)^2}}}.$$

$$\sigma_p^2 = \langle p^2\rangle - \langle p\rangle^2 = \left(\frac{n\pi\hbar}{a}\right)^2; \quad \boxed{\sigma_p = \frac{n\pi\hbar}{a}.} \quad \therefore \sigma_x\sigma_p = \boxed{\frac{\hbar}{2}\sqrt{\frac{(n\pi)^2}{3} - 2}.}$$

The product $\sigma_x\sigma_p$ is $\boxed{\text{smallest for } n = 1;}$ in that case, $\sigma_x\sigma_p = \frac{\hbar}{2}\sqrt{\frac{\pi^2}{3} - 2} = (1.136)\hbar/2 > \hbar/2.$ ✓

## Problem 2.5

**(a)**

$$|\Psi|^2 = \Psi^2\Psi = |A|^2(\psi_1^* + \psi_2^*)(\psi_1 + \psi_2) = |A|^2[\psi_1^*\psi_1 + \psi_1^*\psi_2 + \psi_2^*\psi_1 + \psi_2^*\psi_2].$$

$$1 = \int |\Psi|^2 dx = |A|^2 \int [|\psi_1|^2 + \psi_1^*\psi_2 + \psi_2^*\psi_1 + |\psi_2|^2]dx = 2|A|^2 \Rightarrow \boxed{A = 1/\sqrt{2}.}$$

**(b)**

$$\Psi(x,t) = \frac{1}{\sqrt{2}}\left[\psi_1 e^{-iE_1 t/\hbar} + \psi_2 e^{-iE_2 t/\hbar}\right] \quad \left(\text{but } \frac{E_n}{\hbar} = n^2\omega\right)$$

$$= \frac{1}{\sqrt{2}}\sqrt{\frac{2}{a}}\left[\sin\left(\frac{\pi}{a}x\right)e^{-i\omega t} + \sin\left(\frac{2\pi}{a}x\right)e^{-i4\omega t}\right] = \boxed{\frac{1}{\sqrt{a}}e^{-i\omega t}\left[\sin\left(\frac{\pi}{a}x\right) + \sin\left(\frac{2\pi}{a}x\right)e^{-3i\omega t}\right].}$$

$$|\Psi(x,t)|^2 = \frac{1}{a}\left[\sin^2\left(\frac{\pi}{a}x\right) + \sin\left(\frac{\pi}{a}x\right)\sin\left(\frac{2\pi}{a}x\right)\left(e^{-3i\omega t} + e^{3i\omega t}\right) + \sin^2\left(\frac{2\pi}{a}x\right)\right]$$

$$= \boxed{\frac{1}{a}\left[\sin^2\left(\frac{\pi}{a}x\right) + \sin^2\left(\frac{2\pi}{a}x\right) + 2\sin\left(\frac{\pi}{a}x\right)\sin\left(\frac{2\pi}{a}x\right)\cos(3\omega t)\right].}$$

**(c)**

$$\langle x \rangle = \int x |\Psi(x,t)|^2 dx$$

$$= \frac{1}{a} \int_0^a x \left[ \sin^2 \left( \frac{\pi}{a} x \right) + \sin^2 \left( \frac{2\pi}{a} x \right) + 2 \sin \left( \frac{\pi}{a} x \right) \sin \left( \frac{2\pi}{a} x \right) \cos(3\omega t) \right] dx$$

$$\int_0^a x \sin^2 \left( \frac{\pi}{a} x \right) dx = \left[ \frac{x^2}{4} - \frac{x \sin \left( \frac{2\pi}{a} x \right)}{4\pi/a} - \frac{\cos \left( \frac{2\pi}{a} x \right)}{8(\pi/a)^2} \right] \Big|_0^a = \frac{a^2}{4} = \int_0^a x \sin^2 \left( \frac{2\pi}{a} x \right) dx.$$

$$\int_0^a x \sin \left( \frac{\pi}{a} x \right) \sin \left( \frac{2\pi}{a} x \right) dx = \frac{1}{2} \int_0^a x \left[ \cos \left( \frac{\pi}{a} x \right) - \cos \left( \frac{3\pi}{a} x \right) \right] dx$$

$$= \frac{1}{2} \left[ \frac{a^2}{\pi^2} \cos \left( \frac{\pi}{a} x \right) + \frac{ax}{\pi} \sin \left( \frac{\pi}{a} x \right) - \frac{a^2}{9\pi^2} \cos \left( \frac{3\pi}{a} x \right) - \frac{ax}{3\pi} \sin \left( \frac{3\pi}{a} x \right) \right]_0^a$$

$$= \frac{1}{2} \left[ \frac{a^2}{\pi^2} \left( \cos(\pi) - \cos(0) \right) - \frac{a^2}{9\pi^2} \left( \cos(3\pi) - \cos(0) \right) \right] = -\frac{a^2}{\pi^2} \left( 1 - \frac{1}{9} \right) = -\frac{8a^2}{9\pi^2}.$$

$$\therefore \langle x \rangle = \frac{1}{a} \left[ \frac{a^2}{4} + \frac{a^2}{4} - \frac{16a^2}{9\pi^2} \cos(3\omega t) \right] = \boxed{ \frac{a}{2} \left[ 1 - \frac{32}{9\pi^2} \cos(3\omega t) \right] }.$$

*Amplitude:* $\boxed{ \frac{32}{9\pi^2} \left( \frac{a}{2} \right) } = 0.3603(a/2);$     *angular frequency:* $\boxed{ 3\omega = \frac{3\pi^2 \hbar}{2ma^2} }.$

**(d)**

$$\langle p \rangle = m \frac{d\langle x \rangle}{dt} = m \left( \frac{a}{2} \right) \left( -\frac{32}{9\pi^2} \right) (-3\omega) \sin(3\omega t) = \boxed{ \frac{8\hbar}{3a} \sin(3\omega t) }.$$

**(e)** You could get either $\boxed{ E_1 = \pi^2 \hbar^2 / 2ma^2 }$ or $\boxed{ E_2 = 2\pi^2 \hbar^2 / ma^2, }$ with equal probability $\boxed{ P_1 = P_2 = 1/2. }$

So $\langle H \rangle = \boxed{ \frac{1}{2}(E_1 + E_2) = \frac{5\pi^2 \hbar^2}{4ma^2} };$ it's the *average* of $E_1$ and $E_2$.

---

## Problem 2.6

From Problem 2.5, we see that

$$\Psi(x,t) = \boxed{ \frac{1}{\sqrt{a}} e^{-i\omega t} \left[ \sin \left( \frac{\pi}{a} x \right) + \sin \left( \frac{2\pi}{a} x \right) e^{-3i\omega t} e^{i\phi} \right] };$$

$$|\Psi(x,t)|^2 = \boxed{ \frac{1}{a} \left[ \sin^2 \left( \frac{\pi}{a} x \right) + \sin^2 \left( \frac{2\pi}{a} x \right) + 2 \sin \left( \frac{\pi}{a} x \right) \sin \left( \frac{2\pi}{a} x \right) \cos(3\omega t - \phi) \right] };$$

and hence $\boxed{\langle x \rangle = \frac{a}{2}\left[1 - \frac{32}{9\pi^2}\cos(3\omega t - \phi)\right].}$ This amounts physically to starting the clock at a different time (i.e., shifting the $t = 0$ point).

If $\phi = \dfrac{\pi}{2}$, so $\Psi(x,0) = A[\psi_1(x) + i\psi_2(x)]$, then $\cos(3\omega t - \phi) = \sin(3\omega t)$; $\langle x \rangle$ starts at $\dfrac{a}{2}$.

If $\phi = \pi$, so $\Psi(x,0) = A[\psi_1(x) - \psi_2(x)]$, then $\cos(3\omega t - \phi) = -\cos(3\omega t)$; $\langle x \rangle$ starts at $\dfrac{a}{2}\left(1 + \dfrac{32}{9\pi^2}\right)$.

## Problem 2.7

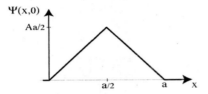

**(a)**

$$1 = A^2 \int_0^{a/2} x^2 dx + A^2 \int_{a/2}^a (a-x)^2 dx = A^2\left[\left.\frac{x^3}{3}\right|_0^{a/2} - \left.\frac{(a-x)^3}{3}\right|_{a/2}^a\right]$$

$$= \frac{A^2}{3}\left(\frac{a^3}{8} + \frac{a^3}{8}\right) = \frac{A^2 a^3}{12} \Rightarrow \boxed{A = \frac{2\sqrt{3}}{\sqrt{a^3}}.}$$

**(b)**

$$c_n = \sqrt{\frac{2}{a}}\frac{2\sqrt{3}}{a\sqrt{a}}\left[\int_0^{a/2} x\sin\left(\frac{n\pi}{a}x\right)dx + \int_{a/2}^a (a-x)\sin\left(\frac{n\pi}{a}x\right)dx\right]$$

$$= \frac{2\sqrt{6}}{a^2}\left\{\left[\left(\frac{a}{n\pi}\right)^2\sin\left(\frac{n\pi}{a}x\right) - \frac{xa}{n\pi}\cos\left(\frac{n\pi}{a}x\right)\right]\Big|_0^{a/2}\right.$$

$$\left. + a\left[-\frac{a}{n\pi}\cos\left(\frac{n\pi}{a}x\right)\right]\Big|_{a/2}^a - \left[\left(\frac{a}{n\pi}\right)^2\sin\left(\frac{n\pi}{a}x\right) - \left(\frac{ax}{n\pi}\right)\cos\left(\frac{n\pi}{a}x\right)\right]\Big|_{a/2}^a\right\}$$

$$= \frac{2\sqrt{6}}{a^2}\left[\left(\frac{a}{n\pi}\right)^2\sin\left(\frac{n\pi}{2}\right) - \cancel{\frac{a^2}{2n\pi}\cos\left(\frac{n\pi}{2}\right)} - \cancel{\frac{a^2}{n\pi}\cos n\pi} + \cancel{\frac{a^2}{n\pi}\cos\left(\frac{n\pi}{2}\right)}\right.$$

$$\left. + \left(\frac{a}{n\pi}\right)^2\sin\left(\frac{n\pi}{2}\right) + \cancel{\frac{a^2}{n\pi}\cos n\pi} - \cancel{\frac{a^2}{2n\pi}\cos\left(\frac{n\pi}{2}\right)}\right]$$

$$= \frac{2\sqrt{6}}{\cancel{a^2}}2\frac{\cancel{a^2}}{(n\pi)^2}\sin\left(\frac{n\pi}{2}\right) = \frac{4\sqrt{6}}{(n\pi)^2}\sin\left(\frac{n\pi}{2}\right) = \begin{cases} 0, & n \text{ even,} \\ (-1)^{(n-1)/2}\frac{4\sqrt{6}}{(n\pi)^2}, & n \text{ odd.} \end{cases}$$

So $\boxed{\Psi(x,t) = \frac{4\sqrt{6}}{\pi^2}\sqrt{\frac{2}{a}}\sum_{n=1,3,5,\ldots}(-1)^{(n-1)/2}\frac{1}{n^2}\sin\left(\frac{n\pi}{a}x\right)e^{-E_n t/\hbar},}$ where $E_n = \dfrac{n^2\pi^2\hbar^2}{2ma^2}.$

**(c)**

$$P_1 = |c_1|^2 = \frac{16 \cdot 6}{\pi^4} = \boxed{0.9855.}$$

**(d)**

$$\langle H \rangle = \sum |c_n|^2 E_n = \frac{96}{\pi^4} \frac{\pi^2 \hbar^2}{2ma^2} \left( \underbrace{\frac{1}{1} + \frac{1}{3^2} + \frac{1}{5^2} + \frac{1}{7^2} + \cdots}_{\pi^2/8} \right) = \frac{48\hbar^2}{\pi^2 ma^2} \frac{\pi^2}{8} = \boxed{\frac{6\hbar^2}{ma^2}.}$$

## Problem 2.8

**(a)**

$$\boxed{\Psi(x,0) = \begin{cases} A, & 0 < x < a/2; \\ 0, & \text{otherwise.} \end{cases}} \quad 1 = A^2 \int_0^{a/2} dx = A^2(a/2) \Rightarrow \boxed{A = \sqrt{\frac{2}{a}}.}$$

**(b)** From Eq. 2.37,

$$c_1 = A\sqrt{\frac{2}{a}} \int_0^{a/2} \sin\left(\frac{\pi}{a}x\right) dx = \frac{2}{a} \left[ -\frac{a}{\pi} \cos\left(\frac{\pi}{a}x\right) \right] \Big|_0^{a/2} = -\frac{2}{\pi} \left[ \cos\left(\frac{\pi}{2}\right) - \cos 0 \right] = \frac{2}{\pi}.$$

$$P_1 = |c_1|^2 = \boxed{(2/\pi)^2 = 0.4053.}$$

## Problem 2.9

$$\hat{H}\Psi(x,0) = -\frac{\hbar^2}{2m} \frac{\partial^2}{\partial x^2} [Ax(a-x)] = -A\frac{\hbar^2}{2m} \frac{\partial}{\partial x}(a - 2x) = A\frac{\hbar^2}{m}.$$

$$\int \Psi(x,0)^* \hat{H}\Psi(x,0)\, dx = A^2 \frac{\hbar^2}{m} \int_0^a x(a-x)\, dx = A^2 \frac{\hbar^2}{m} \left( a\frac{x^2}{2} - \frac{x^3}{3} \right) \Big|_0^a$$

$$= A^2 \frac{\hbar^2}{m} \left( \frac{a^3}{2} - \frac{a^3}{3} \right) = \frac{30}{a^5} \frac{\hbar^2}{m} \frac{a^3}{6} = \boxed{\frac{5\hbar^2}{ma^2}}$$

(same as Example 2.3).

## Problem 2.10

**(a)** Using Eqs. 2.47 and 2.59,

$$a_+ \psi_0 = \frac{1}{\sqrt{2\hbar m\omega}} \left( -\hbar \frac{d}{dx} + m\omega x \right) \left( \frac{m\omega}{\pi\hbar} \right)^{1/4} e^{-\frac{m\omega}{2\hbar}x^2}$$

$$= \frac{1}{\sqrt{2\hbar m\omega}} \left( \frac{m\omega}{\pi\hbar} \right)^{1/4} \left[ -\hbar \left( -\frac{m\omega}{2\hbar} \right) 2x + m\omega x \right] e^{-\frac{m\omega}{2\hbar}x^2} = \frac{1}{\sqrt{2\hbar m\omega}} \left( \frac{m\omega}{\pi\hbar} \right)^{1/4} 2m\omega x e^{-\frac{m\omega}{2\hbar}x^2}.$$

$$(a_+)^2 \psi_0 = \frac{1}{2\hbar m\omega} \left( \frac{m\omega}{\pi\hbar} \right)^{1/4} 2m\omega \left( -\hbar \frac{d}{dx} + m\omega x \right) x e^{-\frac{m\omega}{2\hbar}x^2}$$

$$= \frac{1}{\hbar} \left( \frac{m\omega}{\pi\hbar} \right)^{1/4} \left[ -\hbar \left( 1 - x\frac{m\omega}{2\hbar}2x \right) + m\omega x^2 \right] e^{-\frac{m\omega}{2\hbar}x^2} = \left( \frac{m\omega}{\pi\hbar} \right)^{1/4} \left( \frac{2m\omega}{\hbar}x^2 - 1 \right) e^{-\frac{m\omega}{2\hbar}x^2}.$$

Therefore, from Eq. 2.67,

$$\psi_2 = \frac{1}{\sqrt{2}} (a_+)^2 \psi_0 = \boxed{ \frac{1}{\sqrt{2}} \left( \frac{m\omega}{\pi\hbar} \right)^{1/4} \left( \frac{2m\omega}{\hbar}x^2 - 1 \right) e^{-\frac{m\omega}{2\hbar}x^2}. }$$

**(b)**

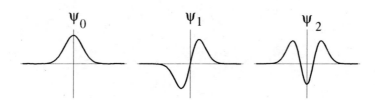

**(c)** Since $\psi_0$ and $\psi_2$ are even, whereas $\psi_1$ is odd, $\int \psi_0^* \psi_1 dx$ and $\int \psi_2^* \psi_1 dx$ vanish automatically. The only one we need to check is $\int \psi_2^* \psi_0 \, dx$:

$$\int \psi_2^* \psi_0 \, dx = \frac{1}{\sqrt{2}} \sqrt{\frac{m\omega}{\pi\hbar}} \int_{-\infty}^{\infty} \left( \frac{2m\omega}{\hbar}x^2 - 1 \right) e^{-\frac{m\omega}{\hbar}x^2} dx$$

$$= -\sqrt{\frac{m\omega}{2\pi\hbar}} \left( \int_{-\infty}^{\infty} e^{-\frac{m\omega}{\hbar}x^2} dx - \frac{2m\omega}{\hbar} \int_{-\infty}^{\infty} x^2 e^{-\frac{m\omega}{\hbar}x^2} dx \right)$$

$$= -\sqrt{\frac{m\omega}{2\pi\hbar}} \left( \sqrt{\frac{\pi\hbar}{m\omega}} - \frac{2m\omega}{\hbar} \frac{\hbar}{2m\omega} \sqrt{\frac{\pi\hbar}{m\omega}} \right) = 0. \checkmark$$

---

## Problem 2.11

**(a)** Note that $\psi_0$ is even, and $\psi_1$ is odd. In either case $|\psi|^2$ is even, so $\langle x \rangle = \int x|\psi|^2 dx = \boxed{0.}$ Therefore $\langle p \rangle = md\langle x \rangle/dt = \boxed{0.}$ (These results hold for *any* stationary state of the harmonic oscillator.)

From Eqs. 2.59 and 2.62, $\psi_0 = \alpha e^{-\xi^2/2}$, $\psi_1 = \sqrt{2}\alpha\xi e^{-\xi^2/2}$. So

<u>$n = 0$</u>:

$$\langle x^2 \rangle = \alpha^2 \int_{-\infty}^{\infty} x^2 e^{-\xi^2/2} dx = \alpha^2 \left( \frac{\hbar}{m\omega} \right)^{3/2} \int_{-\infty}^{\infty} \xi^2 e^{-\xi^2} d\xi = \frac{1}{\sqrt{\pi}} \left( \frac{\hbar}{m\omega} \right) \frac{\sqrt{\pi}}{2} = \boxed{ \frac{\hbar}{2m\omega}. }$$

$$\langle p^2 \rangle = \int \psi_0 \left( \frac{\hbar}{i} \frac{d}{dx} \right)^2 \psi_0 \, dx = -\hbar^2 \alpha^2 \sqrt{\frac{m\omega}{\hbar}} \int_{-\infty}^{\infty} e^{-\xi^2/2} \left( \frac{d^2}{d\xi^2} e^{-\xi^2/2} \right) d\xi$$

$$= -\frac{m\hbar\omega}{\sqrt{\pi}} \int_{-\infty}^{\infty} (\xi^2 - 1) e^{-\xi^2/2} d\xi = -\frac{m\hbar\omega}{\sqrt{\pi}} \left( \frac{\sqrt{\pi}}{2} - \sqrt{\pi} \right) = \boxed{\frac{m\hbar\omega}{2}}.$$

$\underline{n = 1}$:

$$\langle x^2 \rangle = 2\alpha^2 \int_{-\infty}^{\infty} x^2 \xi^2 e^{-\xi^2} dx = 2\alpha^2 \left( \frac{\hbar}{m\omega} \right)^{3/2} \int_{-\infty}^{\infty} \xi^4 e^{-\xi^2} d\xi = \frac{2\hbar}{\sqrt{\pi} m\omega} \frac{3\sqrt{\pi}}{4} = \boxed{\frac{3\hbar}{2m\omega}}.$$

$$\langle p^2 \rangle = -\hbar^2 2\alpha^2 \sqrt{\frac{m\omega}{\hbar}} \int_{-\infty}^{\infty} \xi e^{-\xi^2/2} \left[ \frac{d^2}{d\xi^2} \left( \xi e^{-\xi^2/2} \right) \right] d\xi$$

$$= -\frac{2m\omega\hbar}{\sqrt{\pi}} \int_{-\infty}^{\infty} (\xi^4 - 3\xi^2) e^{-\xi^2} d\xi = -\frac{2m\omega\hbar}{\sqrt{\pi}} \left( \frac{3}{4} \sqrt{\pi} - 3 \frac{\sqrt{\pi}}{2} \right) = \boxed{\frac{3m\hbar\omega}{2}}.$$

**(b)** $\underline{n = 0}$:

$$\sigma_x = \sqrt{\langle x^2 \rangle - \langle x \rangle^2} = \sqrt{\frac{\hbar}{2m\omega}}; \quad \sigma_p = \sqrt{\langle p^2 \rangle - \langle p \rangle^2} = \sqrt{\frac{m\hbar\omega}{2}};$$

$$\sigma_x \sigma_p = \sqrt{\frac{\hbar}{2m\omega}} \sqrt{\frac{m\omega\hbar}{2}} = \frac{\hbar}{2}. \quad \text{(Right } at \text{ the uncertainty limit.)} \checkmark$$

$\underline{n = 1}$:

$$\sigma_x = \sqrt{\frac{3\hbar}{2m\omega}}; \quad \sigma_p = \sqrt{\frac{3m\hbar\omega}{2}}; \quad \sigma_x \sigma_p = 3 \frac{\hbar}{2} > \frac{\hbar}{2}. \checkmark$$

**(c)**

$$\langle T \rangle = \frac{1}{2m} \langle p^2 \rangle = \boxed{ \left\{ \begin{array}{l} \frac{1}{4}\hbar\omega \ (n = 0) \\ \frac{3}{4}\hbar\omega \ (n = 1) \end{array} \right\} }; \quad \langle V \rangle = \frac{1}{2} m\omega^2 \langle x^2 \rangle = \boxed{ \left\{ \begin{array}{l} \frac{1}{4}\hbar\omega \ (n = 0) \\ \frac{3}{4}\hbar\omega \ (n = 1) \end{array} \right\} }.$$

$$\langle T \rangle + \langle V \rangle = \langle H \rangle = \left\{ \begin{array}{l} \frac{1}{2}\hbar\omega \ (n = 0) = E_0 \\ \frac{3}{2}\hbar\omega \ (n = 1) = E_1 \end{array} \right\}, \text{ as expected.}$$

---

## Problem 2.12

From Eq. 2.69,

$$x = \sqrt{\frac{\hbar}{2m\omega}} (a_+ + a_-), \quad p = i\sqrt{\frac{\hbar m\omega}{2}} (a_+ - a_-),$$

so

$$\langle x \rangle = \sqrt{\frac{\hbar}{2m\omega}} \int \psi_n^* (a_+ + a_-) \psi_n \, dx.$$

But (Eq. 2.66)
$$a_+\psi_n = \sqrt{n+1}\psi_{n+1}, \quad a_-\psi_n = \sqrt{n}\psi_{n-1}.$$

So
$$\langle x \rangle = \sqrt{\frac{\hbar}{2m\omega}}\left[\sqrt{n+1}\int \psi_n^*\psi_{n+1}\,dx + \sqrt{n}\int \psi_n^*\psi_{n-1}\,dx\right] = \boxed{0}\ \text{(by orthogonality)}.$$

$$\langle p \rangle = m\frac{d\langle x\rangle}{dt} = \boxed{0.}\quad x^2 = \frac{\hbar}{2m\omega}(a_+ + a_-)^2 = \frac{\hbar}{2m\omega}\left(a_+^2 + a_+a_- + a_-a_+ + a_-^2\right).$$

$$\langle x^2 \rangle = \frac{\hbar}{2m\omega}\int \psi_n^*\left(a_+^2 + a_+a_- + a_-a_+ + a_-^2\right)\psi_n.\quad \text{But}$$

$$\begin{cases}
a_+^2\psi_n &= a_+\left(\sqrt{n+1}\psi_{n+1}\right) = \sqrt{n+1}\sqrt{n+2}\psi_{n+2} = \sqrt{(n+1)(n+2)}\psi_{n+2}. \\
a_+a_-\psi_n &= a_+\left(\sqrt{n}\psi_{n-1}\right) \quad= \sqrt{n}\sqrt{n}\psi_n \qquad\qquad = n\psi_n. \\
a_-a_+\psi_n &= a_-\left(\sqrt{n+1}\psi_{n+1}\right) = \sqrt{n+1}\sqrt{n+1}\psi_n \quad= (n+1)\psi_n. \\
a_-^2\psi_n &= a_-\left(\sqrt{n}\psi_{n-1}\right) \quad= \sqrt{n}\sqrt{n-1}\psi_{n-2} = \sqrt{(n-1)n}\psi_{n-2}.
\end{cases}$$

So
$$\langle x^2 \rangle = \frac{\hbar}{2m\omega}\left[0 + n\int |\psi_n|^2 dx + (n+1)\int |\psi_n|^2 dx + 0\right] = \frac{\hbar}{2m\omega}(2n+1) = \boxed{\left(n+\frac{1}{2}\right)\frac{\hbar}{m\omega}}.$$

$$p^2 = -\frac{\hbar m\omega}{2}(a_+ - a_-)^2 = -\frac{\hbar m\omega}{2}\left(a_+^2 - a_+a_- - a_-a_+ + a_-^2\right) \Rightarrow$$

$$\langle p^2 \rangle = -\frac{\hbar m\omega}{2}\left[0 - n - (n+1) + 0\right] = \frac{\hbar m\omega}{2}(2n+1) = \boxed{\left(n+\frac{1}{2}\right)m\hbar\omega}.$$

$$\langle T \rangle = \langle p^2/2m \rangle = \boxed{\frac{1}{2}\left(n+\frac{1}{2}\right)\hbar\omega}.$$

$$\sigma_x = \sqrt{\langle x^2\rangle - \langle x\rangle^2} = \sqrt{n+\frac{1}{2}}\sqrt{\frac{\hbar}{m\omega}}; \quad \sigma_p = \sqrt{\langle p^2\rangle - \langle p\rangle^2} = \sqrt{n+\frac{1}{2}}\sqrt{m\hbar\omega}; \quad \sigma_x\sigma_p = \left(n+\frac{1}{2}\right)\hbar \geq \frac{\hbar}{2}.\ \checkmark$$

---

## Problem 2.13

(a)

$$1 = \int |\Psi(x,0)|^2 dx = |A|^2\int \left(9|\psi_0|^2 + 12\psi_0^*\psi_1 + 12\psi_1^*\psi_0 + 16|\psi_1|^2\right)dx$$

$$= |A|^2(9 + 0 + 0 + 16) = 25|A|^2 \Rightarrow \boxed{A = 1/5.}$$

**(b)**

$$\Psi(x,t) = \frac{1}{5}\left[3\psi_0(x)e^{-iE_0t/\hbar} + 4\psi_1(x)e^{-iE_1t/\hbar}\right] = \boxed{\frac{1}{5}\left[3\psi_0(x)e^{-i\omega t/2} + 4\psi_1(x)e^{-3i\omega t/2}\right]}.$$

(Here $\psi_0$ and $\psi_1$ are given by Eqs. 2.59 and 2.62; $E_1$ and $E_2$ by Eq. 2.61.)

$$|\Psi(x,t)|^2 = \frac{1}{25}\left[9\psi_0^2 + 12\psi_0\psi_1 e^{i\omega t/2}e^{-3i\omega t/2} + 12\psi_0\psi_1 e^{-i\omega t/2}e^{3i\omega t/2} + 16\psi_1^2\right]$$

$$= \boxed{\frac{1}{25}\left[9\psi_0^2 + 16\psi_1^2 + 24\psi_0\psi_1\cos(\omega t)\right]}.$$

**(c)**

$$\langle x\rangle = \frac{1}{25}\left[9\int x\psi_0^2\,dx + 16\int x\psi_1^2\,dx + 24\cos(\omega t)\int x\psi_0\psi_1\,dx\right].$$

But $\int x\psi_0^2\,dx = \int x\psi_1^2\,dx = 0$ (see Problem 2.11 or 2.12), while

$$\int x\psi_0\psi_1\,dx = \sqrt{\frac{m\omega}{\pi\hbar}}\sqrt{\frac{2m\omega}{\hbar}}\int xe^{-\frac{m\omega}{2\hbar}x^2}xe^{-\frac{m\omega}{2\hbar}x^2}\,dx = \sqrt{\frac{2}{\pi}}\left(\frac{m\omega}{\hbar}\right)\int_{-\infty}^{\infty}x^2e^{-\frac{m\omega}{\hbar}x^2}\,dx$$

$$= \sqrt{\frac{2}{\pi}}\left(\frac{m\omega}{\hbar}\right)2\sqrt{\pi}2\left(\frac{1}{2}\sqrt{\frac{\hbar}{m\omega}}\right)^3 = \sqrt{\frac{\hbar}{2m\omega}}.$$

So

$$\boxed{\langle x\rangle = \frac{24}{25}\sqrt{\frac{\hbar}{2m\omega}}\cos(\omega t);} \quad \langle p\rangle = m\frac{d}{dt}\langle x\rangle = \boxed{-\frac{24}{25}\sqrt{\frac{m\omega\hbar}{2}}\sin(\omega t).}$$

(With $\psi_2$ in place of $\psi_1$ the frequency would be $(E_2 - E_0)/\hbar = [(5/2)\hbar\omega - (1/2)\hbar\omega]/\hbar = 2\omega$.)

Ehrenfest's theorem says $d\langle p\rangle/dt = -\langle\partial V/\partial x\rangle$. Here

$$\frac{d\langle p\rangle}{dt} = -\frac{24}{25}\sqrt{\frac{m\omega\hbar}{2}}\omega\cos(\omega t), \quad V = \frac{1}{2}m\omega^2 x^2 \Rightarrow \frac{\partial V}{\partial x} = m\omega^2 x,$$

so

$$-\langle\frac{\partial V}{\partial x}\rangle = -m\omega^2\langle x\rangle = -m\omega^2\frac{24}{25}\sqrt{\frac{\hbar}{2m\omega}}\cos(\omega t) = -\frac{24}{25}\sqrt{\frac{\hbar m\omega}{2}}\omega\cos(\omega t),$$

so Ehrenfest's theorem holds.

**(d)** You could get $\boxed{E_0 = \frac{1}{2}\hbar\omega,}$ with probability $|c_0|^2 = \boxed{9/25,}$ or $\boxed{E_1 = \frac{3}{2}\hbar\omega,}$ with probability $|c_1|^2 = \boxed{16/25.}$

---

## Problem 2.14

The new allowed energies are $E_n' = (n + \frac{1}{2})\hbar\omega' = 2(n + \frac{1}{2})\hbar\omega = \hbar\omega, 3\hbar\omega, 5\hbar\omega, \ldots$. So the probability of getting $\frac{1}{2}\hbar\omega$ is $\boxed{\text{zero.}}$ The probability of getting $\hbar\omega$ (the new ground state energy) is $P_0 = |c_0|^2$, where $c_0 = \int\Psi(x,0)\psi_0'\,dx$, with

$$\Psi(x,0) = \psi_0(x) = \left(\frac{m\omega}{\pi\hbar}\right)^{1/4}e^{-\frac{m\omega}{2\hbar}x^2}, \quad \psi_0(x)' = \left(\frac{m2\omega}{\pi\hbar}\right)^{1/4}e^{-\frac{m2\omega}{2\hbar}x^2}.$$

So

$$c_0 = 2^{1/4} \sqrt{\frac{m\omega}{\pi\hbar}} \int_{-\infty}^{\infty} e^{-\frac{3m\omega}{2\hbar} x^2} \, dx = 2^{1/4} \sqrt{\frac{m\omega}{\pi\hbar}} 2\sqrt{\pi} \left( \frac{1}{2} \sqrt{\frac{2\hbar}{3m\omega}} \right) = 2^{1/4} \sqrt{\frac{2}{3}}.$$

Therefore

$$P_0 = \boxed{\frac{2}{3}\sqrt{2} = 0.9428.}$$

## Problem 2.15

$$\psi_0 = \left(\frac{m\omega}{\pi\hbar}\right)^{1/4} e^{-\xi^2/2}, \text{ so } P = 2\sqrt{\frac{m\omega}{\pi\hbar}} \int_{x_0}^{\infty} e^{-\xi^2} dx = 2\sqrt{\frac{m\omega}{\pi\hbar}} \sqrt{\frac{\hbar}{m\omega}} \int_{\xi_0}^{\infty} e^{-\xi^2} d\xi.$$

Classically allowed region extends out to: $\frac{1}{2}m\omega^2 x_0^2 = E_0 = \frac{1}{2}\hbar\omega$, or $x_0 = \sqrt{\frac{\hbar}{m\omega}}$, so $\xi_0 = 1$.

$$P = \frac{2}{\sqrt{\pi}} \int_1^{\infty} e^{-\xi^2} d\xi = 2(1 - F(\sqrt{2})) \text{ (in notation of CRC Table)} = \boxed{0.157.}$$

## Problem 2.16

$\underline{n = 5}$: $j = 1 \Rightarrow a_3 = \frac{-2(5-1)}{(1+1)(1+2)} a_1 = -\frac{4}{3}a_1$; $j = 3 \Rightarrow a_5 = \frac{-2(5-3)}{(3+1)(3+2)} a_3 = -\frac{1}{5}a_3 = \frac{4}{15}a_1$; $j = 5 \Rightarrow a_7 = 0$. So $H_5(\xi) = a_1\xi - \frac{4}{3}a_1\xi^3 + \frac{4}{15}a_1\xi^5 = \frac{a_1}{15}(15\xi - 20\xi^3 + 4\xi^5)$. By convention the coefficient of $\xi^5$ is $2^5$, so $a_1 = 15 \cdot 8$, and $\boxed{H_5(\xi) = 120\xi - 160\xi^3 + 32\xi^5}$ (which agrees with Table 2.1).

$\underline{n = 6}$: $j = 0 \Rightarrow a_2 = \frac{-2(6-0)}{(0+1)(0+2)} a_0 = -6a_0$; $j = 2 \Rightarrow a_4 = \frac{-2(6-2)}{(2+1)(2+2)} a_2 = -\frac{2}{3}a_2 = 4a_0$; $j = 4 \Rightarrow a_6 = \frac{-2(6-4)}{(4+1)(4+2)} a_4 = -\frac{2}{15}a_4 = -\frac{8}{15}a_0$; $j = 6 \Rightarrow a_8 = 0$. So $H_6(\xi) = a_0 - 6a_0\xi^2 + 4a_0\xi^4 - \frac{8}{15}\xi^6 a_0$. The coefficient of $\xi^6$ is $2^6$, so $2^6 = -\frac{8}{15}a_0 \Rightarrow a_0 = -15 \cdot 8 = -120$. $\boxed{H_6(\xi) = -120 + 720\xi^2 - 480\xi^4 + 64\xi^6.}$

## Problem 2.17

(a)

$$\frac{d}{d\xi}(e^{-\xi^2}) = -2\xi e^{-\xi^2}; \quad \left(\frac{d}{d\xi}\right)^2 e^{-\xi^2} = \frac{d}{d\xi}(-2\xi e^{-\xi^2}) = (-2 + 4\xi^2)e^{-\xi^2};$$

$$\left(\frac{d}{d\xi}\right)^3 e^{-\xi^2} = \frac{d}{d\xi}\left[(-2 + 4\xi^2)e^{-\xi^2}\right] = \left[8\xi + (-2 + 4\xi^2)(-2\xi)\right]e^{-\xi^2} = (12\xi - 8\xi^3)e^{-\xi^2};$$

$$\left(\frac{d}{d\xi}\right)^4 e^{-\xi^2} = \frac{d}{d\xi}\left[(12\xi - 8\xi^3)e^{-\xi^2}\right] = \left[12 - 24\xi^2 + (12\xi - 8\xi^3)(-2\xi)\right]e^{-\xi^2} = (12 - 48\xi^2 + 16\xi^4)e^{-\xi^2}.$$

$$H_3(\xi) = -e^{\xi^2}\left(\frac{d}{d\xi}\right)^3 e^{-\xi^2} = \boxed{-12\xi + 8\xi^3;} \quad H_4(\xi) = e^{\xi^2}\left(\frac{d}{d\xi}\right)^4 e^{-\xi^2} = \boxed{12 - 48\xi^2 + 16\xi^4.}$$

**(b)**

$$H_5 = 2\xi H_4 - 8H_3 = 2\xi(12 - 48\xi^2 + 16\xi^4) - 8(-12\xi + 8\xi^3) = \boxed{120\xi - 160\xi^3 + 32\xi^5.}$$

$$H_6 = 2\xi H_5 - 10H_4 = 2\xi(120\xi - 160\xi^3 + 32\xi^5) - 10(12 - 48\xi^2 + 16\xi^4) = \boxed{-120 + 720\xi^2 - 480\xi^4 + 64\xi^6.}$$

**(c)**

$$\frac{dH_5}{d\xi} = 120 - 480\xi^2 + 160\xi^4 = 10(12 - 48\xi^2 + 16\xi^4) = (2)(5)H_4. \checkmark$$

$$\frac{dH_6}{d\xi} = 1440\xi - 1920\xi^3 + 384\xi^5 = 12(120\xi - 160\xi^3 + 32\xi^5) = (2)(6)H_5. \checkmark$$

**(d)**

$$\frac{d}{dz}(e^{-z^2+2z\xi}) = (-2z + \xi)e^{-z^2+2z\xi}; \text{ setting } z = 0, \boxed{H_0(\xi) = 2\xi.}$$

$$\left(\frac{d}{dz}\right)^2 (e^{-z^2+2z\xi}) = \frac{d}{dz}\left[(-2z + 2\xi)e^{-z^2+2z\xi}\right]$$
$$= \left[-2 + (-2z + 2\xi)^2\right]e^{-z^2+2z\xi}; \text{ setting } z = 0, \boxed{H_1(\xi) = -2 + 4\xi^2.}$$

$$\left(\frac{d}{dz}\right)^3 (e^{-z^2+2z\xi}) = \frac{d}{dz}\left\{\left[-2 + (-2z + 2\xi)^2\right]e^{-z^2+2z\xi}\right\}$$
$$= \left\{2(-2z + 2\xi)(-2) + \left[-2 + (-2z + 2\xi)^2\right](-2z + 2\xi)\right\}e^{-z^2+2z\xi};$$

$$\text{setting } z = 0, \ H_2(\xi) = -8\xi + (-2 + 4\xi^2)(2\xi) = \boxed{-12\xi + 8\xi^3.}$$

---

## Problem 2.18

$$Ae^{ikx} + Be^{-ikx} = A(\cos kx + i\sin kx) + B(\cos kx - i\sin kx) = (A + B)\cos kx + i(A - B)\sin kx$$
$$= C\cos kx + D\sin kx, \text{ with } \boxed{C = A + B; \ D = i(A - B).}$$

$$C\cos kx + D\sin kx = C\left(\frac{e^{ikx} + e^{-ikx}}{2}\right) + D\left(\frac{e^{ikx} - e^{-ikx}}{2i}\right) = \frac{1}{2}(C - iD)e^{ikx} + \frac{1}{2}(C + iD)e^{-ikx}$$
$$= Ae^{ikx} + Be^{-ikx}, \text{ with } \boxed{A = \frac{1}{2}(C - iD); \ B = \frac{1}{2}(C + iD).}$$

---

## Problem 2.19

Equation 2.94 says $\Psi = Ae^{i(kx - \frac{\hbar k^2}{2m}t)}$, so

$$J = \frac{i\hbar}{2m}\left(\Psi\frac{\partial\Psi^*}{\partial x} - \Psi^*\frac{\partial\Psi}{\partial x}\right) = \frac{i\hbar}{2m}|A|^2\left[e^{i(kx-\frac{\hbar k^2}{2m}t)}(-ik)e^{-i(kx-\frac{\hbar k^2}{2m}t)} - e^{-i(kx-\frac{\hbar k^2}{2m}t)}(ik)e^{i(kx-\frac{\hbar k^2}{2m}t)}\right]$$

$$= \frac{i\hbar}{2m}|A|^2(-2ik) = \boxed{\frac{\hbar k}{m}|A|^2}.$$

It flows in the positive $(x)$ direction (as you would expect).

---

## Problem 2.20

(a)

$$f(x) = b_0 + \sum_{n=1}^{\infty}\frac{a_n}{2i}\left(e^{in\pi x/a} - e^{-in\pi x/a}\right) + \sum_{n=1}^{\infty}\frac{b_n}{2}\left(e^{in\pi x/a} + e^{-in\pi x/a}\right)$$

$$= b_0 + \sum_{n=1}^{\infty}\left(\frac{a_n}{2i} + \frac{b_n}{2}\right)e^{in\pi x/a} + \sum_{n=1}^{\infty}\left(-\frac{a_n}{2i} + \frac{b_n}{2}\right)e^{-in\pi x/a}.$$

Let

$$\boxed{c_0 \equiv b_0;\ c_n = \tfrac{1}{2}\left(-ia_n + b_n\right),\ \text{for } n = 1, 2, 3, \ldots;\ c_n \equiv \tfrac{1}{2}\left(ia_{-n} + b_{-n}\right),\ \text{for } n = -1, -2, -3, \ldots.}$$

Then $f(x) = \displaystyle\sum_{n=-\infty}^{\infty} c_n e^{in\pi x/a}$.    QED

(b)

$$\int_{-a}^{a} f(x)e^{-im\pi x/a}dx = \sum_{n=-\infty}^{\infty} c_n \int_{-a}^{a} e^{i(n-m)\pi x/a}dx.\quad \text{But for } n \neq m,$$

$$\int_{-a}^{a} e^{i(n-m)\pi x/a}dx = \frac{e^{i(n-m)\pi x/a}}{i(n-m)\pi/a}\bigg|_{-a}^{a} = \frac{e^{i(n-m)\pi} - e^{-i(n-m)\pi}}{i(n-m)\pi/a} = \frac{(-1)^{n-m} - (-1)^{n-m}}{i(n-m)\pi/a} = 0,$$

whereas for $n = m$,

$$\int_{-a}^{a} e^{i(n-m)\pi x/a}dx = \int_{-a}^{a} dx = 2a.$$

So all terms except $n = m$ are zero, and

$$\int_{-a}^{a} f(x)e^{-im\pi x/a} = 2ac_m,\ \text{so } c_n = \frac{1}{2a}\int_{-a}^{a} f(x)e^{-in\pi x/a}dx.\quad \text{QED}$$

(c)

$$f(x) = \sum_{n=-\infty}^{\infty}\sqrt{\frac{\pi}{2}}\frac{1}{a}F(k)e^{ikx} = \frac{1}{\sqrt{2\pi}}\sum F(k)e^{ikx}\Delta k,$$

where $\boxed{\Delta k \equiv \dfrac{\pi}{a}}$ is the increment in $k$ from $n$ to $(n+1)$.

$$F(k) = \sqrt{\frac{2}{\pi}} a \frac{1}{2a} \int_{-a}^{a} f(x) e^{-ikx} dx = \frac{1}{\sqrt{2\pi}} \int_{-a}^{a} f(x) e^{-ikx} dx.$$

**(d)** As $a \to \infty$, $k$ becomes a continuous variable,

$$f(x) = \frac{1}{\sqrt{2\pi}} \int_{-\infty}^{\infty} F(k) e^{ikx} dk; \quad F(k) = \frac{1}{\sqrt{2\pi}} \int_{-\infty}^{\infty} f(x) e^{ikx} dx.$$

---

## Problem 2.21

**(a)**

$$1 = \int_{-\infty}^{\infty} |\Psi(x,0)|^2 dx = 2|A|^2 \int_{0}^{\infty} e^{-2ax} dx = 2|A|^2 \frac{e^{-2ax}}{-2a}\bigg|_{0}^{\infty} = \frac{|A|^2}{a} \Rightarrow A = \boxed{\sqrt{a}.}$$

**(b)**

$$\phi(k) = \frac{A}{\sqrt{2\pi}} \int_{-\infty}^{\infty} e^{-a|x|} e^{-ikx} \, dx = \frac{A}{\sqrt{2\pi}} \int_{-\infty}^{\infty} e^{-a|x|} (\cos kx - i \sin kx) dx.$$

The cosine integrand is even, and the sine is odd, so the latter vanishes and

$$
\begin{aligned}
\phi(k) &= 2\frac{A}{\sqrt{2\pi}} \int_{0}^{\infty} e^{-ax} \cos kx \, dx = \frac{A}{\sqrt{2\pi}} \int_{0}^{\infty} e^{-ax} \left( e^{ikx} + e^{-ikx} \right) dx \\
&= \frac{A}{\sqrt{2\pi}} \int_{0}^{\infty} \left( e^{(ik-a)x} + e^{-(ik+a)x} \right) dx = \frac{A}{\sqrt{2\pi}} \left[ \frac{e^{(ik-a)x}}{ik-a} + \frac{e^{-(ik+a)x}}{-(ik+a)} \right]\Bigg|_{0}^{\infty} \\
&= \frac{A}{\sqrt{2\pi}} \left( \frac{-1}{ik-a} + \frac{1}{ik+a} \right) = \frac{A}{\sqrt{2\pi}} \frac{-ik - a + ik - a}{-k^2 - a^2} = \boxed{\sqrt{\frac{a}{2\pi}} \frac{2a}{k^2 + a^2}.}
\end{aligned}
$$

**(c)**

$$\Psi(x,t) = \frac{1}{\sqrt{2\pi}} 2 \sqrt{\frac{a^3}{2\pi}} \int_{-\infty}^{\infty} \frac{1}{k^2 + a^2} e^{i(kx - \frac{\hbar k^2}{2m} t)} dk = \boxed{\frac{a^{3/2}}{\pi} \int_{-\infty}^{\infty} \frac{1}{k^2 + a^2} e^{i(kx - \frac{\hbar k^2}{2m} t)} dk.}$$

**(d)** For *large a*, $\Psi(x,0)$ is a sharp narrow spike whereas $\phi(k) \cong \sqrt{2/\pi a}$ is broad and flat; position is well-defined but momentum is ill-defined. For *small a*, $\Psi(x,0)$ is a broad and flat whereas $\phi(k) \cong (\sqrt{2a^3/\pi})/k^2$ is a sharp narrow spike; position is ill-defined but momentum is well-defined.

---

28						CHAPTER 2. THE TIME-INDEPENDENT SCHRÖDINGER EQUATION

## Problem 2.22

**(a)**

$$1 = |A|^2 \int_{-\infty}^{\infty} e^{-2ax^2} dx = |A|^2 \sqrt{\frac{\pi}{2a}}; \quad \boxed{A = \left(\frac{2a}{\pi}\right)^{1/4}}.$$

**(b)**

$$\int_{-\infty}^{\infty} e^{-(ax^2+bx)} dx = \int_{-\infty}^{\infty} e^{-y^2+(b^2/4a)} \frac{1}{\sqrt{a}} dy = \frac{1}{\sqrt{a}} e^{b^2/4a} \int_{-\infty}^{\infty} e^{-y^2} dy = \sqrt{\frac{\pi}{a}} e^{b^2/4a}.$$

$$\phi(k) = \frac{1}{\sqrt{2\pi}} A \int_{-\infty}^{\infty} e^{-ax^2} e^{-ikx} dx = \frac{1}{\sqrt{2\pi}} \left(\frac{2a}{\pi}\right)^{1/4} \sqrt{\frac{\pi}{a}} e^{-k^2/4a} = \frac{1}{(2\pi a)^{1/4}} e^{-k^2/4a}.$$

$$\Psi(x,t) = \frac{1}{\sqrt{2\pi}} \frac{1}{(2\pi a)^{1/4}} \int_{-\infty}^{\infty} \underbrace{e^{-k^2/4a} e^{i(kx-\hbar k^2 t/2m)}}_{e^{-[(\frac{1}{4a}+i\hbar t/2m)k^2 - ixk]}} dk$$

$$= \frac{1}{\sqrt{2\pi}(2\pi a)^{1/4}} \frac{\sqrt{\pi}}{\sqrt{\frac{1}{4a}+i\hbar t/2m}} e^{-x^2/4(\frac{1}{4a}+i\hbar t/2m)} = \boxed{\left(\frac{2a}{\pi}\right)^{1/4} \frac{e^{-ax^2/(1+2i\hbar at/m)}}{\sqrt{1+2i\hbar at/m}}}.$$

**(c)**

Let $\theta \equiv 2\hbar at/m$. Then $|\Psi|^2 = \sqrt{\frac{2a}{\pi}} \frac{e^{-ax^2/(1+i\theta)} e^{-ax^2/(1-i\theta)}}{\sqrt{(1+i\theta)(1-i\theta)}}$. The exponent is

$$-\frac{ax^2}{(1+i\theta)} - \frac{ax^2}{(1-i\theta)} = -ax^2 \frac{(1-i\theta+1+i\theta)}{(1+i\theta)(1-i\theta)} = \frac{-2ax^2}{1+\theta^2}; \quad |\Psi|^2 = \sqrt{\frac{2a}{\pi}} \frac{e^{-2ax^2/(1+\theta^2)}}{\sqrt{1+\theta^2}}.$$

Or, with $w \equiv \sqrt{\frac{a}{1+\theta^2}}$, $\boxed{|\Psi|^2 = \sqrt{\frac{2}{\pi}} w e^{-2w^2 x^2}}.$ As $t$ increases, the graph of $|\Psi|^2$ flattens out and broadens.

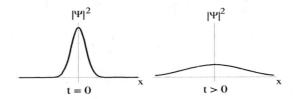

**(d)**

$$\langle x \rangle = \int_{-\infty}^{\infty} x|\Psi|^2 dx = \boxed{0} \text{ (odd integrand)}; \quad \langle p \rangle = m\frac{d\langle x \rangle}{dt} = \boxed{0.}$$

$$\langle x^2 \rangle = \sqrt{\frac{2}{\pi}} w \int_{-\infty}^{\infty} x^2 e^{-2w^2 x^2} dx = \sqrt{\frac{2}{\pi}} w \frac{1}{4w^2} \sqrt{\frac{\pi}{2w^2}} = \boxed{\frac{1}{4w^2}}. \quad \langle p^2 \rangle = -\hbar^2 \int_{-\infty}^{\infty} \Psi^* \frac{d^2\Psi}{dx^2} dx.$$

Write $\Psi = Be^{-bx^2}$, where $B \equiv \left(\dfrac{2a}{\pi}\right)^{1/4} \dfrac{1}{\sqrt{1+i\theta}}$ and $b \equiv \dfrac{a}{1+i\theta}$.

$$\frac{d^2\Psi}{dx^2} = B\frac{d}{dx}\left(-2bxe^{-bx^2}\right) = -2bB(1-2bx^2)e^{-bx^2}.$$

$$\Psi^*\frac{d^2\Psi}{dx^2} = -2b|B|^2(1-2bx^2)e^{-(b+b^*)x^2}; \quad b+b^* = \frac{a}{1+i\theta} + \frac{a}{1-i\theta} = \frac{2a}{1+\theta^2} = 2w^2.$$

$$|B|^2 = \sqrt{\frac{2a}{\pi}}\frac{1}{\sqrt{1+\theta^2}} = \sqrt{\frac{2}{\pi}}w. \quad \text{So } \Psi^*\frac{d^2\Psi}{dx^2} = -2b\sqrt{\frac{2}{\pi}}w(1-2bx^2)e^{-2w^2x^2}.$$

$$\langle p^2\rangle = 2b\hbar^2\sqrt{\frac{2}{\pi}}w\int_{-\infty}^{\infty}(1-2bx^2)e^{-2w^2x^2}dx$$

$$= 2b\hbar^2\sqrt{\frac{2}{\pi}}w\left(\sqrt{\frac{\pi}{2w^2}} - 2b\frac{1}{4w^2}\sqrt{\frac{\pi}{2w^2}}\right) = 2b\hbar^2\left(1-\frac{b}{2w^2}\right).$$

But $1 - \dfrac{b}{2w^2} = 1 - \left(\dfrac{a}{1+i\theta}\right)\left(\dfrac{1+\theta^2}{2a}\right) = 1 - \dfrac{(1-i\theta)}{2} = \dfrac{1+i\theta}{2} = \dfrac{a}{2b}$, so

$$\langle p^2\rangle = 2b\hbar^2\frac{a}{2b} = \boxed{\hbar^2 a.} \quad \boxed{\sigma_x = \frac{1}{2w};} \quad \boxed{\sigma_p = \hbar\sqrt{a}.}$$

**(e)**

$$\sigma_x\sigma_p = \frac{1}{2w}\hbar\sqrt{a} = \frac{\hbar}{2}\sqrt{1+\theta^2} = \frac{\hbar}{2}\sqrt{1+(2\hbar at/m)^2} \geq \frac{\hbar}{2}. \checkmark$$

Closest at $\boxed{t=0,}$ at which time it is right *at* the uncertainty limit.

---

## Problem 2.23

**(a)**

$$(-2)^3 - 3(-2)^2 + 2(-2) - 1 = -8 - 12 - 4 - 1 = \boxed{-25.}$$

**(b)**

$$\cos(3\pi) + 2 = -1 + 2 = \boxed{1.}$$

**(c)**

$\boxed{0}$ ($x=2$ is outside the domain of integration).

---

## Problem 2.24

**(a)** Let $y \equiv cx$, so $dx = \dfrac{1}{c}dy$. $\left\{ \begin{array}{l} \text{If } c > 0, \; y : -\infty \to \infty. \\ \text{If } c < 0, \; y : \infty \to -\infty. \end{array} \right\}$

$$\int_{-\infty}^{\infty} f(x)\delta(cx)dx = \left\{ \begin{array}{l} \frac{1}{c}\int_{-\infty}^{\infty} f(y/c)\delta(y)dy = \frac{1}{c}f(0) \quad (c>0); \text{ or} \\[2ex] \frac{1}{c}\int_{\infty}^{-\infty} f(y/c)\delta(y)dy = -\frac{1}{c}\int_{-\infty}^{\infty} f(y/c)\delta(y)dy = -\frac{1}{c}f(0) \; (c<0). \end{array} \right.$$

In either case, $\displaystyle\int_{-\infty}^{\infty} f(x)\delta(cx)dx = \frac{1}{|c|}f(0) = \int_{-\infty}^{\infty} f(x)\frac{1}{|c|}\delta(x)dx$. So $\delta(cx) = \dfrac{1}{|c|}\delta(x)$. ✓

**(b)**

$$\int_{-\infty}^{\infty} f(x)\frac{d\theta}{dx}dx = f\theta\Big|_{-\infty}^{\infty} - \int_{-\infty}^{\infty}\frac{df}{dx}\theta dx \quad \text{(integration by parts)}$$

$$= f(\infty) - \int_0^{\infty}\frac{df}{dx}dx = f(\infty) - f(\infty) + f(0) = f(0) = \int_{-\infty}^{\infty} f(x)\delta(x)dx.$$

So $d\theta/dx = \delta(x)$. ✓ [Makes sense: The $\theta$ function is constant (so derivative is zero) except at $x = 0$, where the derivative is infinite.]

## Problem 2.25

$$\psi(x) = \frac{\sqrt{m\alpha}}{\hbar}e^{-m\alpha|x|/\hbar^2} = \frac{\sqrt{m\alpha}}{\hbar}\left\{ \begin{array}{ll} e^{-m\alpha x/\hbar^2}, & (x \geq 0), \\ e^{m\alpha x/\hbar^2}, & (x \leq 0). \end{array} \right.$$

$$\langle x \rangle = 0 \text{ (odd integrand)}.$$

$$\langle x^2 \rangle = \int_{-\infty}^{\infty} x^2|\psi|^2 dx = 2\frac{m\alpha}{\hbar^2}\int_0^{\infty} x^2 e^{-2m\alpha x/\hbar^2}dx = \frac{2m\alpha}{\hbar^2}2\left(\frac{\hbar^2}{2m\alpha}\right)^3 = \frac{\hbar^4}{2m^2\alpha^2}; \quad \sigma_x = \frac{\hbar^2}{\sqrt{2}m\alpha}.$$

$$\frac{d\psi}{dx} = \frac{\sqrt{m\alpha}}{\hbar}\left\{ \begin{array}{ll} -\frac{m\alpha}{\hbar^2}e^{-m\alpha x/\hbar^2}, & (x \geq 0) \\ \frac{m\alpha}{\hbar^2}e^{m\alpha x/\hbar^2}, & (x \leq 0) \end{array} \right\} = \left(\frac{\sqrt{m\alpha}}{\hbar}\right)^3\left[-\theta(x)e^{-m\alpha x/\hbar^2} + \theta(-x)e^{m\alpha x/\hbar^2}\right].$$

$$\frac{d^2\psi}{dx^2} = \left(\frac{\sqrt{m\alpha}}{\hbar}\right)^3\left[-\delta(x)e^{-m\alpha x/\hbar^2} + \frac{m\alpha}{\hbar^2}\theta(x)e^{-m\alpha x/\hbar^2} - \delta(-x)e^{m\alpha x/\hbar^2} + \frac{m\alpha}{\hbar^2}\theta(-x)e^{m\alpha x/\hbar^2}\right]$$

$$= \left(\frac{\sqrt{m\alpha}}{\hbar}\right)^3\left[-2\delta(x) + \frac{m\alpha}{\hbar^2}e^{-m\alpha|x|/\hbar^2}\right].$$

In the last step I used the fact that $\delta(-x) = \delta(x)$ (Eq. 2.142), $f(x)\delta(x) = f(0)\delta(x)$ (Eq. 2.112), and $\theta(-x) + \theta(x) = 1$ (Eq. 2.143). Since $d\psi/dx$ is an odd function, $\langle p \rangle = 0$.

$$\langle p^2 \rangle = -\hbar^2\int_{-\infty}^{\infty}\psi\frac{d^2\psi}{dx^2}dx = -\hbar^2\frac{\sqrt{m\alpha}}{\hbar}\left(\frac{\sqrt{m\alpha}}{\hbar}\right)^3\int_{-\infty}^{\infty} e^{-m\alpha|x|/\hbar^2}\left[-2\delta(x) + \frac{m\alpha}{\hbar^2}e^{-m\alpha|x|/\hbar^2}\right]dx$$

$$= \left(\frac{m\alpha}{\hbar}\right)^2\left[2 - 2\frac{m\alpha}{\hbar^2}\int_0^{\infty} e^{-2m\alpha x/\hbar^2}dx\right] = 2\left(\frac{m\alpha}{\hbar}\right)^2\left[1 - \frac{m\alpha}{\hbar^2}\frac{\hbar^2}{2m\alpha}\right] = \left(\frac{m\alpha}{\hbar}\right)^2.$$

Evidently

$$\sigma_p = \frac{m\alpha}{\hbar}, \quad \text{so} \quad \sigma_x\sigma_p = \frac{\hbar^2}{\sqrt{2}m\alpha}\frac{m\alpha}{\hbar} = \sqrt{2}\frac{\hbar}{2} > \frac{\hbar}{2}. \;\checkmark$$

## Problem 2.26

Put $f(x) = \delta(x)$ into Eq. 2.102: $F(k) = \dfrac{1}{\sqrt{2\pi}} \displaystyle\int_{-\infty}^{\infty} \delta(x)e^{-ikx}dx = \boxed{\dfrac{1}{\sqrt{2\pi}}}.$

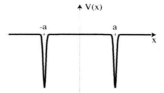

$\therefore f(x) = \delta(x) = \dfrac{1}{\sqrt{2\pi}} \displaystyle\int_{-\infty}^{\infty} \dfrac{1}{\sqrt{2\pi}} e^{ikx}dk = \dfrac{1}{2\pi} \displaystyle\int_{-\infty}^{\infty} e^{ikx}dk.$   QED

---

## Problem 2.27

**(a)**

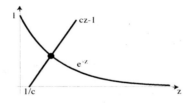

**(b)** From Problem 2.1(c) the solutions are even or odd. Look first for *even solutions*:

$$\psi(x) = \begin{cases} Ae^{-\kappa x} & (x < a), \\ B(e^{\kappa x} + e^{-\kappa x}) & (-a < x < a), \\ Ae^{\kappa x} & (x < -a). \end{cases}$$

Continuity at $a$: $Ae^{-\kappa a} = B(e^{\kappa a} + e^{-\kappa a})$, or $A = B(e^{2\kappa a} + 1)$.

Discontinuous derivative at $a$, $\Delta\dfrac{d\psi}{dx} = -\dfrac{2m\alpha}{\hbar^2}\psi(a)$ :

$$-\kappa Ae^{-\kappa a} - B(\kappa e^{\kappa a} - \kappa e^{-\kappa a}) = -\dfrac{2m\alpha}{\hbar^2}Ae^{-\kappa a} \Rightarrow A + B(e^{2\kappa a} - 1) = \dfrac{2m\alpha}{\hbar^2\kappa}A;\ \text{or}$$

$$B(e^{2\kappa a} - 1) = A\left(\dfrac{2m\alpha}{\hbar^2\kappa} - 1\right) = B(e^{2\kappa a} + 1)\left(\dfrac{2m\alpha}{\hbar^2\kappa} - 1\right) \Rightarrow e^{2\kappa a} - 1 = e^{2\kappa a}\left(\dfrac{2m\alpha}{\hbar^2\kappa} - 1\right) + \dfrac{2m\alpha}{\hbar^2\kappa} - 1.$$

$$1 = \dfrac{2m\alpha}{\hbar^2\kappa} - 1 + \dfrac{2m\alpha}{\hbar^2\kappa}e^{-2\kappa a};\ \dfrac{\hbar^2\kappa}{m\alpha} = 1 + e^{-2\kappa a},\ \text{or}\ \boxed{e^{-2\kappa a} = \dfrac{\hbar^2\kappa}{m\alpha} - 1.}$$

This is a transcendental equation for $\kappa$ (and hence for $E$). I'll solve it graphically: Let $z \equiv 2\kappa a$, $c \equiv \dfrac{\hbar^2}{2am\alpha}$, so $e^{-z} = cz - 1$. Plot both sides and look for intersections:

From the graph, noting that $c$ and $z$ are both positive, we see that there is one (and only one) solution (for even $\psi$). If $\alpha = \frac{\hbar^2}{2ma}$, so $c = 1$, the calculator gives $z = 1.278$, so $\kappa^2 = -\frac{2mE}{\hbar^2} = \frac{z^2}{(2a)^2} \Rightarrow E = -\frac{(1.278)^2}{8}\left(\frac{\hbar^2}{ma^2}\right) = -0.204\left(\frac{\hbar^2}{ma^2}\right)$.

Now look for *odd solutions:*

$$\psi(x) = \begin{cases} Ae^{-\kappa x} & (x < a), \\ B(e^{\kappa x} - e^{-\kappa x}) & (-a < x < a), \\ -Ae^{\kappa x} & (x < -a). \end{cases}$$

Continuity at $a$ : $Ae^{-\kappa a} = B(e^{\kappa a} - e^{-\kappa a})$, or $A = B(e^{2\kappa a} - 1)$.

Discontinuity in $\psi'$ : $-\kappa Ae^{-\kappa a} - B(\kappa e^{\kappa a} + \kappa e^{-\kappa a}) = -\frac{2m\alpha}{\hbar^2}Ae^{-\kappa a} \Rightarrow B(e^{2\kappa a} + 1) = A\left(\frac{2m\alpha}{\hbar^2\kappa} - 1\right)$,

$$e^{2\kappa a} + 1 = (e^{2\kappa a} - 1)\left(\frac{2m\alpha}{\hbar^2\kappa} - 1\right) = e^{2\kappa a}\left(\frac{2m\alpha}{\hbar^2\kappa} - 1\right) - \frac{2m\alpha}{\hbar^2\kappa} + 1,$$

$$1 = \frac{2m\alpha}{\hbar^2\kappa} - 1 - \frac{2m\alpha}{\hbar^2\kappa}e^{-2\kappa a}; \quad \frac{\hbar^2\kappa}{m\alpha} = 1 - e^{-2\kappa a}, \quad \boxed{e^{-2\kappa a} = 1 - \frac{\hbar^2\kappa}{m\alpha}}, \text{ or } e^{-z} = 1 - cz.$$

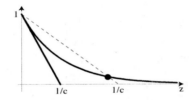

This time there may or may not be a solution. Both graphs have their $y$-intercepts at 1, but if $c$ is too large ($\alpha$ too small), there may be no intersection (solid line), whereas if $c$ is smaller (dashed line) there will be. (Note that $z = 0 \Rightarrow \kappa = 0$ is *not* a solution, since $\psi$ is then non-normalizable.) The slope of $e^{-z}$ (at $z = 0$) is $-1$; the slope of $(1 - cz)$ is $-c$. So there is an *odd* solution $\Leftrightarrow c < 1$, or $\alpha > \hbar^2/2ma$.

Conclusion: $\boxed{\text{One bound state if } \alpha \le \hbar^2/2ma; \text{ two if } \alpha > \hbar^2/2ma.}$

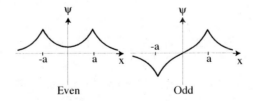

Even                    Odd

$\alpha = \frac{\hbar^2}{ma} \Rightarrow c = \frac{1}{2}.$ $\begin{cases} \text{Even: } e^{-z} = \frac{1}{2}z - 1 \Rightarrow z = 2.21772, \\ \text{Odd: } e^{-z} = 1 - \frac{1}{2}z \Rightarrow z = 1.59362. \end{cases}$

$\boxed{E = -0.615(\hbar^2/ma^2); \quad E = -0.317(\hbar^2/ma^2).}$

$\alpha = \frac{\hbar^2}{4ma} \Rightarrow c = 2.$ *Only even:* $e^{-z} = 2z - 1 \Rightarrow z = 0.738835;$ $\boxed{E = -0.0682(\hbar^2/ma^2).}$

## Problem 2.28

$$\psi = \begin{cases} Ae^{ikx} + Be^{-ikx} & (x < -a) \\ Ce^{ikx} + De^{-ikx} & (-a < x < a) \\ Fe^{ikx} & (x > a) \end{cases}. \quad \text{Impose boundary conditions:}$$

(1) Continuity at $-a$ : $Ae^{ika} + Be^{ika} = Ce^{-ika} + De^{ika} \Rightarrow \beta A + B = \beta C + D$, where $\beta \equiv e^{-2ika}$.

(2) Continuity at $+a$ : $Ce^{ika} + De^{-ika} = Fe^{ika} \Rightarrow F = C + \beta D$.

(3) Discontinuity in $\psi'$ at $-a$ : $ik(Ce^{-ika} - De^{ika}) - ik(Ae^{-ika} - Be^{ika}) = -\frac{2m\alpha}{\hbar^2}(Ae^{-ika} + Be^{ika})$

$\Rightarrow \beta C - D = \beta(\gamma + 1)A + B(\gamma - 1)$, where $\gamma \equiv i2m\alpha/\hbar^2 k$.

(4) Discontinuity in $\psi'$ at $+a$ : $ikFe^{ika} - ik(Ce^{ika} - De^{-ika}) = -\frac{2m\alpha}{\hbar^2}(Fe^{ika})$

$\Rightarrow C - \beta D = (1 - \gamma)F$.

To solve for $C$ and $D$, $\begin{cases} \text{add (2) and (4)} : & 2C = F + (1 - \gamma)F \Rightarrow 2C = (2 - \gamma)F. \\ \text{subtract (2) and (4)} : & 2\beta D = F - (1 - \gamma)F \Rightarrow 2D = (\gamma/\beta)F. \end{cases}$

$\begin{cases} \text{add (1) and (3)} : & 2\beta C = \beta A + B + \beta(\gamma + 1)A + B(\gamma - 1) \Rightarrow 2C = (\gamma + 2)A + (\gamma/\beta)B. \\ \text{subtract (1) and (3)} : & 2D = \beta A + B - \beta(\gamma + 1)A - B(\gamma - 1) \Rightarrow 2D = -\gamma\beta A + (2 - \gamma)B. \end{cases}$

$\begin{cases} \text{Equate the two expressions for } 2C : (2 - \gamma)F = (\gamma + 2)A + (\gamma/\beta)B. \\ \text{Equate the two expressions for } 2D : (\gamma/\beta)F = -\gamma\beta A + (2 - \gamma)B. \end{cases}$

Solve these for $F$ and $B$, in terms of $A$. Multiply the first by $\beta(2 - \gamma)$, the second by $\gamma$, and subtract:

$$\left[\beta(2 - \gamma)^2 F = \beta(4 - \gamma^2)A + \gamma(2 - \gamma)B\right]; \quad \left[(\gamma^2/\beta)F = -\beta\gamma^2 A + \gamma(2 - \gamma)B\right].$$

$$\Rightarrow \left[\beta(2 - \gamma)^2 - \gamma^2/\beta\right] F = \beta\left[4 - \gamma^2 + \gamma\right] A = 4\beta A \Rightarrow \frac{F}{A} = \frac{4}{(2 - \gamma)^2 - \gamma^2/\beta^2}.$$

Let $g \equiv i/\gamma = \frac{\hbar^2 k}{2m\alpha}$; $\phi \equiv 4ka$, so $\gamma = \frac{i}{g}$, $\beta^2 = e^{-i\phi}$. Then: $\frac{F}{A} = \frac{4g^2}{(2g - i)^2 + e^{i\phi}}$.

Denominator: $4g^2 - 4ig - 1 + \cos\phi + i\sin\phi = (4g^2 - 1 + \cos\phi) + i(\sin\phi - 4g)$.

$|\text{Denominator}|^2 = (4g^2 - 1 + \cos\phi)^2 + (\sin\phi - 4g)^2$

$\qquad\qquad = 16g^4 + 1 + \cos^2\phi - 8g^2 - 2\cos\phi + 8g^2\cos\phi + \sin^2\phi - 8g\sin\phi + 16g^2$

$\qquad\qquad = 16g^4 + 8g^2 + 2 + (8g^2 - 2)\cos\phi - 8g\sin\phi.$

$$T = \left|\frac{F}{A}\right|^2 = \boxed{\frac{8g^4}{(8g^4 + 4g^2 + 1) + (4g^2 - 1)\cos\phi - 4g\sin\phi}, \text{ where } g \equiv \frac{\hbar^2 k}{2m\alpha} \text{ and } \phi \equiv 4ka.}$$

## Problem 2.29

In place of Eq. 2.151, we have: $\psi(x) = \begin{cases} Fe^{-\kappa x} & (x > a) \\ D\sin(lx) & (0 < x < a) \\ -\psi(-x) & (x < 0) \end{cases}$ .

Continuity of $\psi$ : $Fe^{-\kappa a} = D\sin(la)$; continuity of $\psi'$ : $-F\kappa e^{-\kappa a} = Dl\cos(la)$.

Divide: $-\kappa = l\cot(la)$, or $-\kappa a = la\cot(la) \Rightarrow \sqrt{z_0^2 - z^2} = -z\cot z$, or $\boxed{-\cot z = \sqrt{(z_0/z)^2 - 1}.}$

**Wide, deep well:** Intersections are at $\pi, 2\pi, 3\pi$, etc. Same as Eq. 2.157, but now for $n$ *even*. This fills in the rest of the states for the infinite square well.

**Shallow, narrow well:** If $z_0 < \pi/2$, there is *no* odd bound state. The corresponding condition on $V_0$ is

$$\boxed{V_0 < \frac{\pi^2\hbar^2}{8ma^2} \Rightarrow \textit{no odd bound state.}}$$

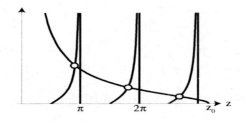

## Problem 2.30

$$1 = 2\int_0^\infty |\psi|^2 dx = 2\left(|D|^2\int_0^a \cos^2 lx\,dx + |F|^2\int_a^\infty e^{-2\kappa x}dx\right)$$

$$= 2\left[|D|^2\left(\frac{x}{2} + \frac{1}{4l}\sin 2lx\right)\Big|_0^a + |F|^2\left(-\frac{1}{2\kappa}e^{-2\kappa x}\right)\Big|_a^\infty\right] = 2\left[|D|^2\left(\frac{a}{2} + \frac{\sin 2la}{4l}\right) + |F|^2\frac{e^{-2\kappa a}}{2\kappa}\right].$$

But $F = De^{\kappa a}\cos la$ (Eq. 2.152), so $1 = |D|^2\left(a + \frac{\sin(2la)}{2l} + \frac{\cos^2(la)}{\kappa}\right)$.

Furthermore $\kappa = l\tan(la)$ (Eq. 2.154), so

$$1 = |D|^2\left(a + \frac{2\sin la\cos la}{2l} + \frac{\cos^3 la}{l\sin la}\right) = |D|^2\left[a + \frac{\cos la}{l\sin la}(\sin^2 la + \cos^2 la)\right]$$

$$= |D|^2\left(a + \frac{1}{l\tan la}\right) = |D|^2\left(a + \frac{1}{\kappa}\right). \qquad \boxed{D = \frac{1}{\sqrt{a + 1/\kappa}},} \qquad \boxed{F = \frac{e^{\kappa a}\cos la}{\sqrt{a + 1/\kappa}}.}$$

## Problem 2.31

Equation 2.155 $\Rightarrow z_0 = \frac{a}{\hbar}\sqrt{2mV_0}$. We want $\alpha = \text{area of potential} = 2aV_0$ held constant as $a \to 0$. Therefore $V_0 = \frac{\alpha}{2a}$; $z_0 = \frac{a}{\hbar}\sqrt{2m\frac{\alpha}{2a}} = \frac{1}{\hbar}\sqrt{m\alpha a} \to 0$. So $z_0$ is *small*, and the intersection in Fig. 2.18 occurs at very small $z$. Solve Eq. 2.156 for very small $z$, by expanding $\tan z$:

$$\tan z \cong z = \sqrt{(z_0/z)^2 - 1} = (1/z)\sqrt{z_0^2 - z^2}.$$

Now (from Eqs. 2.146, 2.148 and 2.155) $z_0^2 - z^2 = \kappa^2 a^2$, so $z^2 = \kappa a$. But $z_0^2 - z^2 = z^4 \ll 1 \Rightarrow z \cong z_0$, so $\kappa a \cong z_0^2$. But we found that $z_0 \cong \frac{1}{\hbar}\sqrt{m\alpha a}$ here, so $\kappa a = \frac{1}{\hbar^2}m\alpha a$, or $\kappa = \frac{m\alpha}{\hbar^2}$. (At this point the $a$'s have canceled, and we can go to the limit $a \to 0$.)

$$\frac{\sqrt{-2mE}}{\hbar} = \frac{m\alpha}{\hbar^2} \Rightarrow -2mE = \frac{m^2\alpha^2}{\hbar^2}. \quad \boxed{E = -\frac{m\alpha^2}{2\hbar^2}} \text{ (which agrees with Eq. 2.129).}$$

In Eq. 2.169, $V_0 \gg E \Rightarrow T^{-1} \cong 1 + \frac{V_0^2}{4EV_0}\sin^2\left(\frac{2a}{\hbar}\sqrt{2mV_0}\right)$. But $V_0 = \frac{\alpha}{2a}$, so the argument of the sine is small, and we can replace $\sin\epsilon$ by $\epsilon$: $T^{-1} \cong 1 + \frac{V_0}{4E}\left(\frac{2a}{\hbar}\right)^2 2mV_0 = 1 + (2aV_0)^2\frac{m}{2\hbar^2 E}$. But $2aV_0 = \alpha$, so $T^{-1} = 1 + \frac{m\alpha^2}{2\hbar^2 E}$, in agreement with Eq. 2.141.

---

## Problem 2.32

Multiply Eq. 2.165 by $\sin la$, Eq. 2.166 by $\frac{1}{l}\cos la$, and add:

$$\left.\begin{array}{l} C\sin^2 la + D\sin la\cos la = Fe^{ika}\sin la \\ C\cos^2 la - D\sin la\cos la = \frac{ik}{l}Fe^{ika}\cos la \end{array}\right\} \quad C = Fe^{ika}\left[\sin la + \frac{ik}{l}\cos la\right].$$

Multiply Eq. 2.165 by $\cos la$, Eq. 2.166 by $\frac{1}{l}\sin la$, and subtract:

$$\left.\begin{array}{l} C\sin la\cos la + D\cos^2 la = Fe^{ika}\cos la \\ C\sin la\cos la - D\sin^2 la = \frac{ik}{l}Fe^{ika}\sin la \end{array}\right\} \quad D = Fe^{ika}\left[\cos la - \frac{ik}{l}\sin la\right].$$

Put these into Eq. 2.163:

**(1)** $Ae^{-ika} + Be^{ika} = -Fe^{ika}\left[\sin la + \frac{ik}{l}\cos la\right]\sin la + Fe^{ika}\left[\cos la - \frac{ik}{l}\sin la\right]\cos la$

$$= Fe^{ika}\left[\cos^2 la - \frac{ik}{l}\sin la\cos la - \sin^2 la - \frac{ik}{l}\sin la\cos la\right]$$

$$= Fe^{ika}\left[\cos(2la) - \frac{ik}{l}\sin(2la)\right].$$

Likewise, from Eq. 2.164:

**(2)** $Ae^{-ika} - Be^{ika} = -\frac{il}{k}Fe^{ika}\left[\left(\sin la + \frac{ik}{l}\cos la\right)\cos la + \left(\cos la - \frac{ik}{l}\sin la\right)\sin la\right]$

$$= -\frac{il}{k}Fe^{ika}\left[\sin la\cos la + \frac{ik}{l}\cos^2 la + \sin la\cos la - \frac{ik}{l}\sin^2 la\right]$$

$$= -\frac{il}{k}Fe^{ika}\left[\sin(2la) + \frac{ik}{l}\cos(2la)\right] = Fe^{ika}\left[\cos(2la) - \frac{il}{k}\sin(2la)\right].$$

Add **(1)** and **(2)**: $2Ae^{-ika} = Fe^{ika} \left[ 2\cos(2la) - i\left( \frac{k}{l} + \frac{l}{k} \right) \sin(2la) \right]$, or:

$$F = \frac{e^{-2ika}A}{\cos(2la) - i\frac{\sin(2la)}{2kl}(k^2 + l^2)} \quad \text{(confirming Eq. 2.168). Now subtract (2) from (1):}$$

$$2Be^{ika} = Fe^{ika}\left[ i\left( \frac{l}{k} - \frac{k}{l} \right)\sin(2la) \right] \Rightarrow B = i\frac{\sin(2la)}{2kl}(l^2 - k^2)F \quad \text{(confirming Eq. 2.167).}$$

$$T^{-1} = \left| \frac{A}{F} \right|^2 = \left| \cos(2la) - i\frac{\sin(2la)}{2kl}(k^2 + l^2) \right|^2 = \cos^2(2la) + \frac{\sin^2(2la)}{(2lk)^2}(k^2 + l^2)^2.$$

But $\cos^2(2la) = 1 - \sin^2(2la)$, so

$$T^{-1} = 1 + \sin^2(2la)\left[ \underbrace{\frac{(k^2 + l^2)^2}{(2lk)^2} - 1}_{\frac{1}{(2kl)^2}[k^4 + 2k^2l^2 + l^4 - 4k^2l^2] = \frac{1}{(2kl)^2}[k^4 - 2k^2l^2 + l^4] = \frac{(k^2 - l^2)^2}{(2kl)^2}.} \right] = 1 + \frac{(k^2 - l^2)^2}{(2kl)^2}\sin^2(2la).$$

But $k = \frac{\sqrt{2mE}}{\hbar}$, $l = \frac{\sqrt{2m(E + V_0)}}{\hbar}$; so $(2la) = \frac{2a}{\hbar}\sqrt{2m(E + V_0)}$; $k^2 - l^2 = -\frac{2mV_0}{\hbar^2}$, and

$$\frac{(k^2 - l^2)^2}{(2kl)^2} = \frac{\left( \frac{2m}{\hbar^2} \right)^2 V_0^2}{4\left( \frac{2m}{\hbar^2} \right)^2 E(E + V_0)} = \frac{V_0^2}{4E(E + V_0)}.$$

$$\therefore T^{-1} = 1 + \frac{V_0^2}{4E(E + V_0)}\sin^2\left( \frac{2a}{\hbar}\sqrt{2m(E + V_0)} \right), \quad \text{confirming Eq. 2.169.}$$

---

## Problem 2.33

$$\underline{\mathbf{E < V_0}}. \qquad \psi = \left\{ \begin{array}{ll} Ae^{ikx} + Be^{-ikx} & (x < -a) \\ Ce^{\kappa x} + De^{-\kappa x} & (-a < x < a) \\ Fe^{ikx} & (x > a) \end{array} \right\} \quad k = \frac{\sqrt{2mE}}{\hbar}; \ \kappa = \frac{\sqrt{2m(V_0 - E)}}{\hbar}.$$

**(1)** Continuity of $\psi$ at $-a$: $Ae^{-ika} + Be^{ika} = Ce^{-\kappa a} + De^{\kappa a}$.

**(2)** Continuity of $\psi'$ at $-a$: $ik(Ae^{-ika} - Be^{ika}) = \kappa(Ce^{-\kappa a} - De^{\kappa a})$.

$$\Rightarrow 2Ae^{-ika} = \left( 1 - i\frac{\kappa}{k} \right)Ce^{-\kappa a} + \left( 1 + i\frac{\kappa}{k} \right)De^{\kappa a}.$$

**(3)** Continuity of $\psi$ at $+a$: $Ce^{\kappa a} + De^{-\kappa a} = Fe^{ika}$.

**(4)** Continuity of $\psi'$ at $+a$: $\kappa(Ce^{\kappa a} - De^{-\kappa a}) = ikFe^{ika}$.

$$\Rightarrow 2Ce^{\kappa a} = \left(1 + \frac{ik}{\kappa}\right)Fe^{ika}; \quad 2De^{-\kappa a} = \left(1 - \frac{ik}{\kappa}\right)Fe^{ika}.$$

$$2Ae^{-ika} = \left(1 - \frac{i\kappa}{k}\right)\left(1 + \frac{ik}{\kappa}\right)Fe^{ika}\frac{e^{-2\kappa a}}{2} + \left(1 + \frac{i\kappa}{k}\right)\left(1 - \frac{ik}{\kappa}\right)Fe^{ika}\frac{e^{2\kappa a}}{2}$$

$$= \frac{Fe^{ika}}{2}\left\{\left[1 + i\left(\frac{k}{\kappa} - \frac{\kappa}{k}\right) + 1\right]e^{-2\kappa a} + \left[1 + i\left(\frac{\kappa}{k} - \frac{k}{\kappa}\right) + 1\right]e^{2\kappa a}\right\}$$

$$= \frac{Fe^{ika}}{2}\left[2\left(e^{-2\kappa a} + e^{2\kappa a}\right) + i\frac{(\kappa^2 - k^2)}{k\kappa}\left(e^{2\kappa a} - e^{-2\kappa a}\right)\right].$$

$$\text{But } \sinh x \equiv \frac{e^x - e^{-x}}{2}, \ \cosh x \equiv \frac{e^x + e^{-x}}{2}, \text{ so}$$

$$= \frac{Fe^{ika}}{2}\left[4\cosh(2\kappa a) + i\frac{(\kappa^2 - k^2)}{k\kappa}2\sinh(2\kappa a)\right]$$

$$= 2Fe^{ika}\left[\cosh(2\kappa a) + i\frac{(\kappa^2 - k^2)}{2k\kappa}\sinh(2\kappa a)\right].$$

$$T^{-1} = \left|\frac{A}{F}\right|^2 = \cosh^2(2\kappa a) + \frac{(\kappa^2 - k^2)^2}{(2\kappa k)^2}\sinh^2(2\kappa a). \quad \text{But } \cosh^2 = 1 + \sinh^2, \text{ so}$$

$$T^{-1} = 1 + \left[\underbrace{1 + \frac{(\kappa^2 - k^2)^2}{(2\kappa k)^2}}_{\bigstar}\right]\sinh^2(2\kappa a) = \boxed{1 + \frac{V_0^2}{4E(V_0 - E)}\sinh^2\left(\frac{2a}{\hbar}\sqrt{2m(V_0 - E)}\right),}$$

$$\text{where } \bigstar = \frac{4\kappa^2 k^2 + k^4 + \kappa^4 - 2\kappa^2 k^2}{(2\kappa k)^2} = \frac{(\kappa^2 + k^2)^2}{(2\kappa k)^2} = \frac{\left(\frac{2mE}{\hbar^2} + \frac{2m(V_0 - E)}{\hbar^2}\right)^2}{4\frac{2mE}{\hbar^2}\frac{2m(V_0 - E)}{\hbar^2}} = \frac{V_0^2}{4E(V_0 - E)}.$$

(You can also get this from Eq. 2.169 by switching the sign of $V_0$ and using $\sin(i\theta) = i\sinh\theta$.)

$$\mathbf{E = V_0}. \qquad \psi = \begin{cases} Ae^{ikx} + Be^{-ikx} & (x < -a) \\ C + Dx & (-a < x < a) \\ Fe^{ikx} & (x > a) \end{cases}$$

(In central region $-\frac{\hbar^2}{2m}\frac{d^2\psi}{dx^2} + V_0\psi = E\psi \Rightarrow \frac{d^2\psi}{dx^2} = 0$, so $\psi = C + Dx$.)

**(1)** Continuous $\psi$ at $-a$: $Ae^{-ika} + Be^{ika} = C - Da$.

**(2)** Continuous $\psi$ at $+a$: $Fe^{ika} = C + Da$.

$$\Rightarrow \mathbf{(2.5)} \ 2Da = Fe^{ika} - Ae^{-ika} - Be^{ika}.$$

**(3)** Continuous $\psi'$ at $-a$: $ik\left(Ae^{-ika} - Be^{ika}\right) = D$.

**(4)** Continuous $\psi'$ at $+a$: $ikFe^{ika} = D$.

$\Rightarrow$ **(4.5)** $Ae^{-2ika} - B = F.$

Use **(4)** to eliminate $D$ in **(2.5)**: $Ae^{-2ika} + B = F - 2aikF = (1 - 2iak)F$, and add to **(4.5)**:

$$2Ae^{-2ika} = 2F(1 - ika), \text{ so } T^{-1} = \left|\frac{A}{F}\right|^2 = 1 + (ka)^2 = \boxed{1 + \frac{2mE}{\hbar^2}a^2.}$$

(You can also get this from Eq. 2.169 by changing the sign of $V_0$ and taking the limit $E \to V_0$, using $\sin \epsilon \cong \epsilon$.)

**E > V$_0$.**      This case is identical to the one in the book, only with $V_0 \to -V_0$. So

$$\boxed{T^{-1} = 1 + \frac{V_0^2}{4E(E - V_0)} \sin^2\left(\frac{2a}{\hbar}\sqrt{2m(E - V_0)}\right).}$$

## Problem 2.34

**(a)**

$$\psi = \begin{cases} Ae^{ikx} + Be^{-ikx} & (x < 0) \\ Fe^{-\kappa x} & (x > 0) \end{cases} \text{ where } k = \frac{\sqrt{2mE}}{\hbar}; \quad \kappa = \frac{\sqrt{2m(V_0 - E)}}{\hbar}.$$

**(1)** Continuity of $\psi$ : $A + B = F.$

**(2)** Continuity of $\psi'$ : $ik(A - B) = -\kappa F.$

$$\Rightarrow A + B = -\frac{ik}{\kappa}(A - B) \Rightarrow A\left(1 + \frac{ik}{\kappa}\right) = -B\left(1 - \frac{ik}{\kappa}\right).$$

$$R = \left|\frac{B}{A}\right|^2 = \frac{|(1 + ik/\kappa)|^2}{|(1 - ik/\kappa)|^2} = \frac{1 + (k/\kappa)^2}{1 + (k/\kappa)^2} = \boxed{1.}$$

Although the wave function penetrates into the barrier, it is eventually all reflected.

**(b)**

$$\psi = \begin{cases} Ae^{ikx} + Be^{-ikx} & (x < 0) \\ Fe^{ilx} & (x > 0) \end{cases} \text{ where } k = \frac{\sqrt{2mE}}{\hbar}; \quad l = \frac{\sqrt{2m(E - V_0)}}{\hbar}.$$

**(1)** Continuity of $\psi$ : $A + B = F.$

**(2)** Continuity of $\psi'$ : $ik(A - B) = ilF.$

$$\Rightarrow A + B = \frac{k}{l}(A - B); \quad A\left(1 - \frac{k}{l}\right) = -B\left(1 + \frac{k}{l}\right).$$

$$R = \left|\frac{B}{A}\right|^2 = \frac{(1 - k/l)^2}{(1 + k/l)^2} = \frac{(k - l)^2}{(k + l)^2} = \frac{(k - l)^4}{(k^2 - l^2)^2}.$$

Now $k^2 - l^2 = \frac{2m}{\hbar^2}(E - E + V_0) = \left(\frac{2m}{\hbar^2}\right)V_0$; $k - l = \frac{\sqrt{2m}}{\hbar}[\sqrt{E} - \sqrt{E - V_0}]$, so

$$\boxed{R = \frac{(\sqrt{E} - \sqrt{E - V_0})^4}{V_0^2}.}$$

**(c)**

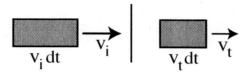

From the diagram, $T = P_t/P_i = |F|^2 v_t/|A|^2 v_i$, where $P_i$ is the probability of finding the incident particle in the box corresponding to the time interval $dt$, and $P_t$ is the probability of finding the transmitted particle in the associated box to the *right* of the barrier.

But $\dfrac{v_t}{v_i} = \dfrac{\sqrt{E - V_0}}{\sqrt{E}}$ (from Eq. 2.98). So $T = \sqrt{\dfrac{E - V_0}{E}} \left|\dfrac{F}{A}\right|^2$ . Alternatively, from Problem 2.19:

$$J_i = \frac{\hbar k}{m}|A|^2; \quad J_t = \frac{\hbar l}{m}|F|^2; \quad T = \frac{J_t}{J_i} = \left|\frac{F}{A}\right|^2 \frac{l}{k} = \left|\frac{F}{A}\right|^2 \sqrt{\frac{E - V_0}{E}}.$$

For $E < V_0$, of course, $\boxed{T = 0.}$

**(d)**

For $E > V_0$, $F = A + B = A + A\dfrac{\left(\frac{k}{l} - 1\right)}{\left(\frac{k}{l} + 1\right)} = A\dfrac{2k/l}{\left(\frac{k}{l} + 1\right)} = \dfrac{2k}{k + l}A.$

$$T = \left|\frac{F}{A}\right|^2 \frac{l}{k} = \left(\frac{2k}{k+l}\right)^2 \frac{l}{k} = \frac{4kl}{(k+l)^2} = \frac{4kl(k-l)^2}{(k^2 - l^2)^2} = \boxed{\frac{4\sqrt{E}\sqrt{E - V_0}(\sqrt{E} - \sqrt{E - V_0})^2}{V_0^2}.}$$

$$T + R = \frac{4kl}{(k+l)^2} + \frac{(k-l)^2}{(k+l)^2} = \frac{4kl + k^2 - 2kl + l^2}{(k+l)^2} = \frac{k^2 + 2kl + l^2}{(k+l)^2} = \frac{(k+l)^2}{(k+l)^2} = 1. \checkmark$$

## Problem 2.35

**(a)**

$$\psi(x) = \begin{cases} Ae^{ikx} + Be^{-ikx} & (x < 0) \\ Fe^{ilx} & (x > 0) \end{cases} \text{ where } k \equiv \frac{\sqrt{2mE}}{\hbar}, \ l \equiv \frac{\sqrt{2m(E + V_0)}}{\hbar}.$$

Continuity of $\psi \Rightarrow A + B = F$
Continuity of $\psi' \Rightarrow ik(A - B) = ilF$ $\Bigg\} \Longrightarrow$

$$A + B = \frac{k}{l}(A - B); \quad A\left(1 - \frac{k}{l}\right) = -B\left(1 + \frac{k}{l}\right); \quad \frac{B}{A} = -\left(\frac{1 - k/l}{1 + k/l}\right).$$

$$R = \left|\frac{B}{A}\right|^2 = \left(\frac{l-k}{l+k}\right)^2 = \left(\frac{\sqrt{E+V_0}-\sqrt{E}}{\sqrt{E+V_0}+\sqrt{E}}\right)^2$$

$$= \left(\frac{\sqrt{1+V_0/E}-1}{\sqrt{1+V_0/E}+1}\right)^2 = \left(\frac{\sqrt{1+3}-1}{\sqrt{1+3}+1}\right)^2 = \left(\frac{2-1}{2+1}\right)^2 = \boxed{\frac{1}{9}}.$$

**(b)** The cliff is *two*-dimensional, and even if we pretend the car drops straight down, the potential *as a function of distance along the* (crooked, but now one-dimensional) *path* is $-mgx$ (with $x$ the vertical coordinate), as shown.

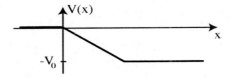

**(c)** Here $V_0/E = 12/4 = 3$, the same as in part (a), so $R = 1/9$, and hence $T = \boxed{8/9 = 0.8889.}$

---

## Problem 2.36

Start with Eq. 2.22: $\psi(x) = A\sin kx + B\cos kx$. This time the boundary conditions are $\psi(a) = \psi(-a) = 0$:

$$A\sin ka + B\cos ka = 0; \quad -A\sin ka + B\cos ka = 0.$$

$$\begin{cases} Subtract: & A\sin ka = 0 \Rightarrow ka = j\pi \text{ or } A = 0, \\ Add: & B\cos ka = 0 \Rightarrow ka = (j-\tfrac{1}{2})\pi \text{ or } B = 0, \end{cases}$$

(where $j = 1, 2, 3, \dots$).

If $B = 0$ (so $A \neq 0$), $k = j\pi/a$. In this case let $n \equiv 2j$ (so $n$ is an *even* integer); then $k = n\pi/2a$, $\psi = A\sin(n\pi x/2a)$. Normalizing: $1 = |A|^2 \int_{-a}^{a} \sin^2(n\pi x/2a)\, dx = |A|^2/2 \Rightarrow A = \sqrt{2}$.

If $A = 0$ (so $B \neq 0$), $k = (j-\tfrac{1}{2})\pi/a$. In this case let $n \equiv 2j-1$ ($n$ is an *odd* integer); again $k = n\pi/2a$, $\psi = B\cos(n\pi x/2a)$. Normalizing: $1 = |B|^2 \int_{-a}^{a} \cos^2(n\pi x/2a)dx = |a|^2/2 \Rightarrow B = \sqrt{2}$.

In either case Eq. 2.21 yields $E = \frac{\hbar^2 k^2}{2m} = \frac{n^2\pi^2\hbar^2}{2m(2a)^2}$ (in agreement with Eq. 2.27 for a well of width $2a$).

The substitution $x \to (x+a)/2$ takes Eq. 2.28 to

$$\sqrt{\frac{2}{a}}\sin\left(\frac{n\pi}{a}\frac{(x+a)}{2}\right) = \sqrt{\frac{2}{a}}\sin\left(\frac{n\pi x}{2a} + \frac{n\pi}{2}\right) = \begin{cases} (-1)^{n/2}\sqrt{\frac{2}{a}}\sin\left(\frac{n\pi x}{2a}\right) & (n \text{ even}), \\[2ex] (-1)^{(n-1)/2}\sqrt{\frac{2}{a}}\cos\left(\frac{n\pi x}{2a}\right) & (n \text{ odd}). \end{cases}$$

So (apart from normalization) we recover the results above. The graphs are the same as Figure 2.2, except that some are upside down (different normalization).

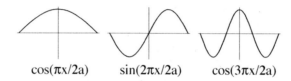

$$\cos(\pi x/2a) \qquad \sin(2\pi x/2a) \qquad \cos(3\pi x/2a)$$

## Problem 2.37

Use the trig identity $\sin 3\theta = 3\sin\theta - 4\sin^3\theta$ to write

$$\sin^3\left(\frac{\pi x}{a}\right) = \frac{3}{4}\sin\left(\frac{\pi x}{a}\right) - \frac{1}{4}\sin\left(\frac{3\pi x}{a}\right). \quad \text{So (Eq. 2.28): } \Psi(x,0) = A\sqrt{\frac{a}{2}}\left[\frac{3}{4}\psi_1(x) - \frac{1}{4}\psi_3(x)\right].$$

Normalize using Eq. 2.38: $|A|^2\dfrac{a}{2}\left(\dfrac{9}{16} + \dfrac{1}{16}\right) = \dfrac{5}{16}a|A|^2 = 1 \Rightarrow \boxed{A = \dfrac{4}{\sqrt{5a}}.}$

So $\Psi(x,0) = \frac{1}{\sqrt{10}}\left[3\psi_1(x) - \psi_3(x)\right]$, and hence (Eq. 2.17)

$$\boxed{\Psi(x,t) = \frac{1}{\sqrt{10}}\left[3\psi_1(x)e^{-iE_1 t/\hbar} - \psi_3(x)e^{-iE_3 t/\hbar}\right].}$$

$$|\Psi(x,t)|^2 = \frac{1}{10}\left[9\psi_1^2 + \psi_3^2 - 6\psi_1\psi_3\cos\left(\frac{E_3 - E_1}{\hbar}t\right)\right]; \text{ so}$$

$$\langle x\rangle = \int_0^a x|\Psi(x,t)|^2 dx = \frac{9}{10}\langle x\rangle_1 + \frac{1}{10}\langle x\rangle_3 - \frac{3}{5}\cos\left(\frac{E_3 - E_1}{\hbar}t\right)\int_0^a x\psi_1(x)\psi_3(x)dx,$$

where $\langle x\rangle_n = a/2$ is the expectation value of $x$ in the $n$th stationary state. The remaining integral is

$$\frac{2}{a}\int_0^a x\sin\left(\frac{\pi x}{a}\right)\sin\left(\frac{3\pi x}{a}\right)dx = \frac{1}{a}\int_0^a x\left[\cos\left(\frac{2\pi x}{a}\right) - \cos\left(\frac{4\pi x}{a}\right)\right]dx$$

$$= \frac{1}{a}\left[\left(\frac{a}{2\pi}\right)^2\cos\left(\frac{2\pi x}{a}\right) + \left(\frac{xa}{2\pi}\right)\sin\left(\frac{2\pi x}{a}\right) - \left(\frac{a}{4\pi}\right)^2\cos\left(\frac{4\pi x}{a}\right) - \left(\frac{xa}{4\pi}\right)\sin\left(\frac{4\pi x}{a}\right)\right]\Bigg|_0^a = 0.$$

Evidently then,

$$\langle x\rangle = \frac{9}{10}\left(\frac{a}{2}\right) + \frac{1}{10}\left(\frac{a}{2}\right) = \boxed{\frac{a}{2}.}$$

## Problem 2.38

**(a)** New allowed energies: $E_n = \dfrac{n^2\pi^2\hbar^2}{2m(2a)^2}$; $\quad \Psi(x,0) = \sqrt{\dfrac{2}{a}}\sin\left(\dfrac{\pi}{a}x\right)$, $\psi_n(x) = \sqrt{\dfrac{2}{2a}}\sin\left(\dfrac{n\pi}{2a}x\right)$.

$$c_n = \frac{\sqrt{2}}{a}\int_0^a \sin\left(\frac{\pi}{a}x\right)\sin\left(\frac{n\pi}{2a}x\right)dx = \frac{\sqrt{2}}{2a}\int_0^a \left\{\cos\left[\left(\frac{n}{2}-1\right)\frac{\pi x}{a}\right] - \cos\left[\left(\frac{n}{2}+1\right)\frac{\pi x}{a}\right]\right\}dx.$$

$$= \frac{1}{\sqrt{2}a}\left\{\frac{\sin\left[\left(\frac{n}{2}-1\right)\frac{\pi x}{a}\right]}{\left(\frac{n}{2}-1\right)\frac{\pi}{a}} - \frac{\sin\left[\left(\frac{n}{2}+1\right)\frac{\pi x}{a}\right]}{\left(\frac{n}{2}+1\right)\frac{\pi}{a}}\right\}\Bigg|_0^a \quad \text{(for } n \neq 2\text{)}$$

$$= \frac{1}{\sqrt{2}\pi}\left\{\frac{\sin\left[\left(\frac{n}{2}-1\right)\pi\right]}{\left(\frac{n}{2}-1\right)} - \frac{\sin\left[\left(\frac{n}{2}+1\right)\pi\right]}{\left(\frac{n}{2}+1\right)}\right\} = \frac{\sin\left[\left(\frac{n}{2}+1\right)\pi\right]}{\sqrt{2}\pi}\left[\frac{1}{\left(\frac{n}{2}-1\right)} - \frac{1}{\left(\frac{n}{2}+1\right)}\right]$$

$$= \frac{4\sqrt{2}}{\pi}\frac{\sin\left[\left(\frac{n}{2}+1\right)\pi\right]}{(n^2-4)} = \left\{\begin{array}{ll} 0, & \text{if } n \text{ is even} \\ \pm\frac{4\sqrt{2}}{\pi(n^2-4)}, & \text{if } n \text{ is odd} \end{array}\right\}.$$

$$c_2 = \frac{\sqrt{2}}{a}\int_0^a \sin^2\left(\frac{\pi}{a}x\right)dx = \frac{\sqrt{2}}{a}\int_0^a \frac{1}{2}dx = \frac{1}{\sqrt{2}}. \quad \text{So the probability of getting } E_n \text{ is}$$

$$P_n = |c_n|^2 = \left\{\begin{array}{ll} \frac{1}{2}, & \text{if } n = 2 \\ \frac{32}{\pi^2(n^2-4)^2}, & \text{if } n \text{ is odd} \\ 0, & \text{otherwise} \end{array}\right\}.$$

Most probable: $E_2 = \boxed{\dfrac{\pi^2\hbar^2}{2ma^2}}$ (same as before).     Probability: $P_2 = \boxed{1/2.}$

**(b)** Next most probable: $E_1 = \boxed{\dfrac{\pi^2\hbar^2}{8ma^2},}$ with probability $P_1 = \boxed{\dfrac{32}{9\pi^2} = 0.36025.}$

**(c)** $\langle H \rangle = \int \Psi^* H \Psi\, dx = \frac{2}{a}\int_0^a \sin\left(\frac{\pi}{a}x\right)\left(-\frac{\hbar^2}{2m}\frac{d^2}{dx^2}\right)\sin\left(\frac{\pi}{a}x\right)dx$, but this is exactly the same as before the wall moved – for which we know the answer: $\boxed{\dfrac{\pi^2\hbar^2}{2ma^2}.}$

---

## Problem 2.39

**(a)** According to Eq. 2.36, the most general solution to the time-dependent Schrödinger equation for the infinite square well is

$$\Psi(x,t) = \sum_{n=1}^{\infty} c_n\psi_n(x)e^{-i(n^2\pi^2\hbar/2ma^2)t}.$$

Now $\dfrac{n^2\pi^2\hbar}{2ma^2}T = \dfrac{n^2\pi^2\hbar}{2ma^2}\dfrac{4ma^2}{\pi\hbar} = 2\pi n^2$, so $e^{-i(n^2\pi^2\hbar/2ma^2)(t+T)} = e^{-i(n^2\pi^2\hbar/2ma^2)t}e^{-i2\pi n^2}$, and since $n^2$ is an integer, $e^{-i2\pi n^2} = 1$. Therefore $\Psi(x,t+T) = \Psi(x,t)$.     QED

**(b)** The classical revival time is the time it takes the particle to go down and back: $T_c = 2a/v$, with the velocity given by

$$E = \frac{1}{2}mv^2 \Rightarrow v = \sqrt{\frac{2E}{m}} \Rightarrow \boxed{T_c = a\sqrt{\frac{2m}{E}}.}$$

(c) The two revival times are equal if

$$\frac{4ma^2}{\pi\hbar} = a\sqrt{\frac{2m}{E}}, \quad \text{or} \quad \boxed{E = \frac{\pi^2\hbar^2}{8ma^2} = \frac{E_1}{4}.}$$

## Problem 2.40

(a) Let $V_0 \equiv 32\hbar^2/ma^2$. This is just like the *odd* bound states for the finite square well, since they are the ones that go to zero at the origin. Referring to the solution to Problem 2.29, the wave function is

$$\psi(x) = \begin{cases} D\sin lx, & l \equiv \sqrt{2m(E+V_0)}/\hbar \quad (0 < x < a), \\ Fe^{-\kappa x}, & \kappa \equiv \sqrt{-2mE}/\hbar \quad (x > a), \end{cases}$$

and the boundary conditions at $x = a$ yield

$$-\cot z = \sqrt{(z_0/z)^2 - 1}$$

with

$$z_0 = \frac{\sqrt{2mV_0}}{\hbar}a = \frac{\sqrt{2m(32\hbar^2/ma^2)}}{\hbar}a = 8.$$

Referring to the figure (Problem 2.29), and noting that $(5/2)\pi = 7.85 < z_0 < 3\pi = 9.42$, we see that there are $\boxed{\text{three bound states.}}$

(b) Let

$$I_1 \equiv \int_0^a |\psi|^2 dx = |D|^2 \int_0^a \sin^2 lx\, dx = |D|^2 \left[\frac{x}{2} - \frac{1}{2l}\sin lx\cos lx\right]\Big|_0^a = |D|^2 \left[\frac{a}{2} - \frac{1}{2l}\sin lz\cos la\right];$$

$$I_2 \equiv \int_a^\infty |\psi|^2 dx = |F|^2 \int_a^\infty e^{-2\kappa x}\, dx = |F|^2 \left[-\frac{e^{-2\kappa x}}{2\kappa}\right]\Big|_a^\infty = |F|^2 \frac{e^{-2\kappa a}}{2\kappa}.$$

But continuity at $x = a \Rightarrow Fe^{-\kappa a} = D\sin la$, so $I_2 = |D|^2\frac{\sin^2 la}{2\kappa}$.

Normalizing:

$$1 = I_1 + I_2 = |D|^2\left[\frac{a}{2} - \frac{1}{2l}\sin la\cos la + \frac{\sin^2 la}{2\kappa}\right] = \frac{1}{2\kappa}|D|^2\left[\kappa a - \frac{\kappa}{l}\sin la\cos la + \sin^2 la\right]$$

But (referring again to Problem 2.29) $\kappa/l = -\cot la$, so

$$= \frac{1}{2\kappa}|D|^2\left[\kappa a + \cot la\sin la\cos la + \sin^2 la\right] = |D|^2\frac{(1+\kappa a)}{2\kappa}.$$

So $|D|^2 = 2\kappa/(1+\kappa a)$, and the probability of finding the particle outside the well is

$$P = I_2 = \frac{2\kappa}{1+\kappa a}\frac{\sin^2 la}{2\kappa} = \frac{\sin^2 la}{1+\kappa a}.$$

We can express this in terms of $z \equiv la$ and $z_0$: $\kappa a = \sqrt{z_0^2 - z^2}$ (page 80),

$$\sin^2 la = \sin^2 z = \frac{1}{1+\cot^2 z} = \frac{1}{1+(z_0/z)^2 - 1} = \left(\frac{z}{z_0}\right)^2 \Rightarrow P = \frac{z^2}{z_0^2(1+\sqrt{z_0^2 - z^2})}.$$

So far, this is correct for *any* bound state. In the present case $z_0 = 8$ and $z$ is the third solution to $-\cot z = \sqrt{(8/z)^2 - 1}$, which occurs somewhere in the interval $7.85 < z < 8$. Mathematica gives $z = 7.9573$ and $\boxed{P = 0.54204.}$

```
FindRoot[Cot[z] == -√(8/z)^2-1, {z, 7.9}]
```

$\{z \to 7.95732\}$

```
z^2 / (64 (1 + √64 - z^2))
```

$$\frac{z^2}{64 \left(1 + \sqrt{64-z^2}\right)}$$

```
% /. z -> 7.957321523328964`
```

0.542041

---

## Problem 2.41

**(a)** In the standard notation $\xi \equiv \sqrt{m\omega/\hbar}\,x,\, \alpha \equiv (m\omega/\pi\hbar)^{1/4}$,

$$\Psi(x,0) = A(1-2\xi)^2 e^{-\xi^2/2} = A(1 - 4\xi + 4\xi^2)e^{-\xi^2/2}.$$

It can be expressed as a linear combination of the first three stationary states (Eq. 2.59 and 2.62, and Problem 2.10):

$$\psi_0(x) = \alpha e^{-\xi^2/2}, \qquad \psi_1(x) = \sqrt{2}\,\alpha\xi e^{-\xi^2/2}, \qquad \psi_2(x) = \frac{\alpha}{\sqrt{2}}(2\xi^2-1)e^{-\xi^2/2}.$$

So $\Psi(x,0) = c_0\psi_0 + c_1\psi_1 + c_2\psi_2 = \alpha(c_0 + \sqrt{2}\xi c_1 + \sqrt{2}\xi^2 c_2 - \frac{1}{\sqrt{2}}c_2)e^{-\xi^2/2}$ with (equating like powers)

$$\begin{cases} \alpha\sqrt{2}c_2 = 4A & \Rightarrow c_2 = 2\sqrt{2}A/\alpha, \\ \alpha\sqrt{2}c_1 = -4A & \Rightarrow c_1 = -2\sqrt{2}A/\alpha, \\ \alpha(c_0 - c_2/\sqrt{2}) = A & \Rightarrow c_0 = (A/\alpha) + c_2/\sqrt{2} = (1+2)A/\alpha = 3A/\alpha. \end{cases}$$

Normalizing: $1 = |c_0|^2 + |c_1|^2 + |c_2|^2 = (8+8+9)(A/\alpha)^2 = 25(A/\alpha)^2 \Rightarrow A = \alpha/5.$

$$c_0 = \frac{3}{5}, \quad c_1 = -\frac{2\sqrt{2}}{5}, \quad c_2 = \frac{2\sqrt{2}}{5}.$$

$$\langle H \rangle = \sum |c_n|^2 (n + \tfrac{1}{2})\hbar\omega = \frac{9}{25}\left(\frac{1}{2}\hbar\omega\right) + \frac{8}{25}\left(\frac{3}{2}\hbar\omega\right) + \frac{8}{25}\left(\frac{5}{2}\hbar\omega\right) = \frac{\hbar\omega}{50}(9 + 24 + 40) = \boxed{\frac{73}{50}\hbar\omega.}$$

**(b)**

$$\Psi(x,t) = \frac{3}{5}\psi_0 e^{-i\omega t/2} - \frac{2\sqrt{2}}{5}\psi_1 e^{-3i\omega t/2} + \frac{2\sqrt{2}}{5}\psi_2 e^{-5i\omega t/2} = e^{-i\omega t/2}\left[\frac{3}{5}\psi_0 - \frac{2\sqrt{2}}{5}\psi_1 e^{-i\omega t} + \frac{2\sqrt{2}}{5}\psi_2 e^{-2i\omega t}\right].$$

To change the sign of the middle term we need $e^{-i\omega T} = -1$ (then $e^{-2i\omega T} = 1$); evidently $\omega T = \pi$, or $\boxed{T = \pi/\omega.}$

## Problem 2.42

Everything in Section 2.3.2 still applies, except that there is an additional boundary condition: $\psi(0) = 0$. This eliminates all the *even* solutions ($n = 0, 2, 4, \dots$), leaving only the odd solutions. So

$$E_n = \left( n + \frac{1}{2} \right) \hbar\omega, \ n = 1, 3, 5, \dots .$$

## Problem 2.43

(a) Normalization is the same as before: $A = \left( \frac{2a}{\pi} \right)^{1/4}$.

(b) Equation 2.103 says

$$\phi(k) = \frac{1}{\sqrt{2\pi}} \left( \frac{2a}{\pi} \right)^{1/4} \int_{-\infty}^{\infty} e^{-ax^2} e^{ilx} e^{-ikx} dx \quad [\text{same as before, only } k \to k - l] = \frac{1}{(2\pi a)^{1/4}} e^{-(k-l)^2/4a}.$$

$$\Psi(x,t) = \frac{1}{\sqrt{2\pi}} \frac{1}{(2\pi a)^{1/4}} \int_{-\infty}^{\infty} \underbrace{e^{-(k-l)^2/4a} e^{i(kx - \hbar k^2 t/2m)}}_{e^{-l^2/4a} e^{-\left[ \left( \frac{1}{4a} + i\frac{\hbar t}{2m} \right) k^2 - \left( ix + \frac{l}{2a} \right) k \right]}} \, dk$$

$$= \frac{1}{\sqrt{2\pi}} \frac{1}{(2\pi a)^{1/4}} e^{-l^2/4a} \sqrt{\frac{\pi}{\left( \frac{1}{4a} + i\frac{\hbar t}{2m} \right)}} e^{(ix + l/2a)^2/[4(1/4a + i\hbar t/2m)]}$$

$$= \boxed{ \left( \frac{2a}{\pi} \right)^{1/4} \frac{1}{\sqrt{1 + 2i\hbar at/m}} e^{-l^2/4a} e^{a(ix + l/2a)^2/(1 + 2ia\hbar t/m)} . }$$

(c) Let $\theta \equiv 2\hbar at/m$, as before: $|\Psi|^2 = \sqrt{\frac{2a}{\pi}} \frac{1}{\sqrt{1 + \theta^2}} e^{-l^2/2a} e^{a\left[ \frac{(ix + l/2a)^2}{(1 + i\theta)} + \frac{(-ix + l/2a)^2}{(1 - i\theta)} \right]}$. Expand the term in square brackets:

$$[\ ] = \frac{1}{1 + \theta^2} \left[ (1 - i\theta) \left( ix + \frac{l}{2a} \right)^2 + (1 + i\theta) \left( -ix + \frac{l}{2a} \right)^2 \right]$$

$$= \frac{1}{1 + \theta^2} \left[ \left( -x^2 + \frac{ixl}{a} + \frac{l^2}{4a^2} \right) + \left( -x^2 - \frac{ixl}{a} + \frac{l^2}{4a^2} \right) \right.$$

$$\left. + i\theta \left( x^2 - \frac{ixl}{a} - \frac{l^2}{4a^2} \right) + i\theta \left( -x^2 - \frac{ixl}{a} + \frac{l^2}{4a^2} \right) \right]$$

$$= \frac{1}{1 + \theta^2} \left[ -2x^2 + \frac{l^2}{2a^2} + 2\theta \frac{xl}{a} \right] = \frac{1}{1 + \theta^2} \left[ -2x^2 + 2\theta \frac{xl}{a} - \frac{\theta^2 l^2}{2a^2} + \frac{\theta^2 l^2}{2a^2} + \frac{l^2}{2a^2} \right]$$

$$= \frac{-2}{1 + \theta^2} \left( x - \frac{\theta l}{2a} \right)^2 + \frac{l^2}{2a^2} .$$

$$|\Psi(x,t)|^2 = \sqrt{\frac{2}{\pi}} \sqrt{\frac{a}{1 + \theta^2}} e^{-l^2/2a} e^{-\frac{2a}{1 + \theta^2} (x - \theta l/2a)^2} e^{l^2/2a} = \boxed{ \sqrt{\frac{2}{\pi}} w e^{-2w^2 (x - \theta l/2a)^2} , }$$

where $w \equiv \sqrt{a/(1+\theta^2)}$. The result is the same as before, except $x \to \left(x - \frac{\theta l}{2a}\right) = \left(x - \frac{\hbar l}{m}t\right)$, so $|\Psi|^2$ has the same (flattening Gaussian) shape – only this time the center moves at constant speed $v = \hbar l/m$.

**(d)**

$$\langle x \rangle = \int_{-\infty}^{\infty} x |\Psi(x,t)|^2 dx. \qquad \text{Let } y \equiv x - \theta l/2a = x - vt, \text{ so } x = y + vt.$$

$$= \int_{-\infty}^{\infty} (y + vt)\sqrt{\frac{2}{\pi}} w e^{-2w^2 y^2} dy = vt.$$

(The first integral is trivially zero; the second is 1 by normalization.)

$$= \boxed{\frac{\hbar l}{m}t;} \quad \langle p \rangle = m\frac{d\langle x \rangle}{dt} = \boxed{\hbar l.}$$

$$\langle x^2 \rangle = \int_{-\infty}^{\infty} (y + vt)^2 \sqrt{\frac{2}{\pi}} w e^{-2w^2 y^2} dy = \frac{1}{4w^2} + 0 + (vt)^2 \text{ (the first integral is same as before).}$$

$$\boxed{\langle x^2 \rangle = \frac{1}{4w^2} + \left(\frac{\hbar l t}{m}\right)^2.} \quad \langle p^2 \rangle = -\hbar^2 \int_{-\infty}^{\infty} \Psi^* \frac{d^2 \Psi}{dx^2} dx.$$

$$\Psi = \left(\frac{2a}{\pi}\right)^{1/4} \frac{1}{\sqrt{1+i\theta}} e^{-l^2/4a} e^{a(ix+l/2a)^2/(1+i\theta)}, \text{ so } \frac{d\Psi}{dx} = \frac{2ia\left(ix + \frac{l}{2a}\right)}{(1+i\theta)}\Psi;$$

$$\frac{d^2\Psi}{dx^2} = \left[\frac{2ia(ix+l/2a)}{1+i\theta}\right]\frac{d\Psi}{dx} + \frac{2i^2 a}{1+i\theta}\Psi = \left[\frac{-4a^2\left(ix+l/2a\right)^2}{(1+i\theta)^2} - \frac{2a}{1+i\theta}\right]\Psi.$$

$$\langle p^2 \rangle = \frac{4a^2\hbar^2}{(1+i\theta)^2} \int_{-\infty}^{\infty} \left[\left(ix + \frac{l}{2a}\right)^2 + \frac{(1+i\theta)}{2a}\right]|\Psi|^2 dx$$

$$= \frac{4a^2\hbar^2}{(1+i\theta)^2} \int_{-\infty}^{\infty} \left[-\left(y + vt - \frac{il}{2a}\right)^2 + \frac{(1+i\theta)}{2a}\right]|\Psi|^2 dy$$

$$= \frac{4a^2\hbar^2}{(1+i\theta)^2} \left\{-\int_{-\infty}^{\infty} y^2 |\Psi|^2 dy - 2\left(vt - \frac{il}{2a}\right)\int_{-\infty}^{\infty} y|\Psi|^2 dy \right.$$

$$\left. + \left[-\left(vt - \frac{il}{2a}\right)^2 + \frac{(1+i\theta)}{2a}\right]\int_{-\infty}^{\infty} |\Psi|^2 dy\right\}$$

$$= \frac{4a^2\hbar^2}{(1+i\theta)^2}\left[-\frac{1}{4w^2} + 0 - \left(vt - \frac{il}{2a}\right)^2 + \frac{(1+i\theta)}{2a}\right]$$

$$= \frac{4a^2\hbar^2}{(1+i\theta)^2}\left\{-\frac{1+\theta^2}{4a} - \left[\left(\frac{-il}{2a}\right)(1+i\theta)\right]^2 + \frac{(1+i\theta)}{2a}\right\}$$

$$= \frac{a\hbar}{1+i\theta}\left[-(1-i\theta) + \frac{l^2}{a}(1+i\theta) + 2\right] = \frac{a\hbar^2}{1+i\theta}\left[(1+i\theta)\left(1 + \frac{l^2}{a}\right)\right] = \boxed{\hbar^2(a + l^2).}$$

$$\sigma_x^2 = \langle x^2 \rangle - \langle x \rangle^2 = \frac{1}{4w^2} + \left(\frac{\hbar l t}{m}\right)^2 - \left(\frac{\hbar l t}{m}\right)^2 = \frac{1}{4w^2} \Rightarrow \boxed{\sigma_x = \frac{1}{2w};}$$

$$\sigma_p^2 = \langle p^2 \rangle - \langle p \rangle^2 = \hbar^2 a + \hbar^2 l^2 - \hbar^2 l^2 = \hbar^2 a, \text{ so } \boxed{\sigma_p = \hbar\sqrt{a}.}$$

**(e)** $\sigma_x$ and $\sigma_p$ are same as before, so the uncertainty principle still holds.

## Problem 2.44

Equation 2.22 $\Rightarrow \psi(x) = A\sin kx + B\cos kx$, $0 \le x \le a$, with $k = \sqrt{2mE}/\hbar^2$.

    **Even solutions:** $\psi(x) = \psi(-x) = A\sin(-kx) + B\cos(-kx) = -A\sin kx + B\cos kx \quad (-a \le x \le 0)$.

Boundary conditions
$$\begin{cases} \psi \text{ continuous at } 0: B = B \text{ (no new condition).} \\ \psi' \text{ discontinuous (Eq. 2.125 with sign of } \alpha \text{ switched): } Ak + Ak = \frac{2m\alpha}{\hbar^2}B \Rightarrow B = \frac{\hbar^2 k}{m\alpha}A. \\ \psi \to 0 \text{ at } x = a: \; A\sin(ka) + \frac{\hbar^2 k}{m\alpha}A\cos(ka) = 0 \Rightarrow \tan(ka) = -\frac{\hbar^2 k}{m\alpha}. \end{cases}$$

$$\boxed{\psi(x) = A\left(\sin kx + \frac{\hbar^2 k}{m\alpha}\cos kx\right) \; (0 \le x \le a); \; \psi(-x) = \psi(x).}$$

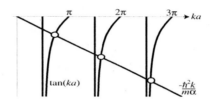

From the graph, the allowed energies are slightly above

$$ka = \frac{n\pi}{2} \; (n = 1, 3, 5, \dots) \quad \text{so} \quad \boxed{E_n \gtrsim \frac{n^2\pi^2\hbar^2}{2m(2a)^2} \; (n = 1, 3, 5, \dots).}$$

These energies are somewhat higher than the corresponding energies for the infinite square well (Eq. 2.27, with $a \to 2a$). As $\alpha \to 0$, the straight line $(-\hbar^2 k/m\alpha)$ gets steeper and steeper, and the intersections get closer to $n\pi/2$; the energies then reduce to those of the ordinary infinite well. As $\alpha \to \infty$, the straight line approaches horizontal, and the intersections are at $n\pi$ $(n = 1, 2, 3, \dots)$, so $E_n \to \frac{n^2\pi^2\hbar^2}{2ma^2}$ – these are the allowed energies for the infinite square well *of width a*. At this point the barrier is impenetrable, and we have two isolated infinite square wells.

    **Odd solutions:** $\psi(x) = -\psi(-x) = -A\sin(-kx) - B\cos(-kx) = A\sin(kx) - B\cos(kx) \quad (-a \le x \le 0)$.

Boundary conditions
$$\begin{cases} \psi \text{ continuous at } 0: \; B = -B \Rightarrow B = 0. \\ \psi' \text{ discontinuous: } Ak - Ak = \frac{2m\alpha}{\hbar^2}(0) \text{ (no new condition).} \\ \psi(a) = 0 \Rightarrow A\sin(ka) = 0 \Rightarrow ka = \frac{n\pi}{2} \; (n = 2, 4, 6, \dots). \end{cases}$$

$$\boxed{\psi(x) = A\sin(kx), \; (-a < x < a); \quad E_n = \frac{n^2\pi^2\hbar^2}{2m(2a)^2} \; (n = 2, 4, 6, \dots).}$$

These are the *exact* (even $n$) energies (and wave functions) for the infinite square well (of width $2a$). The point is that the *odd* solutions (even $n$) are *zero* at the origin, so they never "feel" the delta function at all.

## Problem 2.45

$$\left.\begin{array}{l} -\dfrac{\hbar^2}{2m}\dfrac{d^2\psi_1}{dx^2} + V\psi_1 = E\psi_1 \Rightarrow -\dfrac{\hbar^2}{2m}\psi_2\dfrac{d^2\psi_1}{dx^2} + V\psi_1\psi_2 = E\psi_1\psi_2 \\[4mm] -\dfrac{\hbar^2}{2m}\dfrac{d^2\psi_2}{dx^2} + V\psi_2 = E\psi_2 \Rightarrow -\dfrac{\hbar^2}{2m}\psi_1\dfrac{d^2\psi_2}{dx^2} + V\psi_1\psi_2 = E\psi_1\psi_2 \end{array}\right\} \Rightarrow -\dfrac{\hbar^2}{2m}\left[\psi_2\dfrac{d^2\psi_1}{dx^2} - \psi_1\dfrac{d^2\psi_2}{dx^2}\right] = 0.$$

But $\dfrac{d}{dx}\left[\psi_2\dfrac{d\psi_1}{dx} - \psi_1\dfrac{d\psi_2}{dx}\right] = \dfrac{d\psi_2}{dx}\dfrac{d\psi_1}{dx} + \psi_2\dfrac{d^2\psi_1}{dx^2} - \dfrac{d\psi_1}{dx}\dfrac{d\psi_2}{dx} - \psi_1\dfrac{d^2\psi_2}{dx^2} = \psi_2\dfrac{d^2\psi_1}{dx^2} - \psi_1\dfrac{d^2\psi_2}{dx^2}.$ Since this is

zero, it follows that $\psi_2\dfrac{d\psi_1}{dx} - \psi_1\dfrac{d\psi_2}{dx} = K$ (a constant). But $\psi \to 0$ at $\infty$ so the constant must be zero. Thus

$\psi_2\dfrac{d\psi_1}{dx} = \psi_1\dfrac{d\psi_2}{dx}$, or $\dfrac{1}{\psi_1}\dfrac{d\psi_1}{dx} = \dfrac{1}{\psi_2}\dfrac{d\psi_2}{dx}$, so $\ln\psi_1 = \ln\psi_2 +$ constant, or $\psi_1 = (\text{constant})\psi_2$.     QED

## Problem 2.46

$-\dfrac{\hbar^2}{2m}\dfrac{d^2\psi}{dx^2} = E\psi$ (where $x$ is measured around the circumference), or $\dfrac{d^2\psi}{dx^2} = -k^2\psi$, with $k \equiv \dfrac{\sqrt{2mE}}{\hbar}$, so

$$\psi(x) = Ae^{ikx} + Be^{-ikx}.$$

But $\psi(x + L) = \psi(x)$, since $x + L$ is the same point as $x$, so

$$Ae^{ikx}e^{ikL} + Be^{-ikx}e^{-ikL} = Ae^{ikx} + Be^{-ikx},$$

and this is true for *all* $x$. In particular, for $x = 0$ :

(1)   $Ae^{ikL} + Be^{-ikL} = A + B.$   And for $x = \dfrac{\pi}{2k}$ :

$Ae^{i\pi/2}e^{ikL} + Be^{-i\pi/2}e^{-ikL} = Ae^{i\pi/2} + Be^{-i\pi/2}$, or $iAe^{ikL} - iBe^{-ikL} = iA - iB$, so

(2)   $Ae^{ikL} - Be^{-ikL} = A - B.$   Add (1) and (2): $2Ae^{ikL} = 2A.$

Either $A = 0$, or else $e^{ikL} = 1$, in which case $kL = 2n\pi$ $(n = 0, \pm1, \pm2, \dots)$. But if $A = 0$, then $Be^{-ikL} = B$, leading to the same conclusion. So for every positive $n$ there are *two* solutions: $\psi_n^+(x) = Ae^{i(2n\pi x/L)}$ and $\psi_n^-(x) = Be^{-i(2n\pi x/L)}$ $(n = 0$ is ok too, but in that case there is just *one* solution). Normalizing: $\int_0^L |\psi_\pm|^2 dx = 1 \Rightarrow A = B = 1/\sqrt{L}$. Any *other* solution (with the same energy) is a linear combination of these.

$$\boxed{\psi_n^\pm(x) = \dfrac{1}{\sqrt{L}}e^{\pm i(2n\pi x/L)}; \quad E_n = \dfrac{2n^2\pi^2\hbar^2}{mL^2} \quad (n = 0, 1, 2, 3, \dots).}$$

The theorem fails because here $\psi$ does *not* go to zero at $\infty$; $x$ is restricted to a finite range, and we are unable to determine the constant $K$ (in Problem 2.45).

## Problem 2.47

(a) (i)  $b = 0 \Rightarrow$ ordinary finite square well. Exponential decay outside; sinusoidal inside (cos for $\psi_1$, sin for $\psi_2$). No nodes for $\psi_1$, one node for $\psi_2$.

   (ii) Ground state is *even*. Exponential decay outside, sinusoidal inside the wells, hyperbolic cosine in barrier. First excited state is *odd* – hyperbolic sine in barrier. No nodes for $\psi_1$, one node for $\psi_2$.

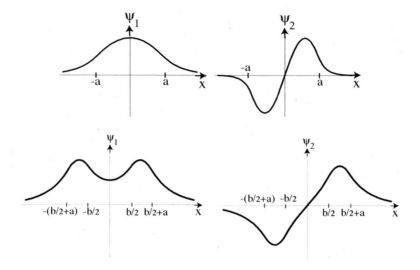

**(iii)** For $b \gg a$, same as (ii), but wave function very small in barrier region. Essentially two isolated finite square wells; $\psi_1$ and $\psi_2$ are degenerate (in energy); they are even and odd linear combinations of the ground states of the two separate wells.

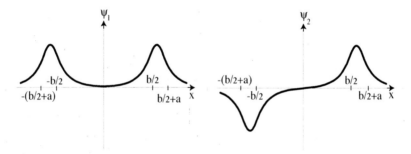

**(b)** From Eq. 2.157 we know that for $b = 0$ the energies fall slightly below

$$\left. \begin{array}{l} E_1 + V_0 \approx \frac{\pi^2 \hbar^2}{2m(2a)^2} = \frac{h}{4} \\ E_2 + V_0 \approx \frac{4\pi^2 \hbar^2}{2m(2a)^2} = h \end{array} \right\} \text{ where } h \equiv \frac{\pi^2 \hbar^2}{2ma^2}.$$

For $b \gg a$, the width of each (isolated) well is $a$, so

$$E_1 + V_0 \approx E_2 + V_0 \approx \frac{\pi^2 \hbar^2}{2ma^2} = h \text{ (again, slightly } below \text{ this).}$$

Hence the graph (next page). [Incidentally, within each well, $\frac{d^2\psi}{dx^2} = -\frac{2m}{\hbar^2}(V_0 + E)\psi$, so the more *curved* the wave function, the higher the energy. This is consistent with the graphs above.]

**(c)** In the (even) ground state the energy is *lowest* in configuration (i), with $b \to 0$, so the electron tends to draw the nuclei $\boxed{\text{together,}}$ promoting *bonding* of the atoms. In the (odd) first excited state, by contrast, the electron drives the nuclei $\boxed{\text{apart.}}$

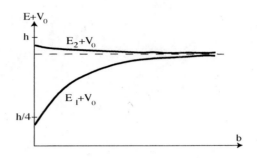

## Problem 2.48

**(a)**

$$\frac{d\Psi}{dx} = \frac{2\sqrt{3}}{a\sqrt{a}} \cdot \left\{ \begin{array}{ll} 1, & (0 < x < a/2) \\ -1, & (a/2 < x < a) \end{array} \right\} = \boxed{\frac{2\sqrt{3}}{a\sqrt{a}}\left[1 - 2\theta\left(x - \frac{a}{2}\right)\right]}.$$

**(b)**

$$\frac{d^2\Psi}{dx^2} = \frac{2\sqrt{3}}{a\sqrt{a}}\left[-2\delta\left(x - \frac{a}{2}\right)\right] = \boxed{-\frac{4\sqrt{3}}{a\sqrt{a}}\delta\left(x - \frac{a}{2}\right)}.$$

**(c)**

$$\langle H\rangle = -\frac{\hbar^2}{2m}\left(-\frac{4\sqrt{3}}{a\sqrt{a}}\right)\int \Psi^*\delta\left(x - \frac{a}{2}\right)dx = \frac{2\sqrt{3}\hbar^2}{ma\sqrt{a}}\underbrace{\Psi^*\left(\frac{a}{2}\right)}_{\sqrt{3/a}} = \frac{2\cdot 3\cdot\hbar^2}{m\cdot a\cdot a} = \boxed{\frac{6\hbar^2}{ma^2}}. \checkmark$$

## Problem 2.49

**(a)**

$$\frac{\partial\Psi}{\partial t} = \left(-\frac{m\omega}{2\hbar}\right)\left[\frac{a^2}{2}\left(-2i\omega e^{-2i\omega t}\right) + \frac{i\hbar}{m} - 2ax(-i\omega)e^{-i\omega t}\right]\Psi, \text{ so}$$

$$i\hbar\frac{\partial\Psi}{\partial t} = \left[-\frac{1}{2}ma^2\omega^2 e^{-2i\omega t} + \frac{1}{2}\hbar\omega + max\omega^2 e^{-i\omega t}\right]\Psi.$$

$$\frac{\partial\Psi}{\partial x} = \left[\left(-\frac{m\omega}{2\hbar}\right)\left(2x - 2ae^{-i\omega t}\right)\right]\Psi = -\frac{m\omega}{\hbar}\left(x - ae^{-i\omega t}\right)\Psi;$$

$$\frac{\partial^2\Psi}{\partial x^2} = -\frac{m\omega}{\hbar}\Psi - \frac{m\omega}{\hbar}\left(x - ae^{-i\omega t}\right)\frac{\partial\Psi}{\partial x} = \left[-\frac{m\omega}{\hbar} + \left(\frac{m\omega}{\hbar}\right)^2\left(x - ae^{-i\omega t}\right)^2\right]\Psi.$$

$$-\frac{\hbar^2}{2m}\frac{\partial^2\Psi}{\partial x^2}+\frac{1}{2}m\omega^2x^2\Psi = -\frac{\hbar^2}{2m}\left[-\frac{m\omega}{\hbar}+\left(\frac{m\omega}{\hbar}\right)^2\left(x-ae^{-i\omega t}\right)^2\right]\Psi+\frac{1}{2}m\omega^2x^2\Psi$$

$$=\left[\frac{1}{2}\hbar\omega-\frac{1}{2}m\omega^2\left(x^2-2axe^{-i\omega t}+a^2e^{-2i\omega t}\right)+\frac{1}{2}m\omega^2x^2\right]\Psi$$

$$=\left[\frac{1}{2}\hbar\omega+max\omega^2e^{-i\omega t}-\frac{1}{2}m\omega^2a^2e^{-2i\omega t}\right]\Psi$$

$$=i\hbar\frac{\partial\Psi}{\partial t}\ \text{(comparing second line above).}\ \checkmark$$

**(b)**

$$|\Psi|^2 = \sqrt{\frac{m\omega}{\pi\hbar}}e^{-\frac{m\omega}{2\hbar}\left[\left(x^2+\frac{a^2}{2}\left(1+e^{2i\omega t}\right)-\frac{i\hbar t}{m}-2axe^{i\omega t}\right)+\left(x^2+\frac{a^2}{2}\left(1+e^{-2i\omega t}\right)+\frac{i\hbar t}{m}-2axe^{-i\omega t}\right)\right]}$$

$$=\sqrt{\frac{m\omega}{\pi\hbar}}e^{-\frac{m\omega}{2\hbar}\left[2x^2+a^2+a^2\cos(2\omega t)-4ax\cos(\omega t)\right]}.\ \ \text{But}\ a^2[1+\cos(2\omega t)]=2a^2\cos^2\omega t,\ \text{so}$$

$$=\sqrt{\frac{m\omega}{\pi\hbar}}e^{-\frac{m\omega}{\hbar}\left[x^2-2ax\cos(\omega t)+a^2\cos^2(\omega t)\right]}=\boxed{\sqrt{\frac{m\omega}{\pi\hbar}}e^{-\frac{m\omega}{\hbar}(x-a\cos\omega t)^2}.}$$

The wave packet is a *Gaussian* of fixed shape, whose *center* oscillates back and forth sinusoidally, with amplitude $a$ and angular frequency $\omega$.

**(c)** Note that this wave function *is* correctly normalized (compare Eq. 2.59). Let $y \equiv x - a\cos\omega t$ :

$$\langle x\rangle = \int x|\Psi|^2 dx = \int (y+a\cos\omega t)|\Psi|^2 dy = 0 + a\cos\omega t\int|\Psi|^2 dy = \boxed{a\cos\omega t.}$$

$$\langle p\rangle = m\frac{d\langle x\rangle}{dt} = \boxed{-ma\omega\sin\omega t.}\ \ \ \frac{d\langle p\rangle}{dt}=-ma\omega^2\cos\omega t.\ \ \ V=\frac{1}{2}m\omega^2x^2\implies\frac{dV}{dx}=m\omega^2x.$$

$$\left\langle-\frac{dV}{dx}\right\rangle = -m\omega^2\langle x\rangle = -m\omega^2a\cos\omega t = \frac{d\langle p\rangle}{dt},\ \text{so Ehrenfest's theorem}\ is\ \text{satisfied.}$$

---

## Problem 2.50

**(a)**

$$\frac{\partial\Psi}{\partial t} = \left[-\frac{m\alpha}{\hbar^2}\frac{\partial}{\partial t}|x-vt|-i\frac{\left(E+\frac{1}{2}mv^2\right)}{\hbar}\right]\Psi;\ \ \ \frac{\partial}{\partial t}|x-vt| = \left\{\begin{array}{l}-v,\ \text{if}\ x-vt>0\\ v,\ \ \ \text{if}\ x-vt<0\end{array}\right\}.$$

We can write this in terms of the $\theta$-function (Eq. 2.143):

$$2\theta(z)-1 = \left\{\begin{array}{l}1,\ \ \ \text{if}\ z>0\\ -1,\ \text{if}\ z<0\end{array}\right\},\ \text{so}\ \frac{\partial}{\partial t}|x-vt| = -v[2\theta(x-vt)-1].$$

$$i\hbar\frac{\partial\Psi}{\partial t} = \left\{i\frac{m\alpha v}{\hbar}[2\theta(x-vt)-1]+E+\frac{1}{2}mv^2\right\}\Psi.\ \ \ \ [\bigstar]$$

$$\frac{\partial \Psi}{\partial x} = \left[ -\frac{m\alpha}{\hbar^2} \frac{\partial}{\partial x} |x - vt| + \frac{imv}{\hbar} \right] \Psi$$

$$\frac{\partial}{\partial x} |x - vt| = \{1, \text{if } x > vt; \ -1, \text{if } x < vt\} = 2\theta(x - vt) - 1.$$

$$= \left\{ -\frac{m\alpha}{\hbar^2} [2\theta(x - vt) - 1] + \frac{imv}{\hbar} \right\} \Psi.$$

$$\frac{\partial^2 \Psi}{\partial x^2} = \left\{ -\frac{m\alpha}{\hbar^2} [2\theta(x - vt) - 1] + \frac{imv}{\hbar} \right\}^2 \Psi - \frac{2m\alpha}{\hbar^2} \left[ \frac{\partial}{\partial x} \theta(x - vt) \right] \Psi.$$

But (from Problem 2.24(b)) $\frac{\partial}{\partial x} \theta(x - vt) = \delta(x - vt)$, so

$$-\frac{\hbar^2}{2m} \frac{\partial^2 \Psi}{\partial x^2} - \alpha\delta(x - vt)\Psi$$

$$= \left( -\frac{\hbar^2}{2m} \left\{ -\frac{m\alpha}{\hbar^2} [2\theta(x - vt) - 1] + \frac{imv}{\hbar} \right\}^2 + \alpha\delta(x - vt) - \alpha\delta(x - vt) \right) \Psi$$

$$= -\frac{\hbar^2}{2m} \left\{ \frac{m^2\alpha^2}{\hbar^4} \underbrace{[2\theta(x - vt) - 1]^2}_{1} - \frac{m^2v^2}{\hbar^2} - 2i \frac{mv}{\hbar} \frac{m\alpha}{\hbar^2} [2\theta(x - vt) - 1] \right\} \Psi$$

$$= \left\{ -\frac{m\alpha^2}{2\hbar^2} + \frac{1}{2} mv^2 + i \frac{mv\alpha}{\hbar} [2\theta(x - vt) - 1] \right\} \Psi = i\hbar \frac{\partial \Psi}{\partial t} \quad (\text{compare } [\bigstar]). \quad \checkmark$$

**(b)**

$$|\Psi|^2 = \frac{m\alpha}{\hbar^2} e^{-2m\alpha|y|/\hbar^2} \quad (y \equiv x - vt).$$

Check normalization: $2\frac{m\alpha}{\hbar^2} \int_0^\infty e^{-2m\alpha y/\hbar^2} dy = \frac{2m\alpha}{\hbar^2} \frac{\hbar^2}{2m\alpha} = 1.$ $\checkmark$

$$\langle H \rangle = \int_{-\infty}^\infty \Psi^* H \Psi dx. \quad \text{But } H\Psi = i\hbar \frac{\partial \Psi}{\partial t}, \text{ which we calculated above } [\bigstar].$$

$$= \int \left\{ \frac{im\alpha v}{\hbar} [2\theta(y) - 1] + E + \frac{1}{2} mv^2 \right\} |\Psi|^2 dy = \boxed{E + \frac{1}{2} mv^2.}$$

(Note that $[2\theta(y) - 1]$ is an *odd* function of $y$.) *Interpretation:* The wave packet is dragged along (at speed $v$) with the delta-function. The total energy is the energy it *would* have in a stationary delta-function ($E$), plus *kinetic* energy due to the motion ($\frac{1}{2}mv^2$).

---

## Problem 2.51

(a) Figure at top of next page.

**(b)** $\frac{d\psi_0}{dx} = -Aa \, \text{sech}(ax) \tanh(ax); \quad \frac{d^2\psi_0}{dx^2} = -Aa^2 \left[ -\text{sech}(ax) \tanh^2(ax) + \text{sech}(ax) \, \text{sech}^2(ax) \right].$

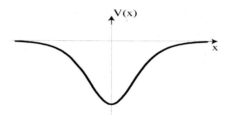

$$H\psi_0 = -\frac{\hbar^2}{2m}\frac{d^2\psi_0}{dx^2} - \frac{\hbar^2 a^2}{m}\operatorname{sech}^2(ax)\psi_0$$

$$= \frac{\hbar^2}{2m}Aa^2\left[-\operatorname{sech}(ax)\tanh^2(ax) + \operatorname{sech}^3(ax)\right] - \frac{\hbar^2 a^2}{m}A\operatorname{sech}^3(ax)$$

$$= \frac{\hbar^2 a^2 A}{2m}\left[-\operatorname{sech}(ax)\tanh^2(ax) + \operatorname{sech}^3(ax) - 2\operatorname{sech}^3(ax)\right]$$

$$= -\frac{\hbar^2 a^2}{2m}A\operatorname{sech}(ax)\left[\tanh^2(ax) + \operatorname{sech}^2(ax)\right].$$

But $(\tanh^2\theta + \operatorname{sech}^2\theta) = \dfrac{\sinh^2\theta}{\cosh^2\theta} + \dfrac{1}{\cosh^2\theta} = \dfrac{\sinh^2\theta + 1}{\cosh^2\theta} = 1$, so

$$= -\frac{\hbar^2 a^2}{2m}\psi_0. \quad \text{QED} \quad \text{Evidently} \quad \boxed{E = -\frac{\hbar^2 a^2}{2m}.}$$

$$1 = |A|^2\int_{-\infty}^{\infty}\operatorname{sech}^2(ax)dx = |A|^2\frac{1}{a}\tanh(ax)\Big|_{-\infty}^{\infty} = \frac{2}{a}|A|^2 \implies \boxed{A = \sqrt{\frac{a}{2}}.}$$

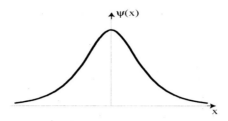

**(c)**

$$\frac{d\psi_k}{dx} = \frac{A}{ik+a}\left[(ik - a\tanh ax)ik - a^2\operatorname{sech}^2 ax\right]e^{ikx}.$$

$$\frac{d^2\psi_k}{dx^2} = \frac{A}{ik+a}\left\{ik\left[(ik - a\tanh ax)ik - a^2\operatorname{sech}^2 ax\right] - a^2 ik\operatorname{sech}^2 ax + 2a^3\operatorname{sech}^2 ax\tanh ax\right\}e^{ikx}.$$

$$-\frac{\hbar^2}{2m}\frac{d^2\psi_k}{dx^2} + V\psi_k = \frac{A}{ik+a}\left\{\frac{-\hbar^2 ik}{2m}\left[-k^2 - iak\tanh ax - a^2\,\text{sech}^2\,ax\right] + \frac{\hbar^2 a^2}{2m}ik\,\text{sech}^2\,ax\right.$$

$$\left.-\frac{\hbar^2 a^3}{m}\,\text{sech}^2\,ax\tanh ax - \frac{\hbar^2 a^2}{m}\,\text{sech}^2\,ax(ik - a\tanh ax)\right\}e^{ikx}$$

$$= \frac{Ae^{ikx}}{ik+a}\frac{\hbar^2}{2m}\left(ik^3 - ak^2\tanh ax + ia^2 k\,\text{sech}^2\,ax + ia^2 k\,\text{sech}^2\,ax\right.$$

$$\left.-2a^3\,\text{sech}^2\,ax\tanh ax - 2ia^2 k\,\text{sech}^2\,ax + 2a^3\,\text{sech}^2\,ax\tanh ax\right)$$

$$= \frac{Ae^{ikx}}{ik+a}\frac{\hbar^2}{2m}k^2(ik - a\tanh ax) = \frac{\hbar^2 k^2}{2m}\psi_k = E\psi_k. \quad \text{QED}$$

As $x \to +\infty$, $\tanh ax \to +1$, so $\boxed{\psi_k(x) \to A\left(\dfrac{ik-a}{ik+a}\right)e^{ikx},}$ which represents a transmitted wave.

$$\boxed{R = 0.} \qquad T = \left|\frac{ik-a}{ik+a}\right|^2 = \left(\frac{-ik-a}{-ik+a}\right)\left(\frac{ik-a}{ik+a}\right) = \boxed{1.}$$

## Problem 2.52

**(a)** (1) From Eq. 2.133: $F + G = A + B$.

(2) From Eq. 2.135: $F - G = (1 + 2i\beta)A - (1 - 2i\beta)B$, where $\beta = m\alpha/\hbar^2 k$.

Subtract: $2G = -2i\beta A + 2(1 - i\beta)B \Rightarrow B = \dfrac{1}{1 - i\beta}(i\beta A + G)$. Multiply (1) by $(1 - 2i\beta)$ and add:

$$2(1 - i\beta)F - 2i\beta G = 2A \Rightarrow F = \frac{1}{1 - i\beta}(A + i\beta G). \qquad \boxed{\mathsf{S} = \frac{1}{1 - i\beta}\begin{pmatrix} i\beta & 1 \\ 1 & i\beta \end{pmatrix}.}$$

**(b)** For an *even* potential, $V(-x) = V(x)$, scattering from the right is the same as scattering from the left, with $x \leftrightarrow -x$, $A \leftrightarrow G$, $B \leftrightarrow F$ (see Fig. 2.22): $F = S_{11}G + S_{12}A$, $B = S_{21}G + S_{22}A$. So $S_{11} = S_{22}$, $S_{21} = S_{12}$. (Note that the delta-well $S$ matrix in (a) has this property.) In the case of the finite square well, Eqs. 2.167 and 2.168 give

$$S_{21} = \frac{e^{-2ika}}{\cos 2la - i\frac{(k^2+l^2)}{2kl}\sin 2la}; \quad S_{11} = \frac{i\frac{(l^2-k^2)}{2kl}\sin 2la\,e^{-2ika}}{\cos 2la - i\frac{(k^2+l^2)}{2kl}\sin 2la}. \quad \text{So}$$

$$\boxed{\mathsf{S} = \frac{e^{-2ika}}{\cos 2la - i\frac{(k^2+l^2)}{2kl}\sin 2la}\begin{pmatrix} i\frac{(l^2-k^2)}{2kl}\sin 2la & 1 \\ 1 & i\frac{(l^2-k^2)}{2kl}\sin 2la \end{pmatrix}.}$$

## Problem 2.53

**(a)**

$$B = S_{11}A + S_{12}G \Rightarrow G = \frac{1}{S_{12}}(B - S_{11}A) = M_{21}A + M_{22}B \Rightarrow M_{21} = -\frac{S_{11}}{S_{12}}, \; M_{22} = \frac{1}{S_{12}}.$$

$$F = S_{21}A + S_{22}B = S_{21}A + \frac{S_{22}}{S_{12}}(B - S_{11}A) = -\frac{(S_{11}S_{22} - S_{12}S_{21})}{S_{12}}A + \frac{S_{22}}{S_{12}}B = M_{11}A + M_{12}B.$$

$$\Rightarrow M_{11} = -\frac{\det S}{S_{12}}, \; M_{12} = \frac{S_{22}}{S_{12}}. \quad \boxed{\mathsf{M} = \frac{1}{S_{12}}\begin{pmatrix} -\det(\mathsf{S}) & S_{22} \\ -S_{11} & 1 \end{pmatrix}.} \quad \text{Conversely:}$$

$$G = M_{21}A + M_{22}B \Rightarrow B = \frac{1}{M_{22}}(G - M_{21}A) = S_{11}A + S_{12}G \Rightarrow S_{11} = -\frac{M_{21}}{M_{22}}; \; S_{12} = \frac{1}{M_{22}}.$$

$$F = M_{11}A + M_{12}B = M_{11}A + \frac{M_{12}}{M_{22}}(G - M_{21}A) = \frac{(M_{11}M_{22} - M_{12}M_{21})}{M_{22}}A + \frac{M_{12}}{M_{22}}G = S_{21}A + S_{22}G.$$

$$\Rightarrow S_{21} = \frac{\det M}{M_{22}}; \; S_{22} = \frac{M_{12}}{M_{22}}. \quad \boxed{\mathsf{S} = \frac{1}{M_{22}}\begin{pmatrix} -M_{21} & 1 \\ \det(\mathsf{M}) & M_{12} \end{pmatrix}.}$$

[It happens that the time-reversal invariance of the Schrödinger equation, plus conservation of probability, requires $M_{22} = M_{11}^*$, $M_{21} = M_{12}^*$, and $\det(\mathsf{M}) = 1$, but I won't use this here. See Merzbacher's *Quantum Mechanics*. Similarly, for *even* potentials $S_{11} = S_{22}$, $S_{12} = S_{21}$ (Problem 2.52).]

$$R_l = |S_{11}|^2 = \boxed{\left|\frac{M_{21}}{M_{22}}\right|^2}, \; T_l = |S_{21}|^2 = \boxed{\left|\frac{\det(\mathsf{M})}{M_{22}}\right|^2}, \; R_r = |S_{22}|^2 = \boxed{\left|\frac{M_{12}}{M_{22}}\right|^2}, \; T_r = |S_{12}|^2 = \boxed{\frac{1}{|M_{22}|^2}}.$$

**(b)**

$$\begin{pmatrix} F \\ G \end{pmatrix} = \mathsf{M}_2\begin{pmatrix} C \\ D \end{pmatrix}, \; \begin{pmatrix} C \\ D \end{pmatrix} = \mathsf{M}_1\begin{pmatrix} A \\ B \end{pmatrix}, \; \text{so} \; \begin{pmatrix} F \\ G \end{pmatrix} = \mathsf{M}_2\mathsf{M}_1\begin{pmatrix} A \\ B \end{pmatrix} = \mathsf{M}\begin{pmatrix} A \\ B \end{pmatrix}, \; \text{with } \mathsf{M} = \mathsf{M}_2\mathsf{M}_1. \quad \text{QED}$$

**(c)**

$$\psi(x) = \begin{cases} Ae^{ikx} + Be^{-ikx} & (x < a) \\ Fe^{ikx} + Ge^{-ikx} & (x > a) \end{cases}.$$

$$\begin{cases} \text{Continuity of } \psi: & Ae^{ika} + Be^{-ika} = Fe^{ika} + Ge^{-ika} \\ \text{Discontinuity of } \psi': & ik\left(Fe^{ika} - Ge^{-ika}\right) - ik\left(Ae^{ika} - Be^{-ika}\right) = -\frac{2m\alpha}{\hbar^2}\psi(a) = -\frac{2m\alpha}{\hbar^2}\left(Ae^{ika} + Be^{-ika}\right). \end{cases}$$

**(1)** $Fe^{2ika} + G = Ae^{2ika} + B.$

**(2)** $Fe^{2ika} - G = Ae^{2ika} - B + i\frac{2m\alpha}{\hbar^2 k}\left(Ae^{2ika} + B\right).$

Add (1) and (2):

$$2Fe^{2ika} = 2Ae^{2ika} + i\frac{2m\alpha}{\hbar^2 k}\left(Ae^{2ika} + B\right) \Rightarrow F = \left(1 + i\frac{m\alpha}{\hbar^2 k}\right)A + i\frac{m\alpha}{\hbar^2 k}e^{-2ika}B = M_{11}A + M_{12}B.$$

So $M_{11} = (1 + i\beta)$; $M_{12} = i\beta e^{-2ika}$; $\beta \equiv \frac{m\alpha}{\hbar^2 k}$.

Subtract (2) from (1):

$$2G = 2B - 2i\beta e^{2ika}A - 2i\beta B \Rightarrow G = (1 - i\beta)B - i\beta e^{2ika}A = M_{21}A + M_{22}B.$$

So $M_{21} = -i\beta e^{2ika}$; $M_{22} = (1 - i\beta)$.  $\boxed{\mathsf{M} = \begin{pmatrix} (1+i\beta) & i\beta e^{-2ika} \\ -i\beta e^{2ika} & (1-i\beta) \end{pmatrix}.}$

**(d)**

$$\mathsf{M}_1 = \begin{pmatrix} (1+i\beta) & i\beta e^{-2ika} \\ -i\beta e^{2ika} & (1-i\beta) \end{pmatrix}; \text{ to get } \mathsf{M}_2, \text{ just switch the sign of } a: \ \mathsf{M}_2 = \begin{pmatrix} (1+i\beta) & i\beta e^{2ika} \\ -i\beta e^{-2ika} & (1-i\beta) \end{pmatrix}.$$

$$\mathsf{M} = \mathsf{M}_2\mathsf{M}_1 = \boxed{\begin{pmatrix} [1 + 2i\beta + \beta^2(e^{4ika} - 1)] & 2i\beta[\cos 2ka + \beta \sin 2ka] \\ -2i\beta[\cos 2ka + \beta \sin 2ka] & [1 - 2i\beta + \beta^2(e^{-4ika} - 1)] \end{pmatrix}.}$$

$$T = T_l = T_r = \frac{1}{|M_{22}|^2} \Rightarrow$$

$$\begin{aligned}
T^{-1} &= [1 + 2i\beta + \beta^2(e^{4ika} - 1)][1 - 2i\beta + \beta^2(e^{-4ika} - 1)] \\
&= 1 - 2i\beta + \beta^2 e^{-4ika} - \beta^2 + 2i\beta + 4\beta^2 + 2i\beta^3 e^{-4ika} - 2i\beta^3 + \beta^2 e^{4ika} \\
&\quad - \beta^2 - 2i\beta^3 e^{4ika} + 2i\beta^3 + \beta^4(1 - e^{4ika} - e^{-4ika} + 1) \\
&= 1 + 2\beta^2 + \beta^2(e^{4ika} + e^{-4ika}) - 2i\beta^3(e^{4ika} - e^{-4ika}) + 2\beta^4 - \beta^4(e^{4ika} + e^{-4ika}) \\
&= 1 + 2\beta^2 + 2\beta^2\cos 4ka - 2i\beta^3 2i\sin 4ka + 2\beta^4 - 2\beta^4\cos 4ka \\
&= 1 + 2\beta^2(1 + \cos 4ka) + 4\beta^3\sin 4ka + 2\beta^4(1 - \cos 4ka) \\
&= 1 + 4\beta^2\cos^2 2ka + 8\beta^3\sin 2ka\cos 2ka + 4\beta^4\sin^2 2ka
\end{aligned}$$

$$\boxed{T = \frac{1}{1 + 4\beta^2(\cos 2ka + \beta\sin 2ka)^2}}$$

## Problem 2.54

I'll just show the first two graphs, and the last two. Evidently $K$ lies between 0.9999 and 1.0001.

```
Plot[Evaluate[u[x] /.
    NDSolve[{u''[x] - (x^2 - 0.9)*u[x] == 0, u[0] == 1,
      u'[0] == 0}, u[x], {x, 10^-8, 10},
    MaxSteps -> 10000]], {x, 0, 10},
  PlotRange -> {-10, 10}];
```

```
Plot[Evaluate[u[x] /.
    NDSolve[{u''[x] - (x^2 - 0.9999)*u[x] == 0, u[0] == 1,
      u'[0] == 0}, u[x], {x, 10^-8, 10}, MaxSteps -> 10000]],
  {x, 4, 5.5}, PlotRange -> {-1, 10}];
```

```
Plot[Evaluate[u[x] /.
    NDSolve[{u''[x] - (x^2 - 1.1)*u[x] == 0, u[0] == 1,
      u'[0] == 0}, u[x], {x, 10^-8, 10},
    MaxSteps -> 10000]], {x, 0, 10},
  PlotRange -> {-10, 10}];
```

```
Plot[Evaluate[u[x] /.
    NDSolve[{u''[x] - (x^2 - 1.0001)*u[x] == 0, u[0] == 1,
      u'[0] == 0}, u[x], {x, 10^-8, 10}, MaxSteps -> 10000]],
  {x, 4, 5.5}, PlotRange -> {-10, 1}];
```

## Problem 2.55

The *correct* values (in Eq. 2.72) are $K = 2n + 1$ (corresponding to $E_n = (n + \frac{1}{2})\hbar\omega$). I'll start by "guessing" 2.9, 4.9, and 6.9, and tweaking the number until I've got 5 reliable significant digits. The results (see below) are $\boxed{3.0000, \ 5.0000, \ 7.0000.}$ (The actual *energies* are these numbers multiplied by $\frac{1}{2}\hbar\omega$.)

58

```
Plot[Evaluate[u[x] /.
    NDSolve[{u''[x] - (x^2 - 2.9)*u[x] == 0, u[0] == 0,
    u'[0] == 1}, u[x], {x, 10^-8, 10},
    MaxSteps -> 10000]], {x, 0, 5},
  PlotRange -> {-1, 5}];
```

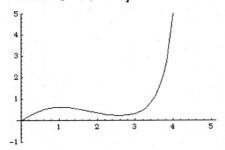

```
Plot[Evaluate[u[x] /.
    NDSolve[{u''[x] - (x^2 - 3.00001)*u[x] == 0,
    u[0] == 0, u'[0] == 1}, u[x], {x, 10^-8, 10},
    MaxSteps -> 10000]], {x, 0, 5.5},
  PlotRange -> {-.5, .7}];
```

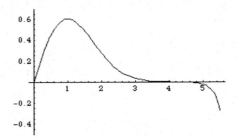

```
Plot[Evaluate[u[x] /.
    NDSolve[{u''[x] - (x^2 - 2.99999)*u[x] == 0,
    u[0] == 0, u'[0] == 1}, u[x], {x, 10^-8, 10},
    MaxSteps -> 10000]], {x, 0, 5.5},
  PlotRange -> {-.1, .7}];
```

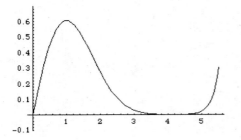

```
Plot[Evaluate[u[x] /.
    NDSolve[{u''[x] - (x^2 - 4.9)*u[x] == 0, u[0] == 1,
    u'[0] == 0}, u[x], {x, 10^-8, 10},
    MaxSteps -> 10000]], {x, 0, 4},
  PlotRange -> {-1.5, 1.2}];
```

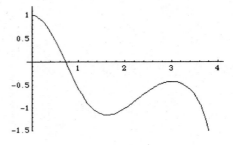

```
Plot[Evaluate[u[x] /.
    NDSolve[{u''[x] - (x^2 - 4.99999) * u[x] == 0,
      u[0] == 1, u'[0] == 0}, u[x], {x, 10^-8, 10},
      MaxSteps -> 10000]], {x, 0, 6},
    PlotRange -> {-1.5, 1.2}];
```

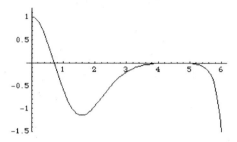

```
Plot[Evaluate[u[x] /.
    NDSolve[{u''[x] - (x^2 - 6.9) * u[x] == 0, u[0] == 0,
      u'[0] == 1}, u[x], {x, 10^-8, 10},
      MaxSteps -> 10000]], {x, 0, 4.5},
    PlotRange -> {-1, .5}];
```

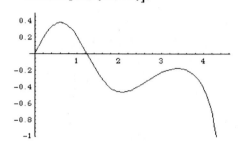

```
Plot[Evaluate[u[x] /.
    NDSolve[{u''[x] - (x^2 - 5.00001) * u[x] == 0,
      u[0] == 1, u'[0] == 0}, u[x], {x, 10^-8, 10},
      MaxSteps -> 10000]], {x, 0, 6},
    PlotRange -> {-1.5, 1.2}];
```

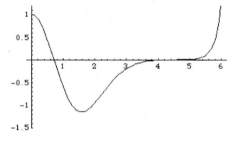

```
Plot[Evaluate[u[x] /.
    NDSolve[{u''[x] - (x^2 - 6.99999) * u[x] == 0,
      u[0] == 0, u'[0] == 1}, u[x], {x, 10^-8, 10},
      MaxSteps -> 10000]], {x, 0, 6.5},
    PlotRange -> {-1, .5}];
```

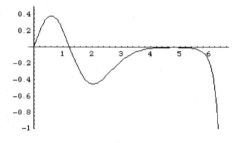

```
Plot[Evaluate[u[x] /.
    NDSolve[{u''[x] - (x^2 - 7.00001)*u[x] == 0,
      u[0] == 0, u'[0] == 1}, u[x], {x, 10^-8, 10},
    MaxSteps -> 10000]], {x, 0, 6.5},
  PlotRange -> {-1, .5}];
```

## Problem 2.56

The Schrödinger equation says $-\frac{\hbar^2}{2m}\psi'' = E\psi$, or, with the *correct* energies (Eq. 2.27) and $a = 1$, $\psi'' + (n\pi)^2\psi = 0$. I'll start with a "guess" using 9 in place of $\pi^2$ (that is, I'll use 9 for the ground state, 36 for the first excited state, 81 for the next, and finally 144). Then I'll tweak the parameter until the graph crosses the axis right at $x = 1$. The results (see below) are, to five significant digits: $\boxed{9.8696, \; 39.478, \; 88.826, \; 157.91.}$ (The actual *energies* are these numbers multiplied by $\hbar^2/2ma^2$.)

```
Plot[Evaluate[u[x] /.
    NDSolve[{u''[x] + (9) *u[x] == 0, u[0] == 0, u'[0] == 1},
    u[x], {x, 10⁻⁸, 1.5}, MaxSteps -> 10000]],
    {x, 0, 1.2}, PlotRange -> {-.5, .5}];
```

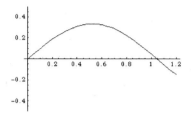

```
Plot[Evaluate[u[x] /.
    NDSolve[{u''[x] + (36) *u[x] == 0, u[0] == 0, u'[0] == 1},
    u[x], {x, 10⁻⁸, 1.5}, MaxSteps -> 10000]],
    {x, 0, 1.2}, PlotRange -> {-.5, .5}];
```

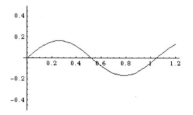

```
Plot[Evaluate[u[x] /.
    NDSolve[{u''[x] + (9.86959) *u[x] == 0, u[0] == 0,
    u'[0] == 1}, u[x], {x, 10⁻⁸, 1.005},
    MaxSteps -> 10000]], {x, 0.99999, 1.00001},
    PlotRange -> {-.00001, .00001}];
```

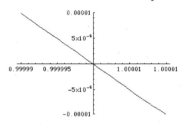

```
Plot[Evaluate[u[x] /.
    NDSolve[{u''[x] + (39.47803) *u[x] == 0, u[0] == 0,
    u'[0] == 1}, u[x], {x, 10⁻⁸, 1.005},
    MaxSteps -> 10000]], {x, 0.99999, 1.00001},
    PlotRange -> {-.00001, .00001}];
```

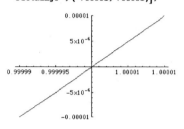

```
Plot[Evaluate[u[x] /.
    NDSolve[{u''[x] + (81) *u[x] == 0, u[0] == 0, u'[0] == 1},
    u[x], {x, 10⁻⁸, 1.5}, MaxSteps -> 10000]],
    {x, 0, 1.2}, PlotRange -> {-.15, .15}];
```

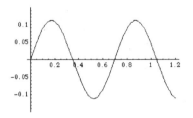

```
Plot[Evaluate[u[x] /.
    NDSolve[{u''[x] + (144) *u[x] == 0, u[0] == 0, u'[0] == 1},
    u[x], {x, 10⁻⁸, 1.5}, MaxSteps -> 10000]],
    {x, 0, 1.2}, PlotRange -> {-.1, .1}];
```

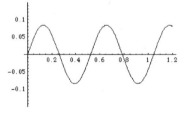

```
Plot[Evaluate[u[x] /.
    NDSolve[{u''[x] + (88.82630) *u[x] == 0, u[0] == 0,
    u'[0] == 1}, u[x], {x, 10⁻⁸, 1.005},
    MaxSteps -> 10000]], {x, 0.99999, 1.00001},
    PlotRange -> {-.00001, .00001}];
```

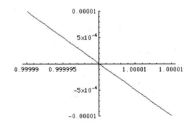

```
Plot[Evaluate[u[x] /.
    NDSolve[{u''[x] + (157.9129) *u[x] == 0, u[0] == 0,
    u'[0] == 1}, u[x], {x, 10⁻⁸, 1.005},
    MaxSteps -> 10000]], {x, 0.99999, 1.00001},
    PlotRange -> {-.00001, .00001}];
```

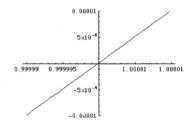

# Chapter 3

# Formalism

## Problem 3.1

**(a)** All conditions are trivial except Eq. A.1: we need to show that the sum of two square-integrable functions is itself square-integrable. Let $h(x) = f(x) + g(x)$, so that $|h|^2 = (f+g)^*(f+g) = |f|^2 + |g|^2 + f^*g + g^*f$ and hence

$$\int |h|^2 \, dx = \int |f|^2 \, dx + \int |g|^2 \, dx + \int f^*g \, dx + \left( \int f^*g \, dx \right)^*.$$

If $f(x)$ and $g(x)$ are square-integrable, then the first two terms are finite, and (by Eq. 3.7) so too are the last two. So $\int |h|^2 dx$ is finite.   QED

The set of all *normalized* functions is certainly *not* a vector space: it doesn't include 0, and the sum of two normalized functions is not (in general) normalized—in fact, if $f(x)$ is normalized, then the square integral of $2f(x)$ is 4.

**(b)** Equation A.19 is trivial:

$$\langle g|f \rangle = \int_a^b g(x)^* f(x) \, dx = \left( \int_a^b f(x)^* g(x) \, dx \right)^* = \langle f|g \rangle^*.$$

Equation A.20 holds (see Eq. 3.9) subject to the understanding in footnote 6. As for Eq. A.21, this is pretty obvious:

$$\langle f|(b|g\rangle + c|h\rangle) \rangle = \int f(x)^* \left( bg(x) + ch(x) \right) dx = b \int f^*g \, dx + c \int f^*h \, dx = b\langle f|g \rangle + c\langle f|h \rangle.$$

---

## Problem 3.2

**(a)**

$$\langle f|f \rangle = \int_0^1 x^{2\nu} \, dx = \frac{1}{2\nu + 1} x^{2\nu+1} \Big|_0^1 = \frac{1}{2\nu + 1} \left( 1 - 0^{2\nu+1} \right).$$

Now $0^{2\nu+1}$ is finite (in fact, *zero*) provided $(2\nu + 1) > 0$, which is to say, $\boxed{\nu > -\frac{1}{2}.}$ If $(2\nu + 1) < 0$ the integral definitely blows up. As for the critical case $\nu = -\frac{1}{2}$, this must be handled separately:

$$\langle f|f \rangle = \int_0^1 x^{-1} \, dx = \ln x \Big|_0^1 = \ln 1 - \ln 0 = 0 + \infty.$$

So $f(x)$ is in Hilbert space only for $\nu$ strictly *greater* than -1/2.

**(b)** For $\nu = 1/2$, we know from (a) that $f(x)$ *is* in Hilbert space: $\boxed{\text{yes.}}$

Since $xf = x^{3/2}$, we know from (a) that it *is* in Hilbert space: $\boxed{\text{yes.}}$

For $df/dx = \frac{1}{2}x^{-1/2}$, we know from (a) that it is *not* in Hilbert space: $\boxed{\text{no.}}$

[*Moral:* Simple operations, such as differenting (or multiplying by $1/x$), can carry a function *out* of Hilbert space.]

---

## Problem 3.3

Suppose $\langle h|\hat{Q}h\rangle = \langle \hat{Q}h|h\rangle$ for all functions $h(x)$. Let $h(x) = f(x) + cg(x)$ for some arbitrary constant $c$. Then

$$\langle h|\hat{Q}h\rangle = \langle(f + cg)|\hat{Q}(f + cg)\rangle = \langle f|\hat{Q}f\rangle + c\langle f|\hat{Q}g\rangle + c^*\langle g|\hat{Q}f\rangle + |c|^2\langle g|\hat{Q}g\rangle;$$
$$\langle \hat{Q}h|h\rangle = \langle \hat{Q}(f + cg)|(f + cg)\rangle = \langle \hat{Q}f|f\rangle + c\langle \hat{Q}f|g\rangle + c^*\langle \hat{Q}g|f\rangle + |c|^2\langle \hat{Q}g|g\rangle.$$

Equating the two and noting that $\langle f|\hat{Q}f\rangle = \langle \hat{Q}f|f\rangle$ and $\langle g|\hat{Q}g\rangle = \langle \hat{Q}g|g\rangle$ leaves

$$c\langle f|\hat{Q}g\rangle + c^*\langle g|\hat{Q}f\rangle = c\langle \hat{Q}f|g\rangle + c^*\langle \hat{Q}g|f\rangle.$$

In particlar, choosing $c = 1$:

$$\langle f|\hat{Q}g\rangle + \langle g|\hat{Q}f\rangle = \langle \hat{Q}f|g\rangle + \langle \hat{Q}g|f\rangle,$$

whereas if $c = i$:

$$\langle f|\hat{Q}g\rangle - \langle g|\hat{Q}f\rangle = \langle \hat{Q}f|g\rangle - \langle \hat{Q}g|f\rangle.$$

Adding the last two equations:

$$\langle f|\hat{Q}g\rangle = \langle \hat{Q}f|g\rangle. \quad \text{QED}$$

---

## Problem 3.4

**(a)** $\langle f|(\hat{H} + \hat{K})g\rangle = \langle f|\hat{H}g\rangle + \langle f|\hat{K}g\rangle = \langle \hat{H}f|g\rangle + \langle \hat{K}f|g\rangle = \langle(\hat{H} + \hat{K})f|g\rangle.$ ✓

**(b)** $\langle f|\alpha\hat{Q}g\rangle = \alpha\langle f|\hat{Q}g\rangle$; $\langle \alpha\hat{Q}f|g\rangle = \alpha^*\langle \hat{Q}f|g\rangle$. Hermitian $\Leftrightarrow$ $\boxed{\alpha \text{ is real.}}$

**(c)** $\langle f|\hat{H}\hat{K}g\rangle = \langle \hat{H}f|\hat{K}g\rangle = \langle \hat{K}\hat{H}f|g\rangle$, so $\hat{H}\hat{K}$ is hermitian $\Leftrightarrow \hat{H}\hat{K} = \hat{K}\hat{H}$, or $\boxed{[\hat{H}, \hat{K}] = 0.}$

**(d)** $\langle f|\hat{x}g\rangle = \int f^*(xg)\,dx = \int(xf)^*g\,dx = \langle \hat{x}f|g\rangle.$ ✓

$$\langle f|\hat{H}g\rangle = \int f^*\left(-\frac{\hbar^2}{2m}\frac{d^2}{dx^2} + V\right)g\,dx = -\frac{\hbar^2}{2m}\int f^*\frac{d^2g}{dx^2}\,dx + \int f^*Vg\,dx.$$

Integrating by parts (twice):

$$\int_{-\infty}^{\infty} f^*\frac{d^2g}{dx^2}\,dx = f^*\frac{dg}{dx}\Big|_{-\infty}^{\infty} - \int_{-\infty}^{\infty}\frac{df^*}{dx}\frac{dg}{dx}\,dx = f^*\frac{dg}{dx}\Big|_{-\infty}^{\infty} - \frac{df^*}{dx}g\Big|_{-\infty}^{\infty} + \int_{-\infty}^{\infty}\frac{d^2f^*}{dx^2}g\,dx.$$

But for functions $f(x)$ and $g(x)$ in Hilbert space the boundary terms vanish, so

$$\int_{-\infty}^{\infty} f^*\frac{d^2g}{dx^2}\,dx = \int_{-\infty}^{\infty}\frac{d^2f^*}{dx^2}g\,dx, \text{ and hence (assuming that } V(x) \text{ is real):}$$

$$\langle f|\hat{H}g\rangle = \int_{-\infty}^{\infty}\left(-\frac{\hbar^2}{2m}\frac{d^2f}{dx^2} + Vf\right)^*g\,dx = \langle \hat{H}f|g\rangle. \quad ✓$$

---

## Problem 3.5

**(a)** $\langle f|xg\rangle = \int f^*(xg)\,dx = \int (xf)^*g\,dx = \langle xf|g\rangle$, so $\boxed{x^\dagger = x.}$

$\langle f|ig\rangle = \int f^*(ig)\,dx = \int (-if)^*g\,dx = \langle -if|g\rangle$, so $\boxed{i^\dagger = -i.}$

$\langle f|\frac{dg}{dx}\rangle = \int_{-\infty}^{\infty} f^*\frac{dg}{dx}\,dx = f^*g\Big|_{-\infty}^{\infty} - \int_{-\infty}^{\infty}\left(\frac{df}{dx}\right)^*g\,dx = -\langle xf|g\rangle$, so $\boxed{\left(\frac{d}{dx}\right)^\dagger = -\frac{d}{dx}.}$

**(b)** $a_+ = \frac{1}{\sqrt{2\hbar m\omega}}(-ip + m\omega x)$. But $p$ and $x$ are hermitian, and $i^\dagger = -i$, so $(a_+)^\dagger = \frac{1}{\sqrt{2\hbar m\omega}}(ip + m\omega x)$, or $\boxed{(a_+)^\dagger = (a_-).}$

**(c)** $\langle f|(\hat{Q}\hat{R})g\rangle = \langle \hat{Q}^\dagger f|\hat{R}g\rangle = \langle \hat{R}^\dagger\hat{Q}^\dagger f|g\rangle = \langle(\hat{Q}\hat{R})^\dagger f|g\rangle$, so $(\hat{Q}\hat{R})^\dagger = \hat{R}^\dagger\hat{Q}^\dagger$. ✓

---

## Problem 3.6

$$\langle f|\hat{Q}g\rangle = \int_0^{2\pi} f^*\frac{d^2g}{d\phi^2}\,d\phi = f^*\frac{dg}{d\phi}\Big|_0^{2\pi} - \int_0^{2\pi}\frac{df^*}{d\phi}\frac{dg}{d\phi}\,d\phi = f^*\frac{dg}{d\phi}\Big|_0^{2\pi} - \frac{df^*}{d\phi}g\Big|_0^{2\pi} + \int_0^{2\pi}\frac{d^2f^*}{d\phi^2}g\,d\phi.$$

As in Example 3.1, for periodic functions (Eq. 3.26) the boundary terms vanish, and we conclude that $\langle f|\hat{Q}g\rangle = \langle\hat{Q}f|g\rangle$, so $\hat{Q}$ is hermitian: $\boxed{\text{yes.}}$

$$\hat{Q}f = qf \Rightarrow \frac{d^2f}{d\phi^2} = qf \Rightarrow f_\pm(\phi) = \boxed{Ae^{\pm\sqrt{q}\phi}.}$$

The periodicity condition (Eq. 3.26) requires that $\sqrt{q}(2\pi) = 2n\pi i$, or $\sqrt{q} = in$, so the eigenvalues are $\boxed{q = -n^2,\ (n = 0, 1, 2, \dots).}$ The spectrum is $\boxed{\text{doubly degenerate;}}$ for a given $n$ there are *two* eigenfunctions (the plus sign or the minus sign, in the exponent), except for the special case $n = 0$, which is not degenerate.

---

## Problem 3.7

**(a)** Suppose $\hat{Q}f = qf$ and $\hat{Q}g = qg$. Let $h(x) = af(x) + bg(x)$, for arbitrary constants $a$ and $b$. Then

$$\hat{Q}h = \hat{Q}(af + bg) = a(\hat{Q}f) + b(\hat{Q}g) = a(qf) + b(qg) = q(af + bg) = qh. \quad ✓$$

**(b)** $\frac{d^2f}{dx^2} = \frac{d^2}{dx^2}(e^x) = \frac{d}{dx}(e^x) = e^x = f$, $\quad \frac{d^2g}{dx^2} = \frac{d^2}{dx^2}(e^{-x}) = \frac{d}{dx}(-e^{-x}) = e^{-x} = g$.

So both of them are eigenfunctions, with the same eigenvalue 1. The simplest orthogonal linear combinations are

$$\boxed{\sinh x = \frac{1}{2}\left(e^x - e^{-x}\right) = \frac{1}{2}(f - g) \quad \text{and} \quad \cosh x = \frac{1}{2}\left(e^x + e^{-x}\right) = \frac{1}{2}(f + g).}$$

(They are clearly orthogonal, since $\sinh x$ is odd while $\cosh x$ is even.)

---

## Problem 3.8

**(a)** The eigenvalues (Eq. 3.29) are $0, \pm 1, \pm 2, \ldots$, which are obviously real. ✓ For any two eigenfunctions, $f = A_q e^{-iq\phi}$ and $g = A_{q'} e^{-iq'\phi}$ (Eq. 3.28), we have

$$\langle f | g \rangle = A_q^* A_{q'} \int_0^{2\pi} e^{iq\phi} e^{-iq'\phi} \, d\phi = A_q^* A_{q'} \left. \frac{e^{i(q-q')\phi}}{i(q-q')} \right|_0^{2\pi} = \frac{A_q^* A_{q'}}{i(q-q')} \left[ e^{i(q-q')2\pi} - 1 \right].$$

But $q$ and $q'$ are *integers*, so $e^{i(q-q')2\pi} = 1$, and hence $\langle f | g \rangle = 0$ (provided $q \neq q'$, so the denominator is nonzero). ✓

**(b)** In Problem 3.6 the eigenvalues are $q = -n^2$, with $n = 0, 1, 2, \ldots$, which are obviously real. ✓ For any two eigenfunctions, $f = A_q e^{\pm in\phi}$ and $g = A_{q'} e^{\pm in'\phi}$, we have

$$\langle f | g \rangle = A_q^* A_{q'} \int_0^{2\pi} e^{\mp in\phi} e^{\pm in'\phi} \, d\phi = A_q^* A_{q'} \left. \frac{e^{\pm i(n'-n)\phi}}{\pm i(n'-n)} \right|_0^{2\pi} = \frac{A_q^* A_{q'}}{\pm i(n'-n)} \left[ e^{\pm i(n'-n)2\pi} - 1 \right] = 0$$

(provided $n \neq n'$). But notice that for each eigenvalue (i.e. each value of $n$) there are *two* eigenfunctions (one with the plus sign and one with the minus sign), and these are *not* orthogonal to one another.

---

## Problem 3.9

**(a)** $\boxed{\text{Infinite square well}}$ (Eq. 2.19).

**(b)** $\boxed{\text{Delta-function barrier}}$ (Fig. 2.16), or the finite rectangular barrier (Prob. 2.33).

**(c)** $\boxed{\text{Delta-function well}}$ (Eq. 2.114), or the finite square well (Eq. 2.145) or the $\text{sech}^2$ potential (Prob. 2.51).

---

## Problem 3.10

From Eq. 2.28, with $n = 1$:

$$\hat{p} \, \psi_1(x) = \frac{\hbar}{i} \frac{d}{dx} \sqrt{\frac{2}{a}} \sin\left(\frac{\pi}{a} x\right) = \frac{\hbar}{i} \sqrt{\frac{2}{a}} \frac{\pi}{a} \cos\left(\frac{\pi}{a} x\right) = \left[ -i \frac{\pi\hbar}{a} \cot\left(\frac{\pi}{a} x\right) \right] \psi_1(x).$$

Since $\hat{p} \, \psi_1$ is *not* a (constant) multiple of $\psi_1$, $\psi_1$ is not an eigenfunction of $\hat{p}$: $\boxed{\text{no.}}$ It's true that the *magnitude* of the momentum, $\sqrt{2mE_1} = \pi\hbar/a$, is determinate, but the particle is just as likely to be found traveling to the left (negative momentum) as to the right (positive momentum).

---

## Problem 3.11

$$\Psi_0(x,t) = \left(\frac{m\omega}{\pi\hbar}\right)^{1/4} e^{-\frac{m\omega}{2\hbar} x^2} e^{-i\omega t/2}; \quad \Phi(p,t) = \frac{1}{\sqrt{2\pi\hbar}} \left(\frac{m\omega}{\pi\hbar}\right)^{1/4} e^{-i\omega/2} \int_{-\infty}^{\infty} e^{-ipx/\hbar} e^{-\frac{m\omega}{2\hbar} x^2} \, dx.$$

From Problem 2.22(b):

$$\Phi(p,t) = \frac{1}{\sqrt{2\pi\hbar}} \left(\frac{m\omega}{\pi\hbar}\right)^{1/4} e^{-i\omega t/2} \sqrt{\frac{2\pi\hbar}{m\omega}} e^{-p^2/2m\omega\hbar} = \boxed{\frac{1}{(\pi m\omega\hbar)^{1/4}} e^{-p^2/2m\omega\hbar} e^{-i\omega t/2}}.$$

$$|\Phi(p,t)|^2 = \frac{1}{\sqrt{\pi m \omega \hbar}} e^{-p^2/m\omega\hbar}. \quad \text{Maximum classical momentum: } \frac{p^2}{2m} = E = \frac{1}{2}\hbar\omega \Longrightarrow p = \sqrt{m\omega\hbar}.$$

So the probability it's outside classical range is:

$$P = \int_{-\infty}^{-\sqrt{m\omega\hbar}} |\Phi|^2 dp + \int_{\sqrt{m\omega\hbar}}^{\infty} |\Phi|^2 dp = 1 - 2\int_{0}^{\sqrt{m\omega\hbar}} |\Phi|^2 dp. \quad \text{Now}$$

$$\int_{0}^{\sqrt{m\omega\hbar}} |\Phi|^2 dp = \frac{1}{\sqrt{\pi m\omega\hbar}} \int_{0}^{\sqrt{m\omega\hbar}} e^{-p^2/m\omega\hbar} dp. \quad \text{Let } z \equiv \sqrt{\frac{2}{m\omega\hbar}}\, p, \text{ so } dp = \sqrt{\frac{m\omega\hbar}{2}}\, dz.$$

$$= \frac{1}{\sqrt{2\pi}} \int_{0}^{\sqrt{2}} e^{-z^2/2} dz = F(\sqrt{2}) - \frac{1}{2}, \quad \text{in CRC Table notation.}$$

$$P = 1 - 2\left[(F(\sqrt{2}) - \frac{1}{2}\right] = 1 - 2F(\sqrt{2}) + 1 = 2\left[1 - F(\sqrt{2})\right] = 0.157.$$

To two digits: $\boxed{0.16}$ (compare Prob. 2.15).

---

## Problem 3.12

From Eq. 3.55: $\Psi(x,t) = \frac{1}{\sqrt{2\pi\hbar}} \int_{-\infty}^{\infty} e^{ipx/\hbar} \Phi(p,t) dp.$

$$\langle x \rangle = \int \Psi^* x \Psi dx = \int \left[ \frac{1}{\sqrt{2\pi\hbar}} \int e^{-ip'x/\hbar} \Phi^*(p',t) dp' \right] x \left[ \frac{1}{\sqrt{2\pi\hbar}} \int e^{+ipx/\hbar} \Phi(p,t) dp \right] dx.$$

But $xe^{ipx/\hbar} = -i\hbar \frac{d}{dp}\left(e^{ipx/\hbar}\right)$, so (integrating by parts):

$$x\int e^{ipx/\hbar} \Phi\, dp = \int \frac{\hbar}{i} \frac{d}{dp}\left(e^{ipx/\hbar}\right) \Phi\, dp = \int e^{ipx/\hbar} \left[ -\frac{\hbar}{i} \frac{\partial}{\partial p} \Phi(p,t) \right] dp.$$

So $\langle x \rangle = \frac{1}{2\pi\hbar} \iiint \left\{ e^{-ip'x/\hbar} \Phi^*(p',t) e^{ipx/\hbar} \left[ -\frac{\hbar}{i} \frac{\partial}{\partial p} \Phi(p,t) \right] \right\} dp'\, dp\, dx.$

Do the $x$ integral first, letting $y \equiv x/\hbar$:

$$\frac{1}{2\pi\hbar} \int e^{-ip'x/\hbar} e^{ipx/\hbar} dx = \frac{1}{2\pi} \int e^{i(p-p')y} dy = \delta(p-p'), \quad \text{(Eq. 2.144), so}$$

$$\langle x \rangle = \iint \Phi^*(p',t) \delta(p-p') \left[ -\frac{\hbar}{i} \frac{\partial}{\partial p} \Phi(p,t) \right] dp'\, dp = \int \Phi^*(p,t) \left[ -\frac{\hbar}{i} \frac{\partial}{\partial p} \Phi(p,t) \right] dp. \quad \text{QED}$$

---

## Problem 3.13

(a) $[AB, C] = ABC - CAB = ABC - ACB + ACB - CAB = A[B, C] + [A, C]B.$  ✓

(b) Introducing a test function $g(x)$, as in Eq. 2.50:

$$[x^n, p]g = x^n \frac{\hbar}{i} \frac{dg}{dx} - \frac{\hbar}{i} \frac{d}{dx}(x^n g) = x^n \frac{\hbar}{i} \frac{dg}{dx} - \frac{\hbar}{i}\left(nx^{n-1}g + x^n \frac{dg}{dx}\right) = i\hbar n x^{n-1} g.$$

So, dropping the test function, $[x^n, p] = i\hbar n x^{n-1}.$  ✓

(c) $[f, p]g = f\frac{\hbar}{i}\frac{dg}{dx} - \frac{\hbar}{i}\frac{d}{dx}(fg) = f\frac{\hbar}{i}\frac{dg}{dx} - \frac{\hbar}{i}\left(\frac{df}{dx}g + f\frac{dg}{dx}\right) = i\hbar\frac{df}{dx}g \Rightarrow [f, p] = i\hbar\frac{df}{dx}.$  ✓

## Problem 3.14

$$\left[x, \frac{p^2}{2m} + V\right] = \frac{1}{2m}\left[x, p^2\right] + [x, V]; \quad \left[x, p^2\right] = xp^2 - p^2 x = xp^2 - pxp + pxp - p^2 x = [x, p]p + p[x, p].$$

Using Eq. 2.51: $\left[x, p^2\right] = i\hbar p + p i\hbar = 2i\hbar p.$   And $[x, V] = 0,$   so $\left[x, \frac{p^2}{2m} + V\right] = \frac{1}{2m}2i\hbar p = \frac{i\hbar p}{m}.$

The generalized uncertainty principle (Eq. 3.62) says, in this case,

$$\sigma_x^2 \sigma_H^2 \geq \left(\frac{1}{2i}\frac{i\hbar}{m}\langle p\rangle\right)^2 = \left(\frac{\hbar}{2m}\langle p\rangle\right)^2 \Rightarrow \sigma_x \sigma_H \geq \frac{\hbar}{2m}|\langle p\rangle|. \quad \text{QED}$$

For stationary states $\sigma_H = 0$ and $\langle p\rangle = 0$, so it just says $0 \geq 0$.

## Problem 3.15

Suppose $\hat{P}f_n = \lambda_n f_n$ and $\hat{Q}f_n = \mu_n f_n$ (that is: $f_n(x)$ is an eigenfunction both of $\hat{P}$ and of $\hat{Q}$), and the set $\{f_n\}$ is complete, so that any function $f(x)$ (in Hilbert space) can be expressed as a linear combination: $f = \sum c_n f_n$. Then

$$[\hat{P}, \hat{Q}]f = (\hat{P}\hat{Q} - \hat{Q}\hat{P})\sum c_n f_n = \hat{P}\left(\sum c_n \mu_n f_n\right) - \hat{Q}\left(\sum c_n \lambda_n f_n\right) = \sum c_n \mu_n \lambda_n f_n - \sum c_n \lambda_n \mu_n f_n = 0.$$

Since this is true for *any* function $f$, it follows that $[\hat{P}, \hat{Q}] = 0$.

## Problem 3.16

$$\frac{d\Psi}{dx} = \frac{i}{\hbar}(iax - ia\langle x\rangle + \langle p\rangle)\Psi = \frac{a}{\hbar}\left(-x + \langle x\rangle + \frac{i}{a}\langle p\rangle\right)\Psi.$$

$$\frac{d\Psi}{\Psi} = \frac{a}{\hbar}\left(-x + \langle x\rangle + \frac{i\langle p\rangle}{a}\right)dx \Rightarrow \ln\Psi = \frac{a}{\hbar}\left(-\frac{x^2}{2} + \langle x\rangle x + \frac{i\langle p\rangle}{a}x\right) + constant.$$

Let $constant = -\frac{\langle x\rangle^2 a}{2\hbar} + B$ ($B$ a new constant). Then $\ln\Psi = -\frac{a}{2\hbar}(x - \langle x\rangle)^2 + \frac{i\langle p\rangle}{\hbar}x + B.$

$$\Psi = e^{-\frac{a}{2\hbar}(x - \langle x\rangle)^2}e^{i\langle p\rangle x/\hbar}e^B = Ae^{-a(x - \langle x\rangle)^2/2\hbar}e^{i\langle p\rangle x/\hbar}, \text{ where } A \equiv e^B.$$

## Problem 3.17

**(a)** 1 commutes with everything, so $\boxed{\dfrac{d}{dt}\langle\Psi|\Psi\rangle = 0}$ (this is the conservation of normalization, which we originally proved in Eq. 1.27).

**(b)** Anything commutes with itself, so $[H, H] = 0$, and hence $\boxed{\dfrac{d}{dt}\langle H\rangle = 0}$ (assuming $H$ has no explicit time dependence); this is conservation of energy, in the sense of the comment following Eq. 2.40.

**(c)** $[H, x] = -\dfrac{i\hbar p}{m}$ (see Problem 3.14). So $\dfrac{d\langle x\rangle}{dt} = \dfrac{i}{\hbar}\left(-\dfrac{i\hbar\langle p\rangle}{m}\right) = \boxed{\dfrac{\langle p\rangle}{m}}$ (Eq. 1.33).

**(d)** $[H, p] = \left[\dfrac{p^2}{2m} + V, p\right] = [V, p] = i\hbar\dfrac{dV}{dx}$ (Problem 3.13(c)). So $\dfrac{d\langle p\rangle}{dt} = \dfrac{i}{\hbar}\left(i\hbar\left\langle\dfrac{\partial V}{\partial x}\right\rangle\right) = \boxed{-\left\langle\dfrac{\partial V}{\partial x}\right\rangle}.$

This is Ehrenfest's theorem (Eq. 1.38).

---

## Problem 3.18

$$\Psi(x, t) = \frac{1}{\sqrt{2}}\left(\psi_1 e^{-iE_1 t/\hbar} + \psi_2 e^{-E_2 t/\hbar}\right). \quad H^2\Psi = \frac{1}{\sqrt{2}}\left[(H^2\psi_1)e^{-E_1 t/\hbar} + (H^2\psi_2)e^{-iE_n t/\hbar}\right].$$

$$H\psi_1 = E_1\psi_1 \Rightarrow H^2\psi_1 = E_1 H\psi_1 = E_1^2\psi_1, \quad \text{and } H^2\psi_2 = E_2^2\psi_2, \quad \text{so}$$

$$\langle H^2\rangle = \frac{1}{2}\langle\left(\psi_1 e^{-iE_1 t/\hbar} + \psi_2 e^{-iE_2 t/\hbar}\right)|\left(E_1^2\psi_1 e^{-iE_1 t/\hbar} + E_2^2\psi_2 e^{-iE_2 t/\hbar}\right)\rangle$$

$$= \frac{1}{2}\left(\langle\psi_1|\psi_1\rangle e^{iE_1 t/\hbar} E_1^2 e^{-iE_1 t/\hbar} + \langle\psi_1|\psi_2\rangle e^{iE_1 t/\hbar} E_2^2 e^{-iE_2 t/\hbar}\right.$$

$$\left. + \langle\psi_2|\psi_1\rangle e^{iE_2 t/\hbar} E_1^2 e^{-iE_1 t/\hbar} + \langle\psi_2|\psi_2\rangle e^{iE_2 t/\hbar} E_2^2 e^{-iE_2 t/\hbar}\right) = \frac{1}{2}\left(E_1^2 + E_2^2\right).$$

Similarly, $\langle H\rangle = \frac{1}{2}(E_1 + E_2)$   (Problem 2.5(e)).

$$\sigma_H^2 = \langle H^2\rangle - \langle H\rangle^2 = \frac{1}{2}\left(E_1^2 + E_2^2\right) - \frac{1}{4}(E_1 + E_2)^2 = \frac{1}{4}\left(2E_1^2 + 2E_2^2 - E_2^2 - E_1^2 - 2E_1 E_2 - E_2^2\right)$$

$$= \frac{1}{4}\left(E_1^2 - 2E_1 E_2 + E_2^2\right) = \frac{1}{4}(E_2 - E_1)^2. \quad \boxed{\sigma_H = \frac{1}{2}(E_2 - E_1).}$$

$$\langle x^2\rangle = \frac{1}{2}\left[\langle\psi_1|x^2|\psi_1\rangle + \langle\psi_2|x^2|\psi_2\rangle + \langle\psi_1|x^2|\psi_2\rangle e^{i(E_1 - E_2)t/\hbar} + \langle\psi_2|x^2|\psi_1\rangle e^{i(E_2 - E_1)t/\hbar}\right].$$

$$\langle\psi_n|x^2|\psi_m\rangle = \frac{2}{a}\int_0^a x^2 \sin\left(\frac{n\pi}{a}x\right)\sin\left(\frac{m\pi}{a}x\right)dx = \frac{1}{a}\int_0^a x^2\left[\cos\left(\frac{n - m}{a}\pi x\right) - \cos\left(\frac{n + m}{a}\pi x\right)\right]dx.$$

$$\text{Now } \int_0^a x^2\cos\left(\frac{k}{a}\pi x\right)dx = \left\{\frac{2a^2 x}{k^2\pi^2}\cos\left(\frac{k}{a}\pi x\right) + \left(\frac{a}{k\pi}\right)^3\left[\left(\frac{k\pi x}{a}\right)^2 - 2\right]\sin\left(\frac{k}{a}\pi x\right)\right\}\Bigg|_0^a$$

$$= \frac{2a^3}{k^2\pi^2}\cos(k\pi) = \frac{2a^3}{k^2\pi^2}(-1)^k \quad \text{(for } k = \text{nonzero integer)}.$$

$$\therefore \langle\psi_n|x^2|\psi_m\rangle = \frac{2a^2}{\pi^2}\left[\frac{(-1)^{n-m}}{(n-m)^2} - \frac{(-1)^{n+m}}{(n+m)^2}\right] = \frac{2a^2}{\pi^2}(-1)^{n+m}\frac{4nm}{(n^2-m^2)^2}.$$

So $\langle\psi_1|x^2|\psi_2\rangle = \langle\psi_2|x^2|\psi_1\rangle = -\frac{16a^2}{9\pi^2}$. Meanwhile, from Problem 2.4, $\langle\psi_n|x^2|\psi_n\rangle = a^2\left[\frac{1}{3} - \frac{1}{2(n\pi)^2}\right]$.

Thus $\langle x^2\rangle = \frac{1}{2}\left\{a^2\left[\frac{1}{3} - \frac{1}{2\pi^2}\right] + a^2\left[\frac{1}{3} - \frac{1}{8\pi^2}\right] - \frac{16a^2}{9\pi^2}\left[\underbrace{e^{i(E_2-E_1)t/\hbar} + e^{-i(E_2-E_1)t/\hbar}}_{2\cos(\frac{E_2-E_1}{\hbar}t)}\right]\right\}.$

$\frac{E_2-E_1}{\hbar} = \frac{(4-1)\pi^2\hbar^2}{2ma^2\hbar} = \frac{3\pi^2\hbar}{2ma^2} = 3\omega$ [in the notation of Problem 2.5(b)].

$\langle x^2\rangle = \frac{a^2}{2}\left[\frac{2}{3} - \frac{5}{8\pi^2} - \frac{32}{9\pi^2}\cos(3\omega t)\right]$. From Problem 2.5(c), $\langle x\rangle = \frac{a}{2}\left[1 - \frac{32}{9\pi^2}\cos(3\omega t)\right]$.

So $\sigma_x^2 = \langle x^2\rangle - \langle x\rangle^2 = \frac{a^2}{4}\left[\frac{4}{3} - \frac{5}{4\pi^2} - \frac{64}{9\pi^2}\cos(3\omega t) - 1 + \frac{64}{9\pi^2}\cos(3\omega t) - \left(\frac{32}{9\pi^2}\right)^2\cos^2(3\omega t)\right].$

$\boxed{\sigma_x^2 = \frac{a^2}{4}\left[\frac{1}{3} - \frac{5}{4\pi^2} - \left(\frac{32}{9\pi^2}\right)^2\cos^2(3\omega t)\right].}$ And, from Problem 2.5(d): $\boxed{\frac{d\langle x\rangle}{dt} = \frac{8\hbar}{3ma}\sin(3\omega t).}$

Meanwhile, the energy-time uncertainty principle (Eq. 3.72) says $\sigma_H^2\sigma_x^2 \geq \frac{\hbar^2}{4}\left(\frac{d\langle x\rangle}{dt}\right)^2$. Here

$\sigma_H^2\sigma_x^2 = \frac{1}{4}(3\hbar\omega)^2\frac{a^2}{4}\left[\frac{1}{3} - \frac{5}{4\pi^2} - \left(\frac{32}{9\pi^2}\right)^2\cos^2(3\omega t)\right] = (\hbar\omega a)^2\left(\frac{3}{4}\right)^2\left[\frac{1}{3} - \frac{5}{4\pi^2} - \left(\frac{32}{9\pi^2}\right)^2\cos^2(3\omega t)\right].$

$\frac{\hbar^2}{4}\left(\frac{d\langle x\rangle}{dt}\right)^2 = \left(\frac{\hbar}{2}\frac{8\hbar}{3ma^2}\right)^2\sin^2(3\omega t) = \left(\frac{8}{3\pi^2}\right)^2(\hbar\omega a)^2\sin^2(3\omega t)$, since $\frac{\hbar}{ma} = \frac{2a\omega}{\pi}$.

So the uncertainty principle holds if

$$\left(\frac{3}{4}\right)^2\left[\frac{1}{3} - \frac{5}{4\pi^2} - \left(\frac{32}{9\pi^2}\right)^2\cos^2(3\omega t)\right] \geq \left(\frac{8}{3\pi^2}\right)^2\sin^2(3\omega t),$$

which is to say, if

$$\frac{1}{3} - \frac{5}{4\pi^2} \geq \left(\frac{32}{9\pi^2}\right)^2\cos^2(3\omega t) + \left(\frac{4}{3}\frac{8}{3\pi^2}\right)^2\sin^2(3\omega t) = \left(\frac{32}{9\pi^2}\right)^2.$$

Evaluating both sides: $\frac{1}{3} - \frac{5}{4\pi^2} = 0.20668$; $\left(\frac{32}{9\pi^2}\right)^2 = 0.12978$. So it holds. (Whew!)

## Problem 3.19

From Problem 2.43, we have:

$$\langle x\rangle = \frac{\hbar l}{m}t, \text{ so } \boxed{\frac{d\langle x\rangle}{dt} = \frac{\hbar l}{m}}, \sigma_x^2 = \frac{1}{4w^2} = \boxed{\frac{1+\theta^2}{4a}}, \text{ where } \theta = \frac{2\hbar at}{m}; \langle H\rangle = \frac{1}{2m}\langle p^2\rangle = \frac{1}{2m}\hbar^2(a+l^2).$$

We need $\langle H^2\rangle$ (to get $\sigma_H$). Now, $H = \frac{p^2}{2m}$, so

$$\langle H^2\rangle = \frac{1}{4m^2}\langle p^4\rangle = \frac{1}{4m^2}\int_{-\infty}^{\infty} p^4|\Phi(p,t)|^2 dp, \text{ where (Eq. 3.54): } \Phi(p,t) = \frac{1}{\sqrt{2\pi\hbar}}\int_{-\infty}^{\infty} e^{-ipx/\hbar}\Psi(x,t)\,dx.$$

From Problem 2.43: $\Psi(x,t) = \left(\frac{2a}{\pi}\right)^{1/4} \frac{1}{\sqrt{1+i\theta}} e^{-\frac{l^2}{4a}} e^{a\left(ix+\frac{l}{2a}\right)^2/(1+i\theta)}$.

So $\Phi(p,t) = \frac{1}{\sqrt{2\pi\hbar}} \left(\frac{2a}{\pi}\right)^{1/4} \frac{1}{\sqrt{1+i\theta}} e^{-l^2/4a} \int_{-\infty}^{\infty} e^{-ipx/\hbar} e^{a\left(ix+\frac{l}{2a}\right)^2/(1+i\theta)} dx$.   Let $y \equiv x - \frac{il}{2a}$.

$\qquad = \frac{1}{\sqrt{2\pi\hbar}} \left(\frac{2a}{\pi}\right)^{1/4} \frac{1}{\sqrt{1+i\theta}} e^{-l^2/4a} e^{pl/2a\hbar} \int_{-\infty}^{\infty} e^{-ipy/\hbar} e^{-ay^2/(1+i\theta)} dy$.

[See Prob. 2.22(a) for the integral.]

$\qquad = \frac{1}{\sqrt{2\pi\hbar}} \left(\frac{2a}{\pi}\right)^{1/4} \frac{1}{\sqrt{1+i\theta}} e^{-l^2/4a} e^{pl/2a\hbar} \sqrt{\frac{\pi(1+i\theta)}{a}} e^{-\frac{p^2(1+i\theta)}{4a\hbar^2}}$

$\qquad = \frac{1}{\sqrt{\hbar}} \left(\frac{1}{2a\pi}\right)^{1/4} e^{-\frac{l^2}{4a}} e^{\frac{pl}{2a\hbar}} e^{-\frac{p^2(1+i\theta)}{4a\hbar^2}}$.

$|\Phi(p,t)|^2 = \frac{1}{\sqrt{2a\pi}} \frac{1}{\hbar} e^{-l^2/2a} e^{pl/a\hbar} e^{-p^2/2a\hbar^2} = \frac{1}{\hbar\sqrt{2a\pi}} e^{\frac{1}{2a}\left(l^2 - \frac{2pl}{\hbar} + \frac{p^2}{\hbar^2}\right)} = \frac{1}{\hbar\sqrt{2a\pi}} e^{-(l-p/\hbar)^2/2a}$.

$\langle p^4 \rangle = \frac{1}{\hbar\sqrt{2a\pi}} \int_{-\infty}^{\infty} p^4 e^{-(l-p/\hbar)^2/2a} dp$.   Let $\frac{p}{\hbar} - l \equiv z$, so $p = \hbar(z+l)$.

$\qquad = \frac{1}{\hbar\sqrt{2a\pi}} \hbar^5 \int_{-\infty}^{\infty} (z+l)^4 e^{-z^2/2a} dz$.   Only even powers of $z$ survive:

$\qquad = \frac{\hbar^4}{\sqrt{2a\pi}} \int_{-\infty}^{\infty} (z^4 + 6z^2 l^2 + l^4) e^{-z^2/2a} dz = \frac{\hbar^4}{\sqrt{2a\pi}} \left[ \frac{3(2a)^2}{4}\sqrt{2a\pi} + 6l^2\frac{(2a)}{2}\sqrt{2a\pi} + l^4\sqrt{2a\pi} \right]$

$\qquad = \hbar^4(3a^2 + 6al^2 + l^4)$.   $\therefore \langle H^2 \rangle = \frac{\hbar^4}{4m^2}(3a^2 + 6al^2 + l^4)$.

$\sigma_H^2 = \langle H^2 \rangle - \langle H \rangle^2 = \frac{\hbar^2}{4m^2}(3a^2 + 6al^2 + l^4 - a^2 - 2al^2 - l^4) = \frac{\hbar^4}{4m^2}(2a^2 + 4al^2) = \boxed{\frac{\hbar^4 a}{2m^2}(a + 2l^2)}$.

$\sigma_H^2 \sigma_x^2 = \frac{\hbar^4 a}{2m^2}(a + 2l^2)\frac{1}{4a}\left[1 + \left(\frac{2\hbar at}{m}\right)^2\right] = \frac{\hbar^4 l^2}{4m^2}\left(1 + \frac{a}{2l^2}\right)\left[1 + \left(\frac{2\hbar at}{m}\right)^2\right]$

$\qquad \geq \frac{\hbar^4 l^2}{4m^2} = \frac{\hbar^2}{4}\left(\frac{\hbar l}{m}\right)^2 = \frac{\hbar^2}{4}\left(\frac{d\langle x \rangle}{dt}\right)^2$, so it works.

---

## Problem 3.20

For $Q = x$, Eq. 3.72 says $\sigma_H \sigma_x \geq \frac{\hbar}{2}\left|\frac{d\langle x \rangle}{dt}\right|$.   But $\langle p \rangle = m\frac{d\langle x \rangle}{dt}$, so $\sigma_x \sigma_H \geq \frac{\hbar}{2m}|\langle p \rangle|$, which is the Griffiths uncertainty principle of Problem 3.14.

---

## Problem 3.21

$P^2|\beta\rangle = P(P|\beta\rangle) = P(\langle\alpha|\beta\rangle|\alpha\rangle) = \langle\alpha|\beta\rangle(P|\alpha\rangle) = \langle\alpha|\beta\rangle \underbrace{\langle\alpha|\alpha\rangle}_{1} |\alpha\rangle = \langle\alpha|\beta\rangle|\alpha\rangle = P|\beta\rangle$.

Since $P^2|\beta\rangle = P|\beta\rangle$ for *any* vector $|\beta\rangle$, $P^2 = P$.  QED  [*Note:* To say two operators are equal *means* that they have the same effect on all vectors.]

If $|\gamma\rangle$ is an eigenvector of $\hat{P}$ with eigenvalue $\lambda$, then $\hat{P}|\gamma\rangle = \lambda|\gamma\rangle$, and it follows that $\hat{P}^2|\gamma\rangle = \lambda\hat{P}|\gamma\rangle = \lambda^2|\gamma\rangle$. But $\hat{P}^2 = \hat{P}$, and $|\gamma\rangle \neq 0$, so $\lambda^2 = \lambda$, and hence the eigenvalues of $\hat{P}$ are $\boxed{0 \text{ and } 1.}$ Any (complex) *multiple* of $|\alpha\rangle$ is an eigenvector of $\hat{P}$, with eigenvalue 1; any vector *orthogonal* to $|\alpha\rangle$ is an eigenvector of $\hat{P}$, with eigenvalue 0.

---

## Problem 3.22

**(a)** $\boxed{\langle\alpha| = -i\langle 1| - 2\langle 2| + i\langle 3|; \quad \langle\beta| = -i\langle 1| + 2\langle 3|.}$

**(b)** $\langle\alpha|\beta\rangle = (-i\langle 1| - 2\langle 2| + i\langle 3|)\,(i|1\rangle + 2|3\rangle) = (-i)(i)\langle 1|1\rangle + (i)(2)\langle 3|3\rangle = \boxed{1 + 2i.}$

$\langle\beta|\alpha\rangle = (-i\langle 1| + 2\langle 3|)\,(i|1\rangle - 2|2\rangle - i|3\rangle) = (-i)(i)\langle 1|1\rangle + (2)(-i)\langle 3|3\rangle = \boxed{1 - 2i} = \langle\alpha|\beta\rangle^*.$  ✓

**(c)**

$$A_{11} = \langle 1|\alpha\rangle\langle\beta|1\rangle = (i)(-i) = 1; \quad A_{12} = \langle 1|\alpha\rangle\langle\beta|2\rangle = (i)(0) = 0; \quad A_{13} = \langle 1|\alpha\rangle\langle\beta|3\rangle = (i)(2) = 2i;$$
$$A_{21} = \langle 2|\alpha\rangle\langle\beta|1\rangle = (-2)(-i) = 2i; \quad A_{22} = \langle 2|\alpha\rangle\langle\beta|2\rangle = (-2)(0) = 0; \quad A_{23} = \langle 2|\alpha\rangle\langle\beta|3\rangle = (-2)(2) = -4;$$
$$A_{31} = \langle 3|\alpha\rangle\langle\beta|1\rangle = (-i)(-i) = -1; \quad A_{32} = \langle 3|\alpha\rangle\langle\beta|2\rangle = (-i)(0) = 0; \quad A_{33} = \langle 3|\alpha\rangle\langle\beta|3\rangle = (-i)(2) = -2i.$$

$$\mathsf{A} = \begin{pmatrix} 1 & 0 & 2i \\ 2i & 0 & -4 \\ -1 & 0 & -2i \end{pmatrix}. \quad \boxed{\text{No,}} \text{ it's } not \text{ hermitian.}$$

---

## Problem 3.23

Write the eigenvector as $|\psi\rangle = c_1|1\rangle + c_2|2\rangle$, and call the eigenvalue $E$. The eigenvalue equation is

$$\hat{H}|\psi\rangle = \epsilon\,(|1\rangle\langle 1| - |2\rangle\langle 2| + |1\rangle\langle 2| + |2\rangle\langle 1|)\,(c_1|1\rangle + c_2|2\rangle) = \epsilon\,(c_1|1\rangle + c_1|2\rangle - c_2|2\rangle + c_2|1\rangle)$$
$$= \epsilon\,[(c_1 + c_2)|1\rangle + (c_1 - c_2)|2\rangle] = E|\psi\rangle = E(c_1|1\rangle + c_2|2\rangle).$$

$$\epsilon(c_1 + c_2) = Ec_1 \Rightarrow c_2 = \left(\frac{E}{\epsilon} - 1\right)c_1; \quad \epsilon(c_1 - c_2) = Ec_2 \Rightarrow c_1 = \left(\frac{E}{\epsilon} + 1\right)c_2.$$

$$c_2 = \left(\frac{E}{\epsilon} - 1\right)\left(\frac{E}{\epsilon} + 1\right)c_2 \quad \Rightarrow \left(\frac{E}{\epsilon}\right)^2 - 1 = 1 \quad \Rightarrow \boxed{E = \pm\sqrt{2}\,\epsilon.}$$

The eigenvectors are: $c_2 = (\pm\sqrt{2} - 1)c_1 \Rightarrow \boxed{|\psi_\pm\rangle = c_1\left[|1\rangle + (\pm\sqrt{2} - 1)|2\rangle\right].}$

The Hamiltonian matrix is $\boxed{\mathsf{H} = \epsilon \begin{pmatrix} 1 & 1 \\ 1 & -1 \end{pmatrix}.}$

---

## Problem 3.24

$$|\alpha\rangle = \sum_n c_n|e_n\rangle \Rightarrow \hat{Q}|\alpha\rangle = \sum_n c_n\hat{Q}|e_n\rangle = \sum_n \langle e_n|\alpha\rangle q_n|e_n\rangle = \left(\sum_n q_n|e_n\rangle\langle e_n|\right)|\alpha\rangle \Rightarrow \hat{Q} = \sum_n q_n|e_n\rangle\langle e_n|. \checkmark$$

---

## Problem 3.25

$$|e_1\rangle = 1; \quad \langle e_1|e_1\rangle = \int_{-1}^{1} 1\,dx = 2. \quad \text{So} \quad \boxed{|e_1'\rangle = \frac{1}{\sqrt{2}}.}$$

$$|e_2\rangle = x; \quad \langle e_1'|e_2\rangle = \frac{1}{\sqrt{2}}\int_{-1}^{1} x\,dx = 0; \quad \langle e_2|e_2\rangle = \int_{-1}^{1} x^2 dx = \frac{x^3}{3}\Big|_{-1}^{1} = \frac{2}{3}. \quad \text{So} \quad \boxed{|e_2'\rangle = \sqrt{\frac{3}{2}}\,x.}$$

$$|e_3\rangle = x^2; \quad \langle e_1'|e_3\rangle = \frac{1}{\sqrt{2}}\int_{-1}^{1} x^2 dx = \frac{1}{\sqrt{2}}\frac{2}{3}; \quad \langle e_2'|e_3\rangle = \sqrt{\frac{2}{3}}\int_{-1}^{1} x^3 dx = 0.$$

So (Problem A.4): $\quad |e_3''\rangle = |e_3\rangle - \frac{1}{\sqrt{2}}\frac{2}{3}|e_1'\rangle = x^2 - \frac{1}{3}.$

$$\langle e_3''|e_3''\rangle = \int_{-1}^{1}\left(x^2 - \frac{1}{3}\right)^2 dx = \left(\frac{x^5}{5} - \frac{2}{3}\cdot\frac{x^3}{3} + \frac{x}{9}\right)\Big|_{-1}^{1} = \frac{2}{5} - \frac{4}{9} + \frac{2}{9} = \frac{8}{45}. \quad \text{So}$$

$$|e_3'\rangle = \sqrt{\frac{45}{8}}\left(x^2 - \frac{1}{3}\right) = \boxed{\sqrt{\frac{5}{2}}\left(\frac{3}{2}x^2 - \frac{1}{2}\right).}$$

$$|e_4\rangle = x^3. \quad \langle e_1'|e_4\rangle = \frac{1}{\sqrt{2}}\int_{-1}^{1} x^3 dx = 0; \quad \langle e_2'|e_4\rangle = \sqrt{\frac{3}{2}}\int_{-1}^{1} x^4 dx = \sqrt{\frac{3}{2}}\cdot\frac{2}{5};$$

$$\langle e_3'|e_4\rangle = \sqrt{\frac{5}{2}}\int_{-1}^{1}\left(\frac{3}{2}x^5 - \frac{1}{2}x^3\right)dx = 0. \quad |e_4''\rangle = |e_4\rangle - \langle e_2'|e_4\rangle|e_2'\rangle = x^3 - \sqrt{\frac{3}{2}}\frac{2}{5}\sqrt{\frac{3}{2}}\,x = x^3 - \frac{3}{5}x.$$

$$\langle e_4''|e_4''\rangle = \int_{-1}^{1}\left(x^3 - \frac{3}{5}x\right)^2 dx = \left[\frac{x^7}{7} - \frac{2\cdot3}{5}\frac{x^5}{5} + \frac{9}{25}\frac{x^3}{3}\right]\Big|_{-1}^{1} = \frac{2}{7} - \frac{12}{25} + \frac{18}{75} = \frac{8}{7\cdot25}.$$

$$|e_4'\rangle = \frac{5}{2}\sqrt{\frac{7}{2}}\left(x^3 - \frac{3}{5}x\right) = \boxed{\sqrt{\frac{7}{2}}\left(\frac{5}{2}x^3 - \frac{3}{2}x\right).}$$

## Problem 3.26

**(a)** $\langle Q\rangle = \langle\psi|\hat{Q}\psi\rangle = \langle\hat{Q}^\dagger\psi|\psi\rangle = -\langle\hat{Q}\psi|\psi\rangle = -(\langle\psi|\hat{Q}\psi\rangle)^* = -\langle Q\rangle^*$, so $\langle Q\rangle$ is imaginary. ✓

**(b)** From Problem 3.5(c) we know that $(\hat{P}\hat{Q})^\dagger = \hat{Q}^\dagger\hat{P}^\dagger$, so if $\hat{P} = \hat{P}^\dagger$ and $\hat{Q} = \hat{Q}^\dagger$ then

$$[\hat{P},\hat{Q}]^\dagger = (\hat{P}\hat{Q} - \hat{Q}\hat{P})^\dagger = \hat{Q}^\dagger\hat{P}^\dagger - \hat{P}^\dagger\hat{Q}^\dagger = \hat{Q}\hat{P} - \hat{P}\hat{Q} = -[\hat{P},\hat{Q}]. \quad ✓$$

If $\hat{P} = -\hat{P}^\dagger$ and $\hat{Q} = -\hat{Q}^\dagger$, then $[\hat{P},\hat{Q}]^\dagger = \hat{Q}^\dagger\hat{P}^\dagger - \hat{P}^\dagger\hat{Q}^\dagger = (-\hat{Q})(-\hat{P}) - (-\hat{P})(-\hat{Q}) = -[\hat{P},\hat{Q}].$

So in either case the commutator is antihermitian.

## Problem 3.27

**(a)** $\boxed{\psi_1.}$

**(b)** $\boxed{b_1 \text{ (with probability } 9/25 \text{) or } b_2 \text{ (with probability } 16/25\text{).}}$

**(c)** Right after the measurement of $B$:

- With probability 9/25 the particle is in state $\phi_1 = (3\psi_1 + 4\psi_2)/5$; in that case the probability of getting $a_1$ is 9/25.

- With probability 16/25 the particle is in state $\phi_2 = (4\psi_1 - 3\psi_2)/5$; in that case the probability of getting $a_1$ is 16/25.

So the total probability of getting $a_1$ is $\dfrac{9}{25} \cdot \dfrac{9}{25} + \dfrac{16}{25} \cdot \dfrac{16}{25} = \boxed{\dfrac{337}{625} = 0.5392.}$

[*Note:* The measurement of $B$ (even if we don't know the *outcome* of that measurement) collapses the wave function, and thereby alters the probabilities for the second measurment of $A$. If the graduate student inadvertently neglected to measure $B$, the second measurement of $A$ would be *certain* to reproduce the result $a_1$.]

---

## Problem 3.28

$$\Psi_n(x,t) = \sqrt{\frac{2}{a}} \sin\left(\frac{n\pi}{a}x\right) e^{-iE_n t/\hbar}, \quad \text{with} \quad E_n = \frac{n^2\pi^2\hbar^2}{2ma^2}.$$

$$\begin{aligned}
\Phi_n(p,t) &= \frac{1}{\sqrt{2\pi\hbar}} \int_{-\infty}^{\infty} e^{-ipx/\hbar} \Psi_n(x,t)\, dx = \frac{1}{\sqrt{2\pi\hbar}} \sqrt{\frac{2}{a}} e^{-iE_n t/\hbar} \int_0^a e^{-ipx/\hbar} \sin\left(\frac{n\pi}{a}x\right) dx \\
&= \frac{1}{\sqrt{\pi\hbar a}} e^{-iE_n t/\hbar} \frac{1}{2i} \int_0^a \left[ e^{i(n\pi/a - p/\hbar)x} - e^{i(-n\pi/a - p/\hbar)x} \right] dx \\
&= \frac{1}{\sqrt{\pi\hbar a}} e^{-iE_n t/\hbar} \frac{1}{2i} \left[ \frac{e^{i(n\pi/a - p/\hbar)x}}{i(n\pi/a - p/\hbar)} - \frac{e^{i(-n\pi/a - p/\hbar)x}}{i(-n\pi/a - p/\hbar)} \right]\Bigg|_0^a \\
&= \frac{-1}{2\sqrt{\pi\hbar a}} e^{-iE_n t/\hbar} \left[ \frac{e^{i(n\pi - pa/\hbar)} - 1}{(n\pi/a - p/\hbar)} + \frac{e^{-i(n\pi + pa/\hbar)} - 1}{(n\pi/a + p/\hbar)} \right] \\
&= \frac{-1}{2\sqrt{\pi\hbar a}} e^{-iE_n t/\hbar} \left[ \frac{(-1)^n e^{-ipa/\hbar} - 1}{(n\pi - ap/\hbar)} a + \frac{(-1)^n e^{-ipa/\hbar} - 1}{(n\pi + ap/\hbar)} a \right] \\
&= -\frac{1}{2}\sqrt{\frac{a}{\pi\hbar}} e^{-iE_n t/\hbar} \frac{2n\pi}{(n\pi)^2 - (ap/\hbar)^2} \left[ (-1)^n e^{-ipa/\hbar} - 1 \right] \\
&= \boxed{\sqrt{\frac{a\pi}{\hbar}} \frac{n e^{-iE_n t/\hbar}}{(n\pi)^2 - (ap/\hbar)^2} \left[ 1 - (-1)^n e^{-ipa/\hbar} \right].}
\end{aligned}$$

Noting that

$$1 - (-1)^n e^{-ipa/\hbar} = e^{-ipa/2\hbar}\left[ e^{ipa/2\hbar} - (-1)^n e^{-ipa/2\hbar} \right] = 2e^{-ipa/2\hbar} \begin{cases} \cos(pa/2\hbar) & (n \text{ odd}), \\ i\sin(pa/2\hbar) & (n \text{ even}), \end{cases}$$

we have

$$|\Phi_1(p,t)|^2 = \frac{4\pi a}{\hbar} \frac{\cos^2(pa/2\hbar)}{[\pi^2 - (pa/\hbar)^2]^2}, \quad |\Phi_2(p,t)|^2 = \frac{16\pi a}{\hbar} \frac{\sin^2(pa/2\hbar)}{[(2\pi)^2 - (pa/\hbar)^2]^2}.$$

Mathematica has no trouble with the points $p = \pm n\pi\hbar/a$, where the denominator vanishes. The reason is that the numerator is also zero there, and the function as a whole is finite—in fact, the graphs show no interesting behavior at these points.

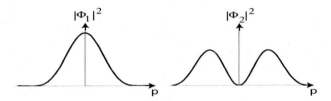

$$\langle p^2 \rangle = \int_{-\infty}^{\infty} p^2 |\Phi_n(p,t)|^2\, dp = \frac{4n^2\pi a}{\hbar} \int_{-\infty}^{\infty} \frac{p^2}{[(n\pi)^2 - (ap/\hbar)^2]^2} \left\{ \begin{array}{c} \cos^2(pa/2\hbar) \\ \sin^2(pa/2\hbar) \end{array} \right\} dp \quad [\text{let } x \equiv \frac{ap}{n\pi\hbar}]$$

$$= \frac{4n\hbar^2}{a^2} \int_{-\infty}^{\infty} \frac{x^2}{(1-x^2)^2} T_n(x)\, dx = \frac{4n\hbar^2}{a^2} I_n,$$

where

$$T_n(x) \equiv \left\{ \begin{array}{ll} \cos^2(n\pi x/2), & \text{if } n \text{ is odd,} \\ \sin^2(n\pi x/2), & \text{if } n \text{ is even.} \end{array} \right\}$$

The integral can be evaluated by partial fractions:

$$\frac{x^2}{(x^2-1)^2} = \frac{1}{4} \left[ \frac{1}{(x-1)^2} + \frac{1}{(x+1)^2} + \frac{1}{(x-1)} - \frac{1}{(x+1)} \right] \Rightarrow$$

$$I_n = \frac{1}{4} \left[ \int_{-\infty}^{\infty} \frac{1}{(x-1)^2} T_n(x)\, dx + \int_{-\infty}^{\infty} \frac{1}{(x+1)^2} T_n(x)\, dx + \int_{-\infty}^{\infty} \frac{1}{(x-1)} T_n(x)\, dx - \int_{-\infty}^{\infty} \frac{1}{(x+1)} T_n(x)\, dx \right].$$

For odd $n$:

$$\int_{-\infty}^{\infty} \frac{1}{(x\pm1)^k} \cos^2\left(\frac{n\pi x}{2}\right) dx = \int_{-\infty}^{\infty} \frac{1}{y^k} \cos^2\left[\frac{n\pi}{2}(y \mp 1)\right] dy = \int_{-\infty}^{\infty} \frac{1}{y^k} \sin^2\left(\frac{n\pi y}{2}\right) dy.$$

For even $n$:

$$\int_{-\infty}^{\infty} \frac{1}{(x\pm1)^k} \sin^2\left(\frac{n\pi x}{2}\right) dx = \int_{-\infty}^{\infty} \frac{1}{y^k} \sin^2\left[\frac{n\pi}{2}(y \mp 1)\right] dy = \int_{-\infty}^{\infty} \frac{1}{y^k} \sin^2\left(\frac{n\pi y}{2}\right) dy.$$

In either case, then,

$$I_n = \frac{1}{2} \int_{-\infty}^{\infty} \frac{1}{y^2} \sin^2\left(\frac{n\pi y}{2}\right) dy = \frac{n\pi}{4} \int_{-\infty}^{\infty} \frac{\sin^2 u}{u^2}\, du = \frac{n\pi^2}{4}.$$

Therefore

$$\langle p^2 \rangle = \frac{4n\hbar^2}{a^2} I_n = \frac{4n\hbar^2}{a^2} \frac{n\pi^2}{4} = \left(\frac{n\pi\hbar}{a}\right)^2 \quad \text{(same as Problem 2.4).}$$

## Problem 3.29

$$\Phi(p,0) = \frac{1}{\sqrt{2\pi\hbar}} \int_{-\infty}^{\infty} e^{-ipx/\hbar} \Psi(x,0)\,dx = \frac{1}{2\sqrt{n\pi\hbar\lambda}} \int_{-n\lambda}^{n\lambda} e^{i(2\pi/\lambda - p/\hbar)x}\,dx$$

$$= \frac{1}{2\sqrt{n\pi\hbar\lambda}} \frac{e^{i(2\pi/\lambda - p/\hbar)x}}{i(2\pi/\lambda - p/\hbar)} \bigg|_{-n\lambda}^{n\lambda} = \frac{1}{2\sqrt{n\pi\hbar\lambda}} \frac{e^{i2\pi n}e^{-ipn\lambda/\hbar} - e^{-i2\pi n}e^{ipn\lambda/\hbar}}{i(2\pi/\lambda - p/\hbar)}$$

$$= \boxed{\sqrt{\frac{\hbar\lambda}{n\pi}} \frac{\sin(np\lambda/\hbar)}{(p\lambda - 2\pi\hbar)}}.$$

$$|\Psi(x,0)|^2 = \frac{1}{2n\lambda} \quad (-n\lambda < x < n\lambda); \quad |\Phi(p,0)|^2 = \frac{\lambda\hbar}{n\pi} \frac{\sin^2(np\lambda/\hbar)}{(p\lambda - 2\pi\hbar)^2}.$$

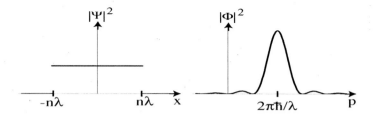

The width of the $|\Psi|^2$ graph is $\boxed{w_x = 2n\lambda.}$ The $|\Phi|^2$ graph is a maximum at $2\pi\hbar/\lambda$, and goes to zero on either side at $\dfrac{2\pi\hbar}{\lambda}\left(1 \pm \dfrac{1}{2n}\right)$, so $\boxed{w_p = \dfrac{2\pi\hbar}{n\lambda}.}$ As $n \to \infty$, $w_x \to \infty$ and $w_p \to 0$; in this limit the particle has a well-defined momentum, but a completely indeterminate position. In general,

$$w_x w_p = (2n\lambda)\frac{2\pi\hbar}{n\lambda} = 4\pi\hbar > \hbar/2,$$

so the uncertainty principle is satisfied (using the widths as a measure of uncertainty). If we try to check the uncertainty principle more rigorously, using standard deviation as the measure, we get an uninformative result, because

$$\langle p^2 \rangle = \frac{\lambda\hbar}{n\pi} \int_{-\infty}^{\infty} p^2 \frac{\sin^2(np\lambda/\hbar)}{(p\lambda - 2\pi\hbar)^2}\,dp = \infty.$$

(At large $|p|$ the integrand is approximately $(1/\lambda^2)\sin^2(np\lambda/\hbar)$, so the integral blows up.) Meanwhile $\langle p \rangle$ is zero, so $\sigma_p = \infty$, and the uncertainty principle tells us nothing. The source of the problem is the discontinuity in $\Psi$ at the end points; here $\hat{p}\Psi = -i\hbar\,d\Psi/dx$ picks up a delta function, and $\langle \Psi|\hat{p}^2\Psi\rangle = \langle \hat{p}\Psi|\hat{p}\Psi\rangle \to \infty$ because the integral of the *square* of the delta function blows up. In general, if you want $\sigma_p$ to be finite, you cannot allow discontinuities in $\Psi$.

---

## Problem 3.30

(a)

$$1 = |A|^2 \int_{-\infty}^{\infty} \frac{1}{(x^2+a^2)^2}\,dx = 2|A|^2 \int_{0}^{\infty} \frac{1}{(x^2+a^2)^2}\,dx = 2|A|^2 \frac{1}{2a^2}\left[\frac{x}{x^2+a^2} + \frac{1}{a}\tan^{-1}\left(\frac{x}{a}\right)\right]\bigg|_0^{\infty}$$

$$= \frac{1}{a^2}|A|^2 \frac{1}{a}\tan^{-1}(\infty) = \frac{\pi}{2a^3}|A|^2 \quad \Rightarrow \quad \boxed{A = a\sqrt{\frac{2a}{\pi}}.}$$

**(b)**

$$\langle x \rangle = A^2 \int_{-\infty}^{\infty} \frac{x}{(a^2 + x^2)^2} \, dx = \boxed{0.}$$

$$\langle x^2 \rangle = 2A^2 \int_0^{\infty} \frac{x^2}{(a^2 + x^2)^2} \, dx. \quad [\text{Let } y \equiv \frac{x^2}{a^2}, \; x = a\sqrt{y}, \; dx = \frac{a}{2\sqrt{y}} \, dy.]$$

$$= \frac{2a^2}{\pi} \int_0^{\infty} \frac{y^{1/2}}{(1+y)^2} \, dy = \frac{2a^2}{\pi} \frac{\Gamma(3/2)\Gamma(1/2)}{\Gamma(2)} = \frac{2a^2}{\pi} \frac{(\sqrt{\pi}/2)(\sqrt{\pi})}{1} = \boxed{a^2.}$$

$$\sigma_x = \sqrt{\langle x^2 \rangle - \langle x \rangle^2} = \boxed{a.}$$

**(c)**

$$\Phi(p,0) = \frac{A}{\sqrt{2\pi\hbar}} \int_{-\infty}^{\infty} e^{-ipx/\hbar} \frac{1}{x^2 + a^2} \, dx. \quad [\text{But } e^{-ipx/\hbar} = \cos\left(\frac{px}{\hbar}\right) - i \sin\left(\frac{px}{\hbar}\right), \text{ and sine is odd.}]$$

$$= \frac{2A}{\sqrt{2\pi\hbar}} \int_0^{\infty} \frac{\cos(px/\hbar)}{x^2 + a^2} \, dx = \frac{2A}{\sqrt{2\pi\hbar}} \left(\frac{\pi}{2a} e^{-|p|a/\hbar}\right) = \boxed{\sqrt{\frac{a}{\hbar}} \, e^{-|p|a/\hbar}.}$$

$$\int_{-\infty}^{\infty} |\Phi(p,0)|^2 \, dp = \frac{a}{\hbar} \int_{-\infty}^{\infty} e^{-2|p|a/\hbar} \, dp = \frac{2a}{\hbar} \left(\frac{e^{-2pa/\hbar}}{-2a/\hbar}\right)\Big|_0^{\infty} = 1. \quad \checkmark$$

**(d)**

$$\langle p \rangle = \frac{a}{\hbar} \int_{-\infty}^{\infty} p e^{-2|p|a/\hbar} \, dp = \boxed{0.}$$

$$\langle p^2 \rangle = 2\frac{a}{\hbar} \int_0^{\infty} p^2 e^{-2pa/\hbar} \, dp = \frac{2a}{\hbar} 2 \left(\frac{\hbar}{2a}\right)^3 = \boxed{\frac{\hbar^2}{2a^2}.} \quad \sigma_p = \sqrt{\langle p^2 \rangle - \langle p \rangle^2} = \boxed{\frac{\hbar}{\sqrt{2}\,a}.}$$

**(e)**

$$\sigma_x \sigma_p = a \frac{\hbar}{\sqrt{2}\,a} = \sqrt{2} \frac{\hbar}{2} > \frac{\hbar}{2}. \quad \checkmark$$

---

## Problem 3.31

Equation 3.71 $\Rightarrow \frac{d}{dt}\langle xp \rangle = \frac{i}{\hbar}\langle [H, xp] \rangle$; Eq. 3.64 $\Rightarrow [H, xp] = [H, x]p + x[H, p]$; Problem 3.14 $\Rightarrow [H, x] = -\frac{i\hbar p}{m}$; Problem 3.17(d) $\Rightarrow [H, p] = i\hbar \frac{dV}{dx}$. So

$$\frac{d}{dt}\langle xp \rangle = \frac{i}{\hbar}\left[-\frac{i\hbar}{m}\langle p^2 \rangle + i\hbar\langle x\frac{dV}{dx}\rangle\right] = 2\langle \frac{p^2}{2m}\rangle - \langle x\frac{dV}{dx}\rangle = 2\langle T \rangle - \langle x\frac{dV}{dx}\rangle. \quad \text{QED}$$

In a stationary state all expectation values (at least, for operators that do not depend explicitly on $t$) are time-independent (see item 1 on p. 26), so $d\langle xp \rangle/dt = 0$, and we are left with Eq. 3.97.

For the harmonic oscillator:

$$V = \frac{1}{2}m\omega^2 x^2 \Rightarrow \frac{dV}{dx} = m\omega^2 x \Rightarrow x\frac{dV}{dx} = m\omega^2 x^2 = 2V \Rightarrow 2\langle T \rangle = 2\langle V \rangle \Rightarrow \langle T \rangle = \langle V \rangle. \quad \text{QED}$$

In Problem 2.11(c) we found that $\langle T \rangle = \langle V \rangle = \frac{1}{4}\hbar\omega$ (for $n = 0$); $\langle T \rangle = \langle V \rangle = \frac{3}{4}\hbar\omega$ (for $n = 1$). $\checkmark$
In Problem 2.12 we found that $\langle T \rangle = \frac{1}{2}(n+\frac{1}{2})\hbar\omega$, while $\langle x^2 \rangle = (n+\frac{1}{2})\hbar/m\omega$, so $\langle V \rangle = \frac{1}{2}m\omega^2\langle x^2 \rangle = \frac{1}{2}(n+\frac{1}{2})\hbar\omega$, and hence $\langle T \rangle = \langle V \rangle$ for *all* stationary states. $\checkmark$

---

## Problem 3.32

$$\Psi(x,t) = \frac{1}{\sqrt{2}}\left(\psi_1 e^{-iE_1 t/\hbar} + \psi_2 e^{-iE_2 t/\hbar}\right); \qquad \langle\Psi(x,t)|\Psi(x,0)\rangle = 0 \Rightarrow$$

$$\frac{1}{2}\left(e^{iE_1 t/\hbar}\langle\psi_1|\psi_1\rangle + e^{iE_1 t/\hbar}\langle\psi_1|\psi_2\rangle + e^{iE_2 t/\hbar}\langle\psi_2|\psi_1\rangle + e^{iE_2 t/\hbar}\langle\psi_2|\psi_2\rangle\right)$$

$$= \frac{1}{2}\left(e^{iE_1 t/\hbar} + e^{iE_2 t/\hbar}\right) = 0, \text{ or } e^{iE_2 t/\hbar} = -e^{iE_1 t/\hbar}, \text{ so } e^{i(E_2-E_1)t/\hbar} = -1 = e^{i\pi}.$$

Thus $(E_2 - E_1)t/\hbar = \pi$ (orthogonality also at $3\pi$, $5\pi$, etc., but this is the *first* occurrence).

$$\therefore \Delta t \equiv \frac{t}{\pi} = \frac{\hbar}{E_2 - E_1}. \quad \text{But } \Delta E = \sigma_H = \frac{1}{2}(E_2 - E_1) \text{ (Problem 3.18).} \quad \text{So } \Delta t\,\Delta E = \frac{\hbar}{2}. \quad \checkmark$$

## Problem 3.33

Equation 2.69: $x = \sqrt{\dfrac{\hbar}{2m\omega}}(a_+ + a_-), \quad p = i\sqrt{\dfrac{\hbar m\omega}{2}}(a_+ - a_-);$ Eq. 2.66: $\begin{cases} a_+|n\rangle = \sqrt{n+1}\,|n+1\rangle, \\ a_-|n\rangle = \sqrt{n}\,|n-1\rangle. \end{cases}$

$$\langle n|x|n'\rangle = \sqrt{\frac{\hbar}{2m\omega}}\langle n|(a_+ + a_-)|n'\rangle = \sqrt{\frac{\hbar}{2m\omega}}\left[\sqrt{n'+1}\,\langle n|n'+1\rangle + \sqrt{n'}\,\langle n|n'-1\rangle\right]$$

$$= \sqrt{\frac{\hbar}{2m\omega}}\left(\sqrt{n'+1}\,\delta_{n,n'+1} + \sqrt{n'}\,\delta_{n,n'-1}\right) = \boxed{\sqrt{\frac{\hbar}{2m\omega}}\left(\sqrt{n}\,\delta_{n',n-1} + \sqrt{n'}\,\delta_{n,n'-1}\right)}.$$

$$\langle n|p|n'\rangle = \boxed{i\sqrt{\frac{m\hbar\omega}{2}}\left(\sqrt{n}\,\delta_{n',n-1} - \sqrt{n'}\,\delta_{n,n'-1}\right)}.$$

Noting that $n$ and $n'$ run from zero to infinity, the matrices are:

$$\mathsf{X} = \sqrt{\frac{\hbar}{2m\omega}}\begin{pmatrix} 0 & \sqrt{1} & 0 & 0 & 0 & 0 \\ \sqrt{1} & 0 & \sqrt{2} & 0 & 0 & 0 \\ 0 & \sqrt{2} & 0 & \sqrt{3} & 0 & 0 \\ 0 & 0 & \sqrt{3} & 0 & \sqrt{4} & 0 \\ 0 & 0 & 0 & \sqrt{4} & 0 & \sqrt{5} \\ & & & \cdots & & \end{pmatrix}; \quad \mathsf{P} = i\sqrt{\frac{m\hbar\omega}{2}}\begin{pmatrix} 0 & -\sqrt{1} & 0 & 0 & 0 & 0 \\ \sqrt{1} & 0 & -\sqrt{2} & 0 & 0 & 0 \\ 0 & \sqrt{2} & 0 & -\sqrt{3} & 0 & 0 \\ 0 & 0 & \sqrt{3} & 0 & -\sqrt{4} & 0 \\ 0 & 0 & 0 & \sqrt{4} & & -\sqrt{5} \\ & & & \cdots & & \end{pmatrix}.$$

Squaring these matrices:

$$\mathsf{X}^2 = \frac{\hbar}{2m\omega}\begin{pmatrix} 1 & 0 & \sqrt{1\cdot 2} & 0 & 0 & 0 \\ 0 & 3 & 0 & \sqrt{2\cdot 3} & 0 & 0 \\ \sqrt{1\cdot 2} & 0 & 5 & 0 & \sqrt{3\cdot 4} & 0 \\ 0 & \sqrt{2\cdot 3} & 0 & 7 & 0 & \sqrt{4\cdot 5} \\ & & & \cdots & & \end{pmatrix};$$

$$\mathsf{P}^2 = -\frac{m\hbar\omega}{2}\begin{pmatrix} -1 & 0 & \sqrt{1\cdot 2} & 0 & 0 & 0 \\ 0 & -3 & 0 & \sqrt{2\cdot 3} & 0 & 0 \\ \sqrt{1\cdot 2} & 0 & -5 & 0 & \sqrt{3\cdot 4} & 0 \\ 0 & \sqrt{2\cdot 3} & 0 & -7 & 0 & \sqrt{4\cdot 5} \\ & & & \cdots & & \end{pmatrix}.$$

So the Hamiltonian, in matrix form, is

$$\mathsf{H} = \frac{1}{2m}\mathsf{P}^2 + \frac{m\omega^2}{2}\mathsf{X}^2$$

$$= -\frac{\hbar\omega}{4}\begin{pmatrix} -1 & 0 & \sqrt{1\cdot 2} & 0 & 0 & 0 \\ 0 & -3 & 0 & \sqrt{2\cdot 3} & 0 & 0 \\ \sqrt{1\cdot 2} & 0 & -5 & 0 & \sqrt{3\cdot 4} & 0 \\ 0 & \sqrt{2\cdot 3} & 0 & -7 & 0 & \sqrt{4\cdot 5} \\ & & & \cdots & & \end{pmatrix} \vdots$$

$$+ \frac{\hbar\omega}{4}\begin{pmatrix} 1 & 0 & \sqrt{1\cdot 2} & 0 & 0 & 0 \\ 0 & 3 & 0 & \sqrt{2\cdot 3} & 0 & 0 \\ \sqrt{1\cdot 2} & 0 & 5 & 0 & \sqrt{3\cdot 4} & 0 \\ 0 & \sqrt{2\cdot 3} & 0 & 7 & 0 & \sqrt{4\cdot 5} \\ & & & \cdots & & \end{pmatrix} \vdots = \frac{\hbar\omega}{2}\begin{pmatrix} 1 & 0 & 0 & 0 \\ 0 & 3 & 0 & 0 \\ 0 & 0 & 5 & 0 \\ 0 & 0 & 0 & 7 \\ & & & & \ddots \end{pmatrix}.$$

It's plainly diagonal, and the nonzero elements are $H_{nn} = \left(n + \frac{1}{2}\right)\hbar\omega$, as they should be.

---

## Problem 3.34

Evidently $\Psi(x,t) = c_0\psi_0(x)e^{-iE_0 t/\hbar} + c_1\psi_1(x)e^{-iE_1 t/\hbar}$, with $|c_0|^2 = |c_1|^2 = 1/2$, so $c_0 = e^{i\theta_0}/\sqrt{2}$, $c_1 = e^{i\theta_1}/\sqrt{2}$, for some real $\theta_0, \theta_1$.

$$\langle p \rangle = |c_0|^2\langle\psi_0|p\psi_0\rangle + |c_1|^2\langle\psi_1|p\psi_1\rangle + c_0^* c_1 e^{i(E_0-E_1)t/\hbar}\langle\psi_0|p\psi_1\rangle + c_1^* c_0 e^{i(E_1-E_0)t/\hbar}\langle\psi_1|p\psi_0\rangle.$$

But $E_1 - E_0 = \left(\frac{3}{2}\hbar\omega\right) - \left(\frac{1}{2}\hbar\omega\right) = \hbar\omega$, and (Problem 2.11) $\langle\psi_0|p\psi_0\rangle = \langle\psi_1|p\psi_1\rangle = 0$, while (Eqs. 2.69 and 2.66)

$$\langle\psi_0|p\psi_1\rangle = i\sqrt{\frac{\hbar m\omega}{2}}\langle\psi_0|(a_+ - a_-)\psi_1\rangle = i\sqrt{\frac{\hbar m\omega}{2}}\left[\langle\psi_0|\sqrt{2}\psi_2\rangle - \langle\psi_0|\sqrt{1}\psi_0\rangle\right] = -i\sqrt{\frac{\hbar m\omega}{2}}; \ \langle\psi_1|p\psi_0\rangle = i\sqrt{\frac{\hbar m\omega}{2}}.$$

$$\langle p \rangle = \frac{1}{\sqrt{2}}e^{-i\theta_0}\frac{1}{\sqrt{2}}e^{i\theta_1}e^{-i\omega t}\left(-i\sqrt{\frac{\hbar m\omega}{2}}\right) + \frac{1}{\sqrt{2}}e^{-i\theta_1}\frac{1}{\sqrt{2}}e^{i\theta_0}e^{i\omega t}\left(i\sqrt{\frac{\hbar m\omega}{2}}\right)$$

$$= \frac{i}{2}\sqrt{\frac{\hbar m\omega}{2}}\left[-e^{-i(\omega t - \theta_1 + \theta_0)} + e^{i(\omega t - \theta_1 + \theta_0)}\right] = -\sqrt{\frac{\hbar m\omega}{2}}\sin(\omega t + \theta_0 - \theta_1).$$

The maximum is $\boxed{\sqrt{\hbar m\omega/2};}$ it occurs at $t = 0 \Leftrightarrow \sin(\theta_0 - \theta_1) = -1$, or $\theta_1 = \theta_0 + \pi/2$. We might as well pick $\theta_0 = 0$, $\theta_1 = \pi/2$; then

$$\Psi(x,t) = \frac{1}{\sqrt{2}}\left[\psi_0 e^{-i\omega t/2} + \psi_1 e^{i\pi/2}e^{-3i\omega t/2}\right] = \boxed{\frac{1}{\sqrt{2}}e^{-i\omega t/2}\left(\psi_0 + i\psi_1 e^{-i\omega t}\right).}$$

---

# Problem 3.35

**(a)** $\langle x \rangle = \langle \alpha | x \alpha \rangle = \sqrt{\dfrac{\hbar}{2m\omega}} \langle \alpha | (a_+ + a_-)\alpha \rangle = \sqrt{\dfrac{\hbar}{2m\omega}} \left( \langle a_-\alpha | \alpha \rangle + \langle \alpha | a_-\alpha \rangle \right) = \boxed{\sqrt{\dfrac{\hbar}{2m\omega}} (\alpha + \alpha^*).}$

$$x^2 = \frac{\hbar}{2m\omega} \left( a_+^2 + a_+a_- + a_-a_+ + a_-^2 \right). \quad \text{But } a_-a_+ = [a_-, a_+] + a_+a_- = 1 + a_+a_- \quad \text{(Eq. 2.55)}.$$

$$= \frac{\hbar}{2m\omega} \left( a_+^2 + 2a_+a_- + 1 + a_-^2 \right).$$

$$\langle x^2 \rangle = \frac{\hbar}{2m\omega} \langle \alpha | \left( a_+^2 + 2a_+a_- + 1 + a_-^2 \right) \alpha \rangle = \frac{\hbar}{2m\omega} \left( \langle a_-^2 \alpha | \alpha \rangle + 2\langle a_-\alpha | a_-\alpha \rangle + \langle \alpha | \alpha \rangle + \langle \alpha | a_-^2 \alpha \rangle \right)$$

$$= \frac{\hbar}{2m\omega} \left[ (\alpha^*)^2 + 2(\alpha^*)\alpha + 1 + \alpha^2 \right] = \boxed{\frac{\hbar}{2m\omega} \left[ 1 + (\alpha + \alpha^*)^2 \right].}$$

$$\langle p \rangle = \langle \alpha | p\alpha \rangle = i\sqrt{\frac{\hbar m\omega}{2}} \langle \alpha | (a_+ - a_-)\alpha \rangle = i\sqrt{\frac{\hbar m\omega}{2}} \left( \langle a_-\alpha | \alpha \rangle - \langle \alpha | a_-\alpha \rangle \right) = \boxed{-i\sqrt{\frac{\hbar m\omega}{2}} (\alpha - \alpha^*).}$$

$$p^2 = -\frac{\hbar m\omega}{2} \left( a_+^2 - a_+a_- - a_-a_+ + a_-^2 \right) = -\frac{\hbar m\omega}{2} \left( a_+^2 - 2a_+a_- - 1 + a_-^2 \right).$$

$$\langle p^2 \rangle = -\frac{\hbar m\omega}{2} \langle \alpha | \left( a_+^2 - 2a_+a_- - 1 + a_-^2 \right) \alpha \rangle = -\frac{\hbar m\omega}{2} \left( \langle a_-^2 \alpha | \alpha \rangle - 2\langle a_-\alpha | a_-\alpha \rangle - \langle \alpha | \alpha \rangle + \langle \alpha | a_-^2 \alpha \rangle \right)$$

$$= -\frac{\hbar m\omega}{2} \left[ (\alpha^*)^2 - 2(\alpha^*)\alpha - 1 + \alpha^2 \right] = \boxed{\frac{\hbar m\omega}{2} \left[ 1 - (\alpha - \alpha^*)^2 \right].}$$

**(b)**

$$\sigma_x^2 = \langle x^2 \rangle - \langle x \rangle^2 = \frac{\hbar}{2m\omega} \left[ 1 + (\alpha + \alpha^*)^2 - (\alpha + \alpha^*)^2 \right] = \frac{\hbar}{2m\omega};$$

$$\sigma_p^2 = \langle p^2 \rangle - \langle p \rangle^2 = \frac{\hbar m\omega}{2} \left[ 1 - (\alpha - \alpha^*)^2 + (\alpha - \alpha^*)^2 \right] = \frac{\hbar m\omega}{2}. \quad \sigma_x\sigma_p = \sqrt{\frac{\hbar}{2m\omega}}\sqrt{\frac{\hbar m\omega}{2}} = \frac{\hbar}{2}. \quad \text{QED}$$

**(c)** Using Eq. 2.67 for $\psi_n$:

$$c_n = \langle \psi_n | \alpha \rangle = \frac{1}{\sqrt{n!}} \langle (a_+)^n \psi_0 | \alpha \rangle = \frac{1}{\sqrt{n!}} \langle \psi_0 | (a_-)^n \alpha \rangle = \frac{1}{\sqrt{n!}} \alpha^n \langle \psi_0 | \alpha \rangle = \frac{\alpha^n}{\sqrt{n!}} c_0. \quad \checkmark$$

**(d)** $1 = \displaystyle\sum_{n=0}^{\infty} |c_n|^2 = |c_0|^2 \sum_{n=0}^{\infty} \frac{|\alpha|^{2n}}{n!} = |c_0|^2 e^{|\alpha|^2} \quad \Rightarrow \quad \boxed{c_0 = e^{-|\alpha|^2/2}.}$

**(e)** $|\alpha(t)\rangle = \displaystyle\sum_{n=0}^{\infty} c_n e^{-iE_n t/\hbar} |n\rangle = \sum_{n=0}^{\infty} \frac{\alpha^n}{\sqrt{n!}} e^{-|\alpha|^2/2} e^{-i(n+\frac{1}{2})\omega t} |n\rangle = e^{-i\omega t/2} \sum_{n=0}^{\infty} \frac{(\alpha e^{-i\omega t})^n}{\sqrt{n!}} e^{-|\alpha|^2/2} |n\rangle.$

Apart form the overall phase factor $e^{-i\omega t/2}$ (which doesn't affect its status as an eigenfunction of $a_-$, or its eigenvalue), $|\alpha(t)\rangle$ is the same as $|\alpha\rangle$, but with eigenvalue $\alpha(t) = e^{-i\omega t}\alpha$. $\checkmark$

**(f)** Equation 2.58 says $a_-|\psi_0\rangle = 0$, so $\boxed{\text{yes,}}$ it *is* a coherent state, with eigenvalue $\boxed{\alpha = 0.}$

## Problem 3.36

**(a)** Equation 3.60 becomes $|z|^2 = [\text{Re}(z)]^2 + [\text{Im}(z)]^2 = \left[\frac{1}{2}(z+z^*)\right]^2 + \left[\frac{1}{2i}(z-z^*)\right]^2$ ; Eq. 3.61 generalizes to

$$\sigma_A^2 \sigma_B^2 \geq \left[\frac{1}{2}\left(\langle f|g\rangle + \langle g|f\rangle\right)\right]^2 + \left[\frac{1}{2i}\left(\langle f|g\rangle - \langle g|f\rangle\right)\right]^2 .$$

But $\langle f|g\rangle - \langle g|f\rangle = \langle[\hat{A},\hat{B}]\rangle$ (p. 111), and, by the same argument,

$$\langle f|g\rangle + \langle g|f\rangle = \langle\hat{A}\hat{B}\rangle - \langle A\rangle\langle B\rangle + \langle\hat{B}\hat{A}\rangle - \langle A\rangle\langle B\rangle = \langle\hat{A}\hat{B} + \hat{B}\hat{A} - 2\langle A\rangle\langle B\rangle\rangle = \langle D\rangle.$$

So $\sigma_A^2 \sigma_B^2 \geq \frac{1}{4}\left(\langle D\rangle^2 + \langle C\rangle^2\right)$.  ✓

**(b)** If $\hat{B} = \hat{A}$,  then $\hat{C} = 0$,  $\hat{D} = 2\left(\hat{A}^2 - \langle A\rangle^2\right)$;  $\langle D\rangle = 2\left(\langle\hat{A}^2\rangle - \langle A\rangle^2\right) = 2\sigma_A^2$.  So Eq. 3.99 says $\sigma_A^2 \sigma_A^2 \geq (1/4)4\sigma_A^4 = \sigma_A^4$, which is *true*, but not very informative.

---

## Problem 3.37

First find the eigenvalues and eigenvectors of the Hamiltonian. The characteristic equation says

$$\begin{vmatrix} (a-E) & 0 & b \\ 0 & (c-E) & 0 \\ b & 0 & (a-E) \end{vmatrix} = (a-E)(c-E)(a-E) - b^2(c-E) = (c-E)\left[(a-E)^2 - b^2\right] = 0,$$

Either $E = c$, or else $(a-E)^2 = b^2 \Rightarrow E = a \pm b$. So the eigenvalues are

$$E_1 = c, \quad E_2 = a+b, \quad E_3 = a-b.$$

To find the corresponding eigenvectors, write

$$\begin{pmatrix} a & 0 & b \\ 0 & c & 0 \\ b & 0 & a \end{pmatrix} \begin{pmatrix} \alpha \\ \beta \\ \gamma \end{pmatrix} = E_n \begin{pmatrix} \alpha \\ \beta \\ \gamma \end{pmatrix} .$$

(1)

$$\left. \begin{array}{l} a\alpha + b\gamma = c\alpha \Rightarrow (a-c)\alpha + b\gamma = 0; \\ c\beta = c\beta \quad \text{(redundant)} \quad ; \\ b\alpha + a\gamma = c\gamma \Rightarrow (a-c)\gamma + b\alpha = 0. \end{array} \right\} \Rightarrow \left[(a-c)^2 - b^2\right]\alpha = 0.$$

So (excluding the degenerate case $a - c = \pm b$) $\alpha = 0$, and hence also $\gamma = 0$.

(2)

$$\begin{array}{ll} a\alpha + b\gamma = (a+b)\alpha \Rightarrow & \alpha - \gamma = 0; \\ c\beta = (a+b)\beta \Rightarrow & \beta = 0; \\ b\alpha + a\gamma = (a+b)\gamma & \text{(redundant)}. \end{array}$$

So $\alpha = \gamma$ and $\beta = 0$.

(3)

$$aα + bγ = (a − b)α \Rightarrow \qquad α + γ = 0;$$
$$cβ = (a − b)β \Rightarrow \qquad β = 0;$$
$$bα + aγ = (a − b)γ \qquad \text{(redundant)}.$$

So $α = −γ$ and $β = 0$.

*Conclusion:* The (normalized) eigenvectors of **H** are

$$|s_1\rangle = \begin{pmatrix} 0 \\ 1 \\ 0 \end{pmatrix}, \quad |s_2\rangle = \frac{1}{\sqrt{2}} \begin{pmatrix} 1 \\ 0 \\ 1 \end{pmatrix}, \quad |s_3\rangle = \frac{1}{\sqrt{2}} \begin{pmatrix} 1 \\ 0 \\ -1 \end{pmatrix}.$$

**(a)** Here $|\mathcal{S}(0)\rangle = |s_1\rangle$, so

$$|\mathcal{S}(t)\rangle = e^{-iE_1 t/\hbar}|s_1\rangle = \boxed{e^{-ict/\hbar} \begin{pmatrix} 0 \\ 1 \\ 0 \end{pmatrix}}.$$

**(b)**

$$|\mathcal{S}(0)\rangle = \frac{1}{\sqrt{2}}\left(|s_2\rangle + |s_3\rangle\right).$$

$$|\mathcal{S}(t)\rangle = \frac{1}{\sqrt{2}}\left(e^{-iE_2 t/\hbar}|s_2\rangle + e^{-iE_3 t/\hbar}|s_3\rangle\right) = \frac{1}{\sqrt{2}}\left[e^{-i(a+b)t/\hbar}\frac{1}{\sqrt{2}}\begin{pmatrix} 1 \\ 0 \\ 1 \end{pmatrix} + e^{-i(a-b)t/\hbar}\frac{1}{\sqrt{2}}\begin{pmatrix} 1 \\ 0 \\ -1 \end{pmatrix}\right]$$

$$= \frac{1}{2}e^{-iat/\hbar}\begin{pmatrix} e^{-ibt/\hbar} + e^{ibt/\hbar} \\ 0 \\ e^{-ibt/\hbar} - e^{ibt/\hbar} \end{pmatrix} = \boxed{e^{-iat/\hbar}\begin{pmatrix} \cos(bt/\hbar) \\ 0 \\ -i\sin(bt/\hbar) \end{pmatrix}}.$$

---

## Problem 3.38

**(a)** H:

$$\boxed{E_1 = \hbar\omega, \ E_2 = E_3 = 2\hbar\omega; \quad |h_1\rangle = \begin{pmatrix} 1 \\ 0 \\ 0 \end{pmatrix}, \ |h_2\rangle = \begin{pmatrix} 0 \\ 1 \\ 0 \end{pmatrix}, \ |h_3\rangle = \begin{pmatrix} 0 \\ 0 \\ 1 \end{pmatrix}.}$$

A:

$$\begin{vmatrix} -a & λ & 0 \\ λ & -a & 0 \\ 0 & 0 & (2λ - a) \end{vmatrix} = a^2(2λ - a) - (2λ - a)λ^2 = 0 \Rightarrow \boxed{a_1 = 2λ, \ a_2 = λ, \ a_3 = -λ.}$$

$$λ\begin{pmatrix} 0 & 1 & 0 \\ 1 & 0 & 0 \\ 0 & 0 & 2 \end{pmatrix}\begin{pmatrix} α \\ β \\ γ \end{pmatrix} = a\begin{pmatrix} α \\ β \\ γ \end{pmatrix} \Rightarrow \begin{cases} λβ = aα \\ λα = aβ \\ 2λγ = aγ \end{cases}$$

**(1)**

$$\left.\begin{array}{l} \lambda\beta = 2\lambda\alpha \;\Rightarrow\; \beta = 2\alpha, \\ \lambda\alpha = 2\lambda\beta \;\Rightarrow\; \alpha = 2\beta, \\ 2\lambda\gamma = 2\lambda\gamma; \end{array}\right\} \quad \alpha = \beta = 0; \quad \boxed{|a_1\rangle = \begin{pmatrix} 0 \\ 0 \\ 1 \end{pmatrix}.}$$

**(2)**

$$\left.\begin{array}{l} \lambda\beta = \lambda\alpha \;\Rightarrow\; \beta = \alpha, \\ \lambda\alpha = \lambda\beta \;\Rightarrow\; \alpha = \beta, \\ 2\lambda\gamma = \lambda\gamma; \;\Rightarrow\; \gamma = 0. \end{array}\right\} \quad \boxed{|a_2\rangle = \frac{1}{\sqrt{2}}\begin{pmatrix} 1 \\ 1 \\ 0 \end{pmatrix}.}$$

**(3)**

$$\left.\begin{array}{l} \lambda\beta = -\lambda\alpha \;\Rightarrow\; \beta = -\alpha, \\ \lambda\alpha = -\lambda\beta \;\Rightarrow\; \alpha = -\beta, \\ 2\lambda\gamma = -\lambda\gamma; \;\Rightarrow\; \gamma = 0. \end{array}\right\} \quad \boxed{|a_3\rangle = \frac{1}{\sqrt{2}}\begin{pmatrix} 1 \\ -1 \\ 0 \end{pmatrix}.}$$

**B:**

$$\begin{vmatrix} (2\mu - b) & 0 & 0 \\ 0 & -b & \mu \\ 0 & \mu & -b \end{vmatrix} = b^2(2\mu - b) - (2\mu - b)\mu^2 = 0 \;\Rightarrow\; \boxed{b_1 = 2\mu, \; b_2 = \mu, \; b_3 = -\mu.}$$

$$\mu\begin{pmatrix} 2 & 0 & 0 \\ 0 & 0 & 1 \\ 0 & 1 & 0 \end{pmatrix}\begin{pmatrix} \alpha \\ \beta \\ \gamma \end{pmatrix} = b\begin{pmatrix} \alpha \\ \beta \\ \gamma \end{pmatrix} \;\Rightarrow\; \left\{\begin{array}{l} 2\mu\alpha = b\alpha \\ \mu\gamma = b\beta \\ \mu\beta = b\gamma \end{array}\right.$$

**(1)**

$$\left.\begin{array}{l} 2\mu\alpha = 2\mu\alpha, \\ \mu\gamma = 2\mu\beta \;\Rightarrow\; \gamma = 2\beta, \\ \mu\beta = 2\mu\gamma \;\Rightarrow\; \beta = 2\gamma; \end{array}\right\} \quad \beta = \gamma = 0; \quad \boxed{|b_1\rangle = \begin{pmatrix} 1 \\ 0 \\ 0 \end{pmatrix}.}$$

**(2)**

$$\left.\begin{array}{l} 2\mu\alpha = \mu\alpha \;\Rightarrow\; \alpha = 0, \\ \mu\gamma = \mu\beta \;\Rightarrow\; \gamma = \beta, \\ \mu\beta = \mu\gamma; \;\Rightarrow\; \beta = \gamma. \end{array}\right\} \quad \boxed{|b_2\rangle = \frac{1}{\sqrt{2}}\begin{pmatrix} 0 \\ 1 \\ 1 \end{pmatrix}.}$$

**(3)**

$$\left.\begin{array}{l} 2\mu\alpha = -\mu\alpha \;\Rightarrow\; \alpha = 0, \\ \mu\gamma = -\mu\beta \;\Rightarrow\; \gamma = -\beta, \\ \mu\beta = -\mu\gamma; \;\Rightarrow\; \beta = -\gamma. \end{array}\right\} \quad \boxed{|b_3\rangle = \frac{1}{\sqrt{2}}\begin{pmatrix} 0 \\ 1 \\ -1 \end{pmatrix}.}$$

**(b)**

$$\langle H \rangle = \langle \mathcal{S}(0)|H|\mathcal{S}(0)\rangle = \hbar\omega \begin{pmatrix} c_1^* & c_2^* & c_3^* \end{pmatrix} \begin{pmatrix} 1 & 0 & 0 \\ 0 & 2 & 0 \\ 0 & 0 & 2 \end{pmatrix} \begin{pmatrix} c_1 \\ c_2 \\ c_3 \end{pmatrix} = \boxed{\hbar\omega \left(|c_1|^2 + 2|c_2|^2 + 2|c_3|^2\right).}$$

$$\langle A \rangle = \langle \mathcal{S}(0)|A|\mathcal{S}(0)\rangle = \lambda \begin{pmatrix} c_1^* & c_2^* & c_3^* \end{pmatrix} \begin{pmatrix} 0 & 1 & 0 \\ 1 & 0 & 0 \\ 0 & 0 & 2 \end{pmatrix} \begin{pmatrix} c_1 \\ c_2 \\ c_3 \end{pmatrix} = \boxed{\lambda \left(c_1^* c_2 + c_2^* c_1 + 2|c_3|^2\right).}$$

$$\langle B \rangle = \langle \mathcal{S}(0)|B|\mathcal{S}(0)\rangle = \mu \begin{pmatrix} c_1^* & c_2^* & c_3^* \end{pmatrix} \begin{pmatrix} 2 & 0 & 0 \\ 0 & 0 & 1 \\ 0 & 1 & 0 \end{pmatrix} \begin{pmatrix} c_1 \\ c_2 \\ c_3 \end{pmatrix} = \boxed{\mu \left(2|c_1|^2 + c_2^* c_3 + c_3^* c_2\right).}$$

**(c)**

$$|\mathcal{S}(0)\rangle = c_1|h_1\rangle + c_2|h_2\rangle + c_3|h_3\rangle \quad \Rightarrow$$
$$|\mathcal{S}(t)\rangle = c_1 e^{-iE_1 t/\hbar}|h_1\rangle + c_2 e^{-iE_2 t/\hbar}|h_2\rangle + c_3 e^{-iE_3 t/\hbar}|h_3\rangle = c_1 e^{-i\omega t}|h_1\rangle + c_2 e^{-2i\omega t}|h_2\rangle + c_3 e^{-2i\omega t}|h_3\rangle$$

$$= e^{-2i\omega t}\left[c_1 e^{i\omega t}\begin{pmatrix}1\\0\\0\end{pmatrix} + c_2\begin{pmatrix}0\\1\\0\end{pmatrix} + c_3\begin{pmatrix}0\\0\\1\end{pmatrix}\right] = \boxed{e^{-2i\omega t}\begin{pmatrix}c_1 e^{i\omega t}\\ c_2\\ c_3\end{pmatrix}.}$$

H: $\boxed{h_1 = \hbar\omega, \text{ probability } |c_1|^2; \quad h_2 = h_3 = 2\hbar\omega, \text{ probability } (|c_2|^2 + |c_3|^2).}$

A: $\boxed{a_1 = 2\lambda,}$ $\quad \langle a_1|\mathcal{S}(t)\rangle = e^{-2i\omega t}\begin{pmatrix}0 & 0 & 1\end{pmatrix}\begin{pmatrix}c_1 e^{i\omega t}\\ c_2\\ c_3\end{pmatrix} = e^{-2i\omega t}c_3 \Rightarrow \boxed{\text{probability } |c_3|^2.}$

$\boxed{a_2 = \lambda,}$ $\quad \langle a_2|\mathcal{S}(t)\rangle = e^{-2i\omega t}\frac{1}{\sqrt{2}}\begin{pmatrix}1 & 1 & 0\end{pmatrix}\begin{pmatrix}c_1 e^{i\omega t}\\ c_2\\ c_3\end{pmatrix} = \frac{1}{\sqrt{2}}e^{-2i\omega t}\left(c_1 e^{i\omega t} + c_2\right) \Rightarrow$

probability $= \frac{1}{2}\left(c_1^* e^{-i\omega t} + c_2^*\right)\left(c_1 e^{i\omega t} + c_2\right) = \boxed{\frac{1}{2}\left(|c_1|^2 + |c_2|^2 + c_1^* c_2 e^{-i\omega t} + c_2^* c_1 e^{i\omega t}\right).}$

$\boxed{a_3 = -\lambda,}$ $\quad \langle a_3|\mathcal{S}(t)\rangle = e^{-2i\omega t}\frac{1}{\sqrt{2}}\begin{pmatrix}1 & -1 & 0\end{pmatrix}\begin{pmatrix}c_1 e^{i\omega t}\\ c_2\\ c_3\end{pmatrix} = \frac{1}{\sqrt{2}}e^{-2i\omega t}\left(c_1 e^{i\omega t} - c_2\right) \Rightarrow$

probability $= \frac{1}{2}\left(c_1^* e^{-i\omega t} - c_2^*\right)\left(c_1 e^{i\omega t} - c_2\right) = \boxed{\frac{1}{2}\left(|c_1|^2 + |c_2|^2 - c_1^* c_2 e^{-i\omega t} - c_2^* c_1 e^{i\omega t}\right).}$

Note that the sum of the probabilities is 1.

B: $\boxed{b_1 = 2\mu,}$ $\quad \langle b_1|\mathcal{S}(t)\rangle = e^{-2i\omega t}\begin{pmatrix}1 & 0 & 0\end{pmatrix}\begin{pmatrix}c_1 e^{i\omega t}\\ c_2\\ c_3\end{pmatrix} = e^{-2i\omega t}c_1 \Rightarrow \boxed{\text{probability } |c_1|^2.}$

$\boxed{b_2 = \mu,}$ $\quad \langle b_2|\mathcal{S}(t)\rangle = e^{-2i\omega t}\frac{1}{\sqrt{2}}\begin{pmatrix}0 & 1 & 1\end{pmatrix}\begin{pmatrix}c_1 e^{i\omega t}\\ c_2\\ c_3\end{pmatrix} = \frac{1}{\sqrt{2}}e^{-2i\omega t}\left(c_2 + c_3\right) \Rightarrow$

probability $= \frac{1}{2}\left(c_1^* + c_2^*\right)\left(c_1 + c_2\right) = \boxed{\frac{1}{2}\left(|c_1|^2 + |c_2|^2 + c_1^* c_2 + c_2^* c_1\right).}$

$$\boxed{b_3 = -\mu,} \quad \langle b_3|\mathcal{S}(t)\rangle = e^{-2i\omega t}\frac{1}{\sqrt{2}}\begin{pmatrix}0 & 1 & -1\end{pmatrix}\begin{pmatrix}c_1 e^{i\omega t}\\ c_2 \\ c_3\end{pmatrix} = \frac{1}{\sqrt{2}}e^{-2i\omega t}(c_2 - c_3) \Rightarrow$$

$$\text{probability} = \frac{1}{2}(c_2^* - c_3^*)(c_2 - c_3) = \boxed{\frac{1}{2}\left(|c_2|^2 + |c_3|^2 - c_2^* c_3 - c_3^* c_2\right).}$$

Again, the sum of the probabilities is 1.

---

## Problem 3.39

**(a)**

Expanding in a Taylor series: $f(x + x_0) = \sum_{n=0}^{\infty} \frac{1}{n!} x_0^n \left(\frac{d}{dx}\right)^n f(x).$

But $p = \frac{\hbar}{i}\frac{d}{dx}$, so $\frac{d}{dx} = \frac{ip}{\hbar}$. Therefore $f(x + x_0) = \sum_{n=0}^{\infty} \frac{1}{n!} x_0^n \left(\frac{ip}{\hbar}\right)^n f(x) = e^{ipx_0/\hbar} f(x).$

**(b)**

$$\Psi(x, t + t_0) = \sum_{n=0}^{\infty} \frac{1}{n!} t_0^n \left(\frac{\partial}{\partial t}\right)^n \Psi(x, t); \quad i\hbar\frac{\partial\Psi}{\partial t} = H\Psi.$$

[*Note:* It is emphatically *not* the case that $i\hbar\frac{\partial}{\partial t} = H$. These two operators have the same effect *only* when (as here) they are acting on solutions to the (time-dependent) Schrödinger equation.] Also,

$$\left(i\hbar\frac{\partial}{\partial t}\right)^2 \Psi = i\hbar\frac{\partial}{\partial t}(H\Psi) = H\left(i\hbar\frac{\partial\Psi}{\partial t}\right) = H^2\Psi,$$

provided $H$ is not explicitly dependent on $t$. And so on. So

$$\Psi(x, t + t_0) = \sum_{n=0}^{\infty} \frac{1}{n!} t_0^n \left(-\frac{i}{\hbar}H\right)^n \Psi = e^{-iHt_0/\hbar}\Psi(x, t).$$

**(c)**

$$\langle Q\rangle_{t+t_0} = \langle\Psi(x, t + t_0)|Q(x, p, t + t_0)|\Psi(x, t + t_0)\rangle.$$

But $\Psi(x, t + t_0) = e^{-iHt_0/\hbar}\Psi(x, t)$, so, using the hermiticity of $H$ to write $\left(e^{-iHt_0/\hbar}\right)^\dagger = e^{iHt_0/\hbar}$ :

$$\langle Q\rangle_{t+t_0} = \langle\Psi(x, t)|e^{iHt_0/\hbar}Q(x, p, t + t_0)e^{-iHt_0/\hbar}|\Psi(x, t)\rangle.$$

If $t_0 = dt$ is very small, expanding to first order, we have:

$$\langle Q\rangle_t + \frac{d\langle Q\rangle}{dt}dt = \langle\Psi(x, t)|\underbrace{\left(1 + \frac{iH}{\hbar}dt\right)\left[Q(x, p, t) + \frac{\partial Q}{\partial t}dt\right]\left(1 - \frac{iH}{\hbar}dt\right)}_{\star}|\Psi(x, t)\rangle$$

$$\left[\star = Q(x, p, t) + \frac{iH}{\hbar}dt\,Q - Q\left(\frac{iH}{\hbar}dt\right) + \frac{\partial Q}{\partial t}dt = Q + \frac{i}{\hbar}[H, Q]dt + \frac{\partial Q}{\partial t}dt\right]$$

$$= \langle Q\rangle_t + \frac{i}{\hbar}\langle[H, Q]\rangle dt + \langle\frac{\partial Q}{\partial t}\rangle dt.$$

$$\therefore \frac{d\langle Q\rangle}{dt} = \frac{i}{\hbar}\langle[H,Q]\rangle + \langle\frac{\partial Q}{\partial t}\rangle. \quad \text{QED}$$

## Problem 3.40

**(a)** For the free particle, $V(x) = 0$, so the time-dependent Schrödinger equation reads

$$i\hbar\frac{\partial\Psi}{\partial t} = -\frac{\hbar^2}{2m}\frac{\partial^2\Psi}{\partial x^2}. \quad \Psi(x,t) = \frac{1}{\sqrt{2\pi\hbar}}\int_{-\infty}^{\infty} e^{ipx/\hbar}\Phi(p,t)\,dp \Rightarrow$$

$$\frac{\partial\Psi}{\partial t} = \frac{1}{\sqrt{2\pi\hbar}}\int_{-\infty}^{\infty} e^{ipx/\hbar}\frac{\partial\Phi}{\partial t}\,dp, \quad \frac{\partial^2\Psi}{\partial x^2} = \frac{1}{\sqrt{2\pi\hbar}}\int_{-\infty}^{\infty}\left(-\frac{p^2}{\hbar^2}\right)e^{ipx/\hbar}\Phi\,dp. \quad \text{So}$$

$$\frac{1}{\sqrt{2\pi\hbar}}\int_{-\infty}^{\infty} e^{ipx/\hbar}\left[i\hbar\frac{\partial\Phi}{\partial t}\right]dp = \frac{1}{\sqrt{2\pi\hbar}}\int_{-\infty}^{\infty} e^{ipx/\hbar}\left[\frac{p^2}{2m}\Phi\right]dp.$$

But two functions with the same Fourier transform are equal (as you can easily prove using Plancherel's theorem), so

$$\boxed{i\hbar\frac{\partial\Phi}{\partial t} = \frac{p^2}{2m}\Phi.} \quad \frac{1}{\Phi}\,d\Phi = -\frac{ip^2}{2m\hbar}\,dt \quad \Rightarrow \quad \boxed{\Phi(p,t) = e^{-ip^2t/2m\hbar}\Phi(p,0).}$$

**(b)**

$$\Psi(x,0) = Ae^{-ax^2}e^{ilx}, \quad A = \left(\frac{2a}{\pi}\right)^{1/4} \quad \text{(Problem2.43(a))}.$$

$$\Phi(p,0) = \frac{1}{\sqrt{2\pi\hbar}}\left(\frac{2a}{\pi}\right)^{1/4}\int_{-\infty}^{\infty} e^{-ipx/\hbar}e^{-ax^2}e^{ilx}\,dx = \frac{1}{(2\pi a\hbar^2)^{1/4}}e^{-(l-p/\hbar)^2/4a} \quad \text{(Problem2.43(b))}.$$

$$\boxed{\Phi(p,t) = \frac{1}{(2\pi a\hbar^2)^{1/4}}e^{-(l-p/\hbar)^2/4a}e^{-ip^2t/2m\hbar}; \qquad |\Phi(p,t)|^2 = \frac{1}{\sqrt{2\pi a}\,\hbar}e^{-(l-p/\hbar)^2/2a}.}$$

**(c)**

$$\langle p\rangle = \int_{-\infty}^{\infty} p|\Phi(p,t)|^2\,dp = \frac{1}{\sqrt{2\pi a}\,\hbar}\int_{-\infty}^{\infty} pe^{-(l-p/\hbar)^2/2a}\,dp$$

$$[\text{Let } y \equiv (p/\hbar) - l, \text{ so } p = \hbar(y+l) \text{ and } dp = \hbar\,dy.]$$

$$= \frac{\hbar}{\sqrt{2\pi a}}\int_{-\infty}^{\infty}(y+l)e^{-y^2/2a}\,dy \quad [\text{but the first term is odd}]$$

$$= \frac{2\hbar l}{\sqrt{2\pi a}}\int_0^{\infty} e^{-y^2/2a}\,dy = \frac{2\hbar l}{\sqrt{2\pi a}}\sqrt{\frac{\pi a}{2}} = \boxed{\hbar l} \quad [\text{as in Problem 2.43(d)}].$$

$$\langle p^2\rangle = \int_{-\infty}^{\infty} p^2|\Phi(p,t)|^2\,dp = \frac{1}{\sqrt{2\pi a}\,\hbar}\int_{-\infty}^{\infty} p^2 e^{-(l-p/\hbar)^2/2a}\,dp = \frac{\hbar^2}{\sqrt{2\pi a}}\int_{-\infty}^{\infty}(y^2+2yl+l^2)e^{-y^2/2a}\,dy$$

$$= \frac{2\hbar^2}{\sqrt{2\pi a}}\left[\int_0^{\infty} y^2 e^{-y^2/2a}\,dy + l^2\int_0^{\infty} e^{-y^2/2a}\,dy\right]$$

$$= \frac{2\hbar^2}{\sqrt{2\pi a}}\left[2\sqrt{\pi}\left(\sqrt{\frac{a}{2}}\right)^3 + l^2\sqrt{\frac{\pi a}{2}}\right] = \boxed{(a+l^2)\hbar^2} \quad [\text{as in Problem 2.43(d)}].$$

**(d)** $H = \dfrac{p^2}{2m}$; $\quad \langle H \rangle = \dfrac{1}{2m}\langle p^2 \rangle = \dfrac{\hbar^2}{2m}(l^2+a) = \dfrac{1}{2m}\langle p \rangle^2 + \dfrac{\hbar^2 a}{2m}$. $\quad$ But $\langle H \rangle_0 = \dfrac{1}{2m}\langle p^2 \rangle_0 = \dfrac{\hbar^2 a}{2m}$ (Problem 2.22(d)).

So $\langle H \rangle = \dfrac{1}{2m}\langle p \rangle^2 + \langle H \rangle_0$. $\quad$ QED $\quad$ *Comment:* The energy of the traveling gaussian is the energy of the same gaussian at rest, plus the kinetic energy ($\langle p \rangle^2/2m$) associated with the motion of the wave packet as a whole.

# Chapter 4

# Quantum Mechanics in Three Dimensions

**Problem 4.1**

**(a)**

$$[x, y] = xy - yx = 0, \text{ etc., so } \boxed{[r_i, r_j] = 0.}$$

$$[p_x, p_y]f = \frac{\hbar}{i} \frac{\partial}{\partial x}\left(\frac{\hbar}{i}\frac{\partial f}{\partial y}\right) - \frac{\hbar}{i}\frac{\partial}{\partial y}\left(\frac{\hbar}{i}\frac{\partial f}{\partial x}\right) = -\hbar^2\left(\frac{\partial^2 f}{\partial x \partial y} - \frac{\partial^2 f}{\partial y \partial x}\right) = 0$$

(by the equality of cross-derivatives), so $\boxed{[p_i, p_j] = 0.}$

$$[x, p_x]f = \frac{\hbar}{i}\left(x\frac{\partial f}{\partial x} - \frac{\partial}{\partial x}(xf)\right) = \frac{\hbar}{i}\left(x\frac{\partial f}{\partial x} - x\frac{\partial f}{\partial x} - f\right) = i\hbar f,$$

so $[x, p_x] = i\hbar$ (likewise $[y, p_y] = i\hbar$ and $[z, p_z] = i\hbar$).

$$[y, p_x]f = \frac{\hbar}{i}\left(y\frac{\partial f}{\partial x} - \frac{\partial}{\partial x}(yf)\right) = \frac{\hbar}{i}\left(y\frac{\partial f}{\partial x} - y\frac{\partial f}{\partial y}\right) = 0 \text{ (since}\frac{\partial y}{\partial x} = 0). \text{ So } [y, p_x] = 0,$$

and same goes for the other "mixed" commutators. Thus $\boxed{[r_i, p_j] = -[p_j, r_i] = i\hbar\delta_{ij}.}$

**(b)** The derivation of Eq. 3.71 (page 115) is identical in three dimensions, so $\dfrac{d\langle x\rangle}{dt} = \dfrac{i}{\hbar}\langle[H, x]\rangle$;

$$[H, x] = \left[\frac{p^2}{2m} + V, x\right] = \frac{1}{2m}[p_x^2 + p_y^2 + p_z^2, x] = \frac{1}{2m}[p_x^2, x]$$

$$= \frac{1}{2m}\left(p_x[p_x, x] + [p_x, x]p_x\right) = \frac{1}{2m}\left[(-i\hbar)p_x + (-i\hbar)p_x\right] = -i\frac{\hbar}{m}p_x.$$

$$\therefore \frac{d\langle x\rangle}{dt} = \frac{i}{\hbar}\left(-i\frac{\hbar}{m}\langle p_x\rangle\right) = \frac{1}{m}\langle p_x\rangle. \text{ The same goes for } y \text{ and } z, \text{ so: } \boxed{\frac{d\langle\mathbf{r}\rangle}{dt} = \frac{1}{m}\langle\mathbf{p}\rangle.}$$

$$\frac{d\langle p_x \rangle}{dt} = \frac{i}{\hbar} \langle [H, p_x] \rangle; \quad [H, p_x] = \left[ \frac{p^2}{2m} + V, p_x \right] = [V, p_x] = i\hbar \frac{\partial V}{\partial x} \quad \text{(Eq. 3.65)}$$

$$= \frac{i}{\hbar} (i\hbar) \left\langle \frac{\partial V}{\partial x} \right\rangle = \left\langle -\frac{\partial V}{\partial x} \right\rangle. \quad \text{Same for } y \text{ and } z, \text{ so: } \boxed{\frac{d\langle \mathbf{p} \rangle}{dt} = \langle -\nabla V \rangle.}$$

(c) From Eq. 3.62: $\sigma_x \sigma_{p_x} \geq \left| \frac{1}{2i} \langle [x, p_x] \rangle \right| = \left| \frac{1}{2i} i\hbar \right| = \frac{\hbar}{2}.$ Generally, $\boxed{\sigma_{r_i} \sigma_{p_j} \geq \frac{\hbar}{2} \delta_{ij}.}$

---

## Problem 4.2

(a) Equation 4.8 $\Rightarrow -\frac{\hbar^2}{2m} \left( \frac{\partial^2 \psi}{\partial x^2} + \frac{\partial^2 \psi}{\partial y^2} + \frac{\partial^2 \psi}{\partial z^2} \right) = E\psi$ (inside the box). Separable solutions: $\psi(x, y, z) = X(x)Y(y)Z(z)$. Put this in, and divide by $XYZ$:

$$\frac{1}{X} \frac{d^2 X}{dx^2} + \frac{1}{Y} \frac{d^2 X}{dy^2} + \frac{1}{Z} \frac{d^2 Z}{dz^2} = -\frac{2m}{\hbar^2} E.$$

The three terms on the left are functions of $x$, $y$, and $z$, respectively, so each must be a constant. Call the separation constants $k_x^2$, $k_y^2$, and $k_z^2$ (as we'll soon seen, they must be positive).

$$\frac{d^2 X}{dx^2} = -k_x^2 X; \quad \frac{d^2 Y}{dy^2} = -k_y^2 Y; \quad \frac{d^2 Z}{dz^2} = -k_z^2 Z, \quad \text{with} \quad E = \frac{\hbar^2}{2m} (k_x^2 + k_y^2 + k_z^2).$$

Solution:

$$X(x) = A_x \sin k_x x + B_x \cos k_x x; \quad Y(y) = A_y \sin k_y y + B_y \cos k_y y; \quad Z(z) = A_z \sin k_z z + B_z \cos k_z z.$$

But $X(0) = 0$, so $B_x = 0$; $Y(0) = 0$, so $B_y = 0$; $Z(0) = 0$, so $B_z = 0$. And $X(a) = 0 \Rightarrow \sin(k_x a) = 0 \Rightarrow k_x = n_x \pi / a$ ($n_x = 1, 2, 3, \dots$). [As before (page 31), $n_x \neq 0$, and negative values are redundant.] Likewise $k_y = n_y \pi / a$ and $k_z = n_z \pi / a$. So

$$\psi(x, y, z) = A_x A_y A_z \sin \left( \frac{n_x \pi}{a} x \right) \sin \left( \frac{n_y \pi}{a} y \right) \sin \left( \frac{n_z \pi}{a} z \right), \quad E = \frac{\hbar^2}{2m} \frac{\pi^2}{a^2} (n_x^2 + n_y^2 + n_z^2).$$

We might as well normalize $X, Y$, and $Z$ separately: $A_x = A_y = A_z = \sqrt{2/a}$. *Conclusion:*

$$\boxed{\psi(x, y, z) = \left( \frac{2}{a} \right)^{3/2} \sin \left( \frac{n_x \pi}{a} x \right) \sin \left( \frac{n_y \pi}{a} y \right) \sin \left( \frac{n_z \pi}{a} z \right); \quad E = \frac{\pi^2 \hbar^2}{2ma^2} (n_x^2 + n_y^2 + n_z^2); \quad n_x, n_y, n_z = 1, 2, 3, \dots}$$

**(b)**

| $n_x$ | $n_y$ | $n_z$ | $(n_x^2 + n_y^2 + n_z^2)$ |
|---|---|---|---|
| 1 | 1 | 1 | 3 |
| | | | |
| 1 | 1 | 2 | 6 |
| 1 | 2 | 1 | 6 |
| 2 | 1 | 1 | 6 |
| | | | |
| 1 | 2 | 2 | 9 |
| 2 | 1 | 2 | 9 |
| 2 | 2 | 1 | 9 |
| | | | |
| 1 | 1 | 3 | 11 |
| 1 | 3 | 1 | 11 |
| 3 | 1 | 1 | 11 |
| | | | |
| 2 | 2 | 2 | 12 |
| | | | |
| 1 | 2 | 3 | 14 |
| 1 | 3 | 2 | 14 |
| 2 | 1 | 3 | 14 |
| 2 | 3 | 1 | 14 |
| 3 | 1 | 2 | 14 |
| 3 | 2 | 1 | 14 |

| Energy | Degeneracy |
|---|---|
| $E_1 = 3\dfrac{\pi^2\hbar^2}{2ma^2};$ | $d = 1$ |
| $E_2 = 6\dfrac{\pi^2\hbar^2}{2ma^2};$ | $d = 3.$ |
| $E_3 = 9\dfrac{\pi^2\hbar^2}{2ma^2};$ | $d = 3.$ |
| $E_4 = 11\dfrac{\pi^2\hbar^2}{2ma^2};$ | $d = 3.$ |
| $E_5 = 12\dfrac{\pi^2\hbar^2}{2ma^2};$ | $d = 1.$ |
| $E_6 = 14\dfrac{\pi^2\hbar^2}{2ma^2};$ | $d = 6.$ |

**(c)** The next combinations are: $E_7(322)$, $E_8(411)$, $E_9(331)$, $E_{10}(421)$, $E_{11}(332)$, $E_{12}(422)$, $E_{13}(431)$, and $E_{14}(333 \text{ and } 511)$. The degeneracy of $E_{14}$ is $\boxed{4.}$ Simple combinatorics accounts for degeneracies of 1 ($n_x = n_y = n_z$), 3 (two the same, one different), or 6 (all three different). But in the case of $E_{14}$ there is a numerical "accident": $3^2 + 3^2 + 3^2 = 27$, but $5^2 + 1^2 + 1^2$ is *also* 27, so the degeneracy is greater than combinatorial reasoning alone would suggest.

---

## Problem 4.3

Eq. 4.32 $\Rightarrow Y_0^0 = \dfrac{1}{\sqrt{4\pi}} P_0^0(\cos\theta)$; Eq. 4.27 $\Rightarrow P_0^0(x) = P_0(x)$; Eq. 4.28 $\Rightarrow P_0(x) = 1$. $\boxed{Y_0^0 = \dfrac{1}{\sqrt{4\pi}}.}$

$$Y_2^1 = -\sqrt{\frac{5}{4\pi}\frac{1}{3\cdot 2}}\, e^{i\phi} P_2^1(\cos\theta); \quad P_2^1(x) = \sqrt{1-x^2}\,\frac{d}{dx}P_2(x);$$

$$P_2(x) = \frac{1}{4\cdot 2}\left(\frac{d}{dx}\right)^2 (x^2-1)^2 = \frac{1}{8}\frac{d}{dx}\left[2(x^2-1)2x\right] = \frac{1}{2}\left[x^2 - 1 + x(2x)\right] = \frac{1}{2}\left(3x^2 - 1\right);$$

$$P_2^1(x) = \sqrt{1-x^2}\,\frac{d}{dx}\left[\frac{3}{2}x^2 - \frac{1}{2}\right] = \sqrt{1-x^2}\,3x; \quad P_2^1(\cos\theta) = 3\cos\theta\sin\theta. \quad \boxed{Y_2^1 = -\sqrt{\frac{15}{8\pi}}\, e^{i\phi}\sin\theta\cos\theta.}$$

Normalization: $\iint |Y_0^0|^2 \sin\theta\, d\theta\, d\phi = \frac{1}{4\pi}\left[\int_0^\pi \sin\theta\, d\theta\right]\left[\int_0^{2\pi} d\phi\right] = \frac{1}{4\pi}(2)(2\pi) = 1.$ ✓

$\iint |Y_2^1|^2 \sin\theta\, d\theta\, d\phi = \frac{15}{8\pi}\int_0^\pi \sin^2\theta\cos^2\theta\sin\theta\, d\theta \int_0^{2\pi} d\phi = \frac{15}{4}\int_0^\pi \cos^2\theta(1-\cos^2\theta)\sin\theta\, d\theta$

$= \frac{15}{4}\left[-\frac{\cos^3\theta}{3}+\frac{\cos^5\theta}{5}\right]\Big|_0^\pi = \frac{15}{4}\left[\frac{2}{3}-\frac{2}{5}\right] = \frac{5}{2}-\frac{3}{2} = 1$ ✓

Orthogonality: $\iint Y_0^{0*}Y_2^1 \sin\theta\, d\theta\, d\phi = -\frac{1}{\sqrt{4\pi}}\sqrt{\frac{15}{8\pi}}\Big[\underbrace{\int_0^\pi \sin\theta\cos\theta\sin\theta\, d\theta}_{(\sin^3\theta)/3|_0^\pi=0}\Big]\Big[\underbrace{\int_0^{2\pi} e^{i\phi}d\phi}_{(e^{i\phi})/i|_0^{2\pi}=0}\Big] = 0.$ ✓

---

## Problem 4.4

$\frac{d\Theta}{d\theta} = \frac{A}{\tan(\theta/2)}\frac{1}{2}\sec^2(\theta/2) = \frac{A}{2}\frac{1}{\sin(\theta/2)\cos(\theta/2)} = \frac{A}{\sin\theta}.$  Therefore  $\frac{d}{d\theta}\left(\sin\theta\frac{d\Theta}{d\theta}\right) = \frac{d}{d\theta}(A) = 0.$

With $l = m = 0$, Eq. 4.25 reads: $\frac{d}{d\theta}\left(\sin\theta\frac{d\Theta}{d\theta}\right) = 0.$  So  $A\ln[\tan(\theta/2)]$  *does* satisfy Eq. 4.25.  However,

$\Theta(0) = A\ln(0) = A(-\infty);\ \ \Theta(\pi) = A\ln\left(\tan\frac{\pi}{2}\right) = A\ln(\infty) = A(\infty).$  $\boxed{\Theta \text{ blows up at } \theta = 0 \text{ and at } \theta = \pi.}$

---

## Problem 4.5

$Y_l^l = (-1)^l\sqrt{\frac{(2l+1)}{4\pi}\frac{1}{(2l)!}}\,e^{il\phi}P_l^l(\cos\theta).$    $P_l^l(x) = (1-x^2)^{l/2}\left(\frac{d}{dx}\right)^l P_l(x).$

$P_l(x) = \frac{1}{2^l l!}\left(\frac{d}{dx}\right)^l (x^2-1)^l,$   so $P_l^l(x) = \frac{1}{2^l l!}(1-x^2)^{l/2}\left(\frac{d}{dx}\right)^{2l}(x^2-1)^l.$

Now $(x^2-1)^l = x^{2l} + \cdots$, where all the other terms involve powers of $x$ *less* than $2l$, and hence give zero when differentiated $2l$ times. So

$P_l^l(x) = \frac{1}{2^l l!}(1-x^2)^{l/2}\left(\frac{d}{dx}\right)^{2l}x^{2l}.$  But $\left(\frac{d}{dx}\right)^n x^n = n!,$   so $P_l^l = \frac{(2l)!}{2^l l!}(1-x^2)^{l/2}.$

$\therefore Y_l^l = (-1)^l\sqrt{\frac{(2l+1)}{4\pi(2l)!}}\,e^{il\phi}\frac{(2l)!}{2^l l!}(\sin\theta)^l = \boxed{\frac{1}{l!}\sqrt{\frac{(2l+1)!}{4\pi}}\left(-\frac{1}{2}e^{i\phi}\sin\theta\right)^l.}$

$$Y_3^2 = \sqrt{\frac{7}{4\pi} \cdot \frac{1}{5!}} \, e^{2i\phi} P_3^2(\cos\theta); \quad P_3^2(x) = (1-x^2)\left(\frac{d}{dx}\right)^2 P_3(x); \quad P_3(x) = \frac{1}{8\cdot 3!}\left(\frac{d}{dx}\right)^3 (x^2-1)^3.$$

$$P_3 = \frac{1}{8\cdot 3\cdot 2}\left(\frac{d}{dx}\right)^2 \left[6x(x^2-1)^2\right] = \frac{1}{8}\frac{d}{dx}\left[(x^2-1)^2 + 4x^2(x^2-1)\right]$$

$$= \frac{1}{8}\left[4x(x^2-1) + 8x(x^2-1) + 4x^2\cdot 2x\right] = \frac{1}{2}\left(x^3 - x + 2x^3 - 2x + 2x^3\right) = \frac{1}{2}\left(5x^3 - 3x\right).$$

$$P_3^2(x) = \frac{1}{2}\left(1-x^2\right)\left(\frac{d}{dx}\right)^2 (5x^3 - 3x) = \frac{1}{2}\left(1-x^2\right)\frac{d}{dx}\left(15x^2 - 3\right) = \frac{1}{2}(1-x^2)30x = 15x(1-x^2).$$

$$Y_3^2 = \sqrt{\frac{7}{4\pi}\frac{1}{5!}}\,15e^{2i\phi}\cos\theta\sin^2\theta = \boxed{\frac{1}{4}\sqrt{\frac{105}{2\pi}}\,e^{2i\phi}\sin^2\theta\cos\theta.}$$

Check that $Y_l^l$ satisfies Eq. 4.18: Let $\quad \frac{1}{l!}\sqrt{\frac{(2l+1)!}{4\pi}}\left(-\frac{1}{2}\right)^l \equiv A$, so $\quad Y_l^l = A(e^{i\phi}\sin\theta)^l.$

$$\frac{\partial Y_l^l}{\partial\theta} = Ae^{il\phi}l(\sin\theta)^{l-1}\cos\theta; \quad \sin\theta\frac{\partial Y_l^l}{\partial\theta} = l\cos\theta Y_l^l;$$

$$\sin\theta\frac{\partial}{\partial\theta}\left(\sin\theta\frac{\partial Y_l^l}{\partial\theta}\right) = l\cos\theta\left(\sin\theta\frac{\partial Y_l^l}{\partial\theta}\right) - l\sin^2\theta Y_l^l = \left(l^2\cos^2\theta - l\sin^2\theta\right)Y_l^l. \quad \frac{\partial^2 Y_l^l}{\partial\phi^2} = -l^2 Y_l^l.$$

So the left side of Eq. 4.18 is $\left[l^2(1-\sin^2\theta) - l\sin^2\theta - l^2\right]Y_l^l = -l(l+1)\sin^2\theta\, Y_l^l$, which matches the right side.

Check that $Y_3^2$ satisfies Eq. 4.18: Let $B \equiv \frac{1}{4}\sqrt{\frac{105}{2\pi}}$, so $Y_3^2 = Be^{2i\phi}\sin^2\theta\cos\theta.$

$$\frac{\partial Y_3^2}{\partial\theta} = Be^{2i\phi}\left(2\sin\theta\cos^2\theta - \sin^3\theta\right); \quad \sin\theta\frac{\partial}{\partial\theta}\left(\sin\theta\frac{\partial Y_3^2}{\partial\theta}\right) = Be^{2i\phi}\sin\theta\frac{\partial}{\partial\theta}\left(2\sin^2\theta\cos^2\theta - \sin^4\theta\right)$$

$$= Be^{2i\phi}\sin\theta\left(4\sin\theta\cos^3\theta - 4\sin^3\theta\cos\theta - 4\sin^3\theta\cos\theta\right) = 4Be^{2i\phi}\sin^2\theta\cos\theta\left(\cos^2\theta - 2\sin^2\theta\right)$$

$$= 4(\cos^2\theta - 2\sin^2\theta)Y_3^2. \quad \frac{\partial^2 Y_3^2}{\partial\phi^2} = -4Y_3^2. \quad \text{So the left side of Eq. 4.18 is}$$

$$4(\cos^2\theta - 2\sin^2\theta - 1)Y_3^2 = 4(-3\sin^2\theta)Y_3^2 = -l(l+1)\sin^2\theta\, Y_3^2,$$

where $l = 3$, so it fits the right side of Eq. 4.18.

## Problem 4.6

$$\int_{-1}^1 P_l(x)P_{l'}(x)dx = \frac{1}{2^l l!}\frac{1}{2^{l'} l'!}\int_{-1}^1 \left[\left(\frac{d}{dx}\right)^l (x^2-1)^l\right]\left[\left(\frac{d}{dx}\right)^{l'}(x^2-1)^{l'}\right]dx.$$

If $l \neq l'$, we may as well let $l$ be the larger of the two ($l > l'$). Integrate by parts, pulling successively each derivative off the first term onto the second:

$$2^l l! 2^{l'} l'! \int_{-1}^{1} P_l(x) P_{l'}(x) dx = \left[ \left(\frac{d}{dx}\right)^{l-1} (x^2 - 1)^l \right] \left[ \left(\frac{d}{dx}\right)^{l'} (x^2 - 1)^{l'} \right] \Bigg|_{-1}^{1}$$

$$- \int_{-1}^{1} \left[ \left(\frac{d}{dx}\right)^{l-1} (x^2 - 1)^l \right] \left[ \left(\frac{d}{dx}\right)^{l'+1} (x^2 - 1)^{l'} \right] dx$$

$$= \ldots (\text{boundary terms}) \ldots + (-1)^l \int_{-1}^{1} (x^2 - 1)^l \left(\frac{d}{dx}\right)^{l'+l} (x^2 - 1)^{l'} dx.$$

But $(d/dx)^{l'+l} (x^2 - 1)^{l'} = 0$, because $(x^2 - 1)^{l'}$ is a polynomial whose highest power is $2l'$, so more than $2l'$ derivatives will kill it, and $l' + l > 2l'$. Now, the boundary terms are of the form:

$$\left[ \left(\frac{d}{dx}\right)^{l-n} (x^2 - 1)^l \right] \left[ \left(\frac{d}{dx}\right)^{l'+n-1} (x^2 - 1)^{l'} \right] \Bigg|_{-1}^{+1}, \quad n = 1, 2, 3, \ldots, l.$$

Look at the first term: $(x^2 - 1)^l = (x^2 - 1)(x^2 - 1) \ldots (x^2 - 1)$; $l$ factors. So $0, 1, 2, \ldots, l - 1$ derivatives will still leave at least one overall factor of $(x^2 - 1)$. [Zero derivatives leaves $l$ factors; one derivative leaves $l - 1$ : $d/dx(x^2-1)^l = 2lx(x^2-1)^{l-1}$; two derivatives leaves $l-2$ : $d^2/dx^2(x^2-1)^l = 2l(x^2-1)^{l-1}+2l(l-1)2x^2(x^2-1)^{l-2}$, and so on.] So the boundary terms are all zero, and hence $\int_{-1}^{1} P_l(x) P_{l'}(x) dx = 0$.

This leaves only the case $l = l'$. Again the boundary terms vanish, but this time the remaining integral does *not*:

$$(2^l l!)^2 \int_{-1}^{1} [P_l(x)]^2 dx = (-1)^l \int_{-1}^{1} (x^2 - 1)^l \underbrace{\left(\frac{d}{dx}\right)^{2l} (x^2 - 1)^l}_{(d/dx)^{2l}(x^{2l})=(2l)!} dx$$

$$= (-1)^l (2l)! \int_{-1}^{1} (x^2 - 1)^l dx = 2(2l)! \int_{0}^{1} (1 - x^2)^l dx.$$

Let $x \equiv \cos\theta$, so $dx = -\sin\theta \, d\theta$, $(1 - x^2) = \sin^2\theta$, $\theta : \pi/2 \to 0$. Then

$$\int_{0}^{1} (1 - x^2)^l dx = \int_{\pi/2}^{0} (\sin\theta)^{2l} (-\sin\theta) d\theta = \int_{0}^{\pi/2} (\sin\theta)^{2l+1} d\theta$$

$$= \frac{(2)(4) \cdots (2l)}{(1)(3)(5) \cdots (2l + 1)} = \frac{(2^l l!)^2}{1 \cdot 2 \cdot 3 \cdot \ldots \cdot (2l + 1)} = \frac{(2^l l!)^2}{(2l + 1)!}.$$

$$\therefore \int_{-1}^{1} [P_l(x)]^2 dx = \frac{1}{(2^l l!)^2} 2(2l)! \frac{(2^l l!)^2}{(2l + 1)!} = \frac{2}{2l + 1}. \quad \text{So} \quad \int_{-1}^{1} P_l(x) P_{l'}(x) dx = \frac{2}{2l + 1} \delta_{ll'}. \quad \text{QED}$$

## Problem 4.7

(a)

$$n_1(x) = -(-x) \frac{1}{x} \frac{d}{dx} \left( \frac{\cos x}{x} \right) = -\frac{\cos x}{x^2} - \frac{\sin x}{x}.$$

$$n_2(x) = -(-x)^2 \left(\frac{1}{x}\frac{d}{dx}\right)^2 \frac{\cos x}{x} = -x^2 \left(\frac{1}{x}\frac{d}{dx}\right)\left[\frac{1}{x}\frac{d}{dx}\left(\frac{\cos x}{x}\right)\right]$$

$$= -x\frac{d}{dx}\left(\frac{1}{x}\cdot\frac{-x\sin x - \cos x}{x^2}\right) = x\frac{d}{dx}\left(\frac{\sin x}{x^2} + \frac{\cos x}{x^3}\right)$$

$$= x\left(\frac{x^2\cos x - 2x\sin x}{x^4} + \frac{-x^3\sin x - 3x^2\cos x}{x^6}\right)$$

$$= \frac{\cos x}{x} - 2\frac{\sin x}{x^2} - \frac{\sin x}{x^2} - \frac{3\cos x}{x^3} = \boxed{-\left(\frac{3}{x^3} - \frac{1}{x}\right)\cos x - \frac{3}{x^2}\sin x.}$$

**(b)** Letting $\sin x \approx x$ and $\cos x \approx 1$, and keeping only the lowest power of $x$:

$$n_1(x) \approx -\frac{1}{x^2} + \frac{1}{x}x \approx \boxed{-\frac{1}{x^2}.} \quad \text{As } x \to 0, \text{ this blows up.}$$

$$n_2(x) \approx -\left(\frac{3}{x^3} - \frac{1}{x}\right) - \frac{3}{x^2}x \approx \boxed{-\frac{3}{x^3},} \quad \text{which again blows up at the origin.}$$

---

## Problem 4.8

**(a)**

$$u = Arj_1(kr) = A\left[\frac{\sin(kr)}{k^2r} - \frac{\cos(kr)}{k}\right] = \frac{A}{k}\left[\frac{\sin(kr)}{(kr)} - \cos(kr)\right].$$

$$\frac{du}{dr} = \frac{A}{k}\left[\frac{k^2r\cos(kr) - k\sin(kr)}{(kr)^2} + k\sin(kr)\right] = A\left[\frac{\cos(kr)}{kr} - \frac{\sin(kr)}{(kr)^2} + \sin(kr)\right].$$

$$\frac{d^2u}{dr^2} = A\left[\frac{-k^2r\sin(kr) - k\cos(kr)}{(kr)^2} - \frac{k^3r^2\cos(kr) - 2k^2r\sin(kr)}{(kr)^4} + k\cos(kr)\right]$$

$$= Ak\left[-\frac{\sin(kr)}{(kr)} - \frac{\cos(kr)}{(kr)^2} - \frac{\cos(kr)}{(kr)^2} + 2\frac{\sin(kr)}{(kr)^3} + \cos(kr)\right]$$

$$= Ak\left[\left(1 - \frac{2}{(kr)^2}\right)\cos(kr) + \left(\frac{2}{(kr)^3} - \frac{1}{(kr)}\right)\sin(kr)\right].$$

With $V = 0$ and $l = 1$, Eq. 4.37 reads: $\dfrac{d^2u}{dr^2} - \dfrac{2}{r^2}u = -\dfrac{2mE}{\hbar^2}u = -k^2u$. In this case the left side is

$$Ak\left[\left(1 - \frac{2}{(kr)^2}\right)\cos(kr) + \left(\frac{2}{(kr)^3} - \frac{1}{(kr)}\right)\sin(kr) - \frac{2}{(kr)^2}\left(\frac{\sin(kr)}{(kr)} - \cos(kr)\right)\right]$$

$$= Ak\left[\cos(kr) - \frac{\sin(kr)}{kr}\right] = -k^2u. \quad \text{So this } u \text{ *does* satisfy Eq. 4.37.}$$

**(b)** Equation $4.48 \Rightarrow j_1(z) = 0$, where $z = ka$. Thus $\frac{\sin z}{z^2} - \frac{\cos z}{z} = 0$, or $\boxed{\tan z = z.}$ For high $z$ (large $n$, if $n = 1, 2, 3, \ldots$ counts the allowed energies in increasing order), the intersections occur slightly below $z = (n + \frac{1}{2})\pi$.

$$\therefore E = \frac{\hbar^2 k^2}{2m} = \frac{\hbar^2 z^2}{2ma^2} = \frac{\hbar^2 \pi^2}{2ma^2} \left( n + \frac{1}{2} \right)^2. \quad \text{QED}$$

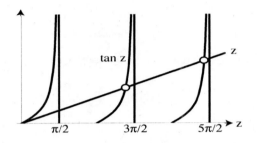

## Problem 4.9

For $r \leq a$, $u(r) = A\sin(kr)$, with $k \equiv \sqrt{2m(E + V_0)}/\hbar$. For $r \geq a$, Eq. 4.37 with $l = 0, V = 0$, and (for a bound state) $E < 0 \Rightarrow$:

$$\frac{d^2 u}{dr^2} = -\frac{2m}{\hbar^2} Eu = \kappa^2 u, \text{ with } \kappa \equiv \sqrt{-2mE}/\hbar \Rightarrow u(r) = Ce^{\kappa r} + De^{-\kappa r}.$$

But the $Ce^{\kappa r}$ term blows up as $r \to \infty$, so $u(r) = De^{-\kappa r}$.

$$\left. \begin{array}{l} \text{Continuity of } u \text{ at } \quad r = a: A\sin(ka) = De^{-\kappa a} \\ \text{Continuity of } u' \text{ at } \quad r = a: Ak\cos(ka) = -D\kappa e^{-\kappa a} \end{array} \right\} \text{ divide: } \frac{1}{k}\tan(ka) = -\frac{1}{\kappa}, \text{ or } -\cot ka = \frac{\kappa}{k}.$$

Let $ka \equiv z$; $\frac{\kappa}{k} = \frac{\sqrt{2mV_0 a^2/\hbar^2 - z^2}}{z}$. Let $z_0 \equiv \frac{\sqrt{2mV_0}}{\hbar}a$. $\boxed{-\cot z = \sqrt{(z_0/z)^2 - 1}.}$ This is exactly the same transcendental equation we encountered in Problem 2.29—see graph there. There is no solution if $z_0 < \pi/2$, which is to say, if $2mV_0 a^2/\hbar^2 < \pi^2/4$, or $V_0 a^2 < \pi^2 \hbar^2/8m$. Otherwise, the ground state energy occurs somewhere between $z = \pi/2$ and $z = \pi$:

$$E + V_0 = \frac{\hbar^2 k^2 a^2}{2ma^2} = \frac{\hbar^2}{2ma^2} z^2, \text{ so } \boxed{\frac{\hbar^2 \pi^2}{8ma^2} < (E_0 + V_0) < \frac{\hbar^2 \pi^2}{2ma^2}} \quad \text{(precise value depends on } V_0\text{).}$$

## Problem 4.10

$R_{30}$ $(n = 3, l = 0)$: Eq. $4.62 \Rightarrow v(\rho) = \sum_{j=0} c_j \rho^j$.

Eq. $4.76 \Rightarrow c_1 = \frac{2(1 - 3)}{(1)(2)} c_0 = -2c_0$; $\quad c_2 = \frac{2(2 - 3)}{(2)(3)} c_1 = -\frac{1}{3}c_1 = \frac{2}{3}c_0$; $\quad c_3 = \frac{2(3 - 3)}{(3)(4)} c_2 = 0$.

Eq. $4.73 \Rightarrow \rho = \frac{r}{3a}$; $\quad$ Eq. $4.75 \Rightarrow R_{30} = \frac{1}{r}\rho e^{-\rho} v(\rho) = \frac{1}{r}\frac{r}{3a} e^{-r/3a} \left[ c_0 - 2c_0 \frac{r}{3a} + \frac{2}{3}c_0 \left( \frac{r}{3a} \right)^2 \right]$

$$R_{30} = \boxed{\left(\frac{c_0}{3a}\right)\left[1 - \frac{2}{3}\left(\frac{r}{a}\right) + \frac{2}{27}\left(\frac{r}{a}\right)^2\right]e^{-r/3a}.}$$

$R_{31}$ $(n=3, l=1)$: $c_1 = \dfrac{2(2-3)}{(1)(4)}c_0 = -\dfrac{1}{2}c_0$; $\quad c_2 = \dfrac{2(3-3)}{(2)(5)}c_1 = 0.$

$$R_{31} = \frac{1}{r}\left(\frac{r}{3a}\right)^2 e^{-r/3a}\left(c_0 - \frac{1}{2}c_0\frac{r}{3a}\right) = \boxed{\left(\frac{c_0}{9a^2}\right)r\left[1 - \frac{1}{6}\left(\frac{r}{a}\right)\right]e^{-r/3a}.}$$

$R_{32}$ $(n=3, l=2)$: $c_1 = \dfrac{2(3-3)}{(1)(6)}c_0 = 0.$ $\quad R_{32} = \dfrac{1}{r}\left(\dfrac{r}{3a}\right)^3 e^{-r/3a}(c_0) = \boxed{\left(\dfrac{c_0}{27a^3}\right)r^2 e^{-r/3a}.}$

## Problem 4.11

**(a)**

Eq. 4.31 $\Rightarrow \displaystyle\int_0^\infty |R|^2 r^2\, dr = 1.$ Eq. 4.82 $\Rightarrow R_{20} = \left(\dfrac{c_0}{2a}\right)\left(1 - \dfrac{r}{2a}\right)e^{-r/2a}.$ Let $z \equiv \dfrac{r}{a}.$

$$1 = \left(\frac{c_0}{2a}\right)^2 a^3 \int_0^\infty \left(1 - \frac{z}{2}\right)^2 e^{-z} z^2\, dz = \frac{c_0^2 a}{4}\int_0^\infty \left(z^2 - z^3 + \frac{1}{4}z^4\right)e^{-z}\,dz = \frac{c_0^2 a}{4}\left(2 - 6 + \frac{24}{4}\right) = \frac{a}{2}c_0^2.$$

$$\therefore \boxed{c_0 = \sqrt{\frac{2}{a}}.}\quad \text{Eq. 4.15} \Rightarrow \psi_{200} = R_{20}Y_0^0. \quad \text{Table 4.3} \Rightarrow Y_0^0 = \frac{1}{\sqrt{4\pi}}.$$

$$\therefore \psi_{200} = \frac{1}{\sqrt{4\pi}}\sqrt{\frac{2}{a}}\frac{1}{2a}\left(1 - \frac{r}{2a}\right)e^{-r/2a} \Rightarrow \boxed{\psi_{200} = \frac{1}{\sqrt{2\pi a}}\frac{1}{2a}\left(1 - \frac{r}{2a}\right)e^{-r/2a}.}$$

**(b)**

$$R_{21} = \frac{c_0}{4a^2}re^{-r/2a}; \quad 1 = \left(\frac{c_0}{4a^2}\right)^2 a^5 \int_0^\infty z^4 e^{-z}\,dz = \frac{c_0^2 a}{16}24 = \frac{3}{2}ac_0^2, \text{ so } \boxed{c_0 = \sqrt{\frac{2}{3a}}.}$$

$$R_{21} = \frac{1}{\sqrt{6a}}\frac{1}{2a^2}re^{-r/2a}; \quad \psi_{21\pm1} = \frac{1}{\sqrt{6a}}\frac{1}{2a^2}re^{-r/2a}\left(\mp\sqrt{\frac{3}{8\pi}}\sin\theta e^{\pm i\phi}\right) = \boxed{\mp\frac{1}{\sqrt{\pi a}}\frac{1}{8a^2}re^{-r/2a}\sin\theta e^{\pm i\phi};}$$

$$\psi_{210} = \frac{1}{\sqrt{6a}}\frac{1}{2a^2}re^{-r/2a}\left(\sqrt{\frac{3}{4\pi}}\cos\theta\right) = \boxed{\frac{1}{\sqrt{2\pi a}}\frac{1}{4a^2}re^{-r/2a}\cos\theta.}$$

## Problem 4.12

**(a)**

$$L_0 = e^x e^{-x} = \boxed{1.} \quad L_1 = e^x \frac{d}{dx}\left(e^{-x}x\right) = e^x\left[e^{-x} - e^{-x}x\right] = \boxed{1 - x.}$$

$$L_2 = e^x \left(\frac{d}{dx}\right)^2 \left(e^{-x}x^2\right) = e^x \frac{d}{dx}\left(2xe^{-x} - e^{-x}x^2\right)$$
$$= e^x\left(2e^{-x} - 2xe^{-x} + e^{-x}x^2 - 2xe^{-x}\right) = \boxed{2 - 4x + x^2.}$$

$$L_3 = e^x \left(\frac{d}{dx}\right)^3 \left(e^{-x}x^3\right) = e^x \left(\frac{d}{dx}\right)^2 \left(-e^{-x}x^3 + 3x^2e^{-x}\right)$$
$$= e^x \frac{d}{dx}\left(e^{-x}x^3 - 3x^2e^{-x} - 3x^2e^{-x} + 6xe^{-x}\right)$$
$$= e^x\left(-e^{-x}x^3 + 3x^2e^{-x} + 6x^2e^{-x} - 12xe^{-x} - 6xe^{-x} + 6e^{-x}\right)$$
$$= \boxed{6 - 18x + 9x^2 - x^3.}$$

**(b)**

$$v(\rho) = L_2^5(2\rho); \quad L_2^5(x) = L_{7-5}^5(x) = (-1)^5 \left(\frac{d}{dx}\right)^5 L_7(x).$$

$$L_7(x) = e^x \left(\frac{d}{dx}\right)^7 \left(x^7 e^{-x}\right) = e^x \left(\frac{d}{dx}\right)^6 \left(7x^6 e^{-x} - x^7 e^{-x}\right)$$
$$= e^x \left(\frac{d}{dx}\right)^5 \left(42x^5 e^{-x} - 7x^6 e^{-x} - 7x^6 e^{-x} + x^7 e^{-x}\right)$$
$$= e^x \left(\frac{d}{dx}\right)^4 \left(210x^4 e^{-x} - 42x^5 e^{-x} - 84x^5 e^{-x} + 14x^6 e^{-x} + 7x^6 e^{-x} - x^7 e^{-x}\right)$$
$$= e^x \left(\frac{d}{dx}\right)^3 \left[840x^3 e^{-x} - (210 + 630)x^4 e^{-x}\right.$$
$$\left. + (126 + 126)x^5 e^{-x} - (21 + 7)x^6 e^{-x} + x^7 e^{-x}\right]$$
$$= e^x \left(\frac{d}{dx}\right)^2 \left(2520x^2 e^{-x} - (840 + 3360)x^3 e^{-x}\right.$$
$$\left. + (840 + 1260)x^4 e^{-x} - (252 + 168)x^5 e^{-x} + (28 + 7)x^6 e^{-x} - x^7 e^{-x}\right)$$
$$= e^x \left(\frac{d}{dx}\right) \left[5040xe^{-x} - (2520 + 12600)x^2 e^{-x} + (4200 + 8400)x^3 e^{-x}\right.$$
$$\left. - (2100 + 2100)x^4 e^{-x} + (420 + 210)x^5 e^{-x} - (35 + 7)x^6 e^{-x} + x^7 e^{-x}\right]$$
$$= e^x \left[5040e^{-x} - (5040 + 30240)xe^{-x} + (15120 + 37800)x^2 e^{-x}\right.$$
$$- (12600 + 8400 + 8400)x^3 e^{-x} + (2100 + 2100 + 3150)x^4 e^{-x}$$
$$\left. - (630 + 252)x^5 e^{-x} + (42 + 7)x^6 e^{-x} - x^7 e^{-x}\right]$$
$$= 5040 - 35280x + 52920x^2 - 29400x^3 + 7350x^4 - 882x^5 + 49x^6 - x^7.$$

$$L_2^5 = -\left(\frac{d}{dx}\right)^5 \left(-882x^5 + 49x^6 - x^7\right)$$

$$= -\left[-882(5 \cdot 4 \cdot 3 \cdot 2) + 49(6 \cdot 5 \cdot 4 \cdot 3 \cdot 2)x - 7 \cdot 6 \cdot 5 \cdot 4 \cdot 3x^2\right]$$

$$= 60\left[(882 \times 2) - (49 \times 12)x + 42x^2\right] = 2520(42 - 14x + x^2).$$

$$v(\rho) = 2520(42 - 28\rho + 4\rho^2) = \boxed{5040\left(21 - 14\rho + 2\rho^2\right).}$$

**(c)**

$$\text{Eq. 4.62} \Rightarrow v(\rho) = \sum_{j=0}^{\infty} c_j \rho^j. \quad \text{Eq. 4.76} \Rightarrow c_1 = \frac{2(3-5)}{(1)(6)}c_0 = -\frac{2}{3}c_0.$$

$$c_2 = \frac{2(4-5)}{(2)(7)}c_1 = -\frac{1}{7}c_1 = \frac{2}{21}c_0; \quad c_3 = \frac{2(5-5)}{(3)(8)}c_2 = 0.$$

$$v(\rho) = c_0 - \frac{2}{3}c_0\rho + \frac{2}{21}c_0\rho^2 = \boxed{\frac{c_0}{21}\left(21 - 14\rho + 2\rho^2\right).} \quad \checkmark$$

## Problem 4.13

**(a)**

$$\psi = \frac{1}{\sqrt{\pi a^3}}e^{-r/a}, \quad \text{so } \langle r^n \rangle = \frac{1}{\pi a^3}\int r^n e^{-2r/a}\left(r^2 \sin\theta\, dr\, d\theta\, d\phi\right) = \frac{4\pi}{\pi a^3}\int_0^\infty r^{n+2}e^{-2r/a}dr.$$

$$\langle r \rangle = \frac{4}{a^3}\int_0^\infty r^3 e^{-2r/a}dr = \frac{4}{a^3}3!\left(\frac{a}{2}\right)^4 = \boxed{\frac{3}{2}a;} \quad \langle r^2 \rangle = \frac{4}{a^3}\int_0^\infty r^4 e^{-2r/a}dr = \frac{4}{a^3}4!\left(\frac{a}{2}\right)^5 = \boxed{3a^2.}$$

**(b)**

$$\boxed{\langle x \rangle = 0;} \quad \langle x^2 \rangle = \frac{1}{3}\langle r^2 \rangle = \boxed{a^2.}$$

**(c)**

$$\psi_{211} = R_{21}Y_1^1 = -\frac{1}{\sqrt{\pi a}}\frac{1}{8a^2}re^{-r/2a}\sin\theta e^{i\phi} \quad (\text{Problem 4.11(b)}).$$

$$\langle x^2 \rangle = \frac{1}{\pi a}\frac{1}{(8a^2)^2}\int \left(r^2 e^{-r/a}\sin^2\theta\right)\left(r^2 \sin^2\theta\cos^2\phi\right)r^2 \sin\theta\, dr\, d\theta\, d\phi$$

$$= \frac{1}{64\pi a^5}\int_0^\infty r^6 e^{-r/a}\, dr \int_0^\pi \sin^5\theta\, d\theta \int_0^{2\pi} \cos^2\phi\, d\phi$$

$$= \frac{1}{64\pi a^5}\left(6!a^7\right)\left(2\frac{2 \cdot 4}{1 \cdot 3 \cdot 5}\right)\left(\frac{1}{2} \cdot 2\pi\right) = \boxed{12a^2.}$$

## Problem 4.14

$$\psi = \frac{1}{\sqrt{\pi a^3}} e^{-r/a}; \quad P = |\psi|^2 4\pi r^2 \, dr = \frac{4}{a^3} e^{-2r/a} r^2 \, dr = p(r) \, dr; \quad p(r) = \frac{4}{a^3} r^2 e^{-2r/a}.$$

$$\frac{dp}{dr} = \frac{4}{a^3} \left[ 2r e^{-2r/a} + r^2 \left( -\frac{2}{a} e^{-2r/a} \right) \right] = \frac{8r}{a^3} e^{-2r/a} \left( 1 - \frac{r}{a} \right) = 0 \Rightarrow \boxed{r = a.}$$

## Problem 4.15

(a) $\Psi(\mathbf{r}, t) = \frac{1}{\sqrt{2}} \left( \psi_{211} e^{-iE_2 t/\hbar} + \psi_{21-1} e^{-iE_2 t/\hbar} \right) = \frac{1}{\sqrt{2}} \left( \psi_{211} + \psi_{21-1} \right) e^{-iE_2 t/\hbar}; \quad E_2 = \frac{E_1}{4} = -\frac{\hbar^2}{8ma^2}.$

From Problem 4.11(b):

$$\psi_{211} + \psi_{21-1} = -\frac{1}{\sqrt{\pi a}} \frac{1}{8a^2} r e^{-r/2a} \sin\theta \left( e^{i\phi} - e^{-i\phi} \right) = -\frac{i}{\sqrt{\pi a} 4a^2} r e^{-r/2a} \sin\theta \sin\phi.$$

$$\boxed{\Psi(\mathbf{r}, t) = -\frac{i}{\sqrt{2\pi a} 4a^2} r e^{-r/2a} \sin\theta \sin\phi \, e^{-iE_2 t/\hbar}.}$$

(b)

$$\langle V \rangle = \int |\Psi|^2 \left( -\frac{e^2}{4\pi\epsilon_0} \frac{1}{r} \right) d^3\mathbf{r} = \frac{1}{(2\pi a)(16a^4)} \left( -\frac{e^2}{4\pi\epsilon_0} \right) \int \left( r^2 e^{-r/a} \sin^2\theta \sin^2\phi \right) \frac{1}{r} r^2 \sin\theta \, dr \, d\theta \, d\phi$$

$$= \frac{1}{32\pi a^5} \left( -\frac{\hbar^2}{ma^2} \right) \int_0^\infty r^3 e^{-r/a} \, dr \int_0^\pi \sin^3\theta \, d\theta \int_0^{2\pi} \sin^2\phi \, d\phi = -\frac{\hbar^2}{32\pi ma^6} (3! a^4) \left( \frac{4}{3} \right) (\pi)$$

$$= \boxed{-\frac{\hbar^2}{4ma^2} = \frac{1}{2} E_1 = \frac{1}{2}(-13.6 \text{eV}) = -6.8 \text{eV}} \quad \text{(independent of } t\text{)}.$$

## Problem 4.16

$$\boxed{E_n(Z) = Z^2 E_n; \quad E_1(Z) = Z^2 E_1; \quad a(Z) = a/Z; \quad R(Z) = Z^2 R.}$$

Lyman lines range from $n_i = 2$ to $n_i = \infty$ (with $n_f = 1$); the wavelengths range from

$$\frac{1}{\lambda_2} = R \left( 1 - \frac{1}{4} \right) = \frac{3}{4} R \Rightarrow \lambda_2 = \frac{4}{3R} \quad \text{down to} \quad \frac{1}{\lambda_1} = R \left( 1 - \frac{1}{\infty} \right) = R \Rightarrow \lambda_1 = \frac{1}{R}.$$

For $Z = 2$: $\quad \lambda_1 = \frac{1}{4R} = \frac{1}{4(1.097 \times 10^7)} = \boxed{2.28 \times 10^{-8} \text{m}}$ to $\lambda_2 = \frac{1}{3R} = \boxed{3.04 \times 10^{-8} \text{ m,}}$ $\boxed{\text{ultraviolet.}}$

For $Z = 3$: $\quad \lambda_1 = \frac{1}{9R} = \boxed{1.01 \times 10^{-8} \text{ m}}$ to $\lambda_2 = \frac{4}{27R} = \boxed{1.35 \times 10^{-8} \text{ m,}}$ also $\boxed{\text{ultraviolet.}}$

## Problem 4.17

(a) $\boxed{V(r) = -G \dfrac{Mm}{r}.}$ So $\dfrac{e^2}{4\pi\epsilon_0} \to GMm$ translates hydrogen results to the gravitational analogs.

**(b)** Equation 4.72: $a = \left(\dfrac{4\pi\epsilon_0}{e^2}\right)\dfrac{\hbar^2}{m}$, so $\boxed{a_g = \dfrac{\hbar^2}{GMm^2}}$

$$= \frac{(1.0546 \times 10^{-34}\text{ Js})^2}{(6.6726 \times 10^{-11}\text{ m}^3/\text{kg}\cdot\text{s}^2)(1.9892 \times 10^{30}\text{ kg})(5.98 \times 10^{24}\text{kg})^2} = \boxed{2.34 \times 10^{-138}\text{ m.}}$$

**(c)** Equation 4.70 $\Rightarrow$ $\boxed{E_n = -\left[\dfrac{m}{2\hbar^2}(GMm)^2\right]\dfrac{1}{n^2}.}$

$E_c = \dfrac{1}{2}mv^2 - G\dfrac{Mm}{r_o}$. But $G\dfrac{Mm}{r_o^2} = \dfrac{mv^2}{r_o} \Rightarrow \dfrac{1}{2}mv^2 = \dfrac{GMm}{2r_o}$, so

$E_c = -\dfrac{GMm}{2r_o} = -\left[\dfrac{m}{2\hbar^2}(GMm)^2\right]\dfrac{1}{n^2} \Rightarrow n^2 = \dfrac{GMm^2}{\hbar^2}r_o = \dfrac{r_o}{a_g} \Rightarrow \boxed{n = \sqrt{\dfrac{r_o}{a_g}}.}$

$r_o = \text{earth-sun distance} = 1.496 \times 10^{11}\text{ m} \Rightarrow n = \sqrt{\dfrac{1.496 \times 10^{11}}{2.34 \times 10^{-138}}} = \boxed{2.53 \times 10^{74}.}$

**(d)**

$$\Delta E = -\left[\frac{G^2 M^2 m^3}{2\hbar^2}\right]\left[\frac{1}{(n+1)^2} - \frac{1}{n^2}\right]. \qquad \frac{1}{(n+1)^2} = \frac{1}{n^2(1+1/n)^2} \approx \frac{1}{n^2}\left(1 - \frac{2}{n}\right).$$

So $\left[\dfrac{1}{(n+1)^2} - \dfrac{1}{n^2}\right] \approx \dfrac{1}{n^2}\left(1 - \dfrac{2}{n} - 1\right) = -\dfrac{2}{n^3}$; $\quad \Delta E = \dfrac{G^2 M^2 m^3}{\hbar^2 n^3}.$

$$\Delta E = \frac{(6.67 \times 10^{-11})^2(1.99 \times 10^{30})^2(5.98 \times 10^{24})^3}{(1.055 \times 10^{-34})^2(2.53\times^{74})^3} = \boxed{2.09 \times 10^{-41}\text{J.}} \quad E_p = \Delta E = h\nu = \frac{hc}{\lambda}.$$

$$\lambda = (3 \times 10^8)(6.63 \times 10^{-34})/(2.09 \times 10^{-41}) = \boxed{9.52 \times 10^{15}\text{ m.}}$$

But $1\text{ ly} = 9.46 \times 10^{15}$ m. Is it a coincidence that $\lambda \approx 1$ ly? No: From part (c), $n^2 = GMm^2 r_o/\hbar^2$, so

$$\lambda = \frac{ch}{\Delta E} = c2\pi\hbar\frac{\hbar^2 n^3}{G^2 M^2 m^3} = c\frac{2\pi\hbar^3}{G^2 M^2 m^3}\left(\frac{GMm^2 r_o}{\hbar^2}\right)^{3/2} = c\left(2\pi\sqrt{\frac{r_o^3}{GM}}\right).$$

But (from (c)) $v = \sqrt{GM/r_o} = 2\pi r_o/T$, where $T$ is the period of the orbit (in this case one year), so $T = 2\pi\sqrt{r_o^3/GM}$, and hence $\boxed{\lambda = cT}$ (one light year). [Incidentally, the same goes for hydrogen: The wavelength of the photon emitted in a transition from a highly excited state to the next lower one is equal to the distance light would travel in one orbital period.]

---

## Problem 4.18

$\langle f|L_\pm g\rangle = \langle f|L_x g\rangle \pm i\langle f|L_y g\rangle = \langle L_x f|g\rangle \pm i\langle L_y f|g\rangle = \langle(L_x \mp iL_y)f|g\rangle = \langle L_\mp f|g\rangle$, so $(L_\pm)^\dagger = L_\mp$.

Now, using Eq. 4.112, in the form $L_\mp L_\pm = L^2 - L_z^2 \mp \hbar L_z$:

$$\langle f_l^m|L_\mp L_\pm f_l^m\rangle = \langle f_l^m|(L^2 - L_z^2 \mp \hbar L_z)f_l^m\rangle = \langle f_l^m|\left[\hbar^2 l(l+1) - \hbar^2 m^2 \mp \hbar^2 m\right]f_l^m\rangle$$
$$= \hbar^2\left[l(l+1) - m(m\pm1)\right]\langle f_l^m|f_l^m\rangle = \hbar^2\left[l(l+1) - m(m\pm1)\right]$$
$$= \langle L_\pm f_l^m|L_\pm f_l^m\rangle = \langle A_l^m f_l^{m\pm1}|A_l^m f_l^{m\pm1}\rangle = |A_l^m|^2\langle f_l^{m\pm1}|f_l^{m\pm1}\rangle = |A_l^m|^2.$$

*Conclusion:*     $\boxed{A_l^m = \hbar\sqrt{l(l+1) - m(m \pm 1)}.}$

## Problem 4.19

### (a)

$$[L_z, x] = [xp_y - yp_x, x] = [xp_y, x] - [yp_x, x] = 0 - y[p_x, x] = i\hbar y. \checkmark$$

$$[L_z, y] = [xp_y - yp_x, y] = [xp_y, y] - [yp_x, y] = x[p_y, y] - 0 = -i\hbar x. \checkmark$$

$$[L_z, z] = [xp_y - yp_x, z] = [xp_y, z] - [yp_x, z] = 0 - 0 = 0. \checkmark$$

$$[L_z, p_x] = [xp_y - yp_x, p_x] = [xp_y, p_x] - [yp_x, p_x] = p_y[x, p_x] - 0 = i\hbar p_y. \checkmark$$

$$[L_z, p_y] = [xp_y - yp_x, p_y] = [xp_y, p_y] - [yp_x, p_y] = 0 - p_x[y, p_y] = -i\hbar p_x. \checkmark$$

$$[L_z, p_z] = [xp_y - yp_x, p_z] = [xp_y, p_z] - [yp_x, p_z] = 0 - 0 = 0. \checkmark$$

### (b)

$$[L_z, L_x] = [L_z, yp_z - zp_y] = [L_z, yp_z] - [L_z, zp_y] = [L_z, y]p_z - [L_z, p_y]z$$
$$= -i\hbar xp_z + i\hbar p_x z = i\hbar(zp_x - xp_z) = i\hbar L_y.$$

(So, by cyclic permutation of the indices, $[L_x, L_y] = i\hbar L_z$.)

### (c)

$$[L_z, r^2] = [L_z, x^2] + [L_z, y^2] + [L_z, z^2] = [L_z, x]x + x[L_z, x] + [L_z, y]y + y[L_z, y] + 0$$
$$= i\hbar yx + xi\hbar y + (-i\hbar x)y + y(-i\hbar x) = \boxed{0.}$$

$$[L_z, p^2] = [L_z, p_x^2] + [L_z, p_y^2] + [L_z, p_z^2] = [L_z, p_x]p_x + p_x[L_z, p_x] + [L_z, p_y]p_y + p_y[L_z, p_y] + 0$$
$$= i\hbar p_y p_x + p_x i\hbar p_y + (-i\hbar p_x)p_y + p_y(-i\hbar p_x) = \boxed{0.}$$

**(d)** It follows from (c) that all three components of **L** commute with $r^2$ and $p^2$, and hence with the whole Hamiltonian, since $H = p^2/2m + V(\sqrt{r^2})$.    QED

## Problem 4.20

(a)

$$\text{Equation 3.71} \Rightarrow \frac{d\langle L_x \rangle}{dt} = \frac{i}{\hbar} \langle [H, L_x] \rangle. \quad [H, L_x] = \frac{1}{2m}[p^2, L_x] + [V, L_x].$$

The first term is zero (Problem 4.19(c)); the second would be too if $V$ were a function only of $r = |\mathbf{r}|$, but in general

$$[H, L_x] = [V, yp_z - zp_y] = y[V, p_z] - z[V, p_y]. \quad \text{Now (Problem 3.13(c)):}$$

$$[V, p_z] = i\hbar \frac{\partial V}{\partial z} \text{ and } [V, p_y] = i\hbar \frac{\partial V}{\partial y}. \quad \text{So } [H, L_x] = yi\hbar\frac{\partial V}{\partial z} - zi\hbar\frac{\partial V}{\partial y} = i\hbar[\mathbf{r} \times (\nabla V)]_x.$$

Thus $\dfrac{d\langle L_x \rangle}{dt} = -\langle [\mathbf{r} \times (\nabla V)]_x \rangle$, and the same goes for the other two components:

$$\frac{d\langle \mathbf{L} \rangle}{dt} = \langle [\mathbf{r} \times (-\nabla V)] \rangle = \langle \mathbf{N} \rangle. \quad \text{QED}$$

(b)

If $V(\mathbf{r}) = V(r)$, then $\nabla V = \dfrac{\partial V}{\partial r}\hat{r}$, and $\mathbf{r} \times \hat{r} = 0$, so $\dfrac{d\langle \mathbf{L} \rangle}{dt} = 0$. QED

---

## Problem 4.21

(a)

$$L_+ L_- f = -\hbar^2 e^{i\phi}\left(\frac{\partial}{\partial\theta} + i\cot\theta\frac{\partial}{\partial\phi}\right)\left[e^{-i\phi}\left(\frac{\partial f}{\partial\theta} - i\cot\theta\frac{\partial f}{\partial\phi}\right)\right]$$

$$= -\hbar^2 e^{i\phi}\left\{e^{-i\phi}\left[\frac{\partial^2 f}{\partial\theta^2} - i\left(-\csc^2\theta\frac{\partial f}{\partial\phi} + \cot\theta\frac{\partial^2 f}{\partial\theta\,\partial\phi}\right)\right]\right.$$

$$\left. + i\cot\theta\left[-ie^{-i\phi}\left(\frac{\partial f}{\partial\theta} - i\cot\theta\frac{\partial f}{\partial\phi}\right) + e^{-i\phi}\left(\frac{\partial^2 f}{\partial\phi\,\partial\theta} - i\cot\theta\frac{\partial^2 f}{\partial\phi^2}\right)\right]\right\}$$

$$= -\hbar^2\left(\frac{\partial^2 f}{\partial\theta^2} + i\csc^2\theta\frac{\partial f}{\partial\phi} - i\cot\theta\frac{\partial^2 f}{\partial\theta\,\partial\phi} + \cot\theta\frac{\partial f}{\partial\theta} - i\cot^2\theta\frac{\partial f}{\partial\phi} + i\cot\theta\frac{\partial^2 f}{\partial\phi\,\partial\theta} + \cot^2\theta\frac{\partial^2 f}{\partial\phi^2}\right)$$

$$= -\hbar^2\left[\frac{\partial^2}{\partial\theta^2} + \cot\theta\frac{\partial}{\partial\theta} + \cot^2\theta\frac{\partial^2}{\partial\phi^2} + i(\csc^2\theta - \cot^2\theta)\frac{\partial}{\partial\phi}\right]f, \quad \text{so}$$

$$L_+ L_- = -\hbar^2\left(\frac{\partial^2}{\partial\theta^2} + \cot\theta\frac{\partial}{\partial\theta} + \cot^2\theta\frac{\partial^2}{\partial\phi^2} + i\frac{\partial}{\partial\phi}\right). \quad \text{QED}$$

(b) Equation 4.129 $\Rightarrow L_z = \dfrac{\hbar}{i}\dfrac{\partial}{\partial\phi}$, Eq. 4.112 $\Rightarrow L^2 = L_+ L_- + L_z^2 - \hbar L_z$, so, using (a):

$$L^2 = -\hbar^2\left(\frac{\partial^2}{\partial\theta^2} + \cot\theta\frac{\partial}{\partial\theta} + \cot^2\theta\frac{\partial^2}{\partial\phi^2} + i\frac{\partial}{\partial\phi}\right) - \hbar^2\frac{\partial^2}{\partial\phi^2} - \hbar\left(\frac{\hbar}{i}\right)\frac{\partial}{\partial\phi}$$

$$= -\hbar^2\left(\frac{\partial^2}{\partial\theta^2} + \cot\theta\frac{\partial}{\partial\theta} + (\cot^2\theta + 1)\frac{\partial^2}{\partial\phi^2} + i\frac{\partial}{\partial\phi} - i\frac{\partial}{\partial\phi}\right) = -\hbar^2\left(\frac{\partial^2}{\partial\theta^2} + \cot\theta\frac{\partial}{\partial\theta} + \frac{1}{\sin^2\theta}\frac{\partial^2}{\partial\phi^2}\right)$$

$$= -\hbar^2\left[\frac{1}{\sin\theta}\frac{\partial}{\partial\theta}\left(\sin\theta\frac{\partial}{\partial\theta}\right) + \frac{1}{\sin^2\theta}\frac{\partial^2}{\partial\phi^2}\right]. \quad \text{QED}$$

## Problem 4.22

**(a)** $\boxed{L_+Y_l^l = 0}$ (top of the ladder).

**(b)**

$$L_z Y_l^l = \hbar l Y_l^l \Rightarrow \frac{\hbar}{i}\frac{\partial}{\partial\phi}Y_l^l = \hbar l Y_l^l, \quad \text{so } \frac{\partial Y_l^l}{\partial\phi} = il Y_l^l, \text{ and hence } Y_l^l = f(\theta)e^{il\phi}.$$

[*Note:* $f(\theta)$ is the "constant" here—it's constant with respect to $\phi$ ... but still can depend on $\theta$.]

$$L_+Y_l^l = 0 \Rightarrow \hbar e^{i\phi}\left(\frac{\partial}{\partial\theta} + i\cot\theta\frac{\partial}{\partial\phi}\right)\left[f(\theta)e^{il\phi}\right] = 0, \quad \text{or } \frac{df}{d\theta}e^{il\phi} + if\cot\theta\, il\, e^{il\phi} = 0, \text{ so}$$

$$\frac{df}{d\theta} = l\cot\theta f \Rightarrow \frac{df}{f} = l\cot\theta d\theta \Rightarrow \int\frac{df}{f} = l\int\frac{\cos\theta}{\sin\theta}\,d\theta \Rightarrow \ln f = l\ln(\sin\theta) + constant.$$

$$\ln f = \ln(\sin^l\theta) + K \Rightarrow \ln\left(\frac{f}{\sin^l\theta}\right) = K \Rightarrow \frac{f}{\sin^l\theta} = constant \Rightarrow f(\theta) = A\sin^l\theta.$$

$$\boxed{Y_l^l(\theta,\phi) = A(e^{i\phi}\sin\theta)^l.}$$

**(c)**

$$1 = A^2\int\sin^{2l}\theta\sin\theta\,d\theta\,d\phi = 2\pi A^2\int_0^\pi \sin^{(2l+1)}\theta\,d\theta = 2\pi A^2\, 2\frac{(2\cdot4\cdot6\cdot\cdots\cdot(2l))}{1\cdot3\cdot5\cdot\cdots\cdot(2l+1)}$$

$$= 4\pi A^2\frac{(2\cdot4\cdot6\cdot\cdots\cdot 2l)^2}{1\cdot2\cdot3\cdot4\cdot5\cdot\cdots\cdot(2l+1)} = 4\pi A^2\frac{(2^l l!)^2}{(2l+1)!}, \quad \text{so } \boxed{A = \frac{1}{2^{l+1}l!}\sqrt{\frac{(2l+1)!}{\pi}},}$$

the same as Problem 4.5, except for an overall factor of $(-1)^l$, which is arbitrary anyway.

## Problem 4.23

$$L_+Y_2^1 = \hbar e^{i\phi}\left(\frac{\partial}{\partial\theta} + i\cot\theta\frac{\partial}{\partial\theta}\right)\left[-\sqrt{\frac{15}{8\pi}}\sin\theta\cos\theta e^{i\phi}\right]$$

$$= -\sqrt{\frac{15}{8\pi}}\hbar e^{i\phi}\left[e^{i\phi}(\cos^2\theta - \sin^2\theta) + i\frac{\cos\theta}{\sin\theta}\sin\theta\cos\theta\, ie^{i\phi}\right]$$

$$= -\sqrt{\frac{15}{8\pi}}\hbar e^{2i\phi}\left(\cos^2\theta - \sin^2\theta - \cos^2\theta\right) = \sqrt{\frac{15}{8\pi}}\hbar\left(e^{i\phi}\sin\theta\right)^2$$

$$= \hbar\sqrt{2\cdot3 - 1\cdot2}\,Y_2^2 = 2\hbar Y_2^2. \quad \therefore \boxed{Y_2^2 = \frac{1}{4}\sqrt{\frac{15}{2\pi}}\left(e^{i\phi}\sin\theta\right)^2.}$$

## Problem 4.24

(a)

$$H = 2\left(\frac{1}{2}mv^2\right) = mv^2; \quad |\mathbf{L}| = 2\frac{a}{2}mv = amv, \quad \text{so } L^2 = a^2m^2v^2, \quad \text{and hence} \quad H = \frac{L^2}{ma^2}.$$

But we know the eigenvalues of $L^2$ : $\hbar^2 l(l+1)$; or, since we usually label energies with $n$:

$$\boxed{E_n = \frac{\hbar^2 n(n+1)}{ma^2} \quad (n = 0, 1, 2, \ldots).}$$

(b) $\boxed{\psi_{nm}(\theta, \phi) = Y_n^m(\theta, \phi),}$ the ordinary spherical harmonics. The degeneracy of the $n$th energy level is the number of $m$-values for given $n$: $\boxed{2n+1.}$

## Problem 4.25

$$r_c = \frac{(1.6 \times 10^{-19})^2}{4\pi(8.85 \times 10^{-12})(9.11 \times 10^{-31})(3.0 \times 10^8)^2} = 2.81 \times 10^{-15} \text{ m.}$$

$$L = \frac{1}{2}\hbar = I\omega = \left(\frac{2}{5}mr^2\right)\left(\frac{v}{r}\right) = \frac{2}{5}mrv \quad \text{so}$$

$$v = \frac{5\hbar}{4mr} = \frac{(5)(1.055 \times 10^{-34})}{(4)(9.11 \times 10^{-31})(2.81 \times 10^{-15})} = \boxed{5.15 \times 10^{10} \text{ m/s.}}$$

Since the speed of light is $3 \times 10^8$ m/s, a point on the equator would be going more than 100 times the speed of light. $\boxed{\text{Nope :}}$ This doesn't look like a very realistic model for spin.

## Problem 4.26

(a)

$$[S_x, S_y] = S_x S_y - S_y S_x = \frac{\hbar^2}{4}\left[\begin{pmatrix} 0 & 1 \\ 1 & 0 \end{pmatrix}\begin{pmatrix} 0 & -i \\ i & 0 \end{pmatrix} - \begin{pmatrix} 0 & -i \\ i & 0 \end{pmatrix}\begin{pmatrix} 0 & 1 \\ 1 & 0 \end{pmatrix}\right]$$

$$= \frac{\hbar^2}{4}\left[\begin{pmatrix} i & 0 \\ 0 & -i \end{pmatrix} - \begin{pmatrix} -i & 0 \\ 0 & i \end{pmatrix}\right] = \frac{\hbar^2}{4}\begin{pmatrix} 2i & 0 \\ 0 & -2i \end{pmatrix} = i\hbar\frac{\hbar}{2}\begin{pmatrix} 1 & 0 \\ 0 & -1 \end{pmatrix} = i\hbar S_z. \quad \checkmark$$

(b)

$$\sigma_x\sigma_x = \begin{pmatrix} 1 & 0 \\ 0 & 1 \end{pmatrix} = 1 = \sigma_y\sigma_y = \sigma_z\sigma_z, \quad \text{so } \sigma_j\sigma_j = 1 \text{ for } j = x, y, \text{ or } z.$$

$$\sigma_x\sigma_y = \begin{pmatrix} i & 0 \\ 0 & -i \end{pmatrix} = i\sigma_z; \quad \sigma_y\sigma_z = \begin{pmatrix} 0 & i \\ i & 0 \end{pmatrix} = i\sigma_x; \quad \sigma_z\sigma_x = \begin{pmatrix} 0 & 1 \\ -1 & 0 \end{pmatrix} = i\sigma_y;$$

$$\sigma_y\sigma_x = \begin{pmatrix} -i & 0 \\ 0 & i \end{pmatrix} = -i\sigma_z; \quad \sigma_z\sigma_y = \begin{pmatrix} 0 & -i \\ -i & 0 \end{pmatrix} = -i\sigma_x; \quad \sigma_x\sigma_z = \begin{pmatrix} 0 & -1 \\ 1 & 0 \end{pmatrix} = -i\sigma_y.$$

Equation 4.153 packages all this in a single formula. $\checkmark$

## Problem 4.27

**(a)**

$$\chi^\dagger \chi = |A|^2(9 + 16) = 25|A|^2 = 1 \Rightarrow \boxed{A = 1/5.}$$

**(b)**

$$\langle S_x \rangle = \chi^\dagger S_x \chi = \frac{1}{25}\frac{\hbar}{2}\begin{pmatrix} -3i & 4 \end{pmatrix}\begin{pmatrix} 0 & 1 \\ 1 & 0 \end{pmatrix}\begin{pmatrix} 3i \\ 4 \end{pmatrix} = \frac{\hbar}{50}\begin{pmatrix} -3i & 4 \end{pmatrix}\begin{pmatrix} 4 \\ 3i \end{pmatrix} = \frac{\hbar}{50}(12i + 12i) = \boxed{0.}$$

$$\langle S_y \rangle = \chi^\dagger S_y \chi = \frac{1}{25}\frac{\hbar}{2}\begin{pmatrix} -3i & 4 \end{pmatrix}\begin{pmatrix} 0 & -i \\ i & 0 \end{pmatrix}\begin{pmatrix} 3i \\ 4 \end{pmatrix} = \frac{\hbar}{50}\begin{pmatrix} -3i & 4 \end{pmatrix}\begin{pmatrix} -4i \\ -3 \end{pmatrix} = \frac{\hbar}{50}(-12 - 12) = \boxed{-\frac{12}{25}\hbar.}$$

$$\langle S_z \rangle = \chi^\dagger S_z \chi = \frac{1}{25}\frac{\hbar}{2}\begin{pmatrix} -3i & 4 \end{pmatrix}\begin{pmatrix} 1 & 0 \\ 0 & -1 \end{pmatrix}\begin{pmatrix} 3i \\ 4 \end{pmatrix} = \frac{\hbar}{50}\begin{pmatrix} -3i & 4 \end{pmatrix}\begin{pmatrix} 3i \\ -4 \end{pmatrix} = \frac{\hbar}{50}(9 - 16) = \boxed{-\frac{7}{50}\hbar.}$$

**(c)**

$$\langle S_x^2 \rangle = \langle S_y^2 \rangle = \langle S_z^2 \rangle = \frac{\hbar^2}{4} \text{ (always, for spin 1/2), so } \sigma_{S_x}^2 = \langle S_x^2 \rangle - \langle S_x \rangle^2 = \frac{\hbar^2}{4} - 0, \boxed{\sigma_{S_x} = \frac{\hbar}{2}.}$$

$$\sigma_{S_y}^2 = \langle S_y^2 \rangle - \langle S_y \rangle^2 = \frac{\hbar}{4} - \left(\frac{12}{25}\right)^2 \hbar^2 = \frac{\hbar^2}{2500}(625 - 576) = \frac{49}{2500}\hbar^2, \boxed{\sigma_{S_y} = \frac{7}{50}\hbar.}$$

$$\sigma_{S_z}^2 = \langle S_z^2 \rangle - \langle S_z \rangle^2 = \frac{\hbar^2}{4} - \left(\frac{7}{50}\right)^2 \hbar^2 = \frac{\hbar^2}{2500}(625 - 49) = \frac{576}{2500}\hbar^2, \boxed{\sigma_{S_z} = \frac{12}{25}\hbar.}$$

**(d)**

$$\sigma_{S_x}\sigma_{S_y} = \frac{\hbar}{2}\cdot\frac{7}{50}\hbar \overset{?}{\geq} \frac{\hbar}{2}|\langle S_z \rangle| = \frac{\hbar}{2}\cdot\frac{7}{50}\hbar \quad \text{(right } at \text{ the uncertainty limit). } \checkmark$$

$$\sigma_{S_y}\sigma_{S_z} = \frac{7}{50}\hbar\cdot\frac{12}{25}\hbar \overset{?}{\geq} \frac{\hbar}{2}|\langle S_x \rangle| = 0 \quad \text{(trivial). } \checkmark$$

$$\sigma_{S_z}\sigma_{S_x} = \frac{12}{25}\hbar\cdot\frac{\hbar}{2} \overset{?}{\geq} \frac{\hbar}{2}|\langle S_y \rangle| = \frac{\hbar}{2}\cdot\frac{12}{25}\hbar \quad \text{(right } at \text{ the uncertainty limit). } \checkmark$$

## Problem 4.28

$$\langle S_x \rangle = \frac{\hbar}{2} \begin{pmatrix} a^* & b^* \end{pmatrix} \begin{pmatrix} 0 & 1 \\ 1 & 0 \end{pmatrix} \begin{pmatrix} a \\ b \end{pmatrix} = \frac{\hbar}{2} \begin{pmatrix} a^* & b^* \end{pmatrix} \begin{pmatrix} b \\ a \end{pmatrix} = \boxed{\frac{\hbar}{2}(a^*b + b^*a)} = \hbar \operatorname{Re}(ab^*).$$

$$\langle S_y \rangle = \frac{\hbar}{2} \begin{pmatrix} a^* & b^* \end{pmatrix} \begin{pmatrix} 0 & -i \\ i & 0 \end{pmatrix} \begin{pmatrix} a \\ b \end{pmatrix} = \frac{\hbar}{2} \begin{pmatrix} a^* & b^* \end{pmatrix} \begin{pmatrix} -ib \\ ia \end{pmatrix}$$

$$= \frac{\hbar}{2}(-ia^*b + iab^*) = \boxed{\frac{\hbar}{2}i(ab^* - a^*b)} = -\hbar \operatorname{Im}(ab^*).$$

$$\langle S_z \rangle = \frac{\hbar}{2} \begin{pmatrix} a^* & b^* \end{pmatrix} \begin{pmatrix} 1 & 0 \\ 0 & -1 \end{pmatrix} \begin{pmatrix} a \\ b \end{pmatrix} = \frac{\hbar}{2} \begin{pmatrix} a^* & b^* \end{pmatrix} \begin{pmatrix} a \\ -b \end{pmatrix} = \frac{\hbar}{2}(a^*a - b^*b) = \boxed{\frac{\hbar}{2}(|a|^2 - |b|^2)}.$$

$$S_x^2 = \frac{\hbar^2}{4} \begin{pmatrix} 0 & 1 \\ 1 & 0 \end{pmatrix} \begin{pmatrix} 0 & 1 \\ 1 & 0 \end{pmatrix} = \frac{\hbar^2}{4} \begin{pmatrix} 1 & 0 \\ 0 & 1 \end{pmatrix} = \frac{\hbar^2}{4}; \quad S_y^2 = \frac{\hbar^2}{4} \begin{pmatrix} 0 & -i \\ i & 0 \end{pmatrix} \begin{pmatrix} 0 & -i \\ i & 0 \end{pmatrix} = \frac{\hbar^2}{4};$$

$$S_z^2 = \frac{\hbar^2}{4} \begin{pmatrix} 1 & 0 \\ 0 & -1 \end{pmatrix} \begin{pmatrix} 1 & 0 \\ 0 & -1 \end{pmatrix} = \frac{\hbar^2}{4}; \quad \text{so} \quad \boxed{\langle S_x^2 \rangle = \langle S_y^2 \rangle = \langle S_z^2 \rangle = \frac{\hbar^2}{4}.}$$

$$\langle S_x^2 \rangle + \langle S_y^2 \rangle + \langle S_z^2 \rangle = \frac{3}{4}\hbar^2 \overset{?}{=} s(s+1)\hbar^2 = \frac{1}{2}(\frac{1}{2}+1)\hbar^2 = \frac{3}{4}\hbar^2 = \langle S^2 \rangle. \checkmark$$

---

## Problem 4.29

**(a)**

$$S_y = \frac{\hbar}{2} \begin{pmatrix} 0 & -i \\ i & 0 \end{pmatrix}; \quad \begin{vmatrix} -\lambda & -i\hbar/2 \\ i\hbar/2 & -\lambda \end{vmatrix} = \lambda^2 - \frac{\hbar^2}{4} \Rightarrow \boxed{\lambda = \pm\frac{\hbar}{2}} \text{ (of course)}.$$

$$\frac{\hbar}{2} \begin{pmatrix} 0 & -i \\ i & 0 \end{pmatrix} \begin{pmatrix} \alpha \\ \beta \end{pmatrix} = \pm\frac{\hbar}{2} \begin{pmatrix} \alpha \\ \beta \end{pmatrix} \Rightarrow -i\beta = \pm\alpha; \quad |\alpha|^2 + |\beta|^2 = 1 \Rightarrow |\alpha|^2 + |\alpha|^2 = 1 \Rightarrow \alpha = \frac{1}{\sqrt{2}}.$$

$$\boxed{\chi_+^{(y)} = \frac{1}{\sqrt{2}} \begin{pmatrix} 1 \\ i \end{pmatrix}; \quad \chi_-^{(y)} = \frac{1}{\sqrt{2}} \begin{pmatrix} 1 \\ -i \end{pmatrix}.}$$

**(b)**

$$c_+ = \left(\chi_+^{(y)}\right)^\dagger \chi = \frac{1}{\sqrt{2}} \begin{pmatrix} 1 & -i \end{pmatrix} \begin{pmatrix} a \\ b \end{pmatrix} = \frac{1}{\sqrt{2}}(a - ib); \quad \boxed{+\frac{\hbar}{2}, \text{ with probability } \frac{1}{2}|a - ib|^2.}$$

$$c_- = \left(\chi_-^{(y)}\right)^\dagger \chi = \frac{1}{\sqrt{2}} \begin{pmatrix} 1 & i \end{pmatrix} \begin{pmatrix} a \\ b \end{pmatrix} = \frac{1}{\sqrt{2}}(a + ib); \quad \boxed{-\frac{\hbar}{2}, \text{ with probability } \frac{1}{2}|a + ib|^2.}$$

$$P_+ + P_- = \frac{1}{2}\left[(a^* + ib^*)(a - ib) + (a^* - ib^*)(a + ib)\right]$$

$$= \frac{1}{2}\left[|a|^2 - ia^*b + iab^* + |b|^2 + |a|^2 + ia^*b - iab^* + |b|^2\right] = |a|^2 + |b|^2 = 1. \checkmark$$

(c) $\boxed{\dfrac{\hbar^2}{4}}$, with probability 1.

---

## Problem 4.30

$$S_r = S \cdot \hat{r} = S_x \sin\theta\cos\phi + S_y \sin\theta\sin\phi + S_z \cos\theta$$
$$= \frac{\hbar}{2}\left[\begin{pmatrix} 0 & \sin\theta\cos\phi \\ \sin\theta\cos\phi & 0 \end{pmatrix} + \begin{pmatrix} 0 & -i\sin\theta\sin\phi \\ i\sin\theta\sin\phi & 0 \end{pmatrix} + \begin{pmatrix} \cos\theta & 0 \\ 0 & -\cos\theta \end{pmatrix}\right]$$
$$= \frac{\hbar}{2}\begin{pmatrix} \cos\theta & \sin\theta(\cos\phi - i\sin\phi) \\ \sin\theta(\cos\phi + i\sin\phi) & -\cos\theta \end{pmatrix} = \boxed{\frac{\hbar}{2}\begin{pmatrix} \cos\theta & e^{-i\phi}\sin\theta \\ e^{i\phi}\sin\theta & -\cos\theta \end{pmatrix}}.$$

$$\left|\begin{matrix} (\frac{\hbar}{2}\cos\theta - \lambda) & \frac{\hbar}{2}e^{-i\phi}\sin\theta \\ \frac{\hbar}{2}e^{i\phi}\sin\theta & (-\frac{\hbar}{2}\cos\theta - \lambda) \end{matrix}\right| = -\frac{\hbar^2}{4}\cos^2\theta + \lambda^2 - \frac{\hbar^2}{4}\sin^2\theta = 0 \Rightarrow$$

$$\lambda^2 = \frac{\hbar^2}{4}(\sin^2\theta + \cos^2\theta) = \frac{\hbar^2}{4} \Rightarrow \boxed{\lambda = \pm\frac{\hbar}{2}} \text{ (of course).}$$

$$\frac{\hbar}{2}\begin{pmatrix} \cos\theta & e^{-i\phi}\sin\theta \\ e^{i\phi}\sin\theta & -\cos\theta \end{pmatrix}\begin{pmatrix} \alpha \\ \beta \end{pmatrix} = \pm\frac{\hbar}{2}\begin{pmatrix} \alpha \\ \beta \end{pmatrix} \Rightarrow \alpha\cos\theta + \beta e^{-i\phi}\sin\theta = \pm\alpha; \quad \beta = e^{i\phi}\frac{(\pm 1 - \cos\theta)}{\sin\theta}\alpha.$$

**Upper sign:** Use $1 - \cos\theta = 2\sin^2\frac{\theta}{2}$, $\sin\theta = 2\sin\frac{\theta}{2}\cos\frac{\theta}{2}$. Then $\beta = e^{i\phi}\dfrac{\sin(\theta/2)}{\cos(\theta/2)}\alpha$. Normalizing:

$$1 = |\alpha|^2 + |\beta|^2 = |\alpha|^2 + \frac{\sin^2(\theta/2)}{\cos^2(\theta/2)}|\alpha|^2 = |\alpha|^2\frac{1}{\cos^2(\theta/2)} \Rightarrow \alpha = \cos\frac{\theta}{2}, \ \beta = e^{i\phi}\sin\frac{\theta}{2}, \ \boxed{\chi_+^{(r)} = \begin{pmatrix} \cos(\theta/2) \\ e^{i\phi}\sin(\theta/2) \end{pmatrix}}.$$

**Lower sign:** Use $1 + \cos\theta = 2\cos^2\frac{\theta}{2}$, $\beta = -e^{i\phi}\dfrac{\cos(\theta/2)}{\sin(\theta/2)}\alpha$; $1 = |\alpha|^2 + \dfrac{\cos^2(\theta/2)}{\sin^2(\theta/2)}|\alpha|^2 = |\alpha|^2\dfrac{1}{\sin^2(\theta/2)}$.

Pick $\alpha = e^{-i\phi}\sin(\theta/2)$; then $\beta = -\cos(\theta/2)$, and $\boxed{\chi_-^{(r)} = \begin{pmatrix} e^{-i\phi}\sin(\theta/2) \\ -\cos(\theta/2) \end{pmatrix}}.$

---

## Problem 4.31

There are three states: $\chi_+ = \begin{pmatrix} 1 \\ 0 \\ 0 \end{pmatrix}$, $\chi_0 = \begin{pmatrix} 0 \\ 1 \\ 0 \end{pmatrix}$, $\chi_- = \begin{pmatrix} 0 \\ 0 \\ 1 \end{pmatrix}$.

$$S_z\chi_+ = \hbar\chi_+, \ S_z\chi_0 = 0, \ S_z\chi_- = -\hbar\chi_-, \ \Rightarrow \boxed{S_z = \hbar\begin{pmatrix} 1 & 0 & 0 \\ 0 & 0 & 0 \\ 0 & 0 & -1 \end{pmatrix}}. \quad \text{From Eq. 4.136:}$$

$$S_+ \chi_+ = 0, \qquad S_+ \chi_0 = \hbar\sqrt{2}\chi_+, \ S_+\chi_- = \hbar\sqrt{2}\chi_0 \atop S_-\chi_+ = \hbar\sqrt{2}\chi_0, \ S_-\chi_0 = \hbar\sqrt{2}\chi_-, \ S_-\chi_- = 0 \bigg\} \Rightarrow S_+ = \sqrt{2}\hbar \begin{pmatrix} 0 & 1 & 0 \\ 0 & 0 & 1 \\ 0 & 0 & 0 \end{pmatrix}, \ S_- = \sqrt{2}\hbar \begin{pmatrix} 0 & 0 & 0 \\ 1 & 0 & 0 \\ 0 & 1 & 0 \end{pmatrix}.$$

$$S_x = \frac{1}{2}(S_+ + S_-) = \boxed{\frac{\hbar}{\sqrt{2}} \begin{pmatrix} 0 & 1 & 0 \\ 1 & 0 & 1 \\ 0 & 1 & 0 \end{pmatrix}}, \quad S_y = \frac{1}{2i}(S_+ - S_-) = \boxed{\frac{i\hbar}{\sqrt{2}} \begin{pmatrix} 0 & -1 & 0 \\ 1 & 0 & -1 \\ 0 & 1 & 0 \end{pmatrix}}.$$

## Problem 4.32

**(a)** Using Eqs. 4.151 and 4.163:

$$c_+^{(x)} = \chi_+^{(x)\dagger}\chi = \frac{1}{\sqrt{2}} (1 \ 1) \begin{pmatrix} \cos\frac{\alpha}{2}e^{i\gamma B_0 t/2} \\ \sin\frac{\alpha}{2}e^{-i\gamma B_0 t/2} \end{pmatrix} = \frac{1}{\sqrt{2}} \left[ \cos\frac{\alpha}{2}e^{i\gamma B_0 t/2} + \sin\frac{\alpha}{2}e^{-i\gamma B_0 t/2} \right].$$

$$P_+^{(x)}(t) = |c_+^{(x)}|^2 = \frac{1}{2} \left[ \cos\frac{\alpha}{2}e^{-i\gamma B_0 t/2} + \sin\frac{\alpha}{2}e^{i\gamma B_0 t/2} \right] \left[ \cos\frac{\alpha}{2}e^{i\gamma B_0 t/2} + \sin\frac{\alpha}{2}e^{-i\gamma B_0 t/2} \right]$$

$$= \frac{1}{2} \left[ \cos^2\frac{\alpha}{2} + \sin^2\frac{\alpha}{2} + \sin\frac{\alpha}{2}\cos\frac{\alpha}{2} \left( e^{i\gamma B_0 t} + e^{-i\gamma B_0 t} \right) \right]$$

$$= \frac{1}{2} \left[ 1 + 2\sin\frac{\alpha}{2}\cos\frac{\alpha}{2}\cos(\gamma B_0 t) \right] = \boxed{\frac{1}{2} \left[ 1 + \sin\alpha\cos(\gamma B_0 t) \right]}.$$

**(b)** From Problem 4.29(a): $\chi_+^{(y)} = \frac{1}{\sqrt{2}} \begin{pmatrix} 1 \\ i \end{pmatrix}.$

$$c_+^{(y)} = \chi_+^{(y)\dagger}\chi = \frac{1}{\sqrt{2}} (1 \ -i) \begin{pmatrix} \cos\frac{\alpha}{2}e^{i\gamma B_0 t/2} \\ \sin\frac{\alpha}{2}e^{i\gamma B_0 t/2} \end{pmatrix} = \frac{1}{\sqrt{2}} \left[ \cos\frac{\alpha}{2}e^{i\gamma B_0 t/2} - i\sin\frac{\alpha}{2}e^{-i\gamma B_0 t/2} \right];$$

$$P_+^{(y)}(t) = |c_+^{(y)}|^2 = \frac{1}{2} \left[ \cos\frac{\alpha}{2}e^{-i\gamma B_0 t/2} + i\sin\frac{\alpha}{2}e^{i\gamma B_0 t/2} \right] \left[ \cos\frac{\alpha}{2}e^{i\gamma B_0 t/2} - i\sin\frac{\alpha}{2}e^{-i\gamma B_0 t/2} \right]$$

$$= \frac{1}{2} \left[ \cos^2\frac{\alpha}{2} + \sin^2\frac{\alpha}{2} + i\sin\frac{\alpha}{2}\cos\frac{\alpha}{2} \left( e^{i\gamma B_0 t} - e^{-i\gamma B_0 t} \right) \right]$$

$$= \frac{1}{2} \left[ 1 - 2\sin\frac{\alpha}{2}\cos\frac{\alpha}{2}\sin(\gamma B_0 t) \right] = \boxed{\frac{1}{2} \left[ 1 - \sin\alpha\sin(\gamma B_0 t) \right]}.$$

**(c)**

$$\chi_+^{(z)} = \begin{pmatrix} 1 \\ 0 \end{pmatrix}; \quad c_+^{(z)} = (1 \ 0) \begin{pmatrix} \cos\frac{\alpha}{2}e^{i\gamma B_0 t/2} \\ \sin\frac{\alpha}{2}e^{-i\gamma B_0 t/2} \end{pmatrix} = \cos\frac{\alpha}{2}e^{i\gamma B_0 t/2}; \quad P_+^{(z)}(t) = |c_+^{(z)}|^2 = \boxed{\cos^2\frac{\alpha}{2}}.$$

## Problem 4.33

**(a)**

$$H = -\gamma \mathbf{B}\cdot\mathbf{S} = -\gamma B_0 \cos\omega t \ S_z = \boxed{-\frac{\gamma B_0 \hbar}{2}\cos\omega t \begin{pmatrix} 1 & 0 \\ 0 & -1 \end{pmatrix}}.$$

**(b)**

$$\chi(t) = \begin{pmatrix} \alpha(t) \\ \beta(t) \end{pmatrix}, \text{ with } \alpha(0) = \beta(0) = \frac{1}{\sqrt{2}}.$$

$$i\hbar \frac{\partial \chi}{\partial t} = i\hbar \begin{pmatrix} \dot{\alpha} \\ \dot{\beta} \end{pmatrix} = \mathsf{H}\chi = -\frac{\gamma B_0 \hbar}{2} \cos \omega t \begin{pmatrix} 1 & 0 \\ 0 & -1 \end{pmatrix} \begin{pmatrix} \alpha \\ \beta \end{pmatrix} = -\frac{\gamma B_0 \hbar}{2} \cos \omega t \begin{pmatrix} \alpha \\ -\beta \end{pmatrix}.$$

$$\dot{\alpha} = i\left(\frac{\gamma B_0}{2}\right)\cos\omega t\, \alpha \Rightarrow \frac{d\alpha}{\alpha} = i\left(\frac{\gamma B_0}{2}\right)\cos\omega t\, dt \Rightarrow \ln\alpha = \frac{i\gamma B_0}{2}\frac{\sin\omega t}{\omega} + constant.$$

$$\alpha(t) = A e^{i(\gamma B_0/2\omega)\sin\omega t}; \quad \alpha(0) = A = \frac{1}{\sqrt{2}}, \quad \text{so } \alpha(t) = \frac{1}{\sqrt{2}} e^{i(\gamma B_0/2\omega)\sin\omega t}.$$

$$\dot{\beta} = -i\left(\frac{\gamma B_0}{2}\right)\cos\omega t\, \beta \Rightarrow \beta(t) = \frac{1}{\sqrt{2}} e^{-i(\gamma B_0/2\omega)\sin\omega t}. \quad \boxed{\chi(t) = \frac{1}{\sqrt{2}}\begin{pmatrix} e^{i(\gamma B_0/2\omega)\sin\omega t} \\ e^{-i(\gamma B_0/2\omega)\sin\omega t} \end{pmatrix}.}$$

**(c)**

$$c_-^{(x)} = \chi_-^{(x)\dagger}\chi = \frac{1}{2}(1 \ {-}1)\begin{pmatrix} e^{i(\gamma B_0/2\omega)\sin\omega t} \\ e^{-i(\gamma B_0/2\omega)\sin\omega t} \end{pmatrix} = \frac{1}{2}\left[ e^{i(\gamma B_0/2\omega)\sin\omega t} - e^{-i(\gamma B_0/2\omega)\sin\omega t}\right]$$

$$= i\sin\left[\frac{\gamma B_0}{2\omega}\sin\omega t\right]. \quad P_-^{(x)}(t) = |c_-^{(x)}|^2 = \boxed{\sin^2\left[\frac{\gamma B_0}{2\omega}\sin\omega t\right].}$$

**(d)** The argument of $\sin^2$ must reach $\pi/2$ (so $P = 1$) $\Rightarrow \dfrac{\gamma B_0}{2\omega} = \dfrac{\pi}{2}$, or $\boxed{B_0 = \dfrac{\pi\omega}{\gamma}.}$

---

## Problem 4.34

**(a)**

$$S_-|1\ 0\rangle = (S_-^{(1)} + S_-^{(2)})\frac{1}{\sqrt{2}}(\uparrow\downarrow + \downarrow\uparrow) = \frac{1}{\sqrt{2}}\left[(S_-\uparrow)\downarrow + (S_-\downarrow)\uparrow + \uparrow(S_-\downarrow) + \downarrow(S_-\uparrow)\right].$$

But $S_-\uparrow = \hbar\downarrow$, $S_-\downarrow = 0$ (Eq. 4.143), so $S_-|10\rangle = \dfrac{1}{\sqrt{2}}\left[\hbar\downarrow\downarrow + 0 + 0 + \hbar\downarrow\downarrow\right] = \sqrt{2}\hbar\downarrow\downarrow = \sqrt{2}\hbar|1 - 1\rangle.\checkmark$

**(b)**

$$S_\pm|0\ 0\rangle = (S_\pm^{(1)} + S_\pm^{(2)})\frac{1}{\sqrt{2}}(\uparrow\downarrow - \downarrow\uparrow) = \frac{1}{\sqrt{2}}\left[(S_\pm\uparrow)\downarrow - (S_\pm\downarrow)\uparrow + \uparrow(S_\pm\downarrow) - \downarrow(S_\pm\uparrow)\right].$$

$$S_+|0\ 0\rangle = \frac{1}{\sqrt{2}}(0 - \hbar\uparrow\uparrow + \hbar\uparrow\uparrow - 0) = 0; \quad S_-|0\ 0\rangle = \frac{1}{\sqrt{2}}(\hbar\downarrow\downarrow - 0 + 0 - \hbar\downarrow\downarrow) = 0.\ \checkmark$$

**(c)**

$$S^2|1\ 1\rangle = \left[ (S^{(1)})^2 + (S^{(2)})^2 + 2\mathbf{S}^{(1)} \cdot \mathbf{S}^{(2)} \right] \uparrow\uparrow$$

$$= (S^2 \uparrow) \uparrow + \uparrow (S^2 \uparrow) + 2\left[ (S_x \uparrow)(S_x \uparrow) + (S_y \uparrow)(S_y \uparrow) + (S_z \uparrow)(S_z \uparrow) \right]$$

$$= \frac{3}{4}\hbar^2 \uparrow\uparrow + \frac{3}{4}\hbar^2 \uparrow\uparrow + 2\left[ \frac{\hbar}{2} \downarrow \frac{\hbar}{2} \downarrow + \frac{i\hbar}{2} \downarrow \frac{i\hbar}{2} \downarrow + \frac{\hbar}{2} \uparrow \frac{\hbar}{2} \uparrow \right]$$

$$= \frac{3}{2}\hbar^2 \uparrow\uparrow + 2\left( \frac{\hbar^2}{4} \uparrow\uparrow \right) = 2\hbar^2 \uparrow\uparrow = 2\hbar^2|1\ 1\rangle = (1)(1+1)\hbar^2|1\ 1\rangle, \text{ as it } should \text{ be.}$$

$$S^2|1\ -1\rangle = \left[ (S^{(1)})^2 + (S^{(2)})^2 + 2\mathbf{S}^{(1)} \cdot \mathbf{S}^{(2)} \right] \downarrow\downarrow$$

$$= \frac{3\hbar^2}{4} \downarrow\downarrow + \frac{3\hbar^2}{4} \downarrow\downarrow + 2\left[ (S_x \downarrow)(S_x \downarrow) + (S_y \downarrow)(S_y \downarrow) + (S_z \downarrow)(S_z \downarrow) \right]$$

$$= \frac{3}{2}\hbar^2 \downarrow\downarrow + 2\left[ \left( \frac{\hbar}{2} \uparrow \right)\left( \frac{\hbar}{2} \uparrow \right) + \left( -\frac{i\hbar}{2} \uparrow \right)\left( -\frac{i\hbar}{2} \uparrow \right) + \left( -\frac{\hbar}{2} \downarrow \right)\left( -\frac{\hbar}{2} \downarrow \right) \right]$$

$$= \frac{3}{2}\hbar^2 \downarrow\downarrow + 2\frac{\hbar^2}{4} \downarrow\downarrow = 2\hbar^2 \downarrow\downarrow = 2\hbar^2|1\ -1\rangle. \checkmark$$

---

## Problem 4.35

**(a)** 1/2 and 1/2 gives 1 or zero; 1/2 and 1 gives 3/2 or 1/2; 1/2 and 0 gives 1/2 only. So baryons can have spin 3/2 or spin 1/2 (and the latter can be acheived in two distinct ways). [Incidentally, the lightest baryons *do* carry spin 1/2 (proton, neutron, etc.) or 3/2 ($\Delta, \Omega^-$, etc.); heavier baryons can have higher total spin, but this is because the quarks have orbital angular momentum as well.]

**(b)** 1/2 and 1/2 gives spin 1 or spin 0. [Again, these *are* the observed spins for the lightest mesons: $\pi$'s and $K$'s have spin 0, $\rho$'s and $\omega$'s have spin 1.]

---

## Problem 4.36

**(a)** From the $2 \times 1$ Clebsch-Gordan table we get

$$|3\ 1\rangle = \sqrt{\frac{1}{15}} |2\ 2\rangle|1\ -1\rangle + \sqrt{\frac{8}{15}} |2\ 1\rangle|1\ 0\rangle + \sqrt{\frac{6}{15}} |2\ 0\rangle|1\ 1\rangle,$$

so you might get $2\hbar$ (probability 1/15), $\hbar$ (probability 8/15), or (probability 6/15).

**(b)** From the $1 \times \frac{1}{2}$ table: $|1\ 0\rangle|\frac{1}{2}\ -\frac{1}{2}\rangle = \sqrt{\frac{2}{3}} |\frac{3}{2}\ -\frac{1}{2}\rangle + \sqrt{\frac{1}{3}} |\frac{1}{2}\ -\frac{1}{2}\rangle$. So the total is 3/2 or 1/2, with $l(l+1)\hbar^2 = 15/4\hbar^2$ and $3/4\hbar^2$, respectively. Thus you get $\frac{15}{4}\hbar^2$ (probability 2/3), or $\frac{3}{4}\hbar^2$ (probability 1/3).

---

## Problem 4.37

Using Eq. 4.179: $[S^2, S_z^{(1)}] = [S^{(1)^2}, S_z^{(1)}] + [S^{(2)^2}, S_z^{(1)}] + 2[\mathbf{S}^{(1)} \cdot \mathbf{S}^{(2)}, S_z^{(1)}]$. But $[S^2, S_z] = 0$ (Eq. 4.102), and anything with superscript (2) commutes with anything with superscript (1). So

$$[S^2, S_z^{(1)}] = 2\left\{ S_x^{(2)}[S_x^{(1)}, S_z^{(1)}] + S_y^{(2)}[S_y^{(1)}, S_z^{(1)}] + S_z^{(2)}[S_z^{(1)}, S_z^{(1)}]\right\}$$

$$= 2\left\{ -i\hbar S_y^{(1)} S_x^{(2)} + i\hbar S_x^{(1)} S_y^{(2)}\right\} = 2i\hbar(\mathbf{S}^{(1)} \times \mathbf{S}^{(2)})z.$$

$$\boxed{[S^2, S_z^{(1)}] = 2i\hbar(S_x^{(1)} S_y^{(2)} - S_y^{(1)} S_x^{(2)}),}$$ and $[S^2, \mathbf{S}^{(1)}] = 2i\hbar(\mathbf{S}^{(1)} \times \mathbf{S}^{(2)})$. Note that $[S^2, \mathbf{S}^{(2)}] = 2i\hbar(\mathbf{S}^{(2)} \times \mathbf{S}^{(1)}) = -2i\hbar(\mathbf{S}^{(1)} \times \mathbf{S}^{(2)})$, so $[S^2, (\mathbf{S}^{(1)} + \mathbf{S}^{(2)})] = 0.]$

---

## Problem 4.38

**(a)**

$$-\frac{\hbar^2}{2m}\left(\frac{\partial^2\psi}{\partial x^2} + \frac{\partial^2\psi}{\partial y^2} + \frac{\partial^2\psi}{\partial z^2}\right) + \frac{1}{2}m\omega^2\left(x^2 + y^2 + z^2\right)\psi = E\psi.$$

Let $\psi(x, y, z) = X(x)Y(y)Z(z)$; plug it in, divide by $XYZ$, and collect terms:

$$\left(-\frac{\hbar^2}{2m}\frac{1}{X}\frac{d^2X}{dx^2} + \frac{1}{2}m\omega^2 x^2\right) + \left(-\frac{\hbar^2}{2m}\frac{1}{Y}\frac{d^2Y}{dy^2} + \frac{1}{2}m\omega^2 y^2\right) + \left(-\frac{\hbar^2}{2m}\frac{1}{Z}\frac{d^2Z}{dz^2} + \frac{1}{2}m\omega^2 z^2\right) = E.$$

The first term is a function only of $x$, the second only of $y$, and the third only of $z$. So each is a constant (call the constants $E_x$, $E_y$, $E_z$, with $E_x + E_y + E_z = E$). Thus:

$$-\frac{\hbar^2}{2m}\frac{d^2X}{dx^2} + \frac{1}{2}m\omega^2 x^2 X = E_x X; \quad -\frac{\hbar^2}{2m}\frac{d^2Y}{dy^2} + \frac{1}{2}m\omega^2 y^2 Y = E_y Y; \quad -\frac{\hbar^2}{2m}\frac{d^2Z}{dz^2} + \frac{1}{2}m\omega^2 z^2 Z = E_z Z.$$

Each of these is simply the one-dimensional harmonic oscillator (Eq. 2.44). We know the allowed energies (Eq. 2.61):

$$E_x = (n_x + \tfrac{1}{2})\hbar\omega; \quad E_y = (n_y + \tfrac{1}{2})\hbar\omega; \quad E_z = (n_z + \tfrac{1}{2})\hbar\omega; \quad \text{where } n_x, n_y, n_z = 0, 1, 2, 3, \ldots.$$

So $E = (n_x + n_y + n_y + \tfrac{3}{2})\hbar\omega = \boxed{(n + \tfrac{3}{2})\hbar\omega,}$ with $n \equiv n_x + n_y + n_z$.

**(b)** The question is: "How many ways can we add three non-negative integers to get sum $n$?"

If $n_x = n$, then $n_y = n_z = 0$; *one* way.

If $n_x = n - 1$, then $n_y = 0, n_z = 1$, or else $n_y = 1, n_z = 0$; *two* ways.

If $n_x = n - 2$, then $n_y = 0, n_z = 2$, or $n_y = 1, n_z = 1$, or $n_y = 2, n_z = 0$; *three* ways.

And so on. Evidently $d(n) = 1 + 2 + 3 + \cdots + (n + 1) = \boxed{\dfrac{(n + 1)(n + 2)}{2}}.$

---

## Problem 4.39

Eq. 4.37:   $-\dfrac{\hbar^2}{2m}\dfrac{d^2u}{dr^2} + \left[\dfrac{1}{2}m\omega^2 r^2 + \dfrac{\hbar^2}{2m}\dfrac{l(l+1)}{r^2}\right]u = Eu.$

Following Eq. 2.71, let $\xi \equiv \sqrt{\dfrac{m\omega}{\hbar}}\,r.$ Then $\quad -\dfrac{\hbar^2}{2m}\dfrac{m\omega}{\hbar}\dfrac{d^2u}{d\xi^2} + \left[\dfrac{1}{2}m\omega^2\dfrac{\hbar}{m\omega}\xi^2 + \dfrac{\hbar^2}{2m}\dfrac{m\omega}{\hbar}\dfrac{l(l+1)}{\xi^2}\right]u = Eu,$

or $\dfrac{d^2u}{d\xi^2} = \left[\xi^2 + \dfrac{l(l+1)}{\xi^2} - K\right]u,$ where $K \equiv \dfrac{2E}{\hbar\omega}$ (as in Eq. 2.73).

At large $\xi$, $\dfrac{d^2u}{d\xi^2} \approx \xi^2 u,$ and $u \sim (\ )e^{-\xi^2/2}$ (see Eq. 2.77).

At small $\xi$, $\dfrac{d^2u}{d\xi^2} \approx \dfrac{l(l+1)}{\xi^2}u,$ and $u \sim (\ )\xi^{l+1}$ (see Eq. 4.59).

So let $u(\xi) \equiv \xi^{l+1}e^{-\xi^2/2}v(\xi).$     [This defines the new function $v(\xi)$.]

$\dfrac{du}{d\xi} = (l+1)\xi^l e^{-\xi^2/2}v - \xi^{l+2}e^{-\xi^2/2}v + \xi^{l+1}e^{-\xi^2/2}v'.$

$\dfrac{d^2u}{d\xi^2} = l(l+1)\xi^{l-1}e^{-\xi^2/2}v - (l+1)\xi^{l+1}e^{-\xi^2/2}v + (l+1)\xi^l e^{-\xi^2/2}v' - (l+2)\xi^{l+1}e^{-\xi^2/2}v$

$\qquad + \xi^{l+3}e^{-\xi^2/2}v - \xi^{l+2}e^{-\xi^2/2}v' + (l+1)\xi^l e^{-\xi^2/2}v' - \xi^{l+2}e^{-\xi^2/2}v' + \xi^{l+1}e^{-\xi^2/2}v''$

$\qquad = \cancel{l(l+1)\xi^{l-1}e^{-\xi^2/2}v} - (2l+3)\xi^{l+1}e^{-\xi^2/2}v + \cancel{\xi^{l+3}e^{-\xi^2/2}v} + 2(l+1)\xi^l e^{-\xi^2/2}v'$

$\qquad - 2\xi^{l+2}e^{-\xi^2/2}v' + \xi^{l+1}e^{-\xi^2/2}v'' = \cancel{\xi^{l+3}e^{-\xi^2/2}v} + \cancel{l(l+1)\xi^{l-1}e^{-\xi^2/2}v} - K\xi^{l+1}e^{-\xi^2/2}v.$

Cancelling the indicated terms, and dividing off $\xi^{l+1}e^{-\xi^2/2}$, we have:

$v'' + 2v'\left(\dfrac{l+1}{\xi} - \xi\right) + (K - 2l - 3)v = 0.$

Let $v(\xi) \equiv \displaystyle\sum_{j=0}^{\infty} a_j\xi^j,$ so $v' = \displaystyle\sum_{j=0}^{\infty} ja_j\xi^{j-1};$    $v'' = \displaystyle\sum_{j=2}^{\infty} j(j-1)a_j\xi^{j-2}.$    Then

$\displaystyle\sum_{j=2}^{\infty} j(j-1)a_j\xi^{j-2} + 2(l+2)\sum_{j=1}^{\infty} ja_j\xi^{j-2} - 2\sum_{j=1}^{\infty} ja_j\xi^j + (K-2l-3)\sum_{j=0}^{\infty} a_j\xi^j = 0.$

In the first two sums, let $j \to j+2$ (rename the dummy index):

$\displaystyle\sum_{j=0}^{\infty}(j+2)(j+1)a_{j+2}\xi^j + 2(l+1)\sum_{j=0}^{\infty}(j+2)a_{j+2}\xi^j - 2\sum_{j=0}^{\infty} ja_j\xi^j + (K-2l-3)\sum_{j=0}^{\infty} a_j\xi^j = 0.$

*Note*: the second sum should start at $j = -1$; to eliminate this term (there is no compensating one in $\xi^{-1}$) we must take $a_1 = 0$. Combining the terms:

$$\sum_{j=0}^{\infty} [(j+2)(j+2l+3)a_{j+2} + (K - 2j - 2l - 3)a_j] = 0, \quad \text{so} \quad \boxed{a_{j+2} = \frac{(2j + 2l + 3 - K)}{(j+2)(j+2l+3)} a_j.}$$

Since $a_1 = 0$, this gives us a single sequence: $a_0, a_2, a_4, \ldots$. But the series must terminate (else we get the wrong behavior as $\xi \to \infty$), so there occurs some maximal (even) number $j_{\max}$ such that $a_{j_{\max}+2} = 0$. Thus $K = 2j_{\max} + 2l + 3$. But $E = \frac{1}{2}\hbar\omega K$, so $E = \left(j_{\max} + l + \frac{3}{2}\right)\hbar\omega$. Or, letting $j_{\max} + l \equiv n$,

$\boxed{E_n = (n + \frac{3}{2})\hbar\omega,}$ and $n$ can be any nonnegative integer.

[Incidentally, we can also determine the degeneracy of $E_n$. Suppose $n$ is *even*; then (since $j_{\max}$ is even) $l = 0, 2, 4, \ldots, n$. For each $l$ there are $(2l + 1)$ values for $m$. So

$$d(n) = \sum_{l=0,2,4,\ldots}^{n} (2l + 1). \quad \text{Let } j = l/2; \quad \text{then } d(n) = \sum_{j=0}^{n/2} (4j + 1) = 4\sum_{j=0}^{n/2} j + \sum_{j=0}^{n/2} 1$$

$$= 4\frac{(\frac{n}{2})(\frac{n}{2}+1)}{2} + (\frac{n}{2} + 1) = (\frac{n}{2} + 1)(n + 1) = \frac{(n+1)(n+2)}{2}, \quad \text{as before (Problem 4.38(b)).}]$$

---

## Problem 4.40

### (a)

$$\frac{d}{dt}\langle \mathbf{r} \cdot \mathbf{p} \rangle = \frac{i}{\hbar}\langle [H, \mathbf{r} \cdot \mathbf{p}]\rangle.$$

$$[H, \mathbf{r} \cdot \mathbf{p}] = \sum_{i=1}^{3} [H, r_i p_i] = \sum_{i=1}^{3} ([H, r_i]p_i + r_i[H, p_i]) = \sum_{i=1}^{3} \left(\frac{1}{2m}[p^2, r_i]p_i + r_i[V, p_i]\right).$$

$$[p^2, r_i] = \sum_{j=1}^{3} [p_j p_j, r_i] = \sum_{j=1}^{3} (p_j[p_j, r_i] + [p_j, r_i]p_j) = \sum_{j=1}^{3} [p_j(-i\hbar\delta_{ij}) + (-i\hbar\delta_{ij})p_j] = -2i\hbar p_i.$$

$$[V, p_i] = i\hbar \frac{\partial V}{\partial r_i} \text{ (Problem 3.13(c)).} \quad [H, \mathbf{r} \cdot \mathbf{p}] = \sum_{i=1}^{3} \left[\frac{1}{2m}(-2i\hbar)p_i p_i + r_i\left(i\hbar\frac{\partial V}{\partial r_i}\right)\right]$$

$$= i\hbar\left(-\frac{p^2}{m} + \mathbf{r} \cdot \nabla V\right). \quad \frac{d}{dt}\langle \mathbf{r} \cdot \mathbf{p} \rangle = \langle \frac{p^2}{m} - \mathbf{r} \cdot \nabla V \rangle = 2\langle T \rangle - \langle \mathbf{r} \cdot \nabla V \rangle.$$

For stationary states $\frac{d}{dt}\langle \mathbf{r} \cdot \mathbf{p} \rangle = 0$, so $2\langle T \rangle = \langle \mathbf{r} \cdot \nabla V \rangle$.   QED

### (b)

$$V(r) = -\frac{e^2}{4\pi\epsilon_0}\frac{1}{r} \Rightarrow \nabla V = \frac{e^2}{4\pi\epsilon_0}\frac{1}{r^2}\hat{r} \Rightarrow \mathbf{r} \cdot \nabla V = \frac{e^2}{4\pi\epsilon_0}\frac{1}{r} = -V. \quad \text{So } 2\langle T \rangle = -\langle V \rangle.$$

But $\langle T \rangle = \langle V \rangle = E_n$, so $\langle T \rangle - 2\langle T \rangle = E_n$, or $\langle T \rangle = -E_n$; $\langle V \rangle = 2E_n$.   QED

**(c)**

$$V = \frac{1}{2}m\omega^2 r^2 \Rightarrow \nabla V = m\omega^2 r\,\hat{r} \Rightarrow \mathbf{r}\cdot\nabla V = m\omega^2 r^2 = 2V. \quad \text{So } 2\langle T\rangle = 2\langle V\rangle, \text{ or } \langle T\rangle = \langle V\rangle.$$

$$\text{But } \langle T\rangle + \langle V\rangle = E_n, \text{ so } \langle T\rangle = \langle V\rangle = \frac{1}{2}E_n. \quad \text{QED}$$

---

## Problem 4.41

**(a)** $\nabla\cdot\mathbf{J} = \dfrac{i\hbar}{2m}\left[\nabla\Psi\cdot\nabla\Psi^* + \Psi(\nabla^2\Psi^*) - \nabla\Psi^*\cdot\nabla\Psi - \Psi^*(\nabla^2\Psi)\right] = \dfrac{i\hbar}{2m}\left[\Psi(\nabla^2\Psi^*) - \Psi^*(\nabla^2\Psi)\right].$

But the Schrödinger equation says $\quad i\hbar\dfrac{\partial\Psi}{\partial t} = -\dfrac{\hbar^2}{2m}\nabla^2\Psi + V\Psi, \quad$ so

$$\nabla^2\Psi = \frac{2m}{\hbar^2}\left(V\Psi - i\hbar\frac{\partial\Psi}{\partial t}\right), \quad \nabla^2\Psi^* = \frac{2m}{\hbar^2}\left(V\Psi^* + i\hbar\frac{\partial\Psi^*}{\partial t}\right). \quad \text{Therefore}$$

$$\begin{aligned}
\nabla\cdot\mathbf{J} &= \frac{i\hbar}{2m}\frac{2m}{\hbar^2}\left[\Psi\left(V\Psi^* + i\hbar\frac{\partial\Psi^*}{\partial t}\right) - \Psi^*\left(V\Psi - i\hbar\frac{\partial\Psi}{\partial t}\right)\right]\\
&= \frac{i}{\hbar}\,i\hbar\left(\Psi\frac{\partial\Psi^*}{\partial t} + \Psi^*\frac{\partial\Psi}{\partial t}\right) = -\frac{\partial}{\partial t}(\Psi^*\Psi) = -\frac{\partial}{\partial t}|\Psi|^2. \quad \checkmark
\end{aligned}$$

**(b)** From Problem 4.11(b), $\quad \Psi_{211} = -\dfrac{1}{\sqrt{\pi a}}\dfrac{1}{8a^2}re^{-r/2a}\sin\theta\, e^{i\phi}e^{-iE_2 t/\hbar}.\quad$ In spherical coordinates,

$$\nabla\Psi = \frac{\partial\Psi}{\partial r}\hat{r} + \frac{1}{r}\frac{\partial\Psi}{\partial\theta}\hat{\theta} + \frac{1}{r\sin\theta}\frac{\partial\Psi}{\partial\phi}\hat{\phi}, \quad \text{so}$$

$$\begin{aligned}
\nabla\Psi_{211} &= -\frac{1}{\sqrt{\pi a}}\frac{1}{8a^2}\left[\left(1 - \frac{r}{2a}\right)e^{-r/2a}\sin\theta\, e^{i\phi}e^{-iE_2 t/\hbar}\hat{r} + \frac{1}{r}re^{-r/2a}\cos\theta\, e^{i\phi}e^{-iE_2 t/\hbar}\hat{\theta}\right.\\
&\quad\left. + \frac{1}{r\sin\theta}re^{-r/2a}\sin\theta\, ie^{i\phi}e^{-iE_2 t/\hbar}\hat{\phi}\right] = \left[\left(1 - \frac{r}{2a}\right)\hat{r} + \cot\theta\,\hat{\theta} + \frac{i}{\sin\theta}\hat{\phi}\right]\frac{1}{r}\Psi_{211}.
\end{aligned}$$

Therefore

$$\begin{aligned}
\mathbf{J} &= \frac{i\hbar}{2m}\left[\left(1 - \frac{r}{2a}\right)\hat{r} + \cot\theta\,\hat{\theta} - \frac{i}{\sin\theta}\hat{\phi} - \left(1 - \frac{r}{2a}\right)\hat{r} - \cot\theta\,\hat{\theta} - \frac{i}{\sin\theta}\hat{\phi}\right]\frac{1}{r}|\Psi_{211}|^2\\
&= \frac{i\hbar}{2m}\frac{(-2i)}{r\sin\theta}|\Psi_{211}|^2\,\hat{\phi} = \frac{\hbar}{m}\frac{1}{\pi a}\frac{1}{64a^4}\frac{r^2 e^{-r/a}\sin^2\theta}{r\sin\theta}\hat{\phi} = \boxed{\frac{\hbar}{64\pi ma^5}re^{-r/a}\sin\theta\,\hat{\phi}.}
\end{aligned}$$

**(c)** Now $\mathbf{r}\times\mathbf{J} = \dfrac{\hbar}{64\pi ma^5}r^2 e^{-r/a}\sin\theta\left(\hat{r}\times\hat{\phi}\right)$, while $\left(\hat{r}\times\hat{\phi}\right) = -\hat{\theta}$ and $\hat{z}\cdot\hat{\theta} = -\sin\theta$, so

$$\mathbf{r}\times\mathbf{J}_z = \frac{\hbar}{64\pi ma^5}r^2 e^{-r/a}\sin^2\theta, \text{ and hence}$$

$$\begin{aligned}
L_z &= m\frac{\hbar}{64\pi ma^5}\int\left(r^2 e^{-r/a}\sin^2\theta\right)r^2\sin\theta\, dr\, d\theta\, d\phi\\
&= \frac{\hbar}{64\pi a^5}\int_0^\infty r^4 e^{-r/a}\, dr\int_0^\pi\sin^3\theta\, d\theta\int_0^{2\pi}d\phi = \frac{\hbar}{64\pi a^5}\left(4!a^5\right)\left(\frac{4}{3}\right)(2\pi) = \boxed{\hbar,}
\end{aligned}$$

as it *should* be, since (Eq. 4.133) $L_z = \hbar m$, and $m = 1$ for this state.

---

## Problem 4.42

(a)

$$\psi = \frac{1}{\sqrt{\pi a^3}} e^{-r/a} \Rightarrow \phi(\mathbf{p}) = \frac{1}{(2\pi\hbar)^{3/2}} \frac{1}{\sqrt{\pi a^3}} \int e^{-i\mathbf{p}\cdot\mathbf{r}/\hbar} e^{-r/a} r^2 \sin\theta \, dr \, d\theta \, d\phi.$$

With axes as suggested, $\mathbf{p} \cdot \mathbf{r} = pr\cos\theta$. Doing the (trivial) $\phi$ integral:

$$\phi(\mathbf{p}) = \frac{2\pi}{(2\pi a\hbar)^{3/2}} \frac{1}{\sqrt{\pi}} \int_0^\infty r^2 e^{-r/a} \left[ \int_0^\pi e^{-ipr\cos\theta/\hbar} \sin\theta \, d\theta \right] dr.$$

$$\int_0^\pi e^{-ipr\cos\theta/\hbar} \sin\theta \, d\theta = \frac{\hbar}{ipr} \, e^{-ipr\cos\theta/\hbar} \Big|_0^\pi = \frac{\hbar}{ipr} \left( e^{ipr/\hbar} - e^{-ipr/\hbar} \right) = \frac{2\hbar}{pr} \sin\left(\frac{pr}{\hbar}\right).$$

$$\phi(\mathbf{p}) = \frac{1}{\pi\sqrt{2}} \frac{1}{(a\hbar)^{3/2}} \frac{2\hbar}{p} \int_0^\infty r e^{-r/a} \sin\left(\frac{pr}{\hbar}\right) dr.$$

$$\int_0^\infty r e^{-r/a} \sin\left(\frac{pr}{\hbar}\right) dr = \frac{1}{2i} \left[ \int_0^\infty r e^{-r/a} e^{ipr/\hbar} dr - \int_0^\infty r e^{-r/a} e^{-ipr/\hbar} dr \right]$$

$$= \frac{1}{2i} \left[ \frac{1}{(1/a - ip/\hbar)^2} - \frac{1}{(1/a + ip/\hbar)^2} \right] = \frac{1}{2i} \frac{(2ip/a\hbar)2}{\left[ (1/a)^2 + (p/\hbar)^2 \right]^2}$$

$$= \frac{(2p/\hbar)a^3}{\left[ 1 + (ap/\hbar)^2 \right]^2}.$$

$$\phi(\mathbf{p}) = \sqrt{\frac{2}{\hbar}} \frac{1}{a^{3/2}} \frac{1}{\pi p} \frac{2pa^3}{\hbar} \frac{1}{\left[ 1 + (ap/\hbar)^2 \right]^2} = \boxed{\frac{1}{\pi} \left(\frac{2a}{\hbar}\right)^{3/2} \frac{1}{\left[ 1 + (ap/\hbar)^2 \right]^2}.}$$

(b)

$$\int |\phi|^2 \, d^3\mathbf{p} = 4\pi \int_0^\infty p^2 |\phi|^2 dp = 4\pi \frac{1}{\pi^2} \left(\frac{2a}{\hbar}\right)^3 \int_0^\infty \frac{p^2}{\left[ 1 + (ap/\hbar)^2 \right]^4} \, dp.$$

From math tables: $\displaystyle \int_0^\infty \frac{x^2}{(m + x^2)^4} \, dx = \frac{\pi}{32} m^{-5/2},$ so

$$\int_0^\infty \frac{p^2}{\left[ 1 + (ap/\hbar)^2 \right]^4} dp = \left(\frac{\hbar}{a}\right)^8 \frac{\pi}{32} \left(\frac{\hbar}{a}\right)^{-5} = \frac{\pi}{32} \left(\frac{\hbar}{a}\right)^3; \quad \int |\phi|^2 d^3\mathbf{p} = \frac{32}{\pi} \left(\frac{a}{\hbar}\right)^3 \frac{\pi}{32} \left(\frac{\hbar}{a}\right)^3 = 1. \checkmark$$

**(c)**

$$\langle p^2 \rangle = \int p^2 |\phi|^2 \, d^3\mathbf{p} = \frac{1}{\pi^2} \left( \frac{2a}{\hbar} \right)^3 4\pi \int_0^\infty \frac{p^4}{[1 + (ap/\hbar)^2]^4} dp. \quad \text{From math tables:}$$

$$\int_0^\infty \frac{x^4}{[m + x^2]^4} dx = \left( \frac{\pi}{32} \right) m^{-3/2}. \quad \text{So} \quad \langle p^2 \rangle = \frac{4}{\pi} \left( \frac{2a}{\hbar} \right)^3 \left( \frac{\hbar}{a} \right)^8 \frac{\pi}{32} \left( \frac{\hbar}{a} \right)^{-3} = \boxed{\frac{\hbar^2}{a^2}}.$$

**(d)**

$$\langle T \rangle = \frac{1}{2m} \langle p^2 \rangle = \frac{1}{2m} \frac{\hbar^2}{a^2} = \frac{\hbar^2}{2m} \frac{m^2}{\hbar^4} \left( \frac{e^2}{4\pi\epsilon_0} \right)^2 = \frac{m}{2\hbar^2} \left( \frac{e^2}{4\pi\epsilon_0} \right)^2 = \boxed{-E_1,}$$

which *is* consistent with Eq. 4.191.

---

## Problem 4.43

**(a)** From Tables 4.3 and 4.7,

$$\psi_{321} = R_{32} Y_2^1 = \frac{4}{81\sqrt{30}} \frac{1}{a^{3/2}} \left( \frac{r}{a} \right)^2 e^{-r/3a} \left[ -\sqrt{\frac{15}{8\pi}} \sin\theta \cos\theta e^{i\phi} \right] = \boxed{-\frac{1}{\sqrt{\pi}} \frac{1}{81a^{7/2}} r^2 e^{-r/3a} \sin\theta \cos\theta e^{i\phi}.}$$

**(b)**

$$\int |\psi|^2 d^3\mathbf{r} = \frac{1}{\pi} \frac{1}{(81)^2 a^7} \int \left( r^4 e^{-2r/3a} \sin^2\theta \cos^2\theta \right) r^2 \sin\theta \, dr \, d\theta \, d\phi$$

$$= \frac{1}{\pi(81)^2 a^7} 2\pi \int_0^\infty r^6 e^{-2r/3a} \, dr \int_0^\pi (1 - \cos^2\theta) \cos^2\theta \sin\theta \, d\theta$$

$$= \frac{2}{(81)^2 a^7} \left[ 6! \left( \frac{3a}{2} \right)^7 \right] \left[ -\frac{\cos^3\theta}{3} + \frac{\cos^5\theta}{5} \right]\Big|_0^\pi$$

$$= \frac{2}{3^8 a^7} 6 \cdot 5 \cdot 4 \cdot 3 \cdot 2 \frac{3^7 a^7}{2^7} \left[ \frac{2}{3} - \frac{2}{5} \right] = \frac{3 \cdot 5}{4} \cdot \frac{4}{15} = 1. \quad \checkmark$$

**(c)**

$$\langle r^s \rangle = \int_0^\infty r^s |R_{32}|^2 r^2 dr = \left( \frac{4}{81} \right)^2 \frac{1}{30} \frac{1}{a^7} \int_0^\infty r^{s+6} e^{-2r/3a} dr$$

$$= \frac{8}{15(81)^2 a^7} (s+6)! \left( \frac{3a}{2} \right)^{s+7} = \boxed{(s+6)! \left( \frac{3a}{2} \right)^5 \frac{1}{720}} = \frac{(s+6)!}{6!} \left( \frac{3a}{2} \right)^3.$$

Finite for $\boxed{s > -7}$.

---

## Problem 4.44

**(a)** From Tables 4.3 and 4.7,

$$\psi_{433} = R_{43} Y_3^3 = \frac{1}{768\sqrt{35}} \frac{1}{a^{3/2}} \left(\frac{r}{a}\right)^3 e^{-r/4a} \left(-\sqrt{\frac{35}{64\pi}} \sin^3\theta \cos\theta e^{3i\phi}\right) = \boxed{-\frac{1}{6144\sqrt{\pi}a^{9/2}} r^3 e^{-r/4a} \sin^3\theta e^{3i\phi}.}$$

**(b)**

$$\langle r \rangle = \int r|\psi|^2 d^3\mathbf{r} = \frac{1}{(6144)^2 \pi a^9} \int r\left(r^6 e^{-r/2a}\sin^6\theta\right) r^2 \sin\theta\, dr\, d\theta\, d\phi$$

$$= \frac{1}{(6144)^2 \pi a^9} \int_0^\infty r^9 e^{-r/2a}\, dr \int_0^\pi \sin^7\theta\, d\theta \int_0^{2\pi} d\phi$$

$$= \frac{1}{(6144)^2 \pi a^9} \left[9!(2a)^{10}\right] \left(2\frac{2\cdot4\cdot6}{3\cdot5\cdot7}\right)(2\pi) = \boxed{18a.}$$

**(c)** Using Eq. 4.133: $L_x^2 + L_y^2 = L^2 - L_z^2 = 4(5)\hbar^2 - (3\hbar)^2 = \boxed{11\hbar^2, \text{ with probability } 1.}$

---

## Problem 4.45

**(a)**

$$P = \int |\psi|^2 d^3\mathbf{r} = \frac{4\pi}{\pi a^3} \int_0^b e^{-2r/a} r^2 dr = \frac{4}{a^3}\left[-\frac{a}{2}r^2 e^{-2r/a} + \frac{a^3}{4}e^{-2r/a}\left(-\frac{2r}{a}-1\right)\right]\Big|_0^b$$

$$= -\left(1 + \frac{2r}{a} + \frac{2r^2}{a^2}\right)e^{-2r/a}\Big|_0^b = \boxed{1 - \left(1 + \frac{2b}{a} + 2\frac{b^2}{a^2}\right)e^{-2b/a}.}$$

**(b)**

$$P = 1 - \left(1 + \epsilon + \frac{1}{2}\epsilon^2\right)e^{-\epsilon} \approx 1 - \left(1 + \epsilon + \frac{1}{2}\epsilon^2\right)\left(1 - \epsilon + \frac{\epsilon^2}{2} - \frac{\epsilon^3}{3!}\right)$$

$$\approx 1 - 1 + \epsilon - \frac{\epsilon^2}{2} + \frac{\epsilon^3}{6} - \epsilon + \epsilon^2 - \frac{\epsilon^3}{2} - \frac{\epsilon^2}{2} + \frac{\epsilon^3}{2} = \epsilon^3\left(\frac{1}{6} - \frac{1}{2} + \frac{1}{2}\right)$$

$$= \frac{1}{6}\left(\frac{2b}{a}\right)^3 = \boxed{\frac{4}{3}\left(\frac{b}{a}\right)^3.}$$

**(c)**

$$|\psi(0)|^2 = \frac{1}{\pi a^3} \Rightarrow P \approx \frac{4}{3}\pi b^3 \frac{1}{\pi a^3} = \frac{4}{3}\left(\frac{b}{a}\right)^3. \quad \checkmark$$

**(d)**

$$P = \frac{4}{3}\left(\frac{10^{-15}}{0.5\times10^{-10}}\right)^3 = \frac{4}{3}\left(2\times10^{-5}\right)^3 = \frac{4}{3}\cdot8\times10^{-15} = \frac{32}{3}\times10^{-15} = \boxed{1.07\times10^{-14}.}$$

---

## Problem 4.46

**(a)** Equation 4.75 $\Rightarrow R_{n(n-1)} = \frac{1}{r}\rho^n e^{-\rho} v(\rho)$, where $\rho \equiv \frac{r}{na}$; Eq. 4.76 $\Rightarrow c_1 = \frac{2(n-n)}{(1)(2n)} c_0 = 0$.

So $v(\rho) = c_0$, and hence $R_{n(n-1)} = N_n r^{n-1} e^{-r/na}$, where $N_n \equiv \frac{c_0}{(na)^n}$.

$$1 = \int_0^\infty |R|^2 r^2 dr = (N_n)^2 \int_0^\infty r^{2n} e^{-2r/na} dr = (N_n)^2 (2n)! \left(\frac{na}{2}\right)^{2n+1}; \quad \boxed{N_n = \left(\frac{2}{na}\right)^n \sqrt{\frac{2}{na(2n)!}}}.$$

**(b)**

$$\langle r^l \rangle = \int_0^\infty |R|^2 r^{l+2} dr = N_n^2 \int_0^\infty r^{2n+l} e^{-2r/na} dr.$$

$$\langle r \rangle = \left(\frac{2}{na}\right)^{2n+1} \frac{1}{(2n)!} (2n+1)! \left(\frac{na}{2}\right)^{2n+2} = \boxed{\left(n + \frac{1}{2}\right) na.}$$

$$\langle r^2 \rangle = \left(\frac{2}{na}\right)^{2n+1} \frac{1}{(2n)!} (2n+2)! \left(\frac{na}{2}\right)^{2n+3} = (2n+2)(2n+1)\left(\frac{na}{2}\right)^2 = \boxed{\left(n + \frac{1}{2}\right)(n+1)(na)^2.}$$

**(c)**

$$\sigma_r^2 = \langle r^2 \rangle - \langle r \rangle^2 = \left[\left(n + \frac{1}{2}\right)(n+1)(na)^2 - \left(n + \frac{1}{2}\right)^2 (na)^2\right]$$

$$= \frac{1}{2}\left(n + \frac{1}{2}\right)(na)^2 = \frac{1}{2(n+1/2)} \langle r \rangle^2; \quad \boxed{\sigma_r = \frac{\langle r \rangle}{\sqrt{2n+1}}.}$$

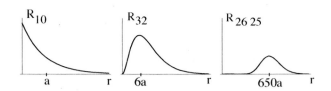

Maxima occur at: $\dfrac{dR_{n,n-1}}{dr} = 0 \Rightarrow (n-1)r^{n-2} e^{-r/na} - \dfrac{1}{na} r^{n-1} e^{-r/na} = 0 \Rightarrow r = na(n-1).$

## Problem 4.47

Here are a couple of examples: {32, 28} and {224,56}; {221, 119} and {119, 91}. For further discussion see D. Wyss and W. Wyss, *Foundations of Physics* **23**, 465 (1993).

## Problem 4.48

**(a)** Using Eqs. 3.64 and 4.122: $[A, B] = [x^2, L_z] = x[x, L_z] + [x, L_z]x = x(-i\hbar y) + (-i\hbar y)x = -2i\hbar xy$.

Equation 3.62 $\Rightarrow \sigma_A^2 \sigma_B^2 \geq \left[ \frac{1}{2i}(-2i\hbar)\langle xy \rangle \right]^2 = \hbar^2 \langle xy \rangle^2 \Rightarrow \boxed{\sigma_A \sigma_B \geq \hbar |\langle xy \rangle|.}$

**(b)** Equation 4.113 $\Rightarrow \langle B \rangle = \langle L_z \rangle = m\hbar$;   $\langle B^2 \rangle = \langle L_z^2 \rangle = m^2 \hbar^2$;   so   $\sigma_B = m^2 \hbar^2 - m^2 \hbar^2 = \boxed{0.}$

**(c)** Since the left side of the uncertainty principle is zero, the right side must also be: $\boxed{\langle xy \rangle = 0,}$ for eigenstates of $L_z$.

---

## Problem 4.49

**(a)** $1 = |A|^2 (1 + 4 + 4) = 9|A|^2$;   $\boxed{A = 1/3.}$

**(b)** $\boxed{\dfrac{\hbar}{2}, \text{ with probability } \dfrac{5}{9}; \ -\dfrac{\hbar}{2}, \text{ with probability } \dfrac{4}{9}.}$ $\langle S_z \rangle = \dfrac{5}{9} \dfrac{\hbar}{2} + \dfrac{4}{9} \left( -\dfrac{\hbar}{2} \right) = \boxed{\dfrac{\hbar}{18}.}$

**(c)** From Eq. 4.151,

$$c_+^{(x)} = \left( \chi_+^{(x)} \right)^\dagger \chi = \frac{1}{3} \frac{1}{\sqrt{2}} \begin{pmatrix} 1 & 1 \end{pmatrix} \begin{pmatrix} 1 - 2i \\ 2 \end{pmatrix} = \frac{1}{3\sqrt{2}} (1 - 2i + 2) = \frac{3 - 2i}{3\sqrt{2}}; \quad |c_+^{(x)}|^2 = \frac{9 + 4}{9 \cdot 2} = \frac{13}{18}.$$

$$c_-^{(x)} = \left( \chi_-^{(x)} \right)^\dagger \chi = \frac{1}{3} \frac{1}{\sqrt{2}} \begin{pmatrix} 1 & -1 \end{pmatrix} \begin{pmatrix} 1 - 2i \\ 2 \end{pmatrix} = \frac{1}{3\sqrt{2}} (1 - 2i - 2) = -\frac{1 + 2i}{3\sqrt{2}}; \quad |c_-^{(x)}|^2 = \frac{1 + 4}{9 \cdot 2} = \frac{5}{18}.$$

$\boxed{\dfrac{\hbar}{2}, \text{ with probability } \dfrac{13}{18}; \ -\dfrac{\hbar}{2}, \text{ with probability } \dfrac{5}{18}.}$ $\langle S_x \rangle = \dfrac{13}{18} \dfrac{\hbar}{2} + \dfrac{5}{18} \left( -\dfrac{\hbar}{2} \right) = \boxed{\dfrac{2\hbar}{9}.}$

**(d)** From Problem 4.29(a),

$$c_+^{(y)} = \left( \chi_+^{(y)} \right)^\dagger \chi = \frac{1}{3} \frac{1}{\sqrt{2}} \begin{pmatrix} 1 & -i \end{pmatrix} \begin{pmatrix} 1 - 2i \\ 2 \end{pmatrix} = \frac{1}{3\sqrt{2}} (1 - 2i - 2i) = \frac{1 - 4i}{3\sqrt{2}}; \quad |c_+^{(y)}|^2 = \frac{1 + 16}{9 \cdot 2} = \frac{17}{18}.$$

$$c_-^{(y)} = \left( \chi_-^{(y)} \right)^\dagger \chi = \frac{1}{3} \frac{1}{\sqrt{2}} \begin{pmatrix} 1 & i \end{pmatrix} \begin{pmatrix} 1 - 2i \\ 2 \end{pmatrix} = \frac{1}{3\sqrt{2}} (1 - 2i + 2i) = \frac{1}{3\sqrt{2}}; \quad |c_-^{(y)}|^2 = \frac{1}{9 \cdot 2} = \frac{1}{18}.$$

$\boxed{\dfrac{\hbar}{2}, \text{ with probability } \dfrac{17}{18}; \ -\dfrac{\hbar}{2}, \text{ with probability } \dfrac{1}{18}.}$ $\langle S_y \rangle = \dfrac{17}{18} \dfrac{\hbar}{2} + \dfrac{1}{18} \left( -\dfrac{\hbar}{2} \right) = \boxed{\dfrac{4\hbar}{9}.}$

---

## Problem 4.50

We may as well choose axes so that $\hat{a}$ lies along the $z$ axis and $\hat{b}$ is in the $xz$ plane. Then $S_a^{(1)} = S_z^{(1)}$, and $S_b^{(2)} = \cos\theta \, S_z^{(2)} + \sin\theta \, S_x^{(2)}$.   $\langle 0 \, 0 | S_a^{(1)} S_b^{(2)} | 0 \, 0 \rangle$ is to be calculated.

$$S_a^{(1)} S_b^{(2)} |0 \, 0\rangle = \frac{1}{\sqrt{2}} \left[ S_z^{(1)} (\cos\theta \, S_z^{(2)} + \sin\theta \, S_x^{(2)}) \right] (\uparrow\downarrow - \downarrow\uparrow)$$

$$= \frac{1}{\sqrt{2}} \left[ (S_z \uparrow)(\cos\theta\, S_z \downarrow + \sin\theta\, S_x \downarrow) - (S_z \downarrow)(\cos\theta\, S_z \uparrow + \sin\theta\, S_x \uparrow) \right]$$

$$= \frac{1}{\sqrt{2}} \left\{ \left( \frac{\hbar}{2} \uparrow \right) \left[ \cos\theta \left( -\frac{\hbar}{2} \downarrow \right) + \sin\theta \left( \frac{\hbar}{2} \uparrow \right) \right] - \left( -\frac{\hbar}{2} \downarrow \right) \left[ \cos\theta \left( \frac{\hbar}{2} \uparrow \right) + \sin\theta \left( \frac{\hbar}{2} \downarrow \right) \right] \right\} \quad \text{(using Eq. 4.145)}$$

$$= \frac{\hbar^2}{4} \left[ \cos\theta \frac{1}{\sqrt{2}} (- \uparrow\downarrow + \downarrow\uparrow) + \sin\theta \frac{1}{\sqrt{2}} (\uparrow\uparrow + \downarrow\downarrow) \right] = \frac{\hbar^2}{4} \left[ - \cos\theta |0\ 0\rangle + \sin\theta \frac{1}{\sqrt{2}} (|1\ 1\rangle + |1\ -1\rangle) \right].$$

so $\langle S_a^{(1)} S_b^{(2)} \rangle = \langle 0\ 0| S_a^{(1)} S_b^{(2)} |0\ 0\rangle = \frac{\hbar^2}{4} \langle 0\ 0| \left[ - \cos\theta |0\ 0\rangle + \sin\theta \frac{1}{\sqrt{2}} (|1\ 1\rangle + |1\ -1\rangle) \right] = -\frac{\hbar^2}{4} \cos\theta \langle 0\ 0|0\ 0\rangle$

(by orthogonality), and hence $\langle S_a^{(1)} S_b^{(2)} \rangle = -\dfrac{\hbar^2}{4} \cos\theta.$ **QED**

---

## Problem 4.51

**(a)** First note from Eqs. 4.136 and 4.144 that

$$S_x |s\ m\rangle = \frac{1}{2} [S_+ |s\ m\rangle + S_- |s\ m\rangle]$$
$$= \frac{\hbar}{2} \left[ \sqrt{s(s+1) - m(m+1)} |s\ m+1\rangle + \sqrt{s(s+1) - m(m-1)} |s\ m-1\rangle \right]$$

$$S_y |s\ m\rangle = \frac{1}{2i} [S_+ |s\ m\rangle - S_- |s\ m\rangle]$$
$$= \frac{\hbar}{2i} \left[ \sqrt{s(s+1) - m(m+1)} |s\ m+1\rangle - \sqrt{s(s+1) - m(m-1)} |s\ m-1\rangle \right]$$

Now, using Eqs. 4.179 and 4.147:

$$S^2 |s\ m\rangle = \left[ (S^{(1)})^2 + (S^{(2)})^2 + 2(S_x^{(1)} S_x^{(2)} + S_y^{(1)} S_y^{(2)} + S_z^{(1)} S_z^{(2)}) \right] \left[ A| \tfrac{1}{2}\ \tfrac{1}{2}\rangle |S_2\ m - \tfrac{1}{2}\rangle + B| \tfrac{1}{2}\ -\tfrac{1}{2}\rangle |s_2\ m + \tfrac{1}{2}\rangle \right]$$

$$= A \Big\{ \left( S^2 |\tfrac{1}{2}\ \tfrac{1}{2}\rangle \right) |s_2\ m - \tfrac{1}{2}\rangle + |\tfrac{1}{2}\ \tfrac{1}{2}\rangle \left( S^2 |s_2\ m - \tfrac{1}{2}\rangle \right)$$

$$+ 2 \left[ \left( S_x |\tfrac{1}{2}\ \tfrac{1}{2}\rangle \right) \left( S_x |s_2\ m - \tfrac{1}{2}\rangle \right) + \left( S_y |\tfrac{1}{2}\ \tfrac{1}{2}\rangle \right) \left( S_y |s_2\ m - \tfrac{1}{2}\rangle \right) + \left( S_z |\tfrac{1}{2}\ \tfrac{1}{2}\rangle \right) \left( S_z |s_2\ m - \tfrac{1}{2}\rangle \right) \right] \Big\}$$

$$+ B \Big\{ \left( S^2 |\tfrac{1}{2}\ -\tfrac{1}{2}\rangle \right) |s_2\ m + \tfrac{1}{2}\rangle + |\tfrac{1}{2}\ -\tfrac{1}{2}\rangle \left( S^2 |s_2\ m + \tfrac{1}{2}\rangle \right)$$

$$+ 2 \left[ \left( S_x |\tfrac{1}{2}\ -\tfrac{1}{2}\rangle \right) \left( S_x |s_2\ m + \tfrac{1}{2}\rangle \right) + \left( S_y |\tfrac{1}{2}\ -\tfrac{1}{2}\rangle \right) \left( S_y |s_2\ m + \tfrac{1}{2}\rangle \right) + \left( S_z |\tfrac{1}{2}\ -\tfrac{1}{2}\rangle \right) \left( S_z |s_2\ m + \tfrac{1}{2}\rangle \right) \right] \Big\}$$

$$= A \Big\{ \tfrac{3}{4} \hbar^2 |\tfrac{1}{2}\ \tfrac{1}{2}\rangle |s_2\ m - \tfrac{1}{2}\rangle + \hbar^2 s_2(s_2 + 1) |\tfrac{1}{2}\ \tfrac{1}{2}\rangle |s_2\ m - \tfrac{1}{2}\rangle$$

$$+ 2 \left[ \tfrac{\hbar}{2} |\tfrac{1}{2}\ -\tfrac{1}{2}\rangle \tfrac{\hbar}{2} \left( \sqrt{s_2(s_2 + 1) - (m - \tfrac{1}{2})(m + \tfrac{1}{2})} |s_2\ m + \tfrac{1}{2}\rangle \right. \right.$$

$$+\sqrt{s_2(s_2+1)-(m-\tfrac{1}{2})(m-\tfrac{3}{2})}|s_2\ m-\tfrac{3}{2}\rangle\Bigg)$$

$$+\left(\tfrac{i\hbar}{2}\right)|\tfrac{1}{2}\ -\tfrac{1}{2}\rangle\tfrac{\hbar}{2i}\Bigg(\sqrt{s_2(s_2+1)-(m-\tfrac{1}{2})(m+\tfrac{1}{2})}|s_2\ m+\tfrac{1}{2}\rangle$$

$$-\sqrt{s_2(s_2+1)-(m-\tfrac{1}{2})(m-\tfrac{3}{2})}|s_2\ m-\tfrac{3}{2}\rangle\Bigg)+\tfrac{\hbar}{2}|\tfrac{1}{2}\ \tfrac{1}{2}\rangle\hbar(m-\tfrac{1}{2})|s_2\ m-\tfrac{1}{2}\rangle\Bigg]\Bigg\}$$

$$+B\Bigg\{\tfrac{3}{4}\hbar^2|\tfrac{1}{2}\ -\tfrac{1}{2}\rangle|s_2\ m+\tfrac{1}{2}\rangle+\hbar^2 s_2(s_2+1)|\tfrac{1}{2}\ -\tfrac{1}{2}\rangle|s_2\ m+\tfrac{1}{2}\rangle$$

$$+2\Bigg[\tfrac{\hbar}{2}|\tfrac{1}{2}\ \tfrac{1}{2}\rangle\tfrac{\hbar}{2}\Bigg(\sqrt{s_2(s_2+1)-(m+\tfrac{1}{2})(m+\tfrac{3}{2})}|s_2\ m+\tfrac{3}{2}\rangle+\sqrt{s_2(s_2+1)-(m+\tfrac{1}{2})(m-\tfrac{1}{2})}|s_2\ m-\tfrac{1}{2}\rangle\Bigg)$$

$$+\left(\tfrac{-i\hbar}{2}\right)|\tfrac{1}{2}\ \tfrac{1}{2}\rangle\tfrac{\hbar}{2i}\Bigg(\sqrt{s_2(s_2+1)-(m+\tfrac{1}{2})(m+\tfrac{3}{2})}|s_2\ m+\tfrac{3}{2}\rangle$$

$$-\sqrt{s_2(s_2+1)-(m+\tfrac{1}{2})(m-\tfrac{1}{2})}|s_2\ m-\tfrac{1}{2}\rangle\Bigg)+\left(\tfrac{-\hbar}{2}\right)|\tfrac{1}{2}\ -\tfrac{1}{2}\rangle\hbar(m+\tfrac{1}{2})|s_2\ m+\tfrac{1}{2}\rangle\Bigg]\Bigg\}$$

$$=\hbar^2\Bigg\{A\left[\tfrac{3}{4}+s_2(s_2+1)+m-\tfrac{1}{2}\right]+B\sqrt{s_2(s_2+1)-m^2+\tfrac{1}{4}}\Bigg\}|\tfrac{1}{2}\ \tfrac{1}{2}\rangle|s_2\ m-\tfrac{1}{2}\rangle$$

$$+\hbar^2\Bigg\{B\left[\tfrac{3}{4}+s_2(s_2+1)-m-\tfrac{1}{2}\right]+A\sqrt{s_2(s_2+1)-m^2+\tfrac{1}{4}}\Bigg\}|\tfrac{1}{2}\ -\tfrac{1}{2}\rangle|s_2\ m+\tfrac{1}{2}\rangle$$

$$=\hbar^2 s(s+1)|s\ m\rangle=\hbar^2 s(s+1)\left[A|\tfrac{1}{2}\ \tfrac{1}{2}\rangle|s_2\ m-\tfrac{1}{2}\rangle+B|\tfrac{1}{2}\ -\tfrac{1}{2}\rangle|s_2\ m+\tfrac{1}{2}\rangle\right].$$

$$\left\{\begin{array}{l}A\left[s_2(s_2+1)+\tfrac{1}{4}+m\right]+B\sqrt{s_2(s_2+1)-m^2+\tfrac{1}{4}}=s(s+1)A,\\ B\left[s_2(s_2+1)+\tfrac{1}{4}-m\right]+A\sqrt{s_2(s_2+1)-m^2+\tfrac{1}{4}}=s(s+1)B,\end{array}\right\}\quad\text{or}$$

$$\left\{\begin{array}{l}A\left[s_2(s_2+1)-s(s+1)+\tfrac{1}{4}+m\right]+B\sqrt{s_2(s_2+1)-m^2+\tfrac{1}{4}}=0,\\ B\left[s_2(s_2+1)-s(s+1)+\tfrac{1}{4}-m\right]+A\sqrt{s_2(s_2+1)-m^2+\tfrac{1}{4}}=0,\end{array}\right\}\quad\text{or}\quad\left\{\begin{array}{l}A(a+m)+Bb=0\\ B(a-m)+Ab=0\end{array}\right\},$$

where $a\equiv s_2(s_2+1)-s(s+1)+\tfrac{1}{4}$, $b\equiv\sqrt{s_2(s_2+1)-m^2+\tfrac{1}{4}}$. Multiply by $(a-b)$ and $b$, then subtract:

$A(a^2-m^2)+Bb(a-m)=0;\ Bb(a-m)+Ab^2=0\Rightarrow A(a^2-m^2-b^2)=0\Rightarrow a^2-b^2=m^2$, or:

$$\left[s_2(s_2+1)-s(s+1)+\tfrac{1}{4}\right]^2-s_2(s_2+1)+m^2-\tfrac{1}{4}=m^2,$$

$$\left[s_2(s_2+1)-s(s+1)+\tfrac{1}{4}\right]^2=s_2^2+s_2+\tfrac{1}{4}=\left(s_2+\tfrac{1}{2}\right)^2,\text{ so}$$

$$s_2(s_2+1)-s(s+1)+\tfrac{1}{4}=\pm\left(s_2+\tfrac{1}{2}\right);\quad s(s+1)=s_2(s_2+1)\mp\left(s_2+\tfrac{1}{2}\right)+\tfrac{1}{4}.$$

Add $\tfrac{1}{4}$ to both sides:

$$s^2+s+\tfrac{1}{4}=\left(s+\tfrac{1}{2}\right)^2=s_2(s_2+1)\mp\left(s_2+\tfrac{1}{2}\right)+\tfrac{1}{2}=\left\{\begin{array}{l}s_2^2+s_2-s_2-\tfrac{1}{2}+\tfrac{1}{2}=s_2^2\\[4pt]s_2^2+s_2+s_2+\tfrac{1}{2}+\tfrac{1}{2}=(s_2+1)^2\end{array}\right\}.$$

$$\text{So }\left\{\begin{array}{l}s+\tfrac{1}{2}=\pm s_2\quad\Rightarrow s=\pm s_2-\tfrac{1}{2}=\left\{\begin{array}{l}s_2-\tfrac{1}{2}\\ -s_2-\tfrac{1}{2}\end{array}\right.\\[12pt]s+\tfrac{1}{2}=\pm(s_2+1)\Rightarrow s=\pm(s_2+1)-\tfrac{1}{2}=\left\{\begin{array}{l}s_2+\tfrac{1}{2}\\ -s_2-\tfrac{3}{2}\end{array}\right.\end{array}\right\}.$$

But $s \geq 0$, so the possibilities are $\boxed{s = s_2 \pm 1/2.}$ Then:

$$a = s_2^2 + s_2 - \left(s_2 \pm \frac{1}{2}\right)\left(s_2 \pm \frac{1}{2} + 1\right) + \frac{1}{4}$$

$$= s_2^2 + s_2 - s_2^2 \mp \frac{1}{2}s_2 - s_2 \mp \frac{1}{2}s_2 - \frac{1}{4} \mp \frac{1}{2} + \frac{1}{4} = \mp s_2 \mp \frac{1}{2} = \mp\left(s_2 + \frac{1}{2}\right).$$

$$b = \sqrt{\left(s_2^2 + s_2 + \frac{1}{4}\right) - m^2} = \sqrt{\left(s_2 + \frac{1}{2}\right)^2 - m^2} = \sqrt{\left(s_2 + \frac{1}{2} + m\right)\left(s_2 + \frac{1}{2} - m\right)}.$$

$$\therefore A\left[\mp\left(s_2 + \tfrac{1}{2}\right) + m\right] = \mp A\left(s_2 + \tfrac{1}{2} \mp m\right) = -Bb = -B\sqrt{\left(s_2 + \tfrac{1}{2} + m\right)\left(s_2 + \tfrac{1}{2} - m\right)}$$

$$\Rightarrow A\sqrt{s_2 + \tfrac{1}{2} \mp m} = \pm B\sqrt{s_2 + \tfrac{1}{2} \pm m}. \quad \text{But } |A|^2 + |B|^2 = 1, \quad \text{so}$$

$$|A|^2 + |A|^2\left(\frac{s_2 + \frac{1}{2} \mp m}{s_2 + \frac{1}{2} \pm m}\right) = \frac{|A|^2}{(s_2 + \frac{1}{2} \pm m)}\left[s_2 + \frac{1}{2} \pm m + s_2 + \frac{1}{2} \mp m\right] = \frac{(2s_2 + 1)}{(s_2 + \frac{1}{2} \pm m)}|A|^2.$$

$$\Rightarrow \boxed{A = \sqrt{\frac{s_2 \pm m + \frac{1}{2}}{2s_2 + 1}}.} \quad B = \pm A\frac{\sqrt{s_2 + \frac{1}{2} \mp m}}{\sqrt{s_2 + \frac{1}{2} \pm m}} = \boxed{\pm\sqrt{\frac{s_2 \mp m + \frac{1}{2}}{2s_2 + 1}}.}$$

**(b)** Here are four examples:

(i) From the $1/2 \times 1/2$ table ($s_2 = 1/2$), pick $s = 1$ (upper signs), $m = 0$. Then

$$A = \sqrt{\frac{\frac{1}{2} + 0 + \frac{1}{2}}{1 + 1}} = \frac{1}{\sqrt{2}}; \quad B = \sqrt{\frac{\frac{1}{2} - 0 + \frac{1}{2}}{1 + 1}} = \frac{1}{\sqrt{2}}.$$

(ii) From the $1 \times 1/2$ table ($s_2 = 1$), pick $s = 3/2$ (upper signs), $m = 1/2$. Then

$$A = \sqrt{\frac{1 + \frac{1}{2} + \frac{1}{2}}{2 + 1}} = \sqrt{\frac{2}{3}}; \quad B = \sqrt{\frac{1 - \frac{1}{2} + \frac{1}{2}}{2 + 1}} = \frac{1}{\sqrt{3}}.$$

(iii) From the $3/2 \times 1/2$ table ($s_2 = 3/2$), pick $s = 1$ (lower signs), $m = -1$. Then

$$A = \sqrt{\frac{\frac{3}{2} + 1 + \frac{1}{2}}{3 + 1}} = \frac{\sqrt{3}}{2}; \quad B = -\sqrt{\frac{\frac{3}{2} - 1 + \frac{1}{2}}{3 + 1}} = -\frac{1}{2}.$$

(iv) From the $2 \times 1/2$ table ($s_2 = 2$), pick $s = 3/2$ (lower signs), $m = 1/2$. Then

$$A = \sqrt{\frac{2 - \frac{1}{2} + \frac{1}{2}}{4 + 1}} = \sqrt{\frac{2}{5}}; \quad B = -\sqrt{\frac{2 + \frac{1}{2} + \frac{1}{2}}{4 + 1}} = -\sqrt{\frac{3}{5}}.$$

These all check with the values on Table 4.8, except that the signs (which are conventional) are reversed in (iii) and (iv). Normalization does not determine the sign of $A$ (nor, therefore, of $B$).

---

## Problem 4.52

$$\left|\tfrac{3}{2}\ \tfrac{3}{2}\right\rangle = \begin{pmatrix} 1 \\ 0 \\ 0 \\ 0 \end{pmatrix}; \quad \left|\tfrac{3}{2}\ \tfrac{1}{2}\right\rangle = \begin{pmatrix} 0 \\ 1 \\ 0 \\ 0 \end{pmatrix}; \quad \left|\tfrac{3}{2}\ \tfrac{-1}{2}\right\rangle = \begin{pmatrix} 0 \\ 0 \\ 1 \\ 0 \end{pmatrix}; \quad \left|\tfrac{3}{2}\ \tfrac{-3}{2}\right\rangle = \begin{pmatrix} 0 \\ 0 \\ 0 \\ 1 \end{pmatrix}. \quad \text{Equation 4.136} \Rightarrow$$

$$\begin{cases} S_+\left|\tfrac{3}{2}\ \tfrac{3}{2}\right\rangle = 0, \quad S_+\left|\tfrac{3}{2}\ \tfrac{1}{2}\right\rangle = \sqrt{3}\hbar\left|\tfrac{3}{2}\ \tfrac{3}{2}\right\rangle, \quad S_+\left|\tfrac{3}{2}\ \tfrac{-1}{2}\right\rangle = 2\hbar\left|\tfrac{3}{2}\ \tfrac{1}{2}\right\rangle, \quad S_+\left|\tfrac{3}{2}\ \tfrac{-3}{2}\right\rangle = \sqrt{3}\hbar\left|\tfrac{3}{2}\ \tfrac{-1}{2}\right\rangle; \\ S_-\left|\tfrac{3}{2}\ \tfrac{3}{2}\right\rangle = \sqrt{3}\hbar\left|\tfrac{3}{2}\ \tfrac{1}{2}\right\rangle, \quad S_-\left|\tfrac{3}{2}\ \tfrac{1}{2}\right\rangle = 2\hbar\left|\tfrac{3}{2}\ \tfrac{-1}{2}\right\rangle, \quad S_-\left|\tfrac{3}{2}\ \tfrac{-1}{2}\right\rangle = \sqrt{3}\hbar\left|\tfrac{3}{2}\ \tfrac{-3}{2}\right\rangle, \quad S_-\left|\tfrac{3}{2}\ \tfrac{-3}{2}\right\rangle = 0. \end{cases}$$

So: $S_+ = \hbar \begin{pmatrix} 0 & \sqrt{3} & 0 & 0 \\ 0 & 0 & 2 & 0 \\ 0 & 0 & 0 & \sqrt{3} \\ 0 & 0 & 0 & 0 \end{pmatrix}$ ; $S_- = \hbar \begin{pmatrix} 0 & 0 & 0 & 0 \\ \sqrt{3} & 0 & 0 & 0 \\ 0 & 2 & 0 & 0 \\ 0 & 0 & \sqrt{3} & 0 \end{pmatrix}$ ; $S_x = \frac{1}{2}(S_+ + S_-) = \boxed{\frac{\hbar}{2} \begin{pmatrix} 0 & \sqrt{3} & 0 & 0 \\ \sqrt{3} & 0 & 2 & 0 \\ 0 & 2 & 0 & \sqrt{3} \\ 0 & 0 & \sqrt{3} & 0 \end{pmatrix}}$ .

$$\begin{vmatrix} -\lambda & \sqrt{3} & 0 & 0 \\ \sqrt{3} & -\lambda & 2 & 0 \\ 0 & 2 & -\lambda & \sqrt{3} \\ 0 & 0 & \sqrt{3} & -\lambda \end{vmatrix} = -\lambda \begin{vmatrix} -\lambda & 2 & 0 \\ 2 & -\lambda & \sqrt{3} \\ 0 & \sqrt{3} & -\lambda \end{vmatrix} - \sqrt{3} \begin{vmatrix} \sqrt{3} & 2 & 0 \\ 0 & -\lambda & \sqrt{3} \\ 0 & \sqrt{3} & -\lambda \end{vmatrix}$$

$$= -\lambda \left[ -\lambda^3 + 3\lambda + 4\lambda \right] - \sqrt{3} \left[ \sqrt{3}\lambda^2 - 3\sqrt{3} \right] = \lambda^4 - 7\lambda^2 - 3\lambda^2 + 9 = 0,$$

or $\lambda^4 - 10\lambda^2 + 9 = 0$; $(\lambda^2 - 9)(\lambda^2 - 1) = 0$; $\lambda = \pm 3, \pm 1$. So the eigenvalues of $S_x$ are $\boxed{\frac{3}{2}\hbar, \ \frac{1}{2}\hbar, \ -\frac{1}{2}\hbar, \ -\frac{3}{2}\hbar.}$

---

## Problem 4.53

From Eq. 4.135, $S_z|s\,m\rangle = \hbar m|s\,m\rangle$. Since $s$ is fixed, here, let's just identify the states by the value of $m$ (which runs from $-s$ to $+s$). The matrix elements of $\mathsf{S}_z$ are

$$\mathsf{S}_{nm} = \langle n|S_z|m\rangle = \hbar m\langle n|m\rangle = \hbar m\delta_{n\,m}.$$

It's a *diagonal* matrix, with elements $m\hbar$, ranging from $m = s$ in the upper left corner to $m = -s$ in the lower right corner:

$$\mathsf{S}_z = \hbar \begin{pmatrix} s & 0 & 0 & \cdots & 0 \\ 0 & s-1 & 0 & \cdots & 0 \\ 0 & 0 & s-2 & \cdots & 0 \\ \vdots & \vdots & \vdots & \ddots & \vdots \\ 0 & 0 & 0 & \cdots & -s \end{pmatrix}.$$

From Eq. 4.136,

$$S_\pm|s\,m\rangle = \hbar\sqrt{s(s+1) - m(m\pm 1)}\,|s\,(m\pm 1)\rangle = \hbar\sqrt{(s \mp m)(s \pm m + 1)}\,|s\,(m\pm 1)\rangle.$$

$$(\mathsf{S}_+)_{nm} = \langle n|S_+|m\rangle = \hbar\sqrt{(s-m)(s+m+1)}\,\langle n|m+1\rangle = \hbar b_{m+1}\delta_{n\,(m+1)} = \hbar b_n\delta_{n\,(m+1)}.$$

All nonzero elements have row index ($n$) one greater than the column index ($m$), so they are on the diagonal just *above* the main diagonal (note that the indices go *down*, here: $s$, $s-1$, $s-2 \ldots, -s$):

$$\mathsf{S}_+ = \hbar \begin{pmatrix} 0 & b_s & 0 & 0 & \cdots & 0 \\ 0 & 0 & b_{s-1} & 0 & \cdots & 0 \\ 0 & 0 & 0 & b_{s-2} & \cdots & 0 \\ \vdots & \vdots & \vdots & \vdots & \ddots & \vdots \\ 0 & 0 & 0 & 0 & \cdots & b_{-s+1} \\ 0 & 0 & 0 & 0 & \cdots & 0 \end{pmatrix}.$$

Similarly

$$(\mathsf{S}_-)_{nm} = \langle n|S_-|m\rangle = \hbar\sqrt{(s+m)(s-m+1)}\,\langle n|m-1\rangle = \hbar b_m\delta_{n\,(m-1)}.$$

This time the nonzero elements are on the diagonal just *below* the main diagonal:

$$S_- = \hbar \begin{pmatrix} 0 & 0 & 0 & \cdots & 0 & 0 \\ b_s & 0 & 0 & \cdots & 0 & 0 \\ 0 & b_{s-1} & 0 & \cdots & 0 & 0 \\ \vdots & \vdots & \vdots & \ddots & \vdots & \vdots \\ 0 & 0 & 0 & \cdots & b_{-s+1} & 0 \end{pmatrix}.$$

To construct $S_x = \frac{1}{2}(S_+ + S_-)$ and $S_y = \frac{1}{2i}(S_+ - S_-)$, simply add and subtract the matrices $S_+$ and $S_-$:

$$S_x = \frac{\hbar}{2} \begin{pmatrix} 0 & b_s & 0 & 0 & \cdots & 0 & 0 \\ b_s & 0 & b_{s-1} & 0 & \cdots & 0 & 0 \\ 0 & b_{s-1} & 0 & b_{s-2} & \cdots & 0 & 0 \\ 0 & 0 & b_{s-2} & 0 & \cdots & 0 & 0 \\ \vdots & \vdots & \vdots & \vdots & \ddots & \vdots & \vdots \\ 0 & 0 & 0 & 0 & \cdots & 0 & b_{-s+1} \\ 0 & 0 & 0 & 0 & \cdots & b_{-s+1} & 0 \end{pmatrix}; \quad S_y = \frac{\hbar}{2i} \begin{pmatrix} 0 & b_s & 0 & 0 & \cdots & 0 & 0 \\ -b_s & 0 & b_{s-1} & 0 & \cdots & 0 & 0 \\ 0 & -b_{s-1} & 0 & b_{s-2} & \cdots & 0 & 0 \\ 0 & 0 & -b_{s-2} & 0 & \cdots & 0 & 0 \\ \vdots & \vdots & \vdots & \vdots & \ddots & \vdots & \vdots \\ 0 & 0 & 0 & 0 & \cdots & 0 & b_{-s+1} \\ 0 & 0 & 0 & 0 & \cdots & -b_{-s+1} & 0 \end{pmatrix}.$$

## Problem 4.54

$L_+ Y_l^m = \hbar \sqrt{l(l+1) - m(m+1)} \, Y_l^{m\pm 1}$  (Eqs. 4.120 and 121).   Equation 4.130 $\Rightarrow$

$$\hbar e^{i\phi} \left( \frac{\partial}{\partial \theta} + i \cot\theta \frac{\partial}{\partial \phi} \right) B_l^m e^{im\phi} P_l^m(\cos\theta) = \hbar \sqrt{l(l+1) - m(m+1)} B_l^{m+1} e^{i(m+1)\phi} P_l^{m+1}(\cos\theta).$$

$$B_l^m \left( \frac{d}{d\theta} - m \cot\theta \right) P_l^m(\cos\theta) = \sqrt{l(l+1) - m(m+1)} B_l^{m+1} P_l^{m+1}(\cos\theta).$$

Let $x \equiv \cos\theta$; $\cot\theta = \dfrac{\cos\theta}{\sin\theta} = \dfrac{x}{\sqrt{1-x^2}}$; $\dfrac{d}{d\theta} = \dfrac{dx}{d\theta}\dfrac{d}{dx} = -\sin\theta \dfrac{d}{dx} = -\sqrt{1-x^2}\dfrac{d}{dx}$.

$$B_l^m \left[ -\sqrt{1-x^2}\frac{d}{dx} - m\frac{x}{\sqrt{1-x^2}} \right] P_l^m(x) = -B_l^m \frac{1}{\sqrt{1-x^2}} \left[ (1-x^2)\frac{dP_l^m}{dx} + mx P_l^m \right] = -B_l^m P_l^{m+1}$$

$$= \sqrt{l(l+1) - m(m+1)} B_l^{m+1} P_l^{m+1}(x). \quad \Rightarrow \quad \boxed{B_l^{m+1} = \frac{-1}{\sqrt{l(l+1) - m(m+1)}} B_l^m.}$$

Now $l(l+1) - m(m+1) = (l-m)(l+m+1)$, so

$$B_l^{m+1} = \frac{-1}{\sqrt{l-m}\sqrt{l+1+m}} B_l^m \Rightarrow B_l^1 = \frac{-1}{\sqrt{l}\sqrt{l+1}} B_l^0; \quad B_l^2 = \frac{-1}{\sqrt{l-1}\sqrt{l+2}} B_l^1 = \frac{1}{\sqrt{l(l-1)}\sqrt{(l+1)(l+2)}} B_l^0;$$

$$B_l^3 = \frac{-1}{\sqrt{l-2}\sqrt{l+3}} B_l^2 = \frac{-1}{\sqrt{(l+3)(l+2)(l+1)l(l-1)(l-2)}} B_l^0, \quad \text{etc.}$$

Evidently there is an overall sign factor $(-1)^m$, and inside the square root the quantity is $[(l+m)!/(l-m)!]$.

Thus: $\boxed{B_l^m = (-1)^m \sqrt{\dfrac{(l-m)!}{(l+m)!}} C(l)}$ (where $C(l) \equiv B_l^0$), for $m \geq 0$. For $m < 0$, we have

$$B_l^{-1} = \frac{-B_l^0}{\sqrt{(l+1)l}}; \quad B_l^{-2} = \frac{-1}{\sqrt{(l+2)(l-1)}} B_l^{-1} = \frac{1}{\sqrt{(l+2)(l+1)l(l-1)}} B_l^0, \quad \text{etc.}$$

Thus $B_l^{-m} = B_l^m$, so in general: $B_l^m = (-1)^m \sqrt{\frac{(l-|m|)!}{(l+|m|)!}} C(l)$.    Now, Problem 4.22 says:

$$Y_l^l = \frac{1}{2^l l!} \sqrt{\frac{(2l+1)!}{\pi}} (e^{i\phi} \sin\theta)^l = B_l^l e^{il\phi} P_l^l(\cos\theta). \quad \text{But}$$

$$P_l^l(x) = (1-x^2)^{l/2} \left(\frac{d}{dx}\right)^l \frac{1}{2^l l!} \left(\frac{d}{dx}\right)^l (x^2-1)^l = \frac{(1-x^2)^{l/2}}{2^l l!} \underbrace{\left(\frac{d}{dx}\right)^{2l} (x^{2l} - \ldots)}_{(2l)!} = \frac{(2l)!}{2^l l!} (1-x^2)^{l/2},$$

so    $P_l^l(\cos\theta) = \frac{(2l)!}{2^l l!} (\sin\theta)^l$.    Therefore

$$\frac{1}{2^l l!} \sqrt{\frac{(2l+1)!}{\pi}} (e^{i\phi} \sin\theta)^l = B_l^l e^{il\phi} \frac{(2l)!}{2^l l!} (\sin\theta)^l \Rightarrow B_l^l = \frac{1}{(2l)!} \sqrt{\frac{(2l+1)!}{\pi}} = \sqrt{\frac{(2l+1)}{\pi(2l)!}}.$$

But $B_l^l = (-1)^l \sqrt{\frac{1}{(2l)!}} C(l)$,    so $\boxed{C(l) = (-1)^l \sqrt{\frac{2l+1}{\pi}},}$    and hence $\boxed{B_l^m = (-1)^{l+m} \sqrt{\frac{(2l+1)}{\pi} \frac{(l-|m|)!}{(l+|m|)!}}.}$

This agrees with Eq. 4.32 except for the overall sign, which of course is purely conventional.

---

## Problem 4.55

**(a)** For both terms, $l = 1$, so    $\hbar^2(1)(2) = \boxed{2\hbar^2, \ P = 1.}$

**(b)** $\boxed{0, \ P = \frac{1}{3},}$ or $\boxed{\hbar, \ P = \frac{2}{3}.}$

**(c)** $\boxed{\frac{3}{4}\hbar^2, \ P = 1.}$

**(d)** $\boxed{\frac{\hbar}{2}, \ P = \frac{1}{3},}$ or $\boxed{-\frac{\hbar}{2}, \ P = \frac{2}{3}.}$

**(e)** From the $1 \times \frac{1}{2}$ Clebsch-Gordan table (or Problem 4.51):

$$\frac{1}{\sqrt{3}} |\tfrac{1}{2} \ \tfrac{1}{2}\rangle |1 \ 0\rangle + \sqrt{\tfrac{2}{3}} |\tfrac{1}{2} \ \tfrac{-1}{2}\rangle |1 \ 1\rangle = \frac{1}{\sqrt{3}} \left[ \sqrt{\tfrac{2}{3}} |\tfrac{3}{2} \ \tfrac{1}{2}\rangle - \frac{1}{\sqrt{3}} |\tfrac{1}{2} \ \tfrac{1}{2}\rangle \right] + \sqrt{\tfrac{2}{3}} \left[ \frac{1}{\sqrt{3}} |\tfrac{3}{2} \ \tfrac{1}{2}\rangle + \sqrt{\tfrac{2}{3}} |\tfrac{1}{2} \ \tfrac{1}{2}\rangle \right]$$

$$= \left(2\tfrac{\sqrt{2}}{3}\right) |\tfrac{3}{2} \ \tfrac{1}{2}\rangle + \left(\tfrac{1}{3}\right) |\tfrac{1}{2} \ \tfrac{1}{2}\rangle. \quad \text{So } s = \tfrac{3}{2} \text{ or } \tfrac{1}{2}. \ \boxed{\frac{15}{4}\hbar^2, \ P = \frac{8}{9},} \text{ or } \boxed{\frac{3}{4}\hbar^2, \ P = \frac{1}{9}.}$$

**(f)** $\boxed{\frac{1}{2}\hbar, \ P = 1.}$

**(g)**

$$|\psi|^2 = |R_{21}|^2 \left\{ \frac{1}{3} |Y_1^0|^2 \underbrace{(\chi_+^\dagger \chi_+)}_{1} + \frac{\sqrt{2}}{3} \left[ Y_1^{0*} Y_1^1 \underbrace{(\chi_+^\dagger \chi_-)}_{0} + Y_1^{1*} Y_1^0 \underbrace{(\chi_-^\dagger \chi_+)}_{0} \right] + \frac{2}{3} |Y_1^1|^2 \underbrace{(\chi_-^\dagger \chi_-)}_{1} \right\}$$

$$= \frac{1}{3} |R_{21}|^2 \left( |Y_1^0|^2 + 2|Y_1^1|^2 \right) = \frac{1}{3} \cdot \frac{1}{24} \cdot \frac{1}{a^3} \cdot \frac{r^2}{a^2} e^{-r/a} \left[ \frac{3}{4\pi} \cos^2\theta + 2\frac{3}{8\pi} \sin^2\theta \right] \quad \text{[Tables 4.3, 4.7]}$$

$$= \frac{1}{3 \cdot 24 \cdot a^5} r^2 e^{-r/a} \cdot \frac{3}{4\pi} (\cos^2\theta + \sin^2\theta) = \boxed{\frac{1}{96\pi a^5} r^2 e^{-r/a}.}$$

---

**(h)**

$$\frac{1}{3}|R_{21}|^2 \int |Y_1^0|^2 \sin^2\theta \, d\theta \, d\phi = \frac{1}{3}|R_{21}|^2 = \frac{1}{3} \cdot \frac{1}{24a^3}r^2 e^{-r/a} = \boxed{\frac{1}{72a^5}r^2 e^{-r/a}}.$$

---

## Problem 4.56

**(a)** Equation 4.129 says $L_z = \frac{\hbar}{i}\frac{\partial}{\partial\phi}$, so this problem is identical to Problem 3.39, with $\hat{p} \to L_z$ and $x \to \phi$.

**(b)** First note that if M is a matrix such that $\mathsf{M}^2 = 1$, then

$$e^{i\mathsf{M}\phi} = 1 + i\mathsf{M}\phi + \frac{1}{2}(i\mathsf{M}\phi)^2 + \frac{1}{3!}(i\mathsf{M}\phi)^3 + \cdots = 1 + i\mathsf{M}\phi - \frac{1}{2}\phi^2 - i\mathsf{M}\frac{1}{3!}\phi^3 + \cdots$$

$$= (1 - \frac{1}{2}\phi^2 + \frac{1}{4!}\phi^4 - \cdots) + i\mathsf{M}(\phi - \frac{1}{3!}\phi^3 + \frac{1}{5!}\phi^5 - \cdots) = \cos\phi + i\mathsf{M}\sin\phi.$$

So $\mathsf{R} = e^{i\pi\sigma_x/2} = \cos\frac{\pi}{2} + i\sigma_x\sin\frac{\pi}{2}$ (because $\sigma_x^2 = 1$ – see Problem 4.26) $= i\sigma_x = \boxed{i\begin{pmatrix} 0 & 1 \\ 1 & 0 \end{pmatrix}}.$

Thus $\mathsf{R}\chi_+ = i\begin{pmatrix} 0 & 1 \\ 1 & 0 \end{pmatrix}\begin{pmatrix} 1 \\ 0 \end{pmatrix} = i\begin{pmatrix} 0 \\ 1 \end{pmatrix} = i\chi_-$; it converts "spin up" into "spin down" (with a factor of $i$).

**(c)**

$$\mathsf{R} = e^{i\pi\sigma_y/4} = \cos\frac{\pi}{4} + i\sigma_y\sin\frac{\pi}{4} = \frac{1}{\sqrt{2}}(1 + i\sigma_y) = \frac{1}{\sqrt{2}}\left[\begin{pmatrix} 1 & 0 \\ 0 & 1 \end{pmatrix} + i\begin{pmatrix} 0 & -i \\ i & 0 \end{pmatrix}\right] = \boxed{\frac{1}{\sqrt{2}}\begin{pmatrix} 1 & 1 \\ -1 & 1 \end{pmatrix}}.$$

$$\mathsf{R}\chi_+ = \frac{1}{\sqrt{2}}\begin{pmatrix} 1 & 1 \\ -1 & 1 \end{pmatrix}\begin{pmatrix} 1 \\ 0 \end{pmatrix} = \frac{1}{\sqrt{2}}\begin{pmatrix} 1 \\ -1 \end{pmatrix} = \frac{1}{\sqrt{2}}(\chi_+ - \chi_-) = \chi_-^{(x)} \text{ (Eq. 4.151)}.$$

What *had* been spin *up* along $z$ is now spin *down* along $x'$ (see figure).

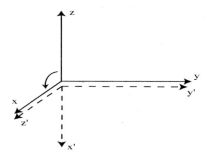

**(d)** $\mathsf{R} = e^{i\pi\sigma_z} = \cos\pi + i\sigma_z\sin\pi = \boxed{-1;}$ rotation by 360° changes the *sign* of the spinor. But since the sign of $\chi$ is arbitrary, it doesn't matter.

**(e)**

$$(\sigma \cdot \hat{n})^2 = (\sigma_x n_x + \sigma_y n_y + \sigma_z n_z)(\sigma_x n_x + \sigma_y n_y + \sigma_z n_z)$$

$$= \sigma_x^2 n_x^2 + \sigma_y^2 n_y^2 + \sigma_z^2 n_z^2 + n_x n_y(\sigma_x\sigma_y + \sigma_y\sigma_x) + n_x n_z(\sigma_x\sigma_z + \sigma_z\sigma_x) + n_y n_z(\sigma_y\sigma_z - \sigma_z\sigma_y).$$

But $\sigma_x^2 = \sigma_y^2 = \sigma_z^2 = 1$, and $\sigma_x\sigma_y + \sigma_y\sigma_x = \sigma_x\sigma_z + \sigma_z\sigma_x = \sigma_y\sigma_z + \sigma_z\sigma_y = 0$ (Problem 4.26), so

$$(\sigma \cdot \hat{n})^2 = n_x^2 + n_y^2 + n_z^2 = 1. \quad \text{So } e^{i(\sigma\cdot\hat{n})\phi/2} = \cos\frac{\phi}{2} + i(\sigma \cdot \hat{n})\sin\frac{\phi}{2}. \quad \text{QED}$$

---

## Problem 4.57

(a)

$$[q_1, q_2] = \frac{1}{2}\left[x + \left(a^2/\hbar\right)p_y, \; x - \left(a^2/\hbar\right)p_y\right] = 0, \text{ because } [x, p_y] = [x, x] = [p_y, p_y] = 0.$$

$$[p_1, p_2] = \frac{1}{2}\left[p_x - \left(\hbar/a^2\right)y, \; p_x + \left(\hbar/a^2\right)y\right] = 0, \text{ because } [y, p_x] = [y, y] = [p_x, p_x] = 0.$$

$$[q_1, p_1] = \frac{1}{2}\left[x + \left(a^2/\hbar\right)p_y, \; p_x - \left(\hbar/a^2\right)y\right] = \frac{1}{2}\left([x, p_x] - [p_y, y]\right) = \frac{1}{2}\left[i\hbar - (-i\hbar)\right] = i\hbar.$$

$$[q_2, p_2] = \frac{1}{2}\left[x - \left(a^2/\hbar\right)p_y, \; p_x + \left(\hbar/a^2\right)y\right] = \frac{1}{2}\left([x, p_x] - [p_y, y]\right) = i\hbar.$$

[See Eq. 4.10 for the canonical commutators.]

(b)

$$q_1^2 - q_2^2 = \frac{1}{2}\left[x^2 + \frac{a^2}{\hbar}(xp_y + p_yx) + \left(\frac{a^2}{\hbar}\right)^2 p_y^2 - x^2 + \frac{a^2}{\hbar}(xp_y + p_yx) - \left(\frac{a^2}{\hbar}\right)^2 p_y^2\right] = \frac{2a}{\hbar}xp_y.$$

$$p_1^2 - p_2^2 = \frac{1}{2}\left[p_x^2 - \frac{\hbar}{a^2}(p_xy + yp_x) + \left(\frac{\hbar}{a^2}\right)^2 y^2 - p_x^2 - \frac{\hbar}{a^2}(p_xy + yp_x) - \left(\frac{\hbar}{a^2}\right)^2 y^2\right] = -\frac{2\hbar}{a^2}yp_x.$$

So $\dfrac{\hbar}{2a^2}(q_1^2 - q_2^2) + \dfrac{a^2}{2\hbar}(p_1^2 - p_2^2) = xp_y - yp_x = L_z.$

(c)

$$H = \frac{1}{2m}p^2 + \frac{1}{2}m\omega^2x^2 = \frac{a^2}{2\hbar}p^2 + \frac{\hbar}{2a^2}x^2 = H(x, p).$$

Then $H(q_1, p_1) = \dfrac{a^2}{2\hbar}p_1^2 + \dfrac{\hbar}{2a^2}q_1^2 \equiv H_1, \quad H(q_2, p_2) = \dfrac{a^2}{2\hbar}p_2^2 + \dfrac{\hbar}{2a^2}q_2^2 \equiv H_2; \quad L_z = H_1 - H_2.$

(d) The eigenvalues of $H_1$ are $(n_1 + \frac{1}{2})\hbar$, and those of $H_2$ are $(n_2 + \frac{1}{2})\hbar$, so the eigenvalues of $L_z$ are

$(n_1 + \frac{1}{2})\hbar - (n_2 + \frac{1}{2})\hbar = (n_1 - n_2)\hbar = m\hbar$, and $m$ is an *integer*, because $n_1$ and $n_2$ are.

---

## Problem 4.58

From Problem 4.28 we know that in the generic state $\chi = \begin{pmatrix} a \\ b \end{pmatrix}$ (with $|a|^2 + |b|^2 = 1$),

$$\langle S_z \rangle = \frac{\hbar}{2}\left(|a|^2 - |b|^2\right), \quad \langle S_x \rangle = \hbar \mathrm{Re}(ab^*), \quad \langle S_y \rangle = -\hbar \mathrm{Im}(ab^*); \quad \langle S_x^2 \rangle = \langle S_y^2 \rangle = \frac{\hbar^2}{4}.$$

Writing $a = |a|e^{i\phi_a}$, $b = |b|e^{i\phi_b}$, we have $ab^* = |a||b|e^{i(\phi_a - \phi_b)} = |a||b|e^{i\theta}$, where $\theta \equiv \phi_a - \phi_b$ is the phase difference between $a$ and $b$. Then

$$\langle S_x \rangle = \hbar \mathrm{Re}(|a||b|e^{i\theta}) = \hbar|a||b|\cos\theta, \quad \langle S_y \rangle = -\hbar\mathrm{Im}(|a||b|e^{i\theta}) = -\hbar|a||b|\sin\theta.$$

$$\sigma_{S_x}^2 = \langle S_x^2 \rangle - \langle S_x \rangle^2 = \frac{\hbar^2}{4} - \hbar^2|a|^2|b|^2\cos^2\theta; \quad \sigma_{S_y}^2 = \langle S_y^2 \rangle - \langle S_y \rangle^2 = \frac{\hbar^2}{4} - \hbar^2|a|^2|b|^2\sin^2\theta.$$

We want $\sigma_{S_x}^2 \sigma_{S_y}^2 = \frac{\hbar^2}{4}\langle S_z \rangle^2$, or

$$\frac{\hbar^2}{4}\left(1 - 4|a|^2|b|^2\cos^2\theta\right)\frac{\hbar^2}{4}\left(1 - 4|a|^2|b|^2\sin^2\theta\right) = \frac{\hbar^2}{4}\frac{\hbar^2}{4}\left(|a|^2 - |b|^2\right)^2.$$

$$1 - 4|a|^2|b|^2\left(\cos^2\theta + \sin^2\theta\right) + 16|a|^4|b|^4\sin^2\theta\cos^2\theta = |a|^4 - 2|a|^2|b|^2 + |b|^4.$$

$$1 + 16|a|^4|b|^4\sin^2\theta\cos^2\theta = |a|^4 + 2|a|^2|b|^2 + |b|^4 = \left(|a|^2 + |b|^2\right)^2 = 1 \quad \Rightarrow |a|^2|b|^2\sin\theta\cos\theta = 0.$$

So either $\theta = 0$ or $\pi$, in which case $a$ and $b$ are relatively real, or else $\theta = \pm\pi/2$, in which case $a$ and $b$ are relatively imaginary (these two options subsume trivially the solutions $a = 0$ and $b = 0$).

---

## Problem 4.59

**(a)**

Start with Eq. 3.71: $\dfrac{d\langle \mathbf{r} \rangle}{dt} = \dfrac{i}{\hbar}\langle [H, \mathbf{r}] \rangle.$

$$H = \frac{1}{2m}(\mathbf{p} - q\mathbf{A}) \cdot (\mathbf{p} - q\mathbf{A}) + q\varphi = \frac{1}{2m}\left[p^2 - q(\mathbf{p}\cdot\mathbf{A} + \mathbf{A}\cdot\mathbf{p}) + q^2 A^2\right] + q\varphi.$$

$$[H, x] = \frac{1}{2m}[p^2, x] - \frac{q}{2m}[(\mathbf{p}\cdot\mathbf{A} + \mathbf{A}\cdot\mathbf{p}), x].$$

$$[p^2, x] = [(p_x^2 + p_y^2 + p_z^2), x] = [p_x^2, x] = p_x[p_x, x] + [p_x, x]p_x = p_x(-i\hbar) + (-i\hbar)p_x = -2i\hbar p_x.$$

$$[\mathbf{p}\cdot\mathbf{A}, x] = [(p_x A_x + p_y A_y + p_z A_z), x] = [p_x A_x, x] = p_x[A_x, x] + [p_x, x]A_x = -i\hbar A_x.$$

$$[\mathbf{A}\cdot\mathbf{p}, x] = [(A_x p_x + A_y p_y + A_z p_z), x] = [A_x p_x, x] = A_x[p_x, x] + [A_x, x]p_x = -i\hbar A_x.$$

$$[H, x] = \frac{1}{2m}(-2i\hbar p_x) - \frac{q}{2m}(-2i\hbar A_x) = -\frac{i\hbar}{m}(p_x - qA_x); \quad [H, \mathbf{r}] = -\frac{i\hbar}{m}(\mathbf{p} - q\mathbf{A}).$$

$$\frac{d\langle \mathbf{r} \rangle}{dt} = \frac{1}{m}\langle (\mathbf{p} - q\mathbf{A}) \rangle. \quad \text{QED}$$

**(b)**

We define the operator $\mathbf{v} \equiv \dfrac{1}{m}(\mathbf{p} - q\mathbf{A})$;    $\dfrac{d\langle \mathbf{v} \rangle}{dt} = \dfrac{i}{\hbar}\langle [H, \mathbf{v}] \rangle + \langle \dfrac{\partial \mathbf{v}}{\partial t} \rangle$;    $\dfrac{\partial \mathbf{v}}{\partial t} = -\dfrac{q}{m}\dfrac{\partial \mathbf{A}}{\partial t}$.

$H = \dfrac{1}{2}mv^2 + q\varphi \Rightarrow [H, \mathbf{v}] = \dfrac{m}{2}[v^2, \mathbf{v}] + q[\varphi, \mathbf{v}]$;    $[\varphi, \mathbf{v}] = \dfrac{1}{m}[\varphi, \mathbf{p}]$.

$[\varphi, p_x] = i\hbar\dfrac{\partial \varphi}{\partial x}$    (Eq. 3.65), so $[\varphi, \mathbf{p}] = i\hbar \nabla \varphi$,  and $[\varphi, \mathbf{v}] = \dfrac{i\hbar}{m}\nabla \varphi$.

$[v^2, v_x] = [(v_x^2 + v_y^2 + v_z^2), v_x] = [v_y^2, v_x] + [v_z^2, v_x] = v_y[v_y, v_x] + [v_y, v_x]v_y + v_z[v_z, v_x] + [v_z, v_x]v_z$.

$[v_y, v_x] = \dfrac{1}{m^2}[(p_y - qA_y), (p_x - qA_x)] = -\dfrac{q}{m^2}\left([A_y, p_x] + [p_y, A_x]\right)$

$\qquad = -\dfrac{q}{m^2}\left(i\hbar\dfrac{\partial A_y}{\partial x} - i\hbar\dfrac{\partial A_x}{\partial y}\right) = -\dfrac{i\hbar q}{m^2}\left(\nabla \times \mathbf{A}\right)_z = -\dfrac{i\hbar q}{m^2}B_z$.

$[v_z, v_x] = \dfrac{1}{m^2}[(p_z - qA_z), (p_x - qA_x)] = -\dfrac{q}{m^2}\left([A_z, p_x] + [p_z, A_x]\right)$

$\qquad = -\dfrac{q}{m^2}\left(i\hbar\dfrac{\partial A_z}{\partial x} - i\hbar\dfrac{\partial A_x}{\partial y}\right) = \dfrac{i\hbar q}{m^2}\left(\nabla \times \mathbf{A}\right)_y = \dfrac{i\hbar q}{m^2}B_y$.

$\therefore [v^2, v_x] = \dfrac{i\hbar q}{m^2}\left(-v_y B_z - B_z v_y + v_z B_y + B_y v_z\right) = \dfrac{i\hbar q}{m^2}\left[-(\mathbf{v} \times \mathbf{B})_x + (\mathbf{B} \times \mathbf{v})_x\right]$.

$[v^2, \mathbf{v}] = \dfrac{i\hbar q}{m^2}\left[(\mathbf{B} \times \mathbf{v}) - (\mathbf{v} \times \mathbf{B})\right]$.   Putting all this together:

$\dfrac{d\langle \mathbf{v} \rangle}{dt} = \dfrac{i}{\hbar}\left\langle \left[\dfrac{m}{2}\dfrac{i\hbar q}{m^2}(\mathbf{B} \times \mathbf{v} - \mathbf{v} \times \mathbf{B}) + \dfrac{qi\hbar}{m}\nabla \varphi\right]\right\rangle - \dfrac{q}{m}\langle\dfrac{\partial \mathbf{A}}{\partial t}\rangle$.

$[\bigstar]\quad m\dfrac{d\langle \mathbf{v} \rangle}{dt} = \dfrac{q}{2}\langle(\mathbf{v} \times \mathbf{B}) - (\mathbf{B} \times \mathbf{v})\rangle + q\left\langle -\nabla\varphi - \dfrac{\partial \mathbf{A}}{dt}\right\rangle = \dfrac{q}{2}\langle(\mathbf{v} \times \mathbf{B} - \mathbf{B} \times \mathbf{v})\rangle + q\langle \mathbf{E}\rangle$.   Or, since

$\mathbf{v} \times \mathbf{B} - \mathbf{B} \times \mathbf{v} = \dfrac{1}{m}\left[(\mathbf{p} - q\mathbf{A}) \times \mathbf{B} - \mathbf{B} \times (\mathbf{p} - q\mathbf{A})\right] = \dfrac{1}{m}\left[\mathbf{p} \times \mathbf{B} - \mathbf{B} \times \mathbf{p}\right] - \dfrac{q}{m}\left[\mathbf{A} \times \mathbf{B} - \mathbf{B} \times \mathbf{A}\right]$.

[*Note:* $\mathbf{p}$ does not commute with $\mathbf{B}$, so the order *does* matter in the first term. But $\mathbf{A}$ commutes with $\mathbf{B}$, so $\mathbf{B} \times \mathbf{A} = -\mathbf{A} \times \mathbf{B}$ in the second.]

$m\dfrac{d\langle \mathbf{v} \rangle}{dt} = q\langle \mathbf{E}\rangle + \dfrac{q}{2m}\langle\mathbf{p} \times \mathbf{B} - \mathbf{B} \times \mathbf{p}\rangle - \dfrac{q^2}{m}\langle \mathbf{A} \times \mathbf{B}\rangle$.   QED

**(c)** Go back to Eq. $\bigstar$, and use $\langle \mathbf{E}\rangle = \mathbf{E}$, $\langle \mathbf{v} \times \mathbf{B}\rangle = \langle \mathbf{v}\rangle \times \mathbf{B}$; $\langle \mathbf{B} \times \mathbf{v}\rangle = \mathbf{B} \times \langle \mathbf{v}\rangle = -\langle \mathbf{v}\rangle \times \mathbf{B}$.   Then

$m\dfrac{d\langle \mathbf{v} \rangle}{dt} = q\langle \mathbf{v}\rangle \times \mathbf{B} + q\mathbf{E}$.   QED

## Problem 4.60

(a)

$$\mathbf{E} = -\nabla\varphi = \boxed{-2Kz\hat{k}.} \qquad \mathbf{B} = \nabla \times \mathbf{A} = \begin{vmatrix} \hat{i} & \hat{j} & \hat{k} \\ \partial/\partial x & \partial/\partial y & \partial/\partial z \\ -B_0 y/2 & B_0 x/2 & 0 \end{vmatrix} = \boxed{B_0\hat{k}.}$$

(b) For time-independent potentials Eq. 4.205 separates in the usual way:

$$\frac{1}{2m}\left(\frac{\hbar}{i}\nabla - q\mathbf{A}\right) \cdot \left(\frac{\hbar}{i}\nabla - q\mathbf{A}\right)\psi + q\varphi\psi = E\psi, \quad \text{or}$$

$$-\frac{\hbar^2}{2m}\nabla^2\psi + \frac{iq\hbar}{2m}\left[\nabla \cdot (\mathbf{A}\psi) + \mathbf{A} \cdot (\nabla\psi)\right] + \frac{q^2}{2m}A^2 + q\varphi\psi = E\psi. \quad \text{But} \quad \nabla \cdot (\mathbf{A}\psi) = (\nabla \cdot \mathbf{A})\psi + \mathbf{A} \cdot (\nabla\psi), \quad \text{so}$$

$$\boxed{-\frac{\hbar^2}{2m}\nabla^2\psi + \frac{iq\hbar}{2m}\left[2\mathbf{A} \cdot (\nabla\psi) + \nabla \cdot (\mathbf{A}\psi)\right] + \left(\frac{q^2}{2m}A^2 + q\varphi\right)\psi = E\psi.}$$

This is the time-independent Schrödinger equation for electrodynamics. In the present case

$$\nabla \cdot \mathbf{A} = 0, \quad \mathbf{A} \cdot (\nabla\psi) = \frac{B_0}{2}\left(x\frac{\partial\psi}{\partial y} - y\frac{\partial\psi}{\partial x}\right), \quad A^2 = \frac{B_0^2}{4}\left(x^2 + y^2\right), \quad \varphi = Kz^2.$$

But $\quad L_z = \frac{\hbar}{i}\left(x\frac{\partial}{\partial y} - y\frac{\partial}{\partial x}\right), \quad$ so $\quad -\frac{\hbar^2}{2m}\nabla^2\psi - \frac{qB_0}{2m}L_z\psi + \left[\frac{q^2 B_0^2}{8m}\left(x^2 + y^2\right) + qKz^2\right]\psi = E\psi.$

Since $L_z$ commutes with $H$, we may as well pick simultaneous eigenfunctions of both: $\quad L_z\psi = \bar{m}\hbar\psi$, where $\bar{m} = 0, \pm 1, \pm 2, \dots$ (with the overbar to distinguish the magnetic quantum number from the mass). Then

$$\left[-\frac{\hbar^2}{2m}\nabla^2 + \frac{(qB_0)^2}{8m}\left(x^2 + y^2\right) + qKz^2\right]\psi = \left(E + \frac{qB_0\hbar}{2m}\bar{m}\right)\psi.$$

Now let $\omega_1 \equiv qB_0/m$, $\quad \omega_2 \equiv \sqrt{2Kq/m}$, and use cylindrical coordinates $(r, \phi, z)$:

$$-\frac{\hbar^2}{2m}\left[\frac{1}{r}\frac{\partial}{\partial r}\left(r\frac{\partial\psi}{\partial r}\right) + \frac{1}{r^2}\frac{\partial^2\psi}{\partial\phi^2} + \frac{\partial^2\psi}{\partial z^2}\right] + \left[\frac{1}{8}m\omega_1^2\left(x^2 + y^2\right) + \frac{1}{2}m\omega_2^2 z^2\right]\psi = \left(E + \frac{1}{2}\bar{m}\hbar\omega_1\right)\psi.$$

But $L_z = \frac{\hbar}{i}\frac{\partial}{\partial\phi}$, so $\frac{\partial^2\psi}{\partial\phi^2} = -\frac{1}{\hbar^2}L_z^2\psi = -\frac{1}{\hbar^2}\bar{m}^2\hbar^2\psi = -\bar{m}^2\psi.$ Use separation of variables: $\psi(r, \phi, z) = R(r)\Phi(\phi)Z(z)$ :

$$-\frac{\hbar^2}{2m}\left[\Phi Z\frac{1}{r}\frac{d}{dr}\left(r\frac{dR}{dr}\right) - \frac{\bar{m}^2}{r^2}R\Phi Z + R\Phi\frac{d^2 Z}{dz^2}\right] + \left(\frac{1}{8}m\omega_1^2 r^2 + \frac{1}{2}m\omega_2^2 z^2\right)R\Phi Z = \left(E + \frac{1}{2}\bar{m}\hbar\omega_1\right)R\Phi Z.$$

Divide by $R\Phi Z$ and collect terms:

$$\left\{-\frac{\hbar^2}{2m}\left[\frac{1}{rR}\frac{d}{dr}\left(r\frac{dR}{dr}\right) - \frac{\bar{m}^2}{r^2}\right] + \frac{1}{8}m\omega_1^2 r^2\right\} + \left\{-\frac{\hbar^2}{2m}\frac{1}{Z}\frac{d^2 Z}{dz^2} + \frac{1}{2}m\omega_2^2 z^2\right\} = \left(E + \frac{1}{2}\bar{m}\hbar\omega_1\right).$$

The first term depends only on $r$, the second only on $z$, so they're both constants; call them $E_r$ and $E_z$:

$$-\frac{\hbar^2}{2m}\left[\frac{1}{r}\frac{d}{dr}\left(r\frac{dR}{dr}\right) - \frac{\bar{m}^2}{r^2}R\right] + \frac{1}{8}m\omega_1^2 r^2 R = E_r R; \qquad -\frac{\hbar^2}{2m}\frac{d^2 Z}{dz^2} + \frac{1}{2}m\omega_2^2 z^2 Z = E_z Z; \qquad E = E_r + E_z - \frac{1}{2}\bar{m}\hbar\omega_1.$$

The $z$ equation is a one-dimensional harmonic oscillator, and we can read off immediately that $E_z = (n_2 + 1/2)\hbar\omega_2$, with $n_2 = 0, 1, 2, \ldots$ . The $r$ equation is actually a two-dimensional harmonic oscillator; to get $E_r$, let $u(r) \equiv \sqrt{r}\, R$, and follow the method of Sections 4.1.3 and 4.2.1:

$$R = \frac{u}{\sqrt{r}}, \quad \frac{dR}{dr} = \frac{u'}{\sqrt{r}} - \frac{u}{2r^{3/2}}, \quad r\frac{dR}{dr} = \sqrt{r}\, u' - \frac{u}{2\sqrt{r}}, \quad \frac{d}{dr}\left(r\frac{dR}{dr}\right) = \sqrt{r}\, u'' + \frac{u}{4r^{3/2}},$$

$$\frac{1}{r}\frac{d}{dr}\left(r\frac{dR}{dr}\right) = \frac{u''}{\sqrt{r}} + \frac{u}{4r^{5/2}}; \quad -\frac{\hbar^2}{2m}\left(\frac{u''}{\sqrt{r}} + \frac{1}{4}\frac{u}{r^2}\frac{1}{\sqrt{r}} - \frac{\bar{m}^2}{r^2}\frac{u}{\sqrt{r}}\right) + \frac{1}{8}m\omega_1^2 r^2 \frac{u}{\sqrt{r}} = E_r \frac{u}{\sqrt{r}}$$

$$-\frac{\hbar^2}{2m}\left[\frac{d^2u}{dr^2} + \left(\frac{1}{4} - \bar{m}^2\right)\frac{u}{r^2}\right] + \frac{1}{8}m\omega_1^2 r^2 u = E_r u.$$

This is identical to the equation we encountered in Problem 4.39 (the three-dimentional harmonic oscillator), only with $\omega \to \omega_1/2, E \to E_r$, and $l(l+1) \to \bar{m}^2 - 1/4$, which is to say, $l^2 + l + 1/4 = \bar{m}^2$, or $(l + 1/2)^2 = \bar{m}^2$, or $l = |\bar{m}| - 1/2$. [Our present equation depends only on $\bar{m}^2$, and hence is the same for either sign, but the solution to Problem 4.39 assumed $l + 1/2 \geq 0$ (else $u$ is not normalizable), so we need $|m|$ here.] Quoting 4.39:

$$E = (j_{\max} + l + 3/2)\hbar\omega \to E_r = (j_{\max} + |\bar{m}| + 1)\hbar\omega_1/2, \quad \text{where} \quad j_{\max} = 0, 2, 4, \ldots.$$

$$E = j_{\max} + |\bar{m}| + 1)\hbar\omega_1/2 + (n_2 + 1/2)\hbar\omega_2 - \bar{m}\hbar\omega_1/2 = \boxed{(n_1 + \tfrac{1}{2})\hbar\omega_1 + (n_2 + \tfrac{1}{2})\hbar\omega_2,}$$

where $n_1 = 0, 1, 2, \ldots$ (if $\bar{m} \geq 0$, then $n_1 = j_{\max}/2$; if $\bar{m} < 0$, then $n_1 = j_{\max}/2 - \bar{m}$).

---

## Problem 4.61

**(a)**

$$\mathbf{B}' = \nabla \times \mathbf{A}' = \nabla \times \mathbf{A} + \nabla \times (\nabla\lambda) = \nabla \times \mathbf{A} = \mathbf{B}.$$

$\left[\nabla \times \nabla\lambda = 0, \text{ by equality of cross-derivatives: } (\nabla \times \nabla\lambda)_x = \dfrac{\partial}{\partial y}\left(\dfrac{\partial\lambda}{\partial z}\right) - \dfrac{\partial}{\partial z}\left(\dfrac{\partial\lambda}{\partial y}\right) = 0, \text{ etc.}\right]$

$$\mathbf{E}' = -\nabla\varphi' - \frac{\partial\mathbf{A}'}{\partial t} = -\nabla\varphi + \nabla\left(\frac{\partial\Lambda}{\partial t}\right) - \frac{\partial\mathbf{A}}{\partial t} - \frac{\partial}{\partial t}(\nabla\Lambda) = -\nabla\varphi - \frac{\partial\mathbf{A}}{\partial t} = \mathbf{E}.$$

$\left[\text{Again: } \nabla\left(\dfrac{\partial\Lambda}{\partial t}\right) = \dfrac{\partial}{\partial t}(\nabla\Lambda) \text{ by the equality of cross-derivatives.}\right]$

**(b)**

$$\left[\frac{\hbar}{i}\nabla - q\mathbf{A} - q(\nabla\Lambda)\right]e^{iq\Lambda/\hbar}\Psi = q(\nabla\Lambda)e^{iq\Lambda/\hbar}\Psi + \frac{\hbar}{i}e^{iq\Lambda/\hbar}\nabla\Psi - q\mathbf{A}e^{iq\Lambda/\hbar}\Psi - q(\nabla\Lambda)e^{iq\Lambda/\hbar}\Psi$$

$$= \frac{\hbar}{i}e^{iq\Lambda/\hbar}\nabla\Psi - q\mathbf{A}e^{iq\Lambda/\hbar}\Psi.$$

$$\left[\frac{\hbar}{i}\nabla - q\mathbf{A} - q(\nabla\Lambda)\right]^2 e^{iq\Lambda/\hbar}\Psi = \left(\frac{\hbar}{i}\nabla - q\mathbf{A} - q(\nabla\Lambda)\right)\left[\frac{\hbar}{i}e^{iq\Lambda/\hbar}\nabla\Psi - q\mathbf{A}e^{iq\Lambda/\hbar}\Psi\right]$$

$$= -\hbar^2 \left[ \frac{iq}{\hbar} (\nabla \Lambda \cdot \nabla \Psi) e^{iq\Lambda/\hbar} + e^{iq\Lambda/\hbar} \nabla^2 \Psi \right] - \frac{\hbar q}{i} (\nabla \cdot \mathbf{A}) e^{iq\Lambda/\hbar} \Psi - q^2 (\mathbf{A} \cdot \nabla \Lambda) e^{iq\Lambda/\hbar} \Psi$$

$$- \frac{q\hbar}{i} e^{iq\Lambda/\hbar} \mathbf{A} \cdot (\nabla \Psi) - \frac{q\hbar}{i} e^{iq\Lambda/\hbar} (\mathbf{A} \cdot \nabla \Psi) + q^2 A^2 e^{iq\Lambda/\hbar} \Psi$$

$$- \frac{q\hbar}{i} e^{iq\Lambda/\hbar} (\nabla \Lambda \cdot \nabla \Psi) + q^2 (\mathbf{A} \cdot \nabla \Lambda) e^{iq\Lambda/\hbar} \Psi$$

$$= e^{iq\Lambda/\hbar} \left\{ \left[ -\hbar^2 \nabla^2 \Psi + i\hbar q (\nabla \cdot \mathbf{A}) \Psi + 2iq\hbar (\mathbf{A} \cdot \nabla \Psi) + q^2 A^2 \Psi \right] \right.$$

$$\left. - iq\hbar (\nabla \Lambda) \cdot (\nabla \Psi) - q^2 (\mathbf{A} \cdot \nabla \Lambda) \Psi + iq\hbar (\nabla \Lambda) \cdot (\nabla \Psi) + q^2 (\mathbf{A} \cdot \nabla \Lambda) \Psi \right\}$$

$$= e^{iq\Lambda/\hbar} \left[ \left( \frac{\hbar}{i} \nabla - q\mathbf{A} \right)^2 \Psi \right].$$

So: $\left[ \dfrac{1}{2m} \left( \dfrac{\hbar}{i} \nabla - q\mathbf{A}' \right)^2 + q\varphi' \right] \Psi' = e^{iq\Lambda/\hbar} \left[ \dfrac{1}{2m} \left( \dfrac{\hbar}{i} \nabla - q\mathbf{A} \right)^2 + q\varphi - q\dfrac{\partial \Lambda}{\partial t} \right] \Psi$

[using Eq. 4.205] $= e^{iq\Lambda/\hbar} \left( i\hbar \dfrac{\partial \Psi}{\partial t} - q\dfrac{\partial \Lambda}{\partial t} \Psi \right) = i\hbar \dfrac{\partial}{\partial t} \left( e^{iq\Lambda/\hbar} \Psi \right) = i\hbar \dfrac{\partial \Psi'}{\partial t}.$    QED

# Chapter 5

# Identical Particles

## Problem 5.1

(a)

$$(m_1 + m_2)\mathbf{R} = m_1\mathbf{r}_1 + m_2\mathbf{r}_2 = m_1\mathbf{r}_1 + m_2(\mathbf{r}_1 - \mathbf{r}) = (m_1 + m_2)\mathbf{r}_1 - m_2\mathbf{r} \quad \Rightarrow$$

$$\mathbf{r}_1 = \mathbf{R} + \frac{m_2}{m_1 + m_2}\mathbf{r} = \mathbf{R} + \frac{\mu}{m_1}\mathbf{r}. \checkmark$$

$$(m_1 + m_2)\mathbf{R} = m_1(\mathbf{r}_2 + \mathbf{r}) + m_2\mathbf{r}_2 = (m_1 + m_2)\mathbf{r}_2 + m_1\mathbf{r} \Rightarrow \mathbf{r}_2 = \mathbf{R} - \frac{m_1}{m_1 + m_2}\mathbf{r} = \mathbf{R} - \frac{\mu}{m_2}\mathbf{r}. \checkmark$$

Let $\mathbf{R} = (X, Y, Z)$, $\mathbf{r} = (x, y, z)$.

$$\begin{aligned}
(\nabla_1)_x &= \frac{\partial}{\partial x_1} = \frac{\partial X}{\partial x_1}\frac{\partial}{\partial X} + \frac{\partial x}{\partial x_1}\frac{\partial}{\partial x} \\
&= \left(\frac{m_1}{m_1 + m_2}\right)\frac{\partial}{\partial X} + (1)\frac{\partial}{\partial x} = \frac{\mu}{m_2}(\nabla_R)_x + (\nabla_r)_x, \quad \text{so} \quad \nabla_1 = \frac{\mu}{m_2}\nabla_R + \nabla_r. \quad \checkmark \\
(\nabla_2)_x &= \frac{\partial}{\partial x_2} = \frac{\partial X}{\partial x_2}\frac{\partial}{\partial X} + \frac{\partial x}{\partial x_2}\frac{\partial}{\partial x} \\
&= \left(\frac{m_2}{m_1 + m_2}\right)\frac{\partial}{\partial X} - (1)\frac{\partial}{\partial x} = \frac{\mu}{m_1}(\nabla_R)_x - (\nabla_r)_x, \quad \text{so} \quad \nabla_2 = \frac{\mu}{m_1}\nabla_R - \nabla_r. \quad \checkmark
\end{aligned}$$

(b)

$$\begin{aligned}
\nabla_1^2\psi &= \nabla_1 \cdot (\nabla_1\psi) = \nabla_1 \cdot \left[\frac{\mu}{m_2}\nabla_R\psi + \nabla_r\psi\right] \\
&= \frac{\mu}{m_2}\nabla_R \cdot \left(\frac{\mu}{m_2}\nabla_R\psi + \nabla_r\psi\right) + \nabla_r \cdot \left(\frac{\mu}{m_2}\nabla_R\psi + \nabla_r\psi\right) \\
&= \left(\frac{\mu}{m_2}\right)^2 \nabla_R^2\psi + 2\frac{\mu}{m_2}(\nabla_r \cdot \nabla_R)\psi + \nabla_r^2\psi.
\end{aligned}$$

Likewise, $\quad \nabla_2^2 \psi = \left(\dfrac{\mu}{m_1}\right)^2 \nabla_R^2 \psi - 2\dfrac{\mu}{m_1}(\nabla_r \cdot \nabla_R) + \nabla_r^2 \psi.$

$$\therefore H\psi = -\frac{\hbar^2}{2m_1}\nabla_1^2\psi - \frac{\hbar^2}{2m_2}\nabla_2^2\psi + V(\mathbf{r}_1, \mathbf{r}_2)\psi$$

$$= -\frac{\hbar^2}{2}\left(\frac{\mu^2}{m_1 m_2^2}\nabla_R^2 + \frac{2\mu}{m_1 m_2}\nabla_r \cdot \nabla_R + \frac{1}{m_1}\nabla_r^2 + \frac{\mu^2}{m_2 m_1^2}\nabla_R^2 - \frac{2\mu}{m_2 m_1}\nabla_r \cdot \nabla_R + \frac{1}{m_2}\nabla_r^2\right)\psi$$

$$+ V(\mathbf{r})\psi = -\frac{\hbar^2}{2}\left[\frac{\mu^2}{m_1 m_2}\left(\frac{1}{m_2} + \frac{1}{m_1}\right)\nabla_R^2 + \left(\frac{1}{m_1} + \frac{1}{m_2}\right)\nabla_r^2\right]\psi + V(\mathbf{r})\psi = E\psi.$$

But $\left(\dfrac{1}{m_1} + \dfrac{1}{m_2}\right) = \dfrac{m_1 + m_2}{m_1 m_2} = \dfrac{1}{\mu}$, so $\dfrac{\mu^2}{m_1 m_2}\left(\dfrac{1}{m_2} + \dfrac{1}{m_1}\right) = \dfrac{\mu}{m_1 m_2} = \dfrac{m_1 m_2}{m_1 m_2 (m_1 + m_2)} + \dfrac{1}{m_1 + m_2}.$

$$-\frac{\hbar^2}{2(m_1 + m_2)}\nabla_R^2\psi - \frac{\hbar^2}{2\mu}\nabla_r^2\psi + V(\mathbf{r})\psi = E\psi. \quad \checkmark$$

(c) Put in $\psi = \psi_r(\mathbf{r})\psi_R(\mathbf{R})$, and divide by $\psi_r\psi_R$:

$$\left[-\frac{\hbar^2}{2(m_1 + m_2)}\frac{1}{\psi_R}\nabla_R^2\psi_R\right] + \left[-\frac{\hbar^2}{2\mu}\frac{1}{\psi_r}\nabla_r^2\psi_r + V(\mathbf{r})\right] = E.$$

The first term depends only on $\mathbf{R}$, the second only on $\mathbf{r}$, so each must be a constant; call them $E_R$ and $E_r$, respectively. Then:

$$\boxed{-\frac{\hbar^2}{2(m_1 + m_2)}\nabla^2\psi_R = E_R\psi_R;} \quad \boxed{-\frac{\hbar^2}{2\mu}\nabla^2\psi_r + V(\mathbf{r})\psi_r = E_r\psi_r,} \quad \text{with} \quad \boxed{E_R + E_r = E.}$$

## Problem 5.2

(a) From Eq. 4.77, $E_1$ is proportional to mass, so $\dfrac{\Delta E_1}{E_1} = \dfrac{\Delta m}{\mu} = \dfrac{m - \mu}{\mu} = \dfrac{m(m + M)}{mM} - \dfrac{M}{M} = \dfrac{m}{M}.$

The fractional error is the ratio of the electron mass to the proton mass:

$\dfrac{9.109 \times 10^{-31}\ \text{kg}}{1.673 \times 10^{-27}\ \text{kg}} = 5.44 \times 10^{-4}.$ The *percent* error is $\boxed{0.054\%}$ (pretty small).

(b) From Eq. 4.94, $R$ is proportional to $m$, so $\dfrac{\Delta(1/\lambda)}{(1/\lambda)} = \dfrac{\Delta R}{R} = \dfrac{\Delta\mu}{\mu} = -\dfrac{(1/\lambda^2)\Delta\lambda}{(1/\lambda)} = -\dfrac{\Delta\lambda}{\lambda}.$

So (in magnitude) $\Delta\lambda/\lambda = \Delta\mu/\mu.$ But $\mu = mM/(m + M)$, where $m$ = electron mass, and $M$ = nuclear mass.

$$\Delta\mu = \frac{m(2m_p)}{m + 2m_p} - \frac{mm_p}{m + m_p} = \frac{mm_p}{(m + m_p)(m + 2m_p)}(2m + 2m_p - m - 2m_p)$$

$$= \frac{m^2 m_p}{(m + m_p)(m + 2m_p)} = \frac{m\mu}{m + 2m_p}.$$

$$\frac{\Delta\lambda}{\lambda} = \frac{\Delta\mu}{\mu} = \frac{m}{m+2m_p} \approx \frac{m}{2m_p}, \quad \text{so} \quad \boxed{\Delta\lambda = \frac{m}{2m_p}\lambda_h}, \quad \text{where } \lambda_h \text{ is the hydrogen wavelength.}$$

$$\frac{1}{\lambda} = R\left(\frac{1}{4}-\frac{1}{9}\right)\frac{5}{36}R \Rightarrow \lambda = \frac{36}{5R} = \frac{36}{5(1.097\times10^7)}\,\text{m} = 6.563\times10^{-7}\,\text{m}.$$

$$\therefore \Delta\lambda = \frac{9.109\times10^{-31}}{2(1.673\times10^{-27})}(6.563\times10^{-7})\text{m} = \boxed{1.79\times10^{-10}\,\text{m.}}$$

(c) $\mu = \frac{mm}{m+m} = \frac{m}{2}$, so the energy is *half* what it would be for hydrogen: $(13.6/2)\text{eV} = \boxed{6.8\,\text{eV.}}$

(d) $\mu = \frac{m_p m_\mu}{m_p + m_\mu}$; $R \propto \mu$, so $R$ is changed by a factor $\frac{m_p m_\mu}{m_p + m_\mu}\cdot\frac{m_p + m_e}{m_p m_e} = \frac{m_\mu(m_p + m_e)}{m_e(m_p + m_\mu)}$, as compared with hydrogen. For hydrogen, $1/\lambda = R(1-1/4) = \frac{3}{4}R \Rightarrow \lambda = 4/3R = 4/3(1.097\times10^7)\,\text{m} = 1.215\times10^{-7}\,\text{m}$, and $\lambda \propto 1/R$, so for muonic hydrogen the Lyman-alpha line is at

$$\lambda = \frac{m_e(m_p + m_\mu)}{m_\mu(m_p + m_e)}(1.215\times10^{-7}\text{m}) = \frac{1}{206.77}\frac{(1.673\times10^{-27}+206.77\times9.109\times10^{-31})}{(1.673\times10^{-27}+9.109\times10^{-31})}(1.215\times10^{-7}\text{m})$$

$$= \boxed{6.54\times10^{-10}\,\text{m.}}$$

## Problem 5.3

The energy of the emitted photon, in a transition from vibrational state $n_i$ to state $n_f$, is $E_p = (n_i + \frac{1}{2})\hbar\omega - (n_f + \frac{1}{2})\hbar\omega = n\hbar\omega$, (where $n \equiv n_i - n_f$). The frequency of the photon is $\nu = \frac{E_p}{h} = \frac{n\omega}{2\pi} = \frac{n}{2\pi}\sqrt{\frac{k}{\mu}}$. The splitting of this line is given by

$$\Delta\nu = \left|\frac{n}{2\pi}\sqrt{k}\left(-\frac{1}{2\mu^{3/2}}\Delta\mu\right)\right| = \frac{1}{2}\frac{n}{2\pi}\sqrt{\frac{k}{\mu}}\frac{\Delta\mu}{\mu} = \frac{1}{2}\nu\frac{\Delta\mu}{\mu}.$$

Now

$$\mu = \frac{m_h m_c}{m_h + m_c} = \frac{1}{\frac{1}{m_c}+\frac{1}{m_h}} \Rightarrow \Delta\mu = \frac{-1}{\left(\frac{1}{m_c}+\frac{1}{m_h}\right)^2}\left(-\frac{1}{m_c^2}\Delta m_c\right) = \frac{\mu^2}{m_c^2}\Delta m_c.$$

$$\Delta\nu = \frac{1}{2}\nu\frac{\mu\Delta m_c}{m_c^2} = \frac{1}{2}\nu\frac{(\Delta m_c/m_c)}{\left(1+\frac{m_c}{m_h}\right)}.$$

Using the average value (36) for $m_c$, we have $\Delta m_c/m_c = 2/36$, and $m_c/m_h = 36/1$, so

$$\Delta\nu = \frac{1}{2}\frac{(1/18)}{(1+36)}\nu = \frac{1}{(36)(37)}\nu = \boxed{7.51\times10^{-4}\,\nu.}$$

## Problem 5.4

**(a)**

$$1 = \int |\psi_\pm|^2 d^3\mathbf{r}_1 d^3\mathbf{r}_2$$

$$= |A|^2 \int [\psi_a(\mathbf{r}_1)\psi_b(\mathbf{r}_2) \pm \psi_b(\mathbf{r}_1)\psi_a(\mathbf{r}_2)]^* [\psi_a(\mathbf{r}_1)\psi_b(\mathbf{r}_2) \pm \psi_b(\mathbf{r}_1)\psi_a(\mathbf{r}_2)] d^3\mathbf{r}_1 d^3\mathbf{r}_2$$

$$= |A|^2 \left[ \int |\psi_a(\mathbf{r}_1)|^2 d^3\mathbf{r}_1 \int |\psi_b(\mathbf{r}_2)|^2 d^3\mathbf{r}_2 \pm \int \psi_a(\mathbf{r}_1)^* \psi_b(\mathbf{r}_1) d^3\mathbf{r}_1 \int \psi_b(\mathbf{r}_2)^* \psi_a(\mathbf{r}_2) d^3\mathbf{r}_2 \right.$$

$$\left. \pm \int \psi_b(\mathbf{r}_1)^* \psi_a(\mathbf{r}_1) d^3\mathbf{r}_1 \int \psi_a(\mathbf{r}_2)^* \psi_b(\mathbf{r}_2) d^3\mathbf{r}_2 + \int |\psi_b(\mathbf{r}_1)|^2 d^3\mathbf{r}_1 \int |\psi_a(\mathbf{r}_2)|^2 d^3\mathbf{r}_2 \right]$$

$$= |A|^2 (1 \cdot 1 \pm 0 \cdot 0 \pm 0 \cdot 0 + 1 \cdot 1) = 2|A|^2 \implies \boxed{A = 1/\sqrt{2}.}$$

**(b)**

$$1 = |A|^2 \int [2\psi_a(\mathbf{r}_1)\psi_a(\mathbf{r}_2)]^* [2\psi_a(\mathbf{r}_1)\psi_a(\mathbf{r}_2)] d^3\mathbf{r}_1 d^3\mathbf{r}_2$$

$$= 4|A|^2 \int |\psi_a(\mathbf{r}_1)|^2 d^3\mathbf{r}_1 \int |\psi_a(\mathbf{r}_2)|^2 d^3\mathbf{r}_2 = 4|A|^2. \qquad \boxed{A = 1/2.}$$

---

## Problem 5.5

**(a)**

$$\boxed{-\frac{\hbar^2}{2m}\frac{\partial^2 \psi}{\partial x_1^2} - \frac{\hbar^2}{2m}\frac{\partial^2 \psi}{\partial x_2^2} = E\psi} \quad \text{(for } 0 \le x_1, x_2 \le a, \text{ otherwise } \psi = 0\text{).}$$

$$\psi = \frac{\sqrt{2}}{a} \left[ \sin\left(\frac{\pi x_1}{a}\right) \sin\left(\frac{2\pi x_2}{a}\right) - \sin\left(\frac{2\pi x_1}{a}\right) \sin\left(\frac{\pi x_2}{a}\right) \right]$$

$$\frac{d^2\psi}{dx_1^2} = \frac{\sqrt{2}}{a} \left[ -\left(\frac{\pi}{a}\right)^2 \sin\left(\frac{\pi x_1}{a}\right) \sin\left(\frac{2\pi x_2}{a}\right) + \left(\frac{2\pi}{a}\right)^2 \sin\left(\frac{2\pi x_1}{a}\right) \sin\left(\frac{\pi x_2}{a}\right) \right]$$

$$\frac{d^2\psi}{dx_2^2} = \frac{\sqrt{2}}{a} \left[ -\left(\frac{2\pi}{a}\right)^2 \sin\left(\frac{\pi x_1}{a}\right) \sin\left(\frac{2\pi x_2}{a}\right) + \left(\frac{\pi}{a}\right)^2 \sin\left(\frac{2\pi x_1}{a}\right) \sin\left(\frac{\pi x_2}{a}\right) \right]$$

$$\left(\frac{d^2\psi}{dx_1^2} + \frac{d^2\psi}{dx_2^2}\right) = -\left[\left(\frac{\pi}{a}\right)^2 + \left(\frac{2\pi}{a}\right)^2\right]\psi = -5\frac{\pi^2}{a^2}\psi,$$

$$-\frac{\hbar^2}{2m}\left(\frac{d^2\psi}{dx_1^2} + \frac{d^2\psi}{dx_2^2}\right) = \frac{5\pi^2\hbar^2}{2ma^2}\psi = E\psi, \quad \text{with} \quad E = \frac{5\pi^2\hbar^2}{2ma^2} = 5K. \quad \checkmark$$

**(b) Distinguishable:**

$$\boxed{\psi_{22} = (2/a)\sin\left(2\pi x_1/a\right)\sin\left(2\pi x_2/a\right), \text{ with } E_{22} = 8K} \quad \text{(nondegenerate).}$$

$$\boxed{\begin{array}{l}\psi_{13} = (2/a)\sin\left(\pi x_1/a\right)\sin\left(3\pi x_2/a\right) \\ \psi_{31} = (2/a)\sin\left(3\pi x_1/a\right)\sin\left(\pi x_2/a\right)\end{array}\right\}, \text{ with } E_{13} = E_{31} = 10K} \quad \text{(doubly degenerate).}$$

**Identical Bosons:**

$$\boxed{\psi_{22} = (2/a)\sin\left(2\pi x_1/a\right)\sin\left(2\pi x_2/a\right), E_{22} = 8K} \quad \text{(nondegenerate).}$$

$$\boxed{\psi_{13} = (\sqrt{2}/a)\left[\sin\left(\pi x_1/a\right)\sin\left(3\pi x_2/a\right) + \sin\left(3\pi x_1/a\right)\sin\left(\pi x_2/a\right)\right], E_{13} = 10K} \quad \text{(nondegenerate).}$$

**Identical Fermions:**

$$\boxed{\psi_{13} = (\sqrt{2}/a)\left[\sin\left(\frac{\pi x_1}{a}\right)\sin\left(\frac{3\pi x_2}{a}\right) - \sin\left(\frac{3\pi x_1}{a}\right)\sin\left(\frac{\pi x_2}{a}\right)\right], E_{13} = 10K} \quad \text{(nondegenerate).}$$

$$\boxed{\psi_{23} = (\sqrt{2}/a)\left[\sin\left(\frac{2\pi x_1}{a}\right)\sin\left(\frac{3\pi x_2}{a}\right) - \sin\left(\frac{3\pi x_1}{a}\right)\sin\left(\frac{2\pi x_2}{a}\right)\right], E_{23} = 13K} \quad \text{(nondegenerate).}$$

---

## Problem 5.6

**(a)** Use Eq. 5.19 and Problem 2.4, with $\langle x \rangle_n = a/2$ and $\langle x^2 \rangle_n = a^2\left(\frac{1}{3} - \frac{1}{2(n\pi)^2}\right)$.

$$\langle (x_1 - x_2)^2 \rangle = a^2\left(\frac{1}{3} - \frac{1}{2(n\pi)^2}\right) + a^2\left(\frac{1}{3} - \frac{1}{2(m\pi)^2}\right) - 2\cdot\frac{a}{2}\cdot\frac{a}{2} = \boxed{a^2\left[\frac{1}{6} - \frac{1}{2\pi^2}\left(\frac{1}{n^2} + \frac{1}{m^2}\right)\right].}$$

**(b)** $\langle x \rangle_{mn} = \frac{2}{a}\int_0^a x\sin\left(\frac{m\pi}{a}x\right)\sin\left(\frac{n\pi}{a}x\right)dx = \frac{1}{a}\int_0^a x\left[\cos\left(\frac{(m-n)\pi}{a}x\right) - \cos\left(\frac{(m+n)\pi}{a}x\right)\right]dx$

$$= \frac{1}{a}\left[\left(\frac{a}{(m-n)\pi}\right)^2\cos\left(\frac{(m-n)\pi}{a}x\right) + \left(\frac{ax}{(m-n)\pi}\right)\sin\left(\frac{(m-n)\pi}{a}x\right)\right.$$

$$\left.-\left(\frac{a}{(m+n)\pi}\right)^2\cos\left(\frac{(m+n)\pi}{a}x\right) - \left(\frac{ax}{(m+n)\pi}\right)\sin\left(\frac{(m+n)\pi}{a}x\right)\right]\Bigg|_0^a$$

$$= \frac{1}{a}\left[\left(\frac{a}{(m-n)\pi}\right)^2(\cos[(m-n)\pi] - 1) - \left(\frac{a}{(m+n)\pi}\right)^2(\cos[(m+n)\pi] - 1)\right].$$

But $\cos[(m \pm n)\pi] = (-1)^{m+n}$, so

$$\langle x \rangle_{mn} = \frac{a}{\pi^2}\left[(-1)^{m+n} - 1\right]\left(\frac{1}{(m-n)^2} - \frac{1}{(m+n)^2}\right) = \begin{cases}\frac{a(-8mn)}{\pi^2(m^2-n^2)^2}, & \text{if } m \text{ and } n \text{ have opposite parity,} \\ 0, & \text{if } m \text{ and } n \text{ have same parity.}\end{cases}$$

So Eq. 5.21 $\Rightarrow \langle (x_1 - x_2)^2 \rangle = \boxed{a^2\left[\frac{1}{6} - \frac{1}{2\pi^2}\left(\frac{1}{n^2} + \frac{1}{m^2}\right)\right]} - \frac{128a^2m^2n^2}{\pi^4(m^2-n^2)^4}.$

(The last term is present only when $m$, $n$ have opposite parity.)

(c) Here Eq. 5.21 $\Rightarrow \langle (x_1 - x_2)^2 \rangle = \boxed{a^2 \left[ \dfrac{1}{6} - \dfrac{1}{2\pi^2} \left( \dfrac{1}{n^2} + \dfrac{1}{m^2} \right) \right] + \dfrac{128a^2m^2n^2}{\pi^4(m^2 - n^2)^4}}$.

(Again, the last term is present only when $m$, $n$ have opposite parity.)

---

## Problem 5.7

(a) $\boxed{\psi(x_1, x_2, x_3) = \psi_a(x_1)\psi_b(x_2)\psi_c(x_3).}$

(b) $\psi(x_1, x_2, x_3) = \boxed{\begin{aligned} &\tfrac{1}{\sqrt{6}}[\psi_a(x_1)\psi_b(x_2)\psi_c(x_3) + \psi_a(x_1)\psi_c(x_2)\psi_b(x_3) + \psi_b(x_1)\psi_a(x_2)\psi_c(x_3) \\ &+ \psi_b(x_1)\psi_c(x_2)\psi_a(x_3) + \psi_c(x_1)\psi_b(x_2)\psi_a(x_3) + \psi_c(x_1)\psi_a(x_2)\psi_b(x_3)] \end{aligned}}$.

(c) $\psi(x_1, x_2, x_3) = \boxed{\begin{aligned} &\tfrac{1}{\sqrt{6}}[\psi_a(x_1)\psi_b(x_2)\psi_c(x_3) - \psi_a(x_1)\psi_c(x_2)\psi_b(x_3) - \psi_b(x_1)\psi_a(x_2)\psi_c(x_3) \\ &+ \psi_b(x_1)\psi_c(x_2)\psi_a(x_3) - \psi_c(x_1)\psi_b(x_2)\psi_a(x_3) + \psi_c(x_1)\psi_a(x_2)\psi_b(x_3)] \end{aligned}}$.

---

## Problem 5.8

$$\psi = A\Big[\psi(\mathbf{r}_1, \mathbf{r}_2, \mathbf{r}_3, \dots, \mathbf{r}_Z) \pm \psi(\mathbf{r}_2, \mathbf{r}_1, \mathbf{r}_3, \dots, \mathbf{r}_Z) + \psi(\mathbf{r}_2, \mathbf{r}_3, \mathbf{r}_1, \dots, \mathbf{r}_Z) + \text{etc.}\Big],$$

where "etc." runs over all permutations of the arguments $\mathbf{r}_1, \mathbf{r}_2, \dots, \mathbf{r}_Z$, with a + sign for all *even* permutations (even number of transpositions $\mathbf{r}_i \leftrightarrow \mathbf{r}_j$, starting from $\mathbf{r}_1, \mathbf{r}_2, \dots, \mathbf{r}_Z$), and $\pm$ for all *odd* permutations (+ for bosons, − for fermions). At the end of the process, normalize the result to determine $A$. (Typically $A = 1/\sqrt{Z!}$, but this may not be right if the starting function is already symmetric under some interchanges.)

---

## Problem 5.9

(a) The energy of each electron is $E = Z^2 E_1/n^2 = 4E_1/4 = E_1 = -13.6\text{eV}$, so the total initial energy is $2 \times (-13.6)$ eV$= -27.2$ eV. One electron drops to the ground state $Z^2 E_1/1 = 4E_1$, so the *other* is left with $2E_1 - 4E_1 = -2E_1 = \boxed{27.2 \text{ eV.}}$

(b) He$^+$ has *one* electron; it's a hydrogenic ion (Problem 4.16) with $Z = 2$, so the spectrum is $\boxed{1/\lambda = 4R\left(1/n_f^2 - 1/n_i^2\right),}$ where $R$ is the hydrogen Rydberg constant, and $n_i, n_f$ are the initial and final quantum numbers (1, 2, 3, ... ).

---

## Problem 5.10

(a) The ground state (Eq. 5.30) is spatially *symmetric*, so it goes with the symmetric (triplet) spin configuration. Thus the ground state is *ortho*helium, and it is triply degerate. The excited states (Eq. 5.32) come in ortho (triplet) and para (singlet) form; since the former go with the symmetric spatial wave function, the orthohelium states are *higher* in energy than the corresponding (nondegenerate) para states.

**(b)** The ground state (Eq. 5.30) and all excited states (Eq. 5.32) come in both ortho and para form. All are quadruply degenerate (or at any rate we have no way *a priori* of knowing whether ortho or para are higher in energy, since we don't know which goes with the symmetric spatial configuration).

---

## Problem 5.11

**(a)**

$$\left\langle \frac{1}{|r_1 - r_2|} \right\rangle = \left(\frac{8}{\pi a^3}\right)^2 \int \underbrace{\left[\int \frac{e^{-4(r_1 + r_2)/a}}{\sqrt{r_1^2 + r_2^2 - 2r_1 r_2 \cos\theta_2}} d^3\mathbf{r}_2\right]}_{\blacklozenge} d^3\mathbf{r}_1$$

$$\blacklozenge = 2\pi \int_0^\infty e^{-4(r_1 + r_2)/a} \underbrace{\left[\int_0^\pi \frac{\sin\theta_2}{\sqrt{r_1^2 + r_2^2 - 2r_1 r_2 \cos\theta_2}} d\theta_2\right]}_{\star} r_2^2 \, dr_2$$

$$\star = \frac{1}{r_1 r_2} \sqrt{r_1^2 + r_2^2 - 2r_1 r_2 \cos\theta_2}\Big|_0^\pi = \frac{1}{r_1 r_2}\left[\sqrt{r_1^2 + r_2^2 + 2r_1 r_2} - \sqrt{r_1^2 + r_2^2 - 2r_1 r_2}\right]$$

$$= \frac{1}{r_1 r_2}\left[(r_1 + r_2) - |r_1 - r_2|\right] = \begin{cases} 2/r_1 & (r_2 < r_1) \\ 2/r_2 & (r_2 > r_1) \end{cases}$$

$$\blacklozenge = 4\pi e^{-4r_1/a}\left[\frac{1}{r_1}\int_0^{r_1} r_2^2 e^{-4r_2/a} dr_2 + \int_{r_1}^\infty r_2 e^{-4r_2/a} dr_2\right].$$

$$\frac{1}{r_1}\int_0^{r_1} r_2^2 e^{-4r_2/a} dr_2 = \frac{1}{r_1}\left[-\frac{a}{4}r_2^2 e^{-4r_2/a} + \frac{a}{2}\left(\frac{a}{4}\right)^2 e^{-4r_2/a}\left(-\frac{4r_2}{a} - 1\right)\right]\Big|_0^{r_1}$$

$$= -\frac{a}{4r_1}\left[r_1^2 e^{-4r_1/a} + \frac{ar_1}{2}e^{-4r_1/a} + \frac{a^2}{8}e^{-4r_1/a} - \frac{a^2}{8}\right].$$

$$\int_{r_1}^\infty r_2 e^{-4r_2/a} dr_2 = \left(\frac{a}{4}\right)^2 e^{-4r_2/a}\left(-\frac{4r_2}{a} - 1\right)\Big|_{r_1}^\infty = \frac{ar_1}{4}e^{-4r_1/a} + \frac{a^2}{16}e^{-4r_1/a}.$$

$$\blacklozenge = 4\pi\left\{\frac{a^3}{32r_1}e^{-4r_1/a} + \left[-\frac{ar_1}{a} - \frac{a^2}{8} - \frac{a^3}{32r_1} + \frac{ar_1}{4} + \frac{a^2}{16}\right]e^{-8r_1/a}\right\}$$

$$= \frac{\pi a^2}{8} \left\{ \frac{a}{r_1} e^{-4r_1/a} - \left( 2 + \frac{a}{r_1} \right) e^{-8r_1/a} \right\}.$$

$$\left\langle \frac{1}{|r_1 - r_2|} \right\rangle = \frac{8}{\pi a^4} \cdot 4\pi \int_0^\infty \left[ \frac{a}{r_1} e^{-4r_1/a} - \left( 2 + \frac{a}{r_1} \right) e^{-8r_1/a} \right] r_1^2 \, dr_1$$

$$= \frac{32}{a^4} \left\{ a \int_0^\infty r_1 e^{-4r_1/a} dr_1 - 2 \int_0^\infty r_1^2 e^{-8r_1/a} dr_1 - a \int_0^\infty r_1 e^{-8r_1/a} dr_1 \right\}$$

$$= \frac{32}{a^4} \left\{ a \cdot \left( \frac{a}{4} \right)^2 - 2 \cdot 2 \left( \frac{a}{8} \right)^3 - a \cdot \left( \frac{a}{8} \right)^2 \right\} = \frac{32}{a} \left( \frac{1}{16} - \frac{1}{128} - \frac{1}{64} \right) = \boxed{\frac{5}{4a}.}$$

**(b)**

$$V_{ee} \approx \frac{e^2}{4\pi\epsilon_0} \left\langle \frac{1}{|r_1 - r_2|} \right\rangle = \boxed{\frac{5}{4} \frac{e^2}{4\pi\epsilon_0} \frac{1}{a}} = \frac{5}{4} \frac{m}{\hbar^2} \left( \frac{e^2}{4\pi\epsilon_0} \right)^2 = \frac{5}{2}(-E_1) = \frac{5}{2}(13.6\,\text{eV}) = \boxed{34\,\text{eV.}}$$

$E_0 + V_{ee} = (-109 + 34)\text{eV} = \boxed{-75\,\text{eV,}}$ which is pretty close to the experimental value $(-79\,\text{eV})$.

---

## Problem 5.12

**(a)** Hydrogen: $(1s)$;  helium: $(1s)^2$;  lithium: $(1s)^2(2s)$;  beryllium: $(1s)^2(2s)^2$; boron: $(1s)^2(2s)^2(2p)$;  carbon: $(1s)^2(2s)^2(2p)^2$;  nitrogen: $(1s)^2(2s)^2(2p)^3$; oxygen: $(1s)^2(2s)^2(2p)^4$;  fluorine: $(1s)^2(2s)^2(2p)^5$;  neon: $(1s)^2(2s)^2(2p)^6$. These values agree with those in Table 5.1—no surprises so far.

**(b)** Hydrogen: $^2S_{1/2}$;  helium: $^1S_0$;  lithium: $^2S_{1/2}$;  beryllium $^1S_0$. (These four are unambiguous, because the *orbital* angular momentum is zero in all cases.) For boron, the spin $(1/2)$ and orbital $(1)$ angular momenta could add to give $3/2$ or $1/2$, so the possibilities are $\boxed{^2P_{3/2} \text{ or } ^2P_{1/2}.}$ For carbon, the two $p$ electrons could combine for orbital angular momentum 2, 1, or 0, and the spins could add to 1 or 0: $\boxed{^1S_0, {}^3S_1, {}^1P_1, {}^3P_2, {}^3P_1, {}^3P_0, {}^1D_2, {}^3D_3, {}^3D_2, {}^3D_1.}$ For nitrogen, the 3 $p$ electrons can add to orbital angular momentum 3, 2, 1, or 0, and the spins to $3/2$ or $1/2$:

$$\boxed{\begin{array}{l} ^2S_{1/2}, {}^4S_{3/2}, {}^2P_{1/2}, {}^2P_{3/2}, {}^4P_{1/2}, {}^4P_{3/2}, {}^4P_{5/2}, {}^2D_{3/2}, {}^2D_{5/2}, \\ ^4D_{1/2}, {}^4D_{3/2}, {}^4D_{5/2}, {}^4D_{7/2}, {}^2F_{5/2}, {}^2F_{3/2}, {}^4F_{3/2}, {}^4F_{5/2}, {}^4F_{7/2}, {}^4F_{9/2}. \end{array}}$$

---

## Problem 5.13

(a) Orthohelium should have lower energy than parahelium, for corresponding states (which is true).

(b) Hund's first rule says $S = 1$ for the ground state of carbon. But this (the triplet) is symmetric, so the orbital state will have to be antisymmetric. Hund's second rule favors $L = 2$, but this is symmetric, as you can see most easily by going to the "top of the ladder": $|2\,2\rangle = |1\,1\rangle_1||1\,1\rangle_2$. So the ground state of carbon will be $S = 1, L = 1$. This leaves three possibilities: $^3P_2, {}^3P_1$, and $^3P_0$.

(c) For boron there is only one electron in the $2p$ subshell (which can accommodate a total of 6), so Hund's third rule says the ground state will have $J = |L - S|$. We found in Problem 5.12(b) that $L = 1$ and $S = 1/2$, so $J = 1/2$, and the configuration is $\boxed{^2P_{1/2}.}$

(d) For carbon we know that $S = 1$ and $L = 1$, and there are only two electrons in the outer subshell, so Hund's third rule says $J = 0$, and the ground state configuration must be $\boxed{^3P_0.}$

   For nitrogen Hund's first rule says $S = 3/2$, which is symmetric (the top of the ladder is $|\frac{3}{2}\,\frac{3}{2}\rangle = |\frac{1}{2}\,\frac{1}{2}\rangle_1|\frac{1}{2}\,\frac{1}{2}\rangle_2|\frac{1}{2}\,\frac{1}{2}\rangle_3$). Hund's second rule favors $L = 3$, but this is also symmetric. In fact, the only *anti*symmetric orbital configuration here is $L = 0$. [You can check this directly by working out the Clebsch-Gordan coefficients, but it's easier to reason as follows: Suppose the three outer electrons are in the "top of the ladder" spin state, so each one has spin up ($|\frac{1}{2}\,\frac{1}{2}\rangle$); then (since the spin states are all the same) the orbital states *have* to be different: $|1\,1\rangle$, $|1\,0\rangle$, and $|1\,-1\rangle$. In particular, the total $z$-component of orbital angular momentum has to be zero. But the only configuration that restricts $L_z$ to zero is $L = 0$.] The outer subshell is exactly half filled (three electrons with $n = 2$, $l = 1$), so Hund's third rule says $J = |L - S| = |0 - \frac{3}{2}| = 3/2$. *Conclusion:* The ground state of nitrogen is $\boxed{^4S_{3/2}.}$ (Table 5.1 confirms this.)

## Problem 5.14

$\boxed{S = 2;\ L = 6;\ J = 8.}$ $\underbrace{(1s)^2(2s)^2(2p)^6(3s)^2(3p)^6(3d)^{10}(4s)^2(4p)^6}_{\text{definite (36 electrons)}}$ $\underbrace{(4d)^{10}(5s)^2(5p)^6(4f)^{10}(6s)^2}_{\text{likely (30 electrons)}}$.

## Problem 5.15

Divide Eq. 5.45 by Eq. 5.43, using Eq. 5.42:

$$\frac{E_{\text{tot}}/Nq}{E_F} = \frac{\hbar^2(3\pi^2 Nq)^{5/3}}{10\pi^2 m V^{2/3}} \frac{1}{Nq} \frac{2m}{\hbar^2(3\pi^2 Nq/V)^{2/3}} = \boxed{\frac{3}{5}.}$$

## Problem 5.16

(a) $E_F = \dfrac{\hbar^2}{2m}(3\rho\pi^2)^{2/3}$. $\rho = \dfrac{Nq}{V} = \dfrac{N}{V} = \dfrac{\text{atoms}}{\text{mole}} \times \dfrac{\text{moles}}{\text{gm}} \times \dfrac{\text{gm}}{\text{volume}} = \dfrac{N_A}{M} \cdot d$, where $N_A$ is Avogadro's number ($6.02 \times 10^{23}$), $M$ = atomic mass = 63.5 gm/mol, $d$ = density = 8.96 gm/cm$^3$.

$$\rho = \frac{(6.02 \times 10^{23})(8.96 \text{ gm/cm}^3)}{(63.5 \text{ gm})} = 8.49 \times 10^{22}/\text{cm}^3 = 8.49 \times 10^{28}/\text{m}^3.$$

$$E_F = \frac{(1.055 \times 10^{-34}\text{J} \cdot \text{s})(6.58 \times 10^{-16}\text{eV} \cdot \text{s})}{(2)(9.109 \times 10^{-31}\text{kg})}(3\pi^2\,8.49 \times 10^{28}/\text{m}^3)^{2/3} = \boxed{7.04 \text{ eV.}}$$

**(b)**

$$7.04 \text{ eV} = \frac{1}{2}(0.511 \times 10^6 \text{eV}/c^2)v^2 \Rightarrow \frac{v^2}{c^2} = \frac{14.08}{.511 \times 10^6} = 2.76 \times 10^{-5} \Rightarrow \frac{v}{c} = 5.25 \times 10^{-3},$$

so it's $\boxed{\text{nonrelativistic.}}$    $v = (5.25 \times 10^{-3}) \times (3 \times 10^8) = \boxed{1.57 \times 10^6 \text{ m/s.}}$

**(c)**

$$T = \frac{7.04 \text{ eV}}{8.62 \times 10^{-5} \text{ eV/K}} = \boxed{8.17 \times 10^4 \text{ K.}}$$

**(d)**

$$P = \frac{(3\pi^2)^{2/3}\hbar^2}{5m}\rho^{5/3} = \frac{(3\pi^2)^{2/3}(1.055 \times 10^{-34})^2}{5(9.109 \times 10^{-31})}(8.49 \times 10^{28})^{5/3} \text{N/m}^2 = \boxed{3.84 \times 10^{10} \text{ N/m}^2.}$$

## Problem 5.17

$$P = \frac{(3\pi^2)^{2/3}\hbar^2}{5m}\left(\frac{Nq}{V}\right)^{5/3} = AV^{-5/3} \Rightarrow B = -V\frac{dP}{dV} = -VA\left(\frac{-5}{3}\right)V^{-5/3-1} = \frac{5}{3}AV^{-5/3} = \frac{5}{3}P.$$

For copper, $B = \frac{5}{3}(3.84 \times 10^{10} \text{ N/m}^2) = \boxed{6.4 \times 10^{10} \text{ N/m}^2.}$

## Problem 5.18

**(a)** Equations 5.59 and 5.63 $\Rightarrow \psi = A\sin kx + B\cos kx;$   $A\sin ka = \left[e^{iKa} - \cos ka\right]B.$  So

$$\psi = A\sin kx + \frac{A\sin ka}{(e^{iKa} - \cos ka)}\cos kx = \frac{A}{(e^{iKa} - \cos ka)}\left[e^{iKa}\sin kx - \sin kx\cos ka + \cos kx\sin ka\right]$$

$$= C\{\sin kx + e^{-iKa}\sin[k(a-x)]\}, \text{ where } C \equiv \frac{Ae^{iKa}}{e^{iKa} - \cos ka}.$$

**(b)** If $z = ka = j\pi$, then $\sin ka = 0$, Eq. 5.64 $\Rightarrow \cos Ka = \cos ka = (-1)^j \Rightarrow \sin Ka = 0$, so $e^{iKa} = \cos Ka + i\sin Ka = (-1)^j$, and the constant $C$ involves division by zero. In this case we must go back to Eq. 5.63, which is a tautology (0=0) yielding no constraint on $A$ or $B$, Eq. 5.61 holds automatically, and Eq. 5.62 gives

$$kA - (-1)^j k\left[A(-1)^j - 0\right] = \frac{2m\alpha}{\hbar^2}B \Rightarrow B = 0. \text{ So } \boxed{\psi = A\sin kx.}$$

Here $\psi$ is *zero* at each delta spike, so the wave function never "feels" the potential at all.

## Problem 5.19

We're looking for a solution to Eq. 5.66 with $\beta = 10$ and $z \lesssim \pi$: $f(z) = \cos z + 10\frac{\sin z}{z} = 1.$

Mathematica gives $z = 2.62768$.  So    $E = \frac{\hbar^2 k^2}{2m} = \frac{\hbar^2 z^2}{2ma^2} = \frac{z^2}{2\beta}\frac{\alpha}{a} = \frac{(2.62768)^2}{20} \text{ eV} = \boxed{0.345 \text{ eV.}}$

## Problem 5.20

<u>Positive-energy solutions.</u> These are the same as before, except that $\alpha$ (and hence also $\beta$) is now a negative number.

<u>Negative-energy solutions.</u> On $0 < x < a$ we have

$$\frac{d^2\psi}{dx^2} = \kappa^2\psi, \quad \text{where} \quad \kappa \equiv \frac{\sqrt{-2mE}}{\hbar} \quad \Rightarrow \quad \psi(x) = A\sinh kx + B\cosh kx.$$

According to Bloch's theorem the solution on $-a < x < 0$ is

$$\psi(x) = e^{-iKa}\left[A\sinh\kappa(x+a) + B\cosh\kappa(x+a)\right].$$

Continuity at $x = 0 \Rightarrow$

$$B = e^{-iKa}\left[A\sinh\kappa a + B\cosh\kappa a\right], \quad \text{or} \quad A\sinh\kappa a = B\left[e^{iKa} - \cosh\kappa a\right]. \tag{1}$$

The discontinuity in $\psi'$ (Eq. 2.125) $\Rightarrow$

$$\kappa A - e^{-iKa}\kappa\left[A\cosh\kappa a + B\sinh\kappa a\right] = \frac{2m\alpha}{\hbar^2}B, \text{ or } A\left[1 - e^{-iKa}\cosh\kappa a\right] = B\left[\frac{2m\alpha}{\hbar^2\kappa} + e^{-iKa}\sinh\kappa a\right]. \tag{2}$$

Plugging (1) into (2) and cancelling $B$:

$$\left(e^{iKa} - \cosh\kappa a\right)\left(1 - e^{-iKa}\cosh\kappa a\right) = \frac{2m\alpha}{\hbar^2\kappa}\sinh\kappa a + e^{-iKa}\sinh^2\kappa a.$$

$$e^{iKa} - 2\cosh\kappa a + e^{-iKa}\cosh^2\kappa a - e^{-iKa}\sinh^2\kappa a = \frac{2m\alpha}{\hbar^2\kappa}\sinh\kappa a.$$

$$e^{iKa} + e^{-iKa} = 2\cosh\kappa a + \frac{2ma}{\hbar^2\kappa}\sinh\kappa a, \quad \boxed{\cos Ka = \cosh\kappa a + \frac{m\alpha}{\hbar^2\kappa}\sinh\kappa a.}$$

This is the analog to Eq. 5.64. As before, we let $\beta \equiv m\alpha a/\hbar^2$ (but remember it's now a *negative* number), and this time we define $z \equiv -\kappa a$, extending Eq. 5.65 to negative $z$, where it represents negative-energy solutions. In this region we define

$$f(z) = \cosh z + \beta\frac{\sinh z}{z}. \tag{3}$$

In the Figure I have plotted $f(z)$ for $\beta = -1.5$, using Eq. 5.66 for postive $z$ and (3) for negative $z$. As before, allowed energies are restricted to the range $-1 \le f(z) \le 1$, and occur at intersections of $f(z)$ with the $N$ horizontal lines $\cos Ka = \cos(2\pi n/Na)$, with $n = 0, 1, 2 \ldots N-1$. Evidently the first band (partly negative, and partly positive) contains $N$ states, as do all the higher bands.

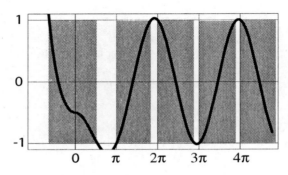

## Problem 5.21

Equation 5.56 says $K = \dfrac{2\pi n}{Na} \Rightarrow Ka = 2\pi \dfrac{n}{N}$; at the bottom of page 227 we found that $n = 0, 1, 2, \ldots, N-1$. Each value of $n$ corresponds to a distinct state. To find the allowed energies we draw $N$ horizontal lines on Figure 5.6, at heights $\cos Ka = \cos(2\pi n/N)$, and look for intersections with $f(z)$. The point is that *almost* all of these lines come in pairs—two different $n$'s yielding the same value of $\cos Ka$:

$\underline{N = 1} \Rightarrow n = 0 \Rightarrow \cos Ka = 1$.   Nondegenerate.

$\underline{N = 2} \Rightarrow n = 0, 1 \Rightarrow \cos Ka = 1, -1$.   Nondegenerate.

$\underline{N = 3} \Rightarrow n = 0, 1, 2 \Rightarrow \cos Ka = 1, -\frac{1}{2}, -\frac{1}{2}$.   The first is nondegenerate, the other two are degenerate.

$\underline{N = 4} \Rightarrow n = 0, 1, 2, 3 \Rightarrow \cos Ka = 1, 0, -1, 0$.   Two are nondegenerate, the others are degenerate.

Evidently they are doubly degenerate (two different $n$'s give same $\cos Ka$) *except* when $\cos Ka = \pm 1$, i.e., at the $\boxed{\text{top or bottom of a band.}}$ The Bloch factors $e^{iKa}$ lie at equal angles in the complex plane, starting with 1 (see Figure, drawn for the case $N = 8$); by symmetry, there is always one with negative imaginary part symmetrically opposite each one with positive imaginary part; these two have the same *real* part ($\cos Ka$). Only points which fall *on* the real axis have no twins.

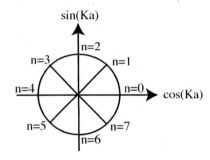

---

## Problem 5.22

(a)

$$\psi(x_A, x_B, x_C) = \frac{1}{\sqrt{6}} \left(\sqrt{\frac{2}{a}}\right)^3 \left[ \sin\left(\frac{5\pi x_A}{a}\right) \sin\left(\frac{7\pi x_B}{a}\right) \sin\left(\frac{17\pi x_C}{a}\right) - \sin\left(\frac{5\pi x_A}{a}\right) \sin\left(\frac{17\pi x_B}{a}\right) \sin\left(\frac{7\pi x_C}{a}\right) \right.$$

$$+ \sin\left(\frac{7\pi x_A}{a}\right) \sin\left(\frac{17\pi x_B}{a}\right) \sin\left(\frac{5\pi x_C}{a}\right) - \sin\left(\frac{7\pi x_A}{a}\right) \sin\left(\frac{5\pi x_B}{a}\right) \sin\left(\frac{17\pi x_C}{a}\right)$$

$$\left. + \sin\left(\frac{17\pi x_A}{a}\right) \sin\left(\frac{5\pi x_B}{a}\right) \sin\left(\frac{7\pi x_C}{a}\right) - \sin\left(\frac{17\pi x_A}{a}\right) \sin\left(\frac{7\pi x_B}{a}\right) \sin\left(\frac{5\pi x_C}{a}\right) \right].$$

(b) (i)

$$\psi = \left(\sqrt{\frac{2}{a}}\right)^3 \left[ \sin\left(\frac{11\pi x_A}{a}\right) \sin\left(\frac{11\pi x_B}{a}\right) \sin\left(\frac{11\pi x_C}{a}\right) \right].$$

(ii)

$$\psi = \frac{1}{\sqrt{3}}\left(\sqrt{\frac{2}{a}}\right)^3\left[\sin\left(\frac{\pi x_A}{a}\right)\sin\left(\frac{\pi x_B}{a}\right)\sin\left(\frac{19\pi x_C}{a}\right)\right.$$

$$\left.+\sin\left(\frac{\pi x_A}{a}\right)\sin\left(\frac{19\pi x_B}{a}\right)\sin\left(\frac{\pi x_C}{a}\right)+\sin\left(\frac{19\pi x_A}{a}\right)\sin\left(\frac{\pi x_B}{a}\right)\sin\left(\frac{\pi x_C}{a}\right)\right].$$

(iii)

$$\psi = \frac{1}{\sqrt{6}}\left(\sqrt{\frac{2}{a}}\right)^3\left[\sin\left(\frac{5\pi x_A}{a}\right)\sin\left(\frac{7\pi x_B}{a}\right)\sin\left(\frac{17\pi x_C}{a}\right)+\sin\left(\frac{5\pi x_A}{a}\right)\sin\left(\frac{17\pi x_B}{a}\right)\sin\left(\frac{7\pi x_C}{a}\right)\right.$$

$$+\sin\left(\frac{7\pi x_A}{a}\right)\sin\left(\frac{17\pi x_B}{a}\right)\sin\left(\frac{5\pi x_C}{a}\right)+\sin\left(\frac{7\pi x_A}{a}\right)\sin\left(\frac{5\pi x_B}{a}\right)\sin\left(\frac{17\pi x_C}{a}\right)$$

$$\left.+\sin\left(\frac{17\pi x_A}{a}\right)\sin\left(\frac{5\pi x_B}{a}\right)\sin\left(\frac{7\pi x_C}{a}\right)+\sin\left(\frac{17\pi x_A}{a}\right)\sin\left(\frac{7\pi x_B}{a}\right)\sin\left(\frac{5\pi x_C}{a}\right)\right].$$

## Problem 5.23

(a) $E_{n_1 n_2 n_3} = (n_1 + n_2 + n_3 + \frac{3}{2})\hbar\omega = \frac{9}{2}\hbar\omega \Rightarrow n_1 + n_2 + n_3 = 3.$  $(n_1, n_2, n_3 = 0, 1, 2, 3\ldots).$

| State | | | Configuration $(N_0, N_1, N_2\ldots)$ | # of States |
|---|---|---|---|---|
| $n_1$ | $n_2$ | $n_3$ | | |
| 0 | 0 | 3 | | |
| 0 | 3 | 0 | $(2,0,0,1,0,0\ldots)$ | 3 |
| 3 | 0 | 0 | | |
| 0 | 1 | 2 | | |
| 0 | 2 | 1 | | |
| 1 | 0 | 2 | $(1,1,1,0,0,0\ldots)$ | 6 |
| 1 | 2 | 0 | | |
| 2 | 0 | 1 | | |
| 2 | 1 | 0 | | |
| 1 | 1 | 1 | $(0,3,0,0,0\ldots)$ | 1 |

Possible single-particle energies:

$E_0 = \hbar\omega/2 : P_0 = 12/30 = 4/10.$
$E_1 = 3\hbar\omega/2 : P_1 = 9/30 = 3/10.$
$E_2 = 5\hbar\omega/2 : P_2 = 6/30 = 2/10.$
$E_3 = 7\hbar\omega/2 : P_3 = 3/30 = 1/10.$

Most probable configuration:  $(1,1,1,0,0,0\ldots).$

Most probable single-particle energy:  $E_0 = \frac{1}{2}\hbar\omega.$

(b) For identical fermions the *only* configuration is $(1,1,1,0,0,0\ldots)$ (one state), so this is also the most probable configuration. The possible one-particle energies are

$E_0 \ (P_0 = 1/3), \quad E_1 \ (P_1 = 1/3), \quad E_2 \ (P_2 = 1/3),$

and they are all equally likely, so it's a 3-way tie for the most probable energy.

(c) For identical bosons all three configurations are possible, and there is one state for each. Possible one-particle energies: $E_0(P_0 = 1/3), E_1(P_1 = 4/9), E_2(P_2 = 1/9), E_3(P_3 = 1/9).$ Most probable energy: $E_1.$

# Problem 5.24

Here $N = 3$, and $d_n = 1$ for all states, so:
$$\begin{cases} \text{Eq. 5.74} \Rightarrow Q = 6 \prod_{n=1}^{\infty} \frac{1}{N_n!} & \text{(distinguishable)}, \\ \text{Eq. 5.75} \Rightarrow Q = \prod_{n=1}^{\infty} \frac{1}{N_n!(1 - N_n)!} & \text{(fermions)}, \\ \text{Eq. 5.77} \Rightarrow Q = 1 & \text{(bosons)}. \end{cases}$$

(In the products, *most* factors are $1/0!$ or $1/1!$, both of which are 1, so I won't write them.)

Configuration 1 ($N_{11} = 3$, others 0):
$$\begin{cases} Q = 6 \times \frac{1}{3!} = \boxed{1} & \text{(distinguishable)}, \\ Q = \frac{1}{3!} \times \frac{1}{(-2)!} = \boxed{0} & \text{(fermions)}, \\ Q = \boxed{1} & \text{(bosons)}. \end{cases}$$

Configuration 2 ($N_5 = 1, N_{13} = 2$):
$$\begin{cases} Q = 6 \times \frac{1}{1!} \times \frac{1}{2!} = \boxed{3} & \text{(distinguishable)}, \\ Q = \frac{1}{1!0!} \times \frac{1}{2!(-1)!} = \boxed{0} & \text{(fermions)}, \\ Q = \boxed{1} & \text{(bosons)}. \end{cases}$$

Configuration 3 ($N_1 = 2, N_{19} = 1$):
$$\begin{cases} Q = 6 \times \frac{1}{2!} \times \frac{1}{1!} = \boxed{3} & \text{(distinguishable)}, \\ Q = \frac{1}{2!(-1)!} \times \frac{1}{1!0!} = \boxed{0} & \text{(fermions)}, \\ Q = \boxed{1} & \text{(bosons)}. \end{cases}$$

Configuration 4 ($N_5 = N_7 = N_{17} = 1$):
$$\begin{cases} Q = 6 \times \frac{1}{1!} \times \frac{1}{1!} \times \frac{1}{1!} = \boxed{6} & \text{(distinguishable)}, \\ Q = \frac{1}{1!0!} \times \frac{1}{1!0!} \times \frac{1}{1!0!} = \boxed{1} & \text{(fermions)}, \\ Q = \boxed{1} & \text{(bosons)}. \end{cases}$$

All of these agree with what we got "by hand" at the top of page 231.

---

# Problem 5.25

$\underline{N = 1}$: - can put the ball in any of $d$ baskets, so $\boxed{d}$ ways.

$\underline{N = 2}$:
$$\begin{cases} \text{- could put both balls in any of the } d \text{ baskets} : d \text{ ways, or} \\ \text{- could put one in one basket (} d \text{ ways), the other in another(} d - 1 \text{) ways—but it} \\ \quad \text{doesn't matter which is which, so divide by 2.} \end{cases}$$

Total: $d + \frac{1}{2}d(d - 1) = \frac{1}{2}d(2 + d - 1) = \boxed{\frac{1}{2}d(d + 1)}$ ways.

$\underline{N = 3}$:
$$\begin{cases} \text{- could put all three in one basket} : d \text{ ways, or} \\ \text{- 2 in one basket, one in another} : d(d - 1) \text{ ways, or} \\ \text{- 1 each in 3 baskets} : d(d - 1)(d - 2)/3! \text{ ways.} \end{cases}$$

Total: $d + d(d - 1) + d(d - 1)(d - 2)/6 = \frac{1}{6}d(6 + 6d - 6 + d^2 - 3d + 2) = \frac{1}{6}d(d^2 + 3d + 2)$

$$= \boxed{\frac{d(d+1)(d+2)}{6}} \text{ ways.}$$

$$\underline{N=4}: \begin{cases} \text{- all in one basket: } d \text{ ways, or} \\ \text{- 3 in one basket, 1 in another: } d(d-1) \text{ ways, or} \\ \text{- 2 in one basket, 2 in another: } d(d-1)/2 \text{ ways, or} \\ \text{- 2 in one basket, one each in others: } d(d-1)(d-2)/2, \text{ or} \\ \text{- all in different baskets: } d(d-1)(d-2)(d-3)/4! \end{cases}$$

$$\underline{\text{Total}}: d + d(d-1) + d(d-1)/2 + d(d-1)(d-2)/2 + d(d-1)(d-2)(d-3)/24$$
$$= \tfrac{1}{24}(24 + 24d - 24 + 12d - 12 + 12d^2 - 36d + 24 + d^3 - 6d^2 + 11d - 6)$$

$$= \tfrac{1}{24}d(d^3 + 6d^2 + 11d + 6) = \boxed{\frac{d(d+1)(d+2)(d+3)}{24}} \text{ ways.}$$

The general formula seems to be $f(N,d) = \dfrac{d(d+1)(d+2)\cdots(d+N-1)}{N!} = \dfrac{(d+N-1)!}{N!(d-1)!} = \boxed{\binom{d+N-1}{N}}.$

<u>Proof:</u> How many ways to put $N$ identical balls in $d$ baskets? Call it $f(N,d)$.
- Could put all of them in the first basket: 1 way.
- Could put all but one in the first basket; there remains 1 ball for $d-1$ baskets: $f(1, d-1)$ ways.
- Could put all but two in the first basket; there remain 2 for $d-1$ baskets: $f(2, d-1)$ ways.

$$\vdots$$

- Could put zero in the first basket, leaving $N$ for $d-1$ baskets: $f(N, d-1)$ ways.

Thus: $f(N,d) = f(0,d-1)+f(1,d-1)+f(2,d-1)+\cdots+f(N,d-1) = \sum_{j=0}^{N} f(j,d-1)$ (where $f(0,d) \equiv 1$).
It follows that $f(N,d) = \sum_{j=0}^{N-1} f(j,d-1) + f(N,d-1) = f(N-1,d) + f(N,d-1)$. Use this recursion relation to confirm the conjectured formula by induction:

$$\binom{d+N-1}{N} \overset{?}{=} \binom{d+N-2}{N-1} + \binom{d+N-2}{N} = \frac{(d+N-2)!}{(N-1)!(d-1)!} + \frac{(d+N-2)!}{N!(d-2)!}$$

$$= \frac{(d+N-2)!}{N!(d-1)!}(N+d-1) = \frac{(d+N-1)!}{N!(d-1)!} = \binom{d+N-1}{d-1}. \quad \checkmark$$

It works for $N=0$: $\binom{d-1}{0} = 1$, and for $d=1$: $\binom{N}{N} = 1$ (which is obviously correct for just one basket). QED

---

## Problem 5.26

$A(x,y) = (2x)(2y) = 4xy$; maximize, subject to the constraint $(x/a)^2 + (y/b)^2 = 1$.

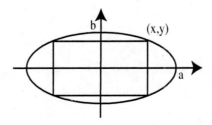

$$G(x,y,\lambda) \equiv 4xy + \lambda\left[(x/a)^2 + (y/b)^2 - 1\right]. \quad \frac{\partial G}{\partial x} = 4y + \frac{2\lambda x}{a^2} = 0 \Rightarrow y = -\frac{\lambda x}{2a^2}.$$

$$\frac{\partial G}{\partial y} = 4x + \frac{2\lambda y}{b^2} = 0 \Rightarrow 4x = -\frac{2\lambda}{b^2}\left(-\frac{\lambda x}{2a^2}\right) \Rightarrow 4x = \frac{\lambda^2}{a^2 b^2}x \Rightarrow x = 0 \text{ (minimum), or else } \lambda = \pm 2ab.$$

So $y = \mp\dfrac{2abx}{2a^2} = \mp\dfrac{b}{a}x$. We may as well pick $x$ and $y$ positive, (as in the figure); then $y = (b/a)x$ (and $\lambda = -2ab$). $\dfrac{\partial G}{\partial \lambda} = 0 \Rightarrow \left(\dfrac{x}{a}\right)^2 + \left(\dfrac{y}{b}\right)^2 = 1$ (of course), so $\dfrac{x^2}{a^2} + \dfrac{b^2 x^2}{a^2 b^2} = 1$, or $\dfrac{2}{a^2}x^2 = 1$, or $x = a/\sqrt{2}$, and hence $y = ba/(a\sqrt{2}) \Rightarrow y = b/\sqrt{2}$. $A = 4\dfrac{a}{\sqrt{2}}\dfrac{b}{\sqrt{2}} = \boxed{2ab.}$

## Problem 5.27

**(a)** $\ln(10!) = \ln(3628800) = 15.1044;$   $10\ln(10) - 10 = 23.026 - 10 = 13.0259;$   $15.1044 - 13.0259 = 2.0785;$   $2.0785/15.1044 = 0.1376,$   or   $\boxed{14\%}$.

| z | % |
|-----|-------|
| 20 | 5.7 |
| 100 | 0.89 |
| 50 | 1.9 |
| 90 | 0.996 |
| 85 | 1.06 |
| 89 | 1.009 |

**(b)** The percent error is: $\dfrac{\ln(z!) - z\ln(z) + z}{\ln(z!)} \times 100.$

Since my calculator cannot compute factorials greater than 69! I used Mathematica to construct the table. Evidently, the smallest integer for which the error is $< 1\%$ is $\boxed{90.}$

## Problem 5.28

Equation 5.108 $\Rightarrow N = \dfrac{V}{2\pi^2}\displaystyle\int_0^\infty k^2 n(\epsilon)\,dk$, where $n(\epsilon)$ is given (as $T \to 0$) by Eq. 5.104.

So $N = \dfrac{V}{2\pi^2}\displaystyle\int_0^{k_{max}} k^2\,dk = \dfrac{V}{2\pi^2}\dfrac{k_{max}^3}{3}$, where $k_{max}$ is given by $\dfrac{\hbar^2 k_{max}^2}{2m} = \mu(0) = E_F \Rightarrow k_{max} = \dfrac{\sqrt{2mE_F}}{\hbar}$.

$\boxed{N = \dfrac{V}{6\pi^2\hbar^3}(2mE_F)^{3/2}.}$   Compare Eq. 5.43, which says

$$E_F = \frac{\hbar^2}{2m}\left(3\pi^2\frac{Nq}{V}\right)^{2/3}, \quad \text{or} \quad \frac{(2mE_F)^{3/2}}{\hbar^3} = 3\pi^2\frac{Nq}{V}, \quad \text{or} \quad N = \frac{V}{3\pi^2 q\hbar^3}(2mE_F)^{3/2}.$$

Here $q = 1$, and Eq. 5.108 needs an extra factor of 2 on the right, to account for spin, so the two formulas agree.

Equation 5.109 $\Rightarrow E_{tot} = \dfrac{V\hbar^2}{4\pi^2 m}\displaystyle\int_0^{k_{max}} k^4\,dk = \dfrac{V\hbar^2}{4\pi^2 m}\dfrac{k_{max}^5}{5} \Rightarrow E_{tot} = \boxed{\dfrac{V}{20\pi^2 m\hbar^3}(2mE_F)^{5/2}.}$

Compare Eq. 5.45, which says $E_{tot} = \dfrac{V\hbar^2}{10\pi^2 m}k_{max}^5$. Again, Eq. 5.109 for electrons has an extra factor of 2, so the two agree.

## Problem 5.29

**(a)** Equation 5.103, $n(\epsilon) > 0 \Rightarrow \dfrac{1}{e^{(\epsilon-\mu)/k_B T} - 1} > 0 \Rightarrow e^{(\epsilon-\mu)/k_B T} > 1 \Rightarrow \dfrac{(\epsilon-\mu)}{k_B T} > 0 \Rightarrow \boxed{\epsilon > \mu(T),}$ for all allowed energies $\epsilon$.

**(b)** For a free particle gas, $E = \dfrac{\hbar^2}{2m} k^2 \to 0$ (as $k \to 0$, in the continuum limit), so $\mu(T)$ *is always negative.* (Technically, the lowest energy is $\dfrac{\hbar^2 \pi^2}{2m}\left(\dfrac{1}{l_x^2} + \dfrac{1}{l_y^2} + \dfrac{1}{l_z^2}\right)$, but we take the dimensions $l_x l_y l_z$ to be very large in the continuum limit.) Equation 5.108 $\Rightarrow N/V = \dfrac{1}{2\pi^2} \displaystyle\int_0^\infty \dfrac{k^2}{e^{(\hbar^2 k^2/2m - \mu)/k_B T} - 1} \, dk$. The integrand is always positive, and the only $T$ dependence is in $\mu(T)$ and $k_B T$. So, as $T$ decreases, $(\hbar^2 k^2/2m) - \mu(T)$ must also decrease, and hence $-\mu(T)$ decreases, or $\mu(T)$ *increases* (always negative).

**(c)** $\dfrac{N}{V} = \dfrac{1}{2\pi^2} \displaystyle\int_0^\infty \dfrac{k^2}{e^{\hbar^2 k^2/2m k_B T} - 1} \, dk$.  Let $x \equiv \dfrac{\hbar^2 k^2}{2m k_B T}$, so $k = \dfrac{\sqrt{2m k_B T}}{\hbar} x^{1/2}$; $dk = \dfrac{\sqrt{2m k_B T}}{\hbar} \dfrac{1}{2} x^{-1/2} \, dx$.

$\dfrac{N}{V} = \dfrac{1}{2\pi^2} \left(\dfrac{2m k_B T}{\hbar^2}\right)^{3/2} \dfrac{1}{2} \displaystyle\int_0^\infty \dfrac{x^{1/2}}{e^x - 1} \, dx$, where $\displaystyle\int_0^\infty \dfrac{x^{3/2 - 1}}{e^x - 1} \, dx = \Gamma(3/2)\zeta(3/2)$.

Now $\Gamma(3/2) = \sqrt{\pi}/2$; $\zeta(3/2) = 2.61238$, so $\dfrac{N}{V} = 2.612 \left(\dfrac{m k_B T}{2\pi \hbar^2}\right)^{3/2}$; $\boxed{T_c = \dfrac{2\pi \hbar^2}{m k_B}\left(\dfrac{N}{2.612 V}\right)^{2/3}.}$

**(d)**

$$\dfrac{N}{V} = \dfrac{\text{mass/volume}}{\text{mass/atom}} = \dfrac{0.15 \times 10^3 \, \text{kg/m}^3}{4(1.67 \times 10^{-27} \, \text{kg})} = 2.2 \times 10^{28} /\text{m}^3.$$

$$T_c = \dfrac{2\pi(1.05 \times 10^{-34} \, \text{J} \cdot \text{s})^2}{4(1.67 \times 10^{-27} \, \text{kg})(1.38 \times 10^{-23} \, \text{J/K})}\left(\dfrac{2.2 \times 10^{28}}{2.61 \, \text{m}^3}\right)^{2/3} = \boxed{3.1 \, \text{K.}}$$

## Problem 5.30

**(a)**

$$\omega = 2\pi\nu = \dfrac{2\pi c}{\lambda}, \quad \text{so} \quad d\omega = -\dfrac{2\pi c}{\lambda^2} \, d\lambda, \quad \text{and} \quad \rho(\omega) = \dfrac{\hbar}{\pi^2 c^3} \dfrac{(2\pi c)^3}{\lambda^3 (e^{2\pi\hbar c/k_B T \lambda} - 1)}.$$

$$\rho(\omega)|d\omega| = 8\pi\hbar \dfrac{1}{\lambda^3(e^{2\pi\hbar c/k_B T\lambda} - 1)} \left|-\dfrac{2\pi c}{\lambda^2} \, d\lambda\right| = \overline{\rho}(\lambda) \, d\lambda \Rightarrow \boxed{\overline{\rho}(\lambda) = \dfrac{16\pi^2 \hbar c}{\lambda^5(e^{2\pi\hbar c/k_B T\lambda} - 1)}.}$$

(For *density*, we want only the *size* of the interval, not its *sign*.)

**(b)** To maximize, set $d\overline{\rho}/d\lambda = 0$:

$$0 = 16\pi^2 \hbar c \left[\dfrac{-5}{\lambda^6(e^{2\pi\hbar c/k_B T\lambda} - 1)} - \dfrac{e^{2\pi\hbar c/k_B T\lambda}(2\pi\hbar c/k_B T)}{\lambda^5(e^{2\pi\hbar c/k_B T\lambda} - 1)^2}\left(-\dfrac{1}{\lambda^2}\right)\right]$$

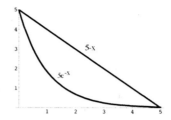

$$\Rightarrow 5(e^{2\pi\hbar c/k_B T\lambda} - 1) = e^{2\pi\hbar c/k_B T\lambda}\left(\frac{2\pi\hbar c}{k_B T\lambda}\right).$$

Let $x \equiv 2\pi\hbar c/k_B T\lambda$; then $5(e^x - 1) = xe^x$; or $5(1 - e^{-x}) = x$, or $5e^{-x} = 5 - x$. From the graph, the solution occurs slightly below $x = 5$.

Mathematica says $x = 4.966$, so $\boxed{\lambda_{\text{max}} = \frac{2\pi\hbar c}{(4.966)k_B}\frac{1}{T}} = \frac{(6.626 \times 10^{-34}\text{ J}\cdot\text{s})(2.998 \times 10^8\text{ m/s})}{(4.966)(1.3807 \times 10^{-23}\text{ J/K})}\frac{1}{T} = $

$\boxed{2.897 \times 10^{-3}\text{ m·K}/T.}$

## Problem 5.31

From Eq. 5.113:

$$\frac{E}{V} = \int_0^\infty \rho(\omega)\,d\omega = \frac{\hbar}{\pi^2 c^3}\int_0^\infty \frac{\omega^3}{(e^{\hbar\omega/k_B T} - 1)}\,d\omega. \quad \text{Let } x \equiv \frac{\hbar\omega}{k_B T}. \quad \text{Then}$$

$$\frac{E}{V} = \frac{\hbar}{\pi^2 c^3}\left(\frac{k_B T}{\hbar}\right)^4\int_0^\infty \frac{x^3}{e^x - 1}\,dx = \frac{(k_B T)^4}{\pi^2 c^3\hbar^3}\Gamma(4)\zeta(4) = \frac{(k_B T)^4}{\pi^2 c^3\hbar^3}\cdot 6\cdot\frac{\pi^4}{90} = \left(\frac{\pi^2 k_B^4}{15 c^3\hbar^3}\right)T^4$$

$$= \left[\frac{\pi^2(1.3807 \times 10^{-23}\text{ J/K})^4}{15(2.998 \times 10^8\text{ m/s})^3(1.0546 \times 10^{-34}\text{ J}\cdot\text{s})^3}\right]T^4 = 7.566 \times 10^{-16}\frac{\text{J}}{\text{m}^3\text{K}^4}T^4. \quad \text{QED}$$

## Problem 5.32

From Problem 2.11(a),

$$\langle x\rangle_0 = \langle x\rangle_1 = 0; \quad \langle x^2\rangle_0 = \frac{\hbar}{2m\omega}; \quad \langle x^2\rangle_1 = \frac{3\hbar}{2m\omega}.$$

From Eq. 3.98,

$$\langle x\rangle_{01} = \int_{-\infty}^\infty x\psi_0(x)\psi_1(x)\,dx = \langle 0|x|1\rangle = \sqrt{\frac{\hbar}{2m\omega}}\left(\sqrt{1}\,\delta_{0\,0} + \sqrt{0}\,\delta_{1\,-1}\right) = \sqrt{\frac{\hbar}{2m\omega}}.$$

(a) Equation 5.19 $\Rightarrow \langle(x_1 - x_2)^2\rangle_d = \frac{\hbar}{2m\omega} + \frac{3\hbar}{2m\omega} - 0 = \boxed{\frac{2\hbar}{m\omega}}.$

(b) Equation 5.21 $\Rightarrow \langle(x_1 - x_2)^2\rangle_+ = \frac{2\hbar}{m\omega} - 2\frac{\hbar}{2m\omega} = \boxed{\frac{\hbar}{m\omega}}.$

**(c)** Equation 5.21 $\Rightarrow \langle (x_1 - x_2)^2 \rangle_- = \dfrac{2\hbar}{m\omega} + 2\dfrac{\hbar}{2m\omega} = \boxed{\dfrac{3\hbar}{m\omega}}.$

---

## Problem 5.33

**(a)** Each particle has 3 possible states: $3 \times 3 \times 3 = \boxed{27.}$

**(b)** All in same state: *aaa, bbb, ccc* $\Rightarrow$ 3.

   2 in one state: *aab, aac, bba, bbc, cca, ccb* $\Rightarrow$ 6 (each symmetrized).

   3 different states: *abc* (symmetrized) $\Rightarrow$ 1.

   Total: $\boxed{10.}$

**(c)** Only *abc* (antisymmetrized) $\Longrightarrow \boxed{1.}$

---

## Problem 5.34

Equation 5.39 $\Rightarrow E_{n_x n_y} = \dfrac{\pi^2 \hbar^2}{2m}\left( \dfrac{n_x^2}{l_x^2} + \dfrac{n_y^2}{l_y^2} \right) = \dfrac{\hbar^2 k^2}{2m}$, with $\mathbf{k} = \left( \dfrac{\pi n_x}{l_x}, \dfrac{\pi n_y}{l_y} \right)$. Each state is represented by an

intersection on a grid in "$\mathbf{k}$-space"—this time a *plane*—and each state occupies an area $\pi^2/l_x l_y = \pi^2/A$ (where $A \equiv l_x l_y$ is the area of the well). Two electrons per state means

$$\frac{1}{4}\pi k_F^2 = \frac{Nq}{2}\left( \frac{\pi^2}{A} \right), \text{ or } k_F = \left( 2\pi \frac{Nq}{A} \right)^{1/2} = (2\pi\sigma)^{1/2},$$

where $\sigma \equiv Nq/A$ is the number of free electrons per unit area.

$$\therefore E_F = \frac{\hbar^2 k_F^2}{2m} = \frac{\hbar^2}{2m} 2\pi\sigma = \boxed{\frac{\pi \hbar^2 \sigma}{m}}.$$

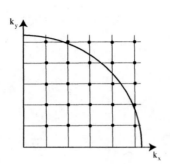

## Problem 5.35

(a)

$$V = \frac{4}{3}\pi R^3, \quad \text{so } E = \frac{\hbar^2 (3\pi^2 Nq)^{5/3}}{10\pi^2 m} \left(\frac{4}{3}\pi R^3\right)^{-2/3} = \boxed{\frac{2\hbar^2}{15\pi m R^2} \left(\frac{9}{4}\pi Nq\right)^{5/3}}.$$

(b) Imagine building up a sphere by layers. When it has reached mass $m$, and radius $r$, the work necessary to bring in the next increment $dm$ is: $dW = -(Gm/r)\,dm$. In terms of the mass density $\rho$, $m = \frac{4}{3}\pi r^3 \rho$, and $dm = 4\pi r^2 dr\rho$, where $dr$ is the resulting increase in radius. Thus:

$$dW = -G\frac{4}{3}\pi r^3 \rho\, 4\pi r^2 \rho\, \frac{dr}{r} = -\frac{16\pi^2}{3}\rho^2 G r^4 dr,$$

and the *total* energy of a sphere of radius $R$ is therefore

$$E_{\text{grav}} = -\frac{16\pi^2}{3}\rho^2 G \int_0^R r^4 \, dr = -\frac{16\pi^2 \rho^2 R^5}{15}G. \quad \text{But } \rho = \frac{NM}{4/3\pi R^3}, \text{ so}$$

$$E_{\text{grav}} = -\frac{16\pi^2 R^5}{15}G\frac{9N^2 M^2}{16\pi^2 R^6} = \boxed{-\frac{3}{5}G\frac{N^2 M^2}{R}}.$$

(c)

$$E_{\text{tot}} = \frac{A}{R^2} - \frac{B}{R}, \quad \text{where } A \equiv \frac{2\hbar^2}{15\pi m}\left(\frac{9}{4}\pi Nq\right)^{5/3} \quad \text{and} \quad B \equiv \frac{3}{5}GN^2 M^2.$$

$$\frac{dE_{\text{tot}}}{dR} = -\frac{2A}{R^3} + \frac{B}{R^2} = 0 \Rightarrow 2A = BR, \quad \text{so} \quad R = \frac{2A}{B} = \frac{4\hbar}{15\pi m}\left(\frac{9}{4}\pi Nq\right)^{5/3}\frac{5}{3GN^2 M^2}.$$

$$R = \left[\left(\frac{4}{9\pi}\right)\left(\frac{9\pi}{4}\right)^{5/3}\right]\left(\frac{N^{5/3}}{N^2}\right)\frac{\hbar^2}{GmM^2}q^{5/3} = \boxed{\left(\frac{9\pi}{4}\right)^{2/3}\frac{\hbar^2}{GmM^2}\frac{q^{5/3}}{N^{1/3}}}.$$

$$R = \left(\frac{9\pi}{4}\right)^{2/3}\frac{(1.055 \times 10^{-34}\,\text{J}\cdot\text{s})^2 (1/2)^{5/3}}{(6.673 \times 10^{-11}\,\text{Nm}^2/\text{kg}^2)(9.109 \times 10^{-31}\,\text{kg})(1.674 \times 10^{-27}\,\text{kg})^2}N^{-1/3}$$

$$= \boxed{(7.58 \times 10^{25}\,\text{m})N^{-1/3}}.$$

(d) Mass of sun: $1.989 \times 10^{30}$ kg, so $N = \dfrac{1.989 \times 10^{30}}{1.674 \times 10^{-27}} = 1.188 \times 10^{57}$; $N^{-1/3} = 9.44 \times 10^{-20}$.

$$R = (7.58 \times 10^{25})(9.44 \times 10^{-20})\,\text{m} = \boxed{7.16 \times 10^6\,\text{m}} \text{ (slightly larger than the earth).}$$

(e)

$$\text{From Eq. 5.43:} \quad E_F = \frac{\hbar^2}{2m}\left(3\pi^2\frac{Nq}{4/3\pi R^3}\right)^{2/3} = \frac{\hbar^2}{2mR^2}\left(\frac{9\pi}{4}Nq\right)^{2/3}. \quad \text{Numerically:}$$

$$E_F = \frac{(1.055 \times 10^{-34} \text{ J} \cdot \text{s})^2}{2(9.109 \times 10^{-31} \text{ kg})(7.16 \times 10^6 \text{ m})^2} \left[ \frac{9\pi}{4}(1.188 \times 10^{57})\frac{1}{2} \right]^{2/3} = 3.102 \times 10^{-14} \text{ J},$$

or, in electron volts:   $E_F = \dfrac{3.102 \times 10^{-14}}{1.602 \times 10^{-19}} \text{ eV} = \boxed{1.94 \times 10^5 \text{ eV.}}$

$E_{\text{rest}} = mc^2 = 5.11 \times 10^5$ eV, so the Fermi energy (which is the energy of the most energetic electrons) is comparable to the rest energy, so they are getting fairly relativistic.

## Problem 5.36

(a)

$$dE = (\hbar ck)\frac{V}{\pi^2}k^2 \, dk \Rightarrow E_{\text{tot}} = \frac{\hbar cV}{\pi^2}\int_0^{k_F} k^3 \, dk = \frac{\hbar cV}{4\pi^2}k_F^4; \quad k_F = \left( \frac{3\pi^2 Nq}{V} \right)^{1/3}.$$

So $E_{\text{tot}} = \boxed{\dfrac{\hbar c}{4\pi^2}(3\pi^2 Nq)^{4/3}V^{-1/3}.}$

(b)

$$V = \frac{4}{3}\pi R^3 \Rightarrow E_{\text{deg}} = \frac{\hbar c}{4\pi^2 R}(3\pi^2 Nq)^{4/3}\left( \frac{4\pi}{3} \right)^{-1/3} = \frac{\hbar c}{3\pi R}\left( \frac{9}{4}\pi Nq \right)^{4/3}.$$

Adding in the gravitational energy, from Problem 5.35(b),

$$E_{\text{tot}} = \frac{A}{R} - \frac{B}{R}, \quad \text{where } A \equiv \frac{\hbar c}{3\pi}\left( \frac{9}{4}\pi Nq \right)^{4/3} \text{ and } B \equiv \frac{3}{5}GN^2 M^2. \quad \frac{dE_{\text{tot}}}{dR} = -\frac{(A - B)}{R^2} = 0 \Rightarrow A = B,$$

but there is no special value of $R$ for which $E_{\text{tot}}$ is minimal. Critical value: $A = B(E_{\text{tot}} = 0) \Rightarrow$
$\dfrac{\hbar c}{3\pi}\left( \dfrac{9}{4}\pi Nq \right)^{4/3} = \dfrac{3}{5}GN^2 M^2$, or

$$\boxed{N_c = \frac{15}{16}\sqrt{5\pi}\left( \frac{\hbar c}{G} \right)^{3/2}\frac{q^2}{M^3}} = \frac{15}{16}\sqrt{5\pi}\left( \frac{1.055 \times 10^{-34} \text{ J} \cdot \text{s} \times 2.998 \times 10^8 \text{ m/s}}{6.673 \times 10^{-11} \text{ N} \cdot \text{m}^2/\text{kg}^2} \right)^{3/2}\frac{(1/2)^2}{(1.674 \times 10^{-27} \text{ kg})^3}$$

$= \boxed{2.04 \times 10^{57}.}$   (About *twice* the value for the sun—Problem 5.35(d).)

(c) Same as Problem 5.35(c), with $m \to M$ and $q \to 1$, so multiply old answer by $(2)^{5/3}m/M$:

$$R = 2^{5/3}\frac{(9.109 \times 10^{-31})}{(1.674 \times 10^{-27})}(7.58 \times 10^{25} \text{ m})N^{-1/3} = (1.31 \times 10^{23} \text{ m})N^{-1/3}. \quad \text{Using } N = 1.188 \times 10^{57},$$

$R = (1.31 \times 10^{23} \text{ m})(9.44 \times 10^{-20}) = \boxed{12.4 \text{ km.}}$ To get $E_F$, use Problem 5.35(e) with $q = 1$, the new $R$, and the neutron mass in place of $m$:

$$E_F = 2^{2/3}\left( \frac{7.16 \times 10^6}{1.24 \times 10^4} \right)^2\left( \frac{9.11 \times 10^{-31}}{1.67 \times 10^{-27}} \right)(1.94 \times 10^5 \text{ eV}) = 5.60 \times 10^7 \text{ eV} = \boxed{56.0 \text{ MeV.}}$$

The rest energy of a neutron is 940 MeV, so a neutron star is reasonably nonrelativistic.

## Problem 5.37

(a) From Problem 4.38: $E_n = (n + \frac{3}{2})\hbar\omega$, with $n = 0, 1, 2, \ldots$; $d_n = \frac{1}{2}(n+1)(n+2)$.

From Eq. 5.103, $n(\epsilon) = e^{-(\epsilon - \mu)/k_B T}$, so $N_n = \frac{1}{2}(n+1)(n+2)e^{(\mu - \frac{3}{2}\hbar\omega)/k_B T}e^{-n\hbar\omega/k_B T}$.

$$N = \sum_{n=0}^{\infty} N_n = \frac{1}{2}e^{(\mu - \frac{3}{2}\hbar\omega)/k_B T}\sum_{n=0}^{\infty}(n+1)(n+2)x^n, \quad \text{where } x \equiv e^{-\hbar\omega/k_B T}. \quad \text{Now}$$

$$\frac{1}{1-x} = \sum_{n=0}^{\infty}x^n \Rightarrow \frac{x}{1-x} = \sum_{n=0}^{\infty}x^{n+1} \Rightarrow \frac{d}{dx}\left(\frac{x}{1-x}\right) = \sum_{n=0}^{\infty}(n+1)x^n \Rightarrow \frac{1}{(1-x)^2} = \sum_{n=0}^{\infty}(n+1)x^n.$$

$$\frac{x^2}{(1-x)^2} = \sum_{n=0}^{\infty}(n+1)x^{n+2}, \quad \text{and hence} \quad \frac{d}{dx}\left(\frac{x^2}{(1-x)^2}\right) = \sum_{n=0}^{\infty}(n+1)(n+2)x^{n+1} = \frac{2x}{(1-x)^3}.$$

$$\sum_{n=0}^{\infty}(n+1)(n+2)x^n = \frac{2}{(1-x)^3}. \quad \text{So } N = e^{\mu/k_B T}e^{-\frac{3}{2}\hbar\omega/k_B T}\frac{1}{(1-e^{-\hbar\omega/k_B T})^3}.$$

$$e^{\mu/k_B T} = N(1 - e^{-\hbar\omega/k_B T})^3 e^{\frac{3}{2}\hbar\omega/k_B T}; \quad \boxed{\mu = k_B T\left[\ln N + 3\ln(1 - e^{-\hbar\omega/k_B T}) + \tfrac{3}{2}\hbar\omega/k_B T\right].}$$

$$E = \sum_{n=0}^{\infty}N_n E_n = \frac{1}{2}\hbar\omega e^{(\mu - \frac{3}{2}\hbar\omega)/k_B T}\sum_{n=0}^{\infty}(n+3/2)(n+1)(n+2)x^n. \quad \text{From above,}$$

$$\frac{2x^{3/2}}{(1-x)^3} = \sum_{n=0}^{\infty}(n+1)(n+2)x^{n+3/2} \Rightarrow \frac{d}{dx}\left(\frac{2x^{3/2}}{(1-x)^3}\right) = \sum_{n=0}^{\infty}(n+3/2)(n+1)(n+2)x^{n+1/2}, \quad \text{or}$$

$$\sum_{n=0}^{\infty}(n+3/2)(n+1)(n+2)x^n = \frac{1}{x^{1/2}}\frac{d}{dx}\left(\frac{2x^{3/2}}{(1-x)^3}\right) = \frac{2}{x^{1/2}}\left[\frac{\frac{3}{2}x^{1/2}}{(1-x)^3} + \frac{3x^{3/2}}{(1-x)^4}\right] = \frac{3(1+x)}{(1-x)^4}.$$

$$E = \frac{1}{2}\hbar\omega e^{(\mu - \frac{3}{2}\hbar\omega)/k_B T}\frac{3(1 + e^{-\hbar\omega/k_B T})}{(1 - e^{-\hbar\omega/k_B T})^4}. \quad \text{But } e^{(\mu - \frac{3}{2}\hbar\omega)/k_B T} = N(1 - e^{-\hbar\omega/k_B T})^3, \quad \text{so}$$

$$\boxed{E = \frac{3}{2}N\hbar\omega\frac{(1 + e^{-\hbar\omega/k_B T})}{(1 - e^{-\hbar\omega/k_B T})}.}$$

(b) $k_B T \ll \hbar\omega$ (low temperature) $\Rightarrow e^{-\hbar\omega/k_B T} \approx 0$, so $\boxed{E \approx \frac{3}{2}N\hbar\omega}$ ($\mu \approx \frac{3}{2}\hbar\omega$). In this limit, *all* particles are in the ground state, $E_0 = \frac{3}{2}\hbar\omega$.

(c) $k_B T \gg \hbar\omega$ (high temperature) $\Rightarrow e^{-\hbar\omega/k_B T} \approx 1 - (\hbar\omega/k_B T)$, so $\boxed{E \approx 3Nk_B T}$
($\mu \approx k_B T\left[\ln N + 3\ln(\hbar\omega/k_B T)\right]$). The equipartition theorem says $E = N\#\frac{1}{2}k_B T$, where $\#$ is the number of degrees of freedom for each particle. In this case $\#/2 = 3$, or $\boxed{\# = 6}$ (3 kinetic, 3 potential, for each particle—one of each for each direction in space).

# Chapter 6

# Time-Independent Perturbation Theory

## Problem 6.1

**(a)**

$$\psi_n^0(x) = \sqrt{\frac{2}{a}} \sin\left(\frac{n\pi}{a}x\right), \text{ so } E_n^1 = \langle \psi_n^0 | H' | \psi_n^0 \rangle = \frac{2}{a}\alpha \int_0^a \sin^2\left(\frac{n\pi}{a}x\right) \delta\left(x - \frac{a}{2}\right) dx.$$

$$E_n^1 = \frac{2\alpha}{a} \sin^2\left(\frac{n\pi}{a}\frac{a}{2}\right) = \frac{2\alpha}{a} \sin^2\left(\frac{n\pi}{2}\right) = \boxed{\left\{ \begin{array}{ll} 0, & \text{if } n \text{ is even,} \\ 2\alpha/a, & \text{if } n \text{ is odd.} \end{array} \right\}}$$

For even $n$ the wave function is zero at the location of the perturbation ($x = a/2$), so it never "feels" $H'$.

**(b)** Here $n = 1$, so we need

$$\langle \psi_m^0 | H' | \psi_1^0 \rangle = \frac{2\alpha}{a} \int \sin\left(\frac{m\pi}{a}x\right) \delta\left(x - \frac{a}{2}\right) \sin\left(\frac{\pi}{a}x\right) dx = \frac{2\alpha}{a} \sin\left(\frac{m\pi}{2}\right) \sin\left(\frac{\pi}{2}\right) = \frac{2\alpha}{a} \sin\left(\frac{m\pi}{2}\right).$$

This is zero for even $m$, so the first three nonzero terms will be $m = 3$, $m = 5$, and $m = 7$. Meanwhile, $E_1^0 - E_m^0 = \dfrac{\pi^2 \hbar^2}{2ma^2}(1 - m^2)$, so

$$\psi_1^1 = \sum_{m=3,5,7,\ldots} \frac{(2\alpha/a)\sin(m\pi/2)}{E_1^0 - E_m^0} \psi_m^0 = \frac{2\alpha}{a} \frac{2ma^2}{\pi^2 \hbar^2} \left[ \frac{-1}{1-9}\psi_3^0 + \frac{1}{1-25}\psi_5^0 + \frac{-1}{1-49}\psi_7^0 + \ldots \right]$$

$$= \frac{4ma\alpha}{\pi^2\hbar^2} \sqrt{\frac{2}{a}} \left[ \frac{1}{8}\sin\left(\frac{3\pi}{a}x\right) - \frac{1}{24}\sin\left(\frac{5\pi}{a}x\right) + \frac{1}{48}\sin\left(\frac{7\pi}{a}x\right) + \ldots \right]$$

$$= \boxed{\frac{m\alpha}{\pi^2\hbar^2} \sqrt{\frac{a}{2}} \left[ \sin\left(\frac{3\pi}{a}x\right) - \frac{1}{3}\sin\left(\frac{5\pi}{a}x\right) + \frac{1}{6}\sin\left(\frac{7\pi}{a}x\right) + \ldots \right].}$$

## Problem 6.2

**(a)** $E_n = (n + \frac{1}{2})\hbar\omega'$, where $\omega' \equiv \sqrt{k(1+\epsilon)/m} = \omega\sqrt{1+\epsilon} = \omega(1 + \frac{1}{2}\epsilon - \frac{1}{8}\epsilon^2 + \frac{1}{16}\epsilon^3 \cdots)$, so

$$\boxed{E_n = (n + \tfrac{1}{2})\hbar\omega\sqrt{1+\epsilon} = (n + \tfrac{1}{2})\hbar\omega(1 + \tfrac{1}{2}\epsilon - \tfrac{1}{8}\epsilon^2 + \cdots).}$$

**(b)** $H' = \frac{1}{2}k'x^2 - \frac{1}{2}kx^2 = \frac{1}{2}kx^2(1 + \epsilon - 1) = \epsilon(\frac{1}{2}kx^2) = \epsilon V$, where $V$ is the unperturbed potential energy. So $E_n^1 = \langle \psi_n^0 | H' | \psi_n^0 \rangle = \epsilon \langle n | V | n \rangle$, with $\langle n | V | n \rangle$ the expectation value of the (unperturbed) potential energy in the $n^{th}$ unperturbed state. This is most easily obtained from the virial theorem (Problem 3.31), but it can also be derived algebraically. In this case the virial theorem says $\langle T \rangle = \langle V \rangle$. But $\langle T \rangle + \langle V \rangle = E_n$. So $\langle V \rangle = \frac{1}{2}E_n^0 = \frac{1}{2}(n + \frac{1}{2})\hbar\omega;$ $\boxed{E_n^1 = \frac{\epsilon}{2}(n + \frac{1}{2})\hbar\omega,}$ which is precisely the $\epsilon^1$ term in the power series from part (a).

---

## Problem 6.3

**(a)** In terms of the one-particle states (Eq. 2.28) and energies (Eq. 2.27):

Ground state: $\psi_1^0(x_1, x_2) = \psi_1(x_1)\psi_1(x_2) = \boxed{\frac{2}{a}\sin\left(\frac{\pi x_1}{a}\right)\sin\left(\frac{\pi x_2}{a}\right);}$ $E_1^0 = 2E_1 = \boxed{\frac{\pi^2 \hbar^2}{ma^2}.}$

First excited state: $\psi_2^0(x_1, x_2) = \frac{1}{\sqrt{2}}[\psi_1(x_1)\psi_2(x_2) + \psi_2(x_1)\psi_1(x_2)]$

$$= \boxed{\frac{\sqrt{2}}{a}\left[\sin\left(\frac{\pi x_1}{a}\right)\sin\left(\frac{2\pi x_2}{a}\right) + \sin\left(\frac{2\pi x_1}{a}\right)\sin\left(\frac{\pi x_2}{a}\right)\right];} \quad E_2^0 = E_1 + E_2 = \boxed{\frac{5}{2}\frac{\pi^2 \hbar^2}{ma^2}.}$$

**(b)**

$$E_1^1 = \langle \psi_1^0 | H' | \psi_1^0 \rangle = (-aV_0)\left(\frac{2}{a}\right)^2 \int_0^a \int_0^a \sin^2\left(\frac{\pi x_1}{a}\right)\sin^2\left(\frac{\pi x_2}{a}\right)\delta(x_2 - x_2)\,dx_1\,dx_2$$

$$= -\frac{4V_0}{a}\int_0^a \sin^4\left(\frac{\pi x}{a}\right)dx = -\frac{4V_0}{a}\frac{a}{\pi}\int_0^\pi \sin^4 y\,dy = -\frac{4V_0}{\pi}\cdot\frac{3\pi}{8} = \boxed{-\frac{3}{2}V_0.}$$

$$E_2^1 = \langle \psi_2^0 | H' | \psi_2^0 \rangle$$

$$= (-aV_0)\left(\frac{2}{a^2}\right)\iint_0^a \left[\sin\left(\frac{\pi x_1}{a}\right)\sin\left(\frac{2\pi x_2}{a}\right) + \sin\left(\frac{2\pi x_1}{a}\right)\sin\left(\frac{\pi x_2}{a}\right)\right]^2 \delta(x_1 - x_2)\,dx_1\,dx_2$$

$$= -\frac{2V_0}{a}\int_0^a \left[\sin\left(\frac{\pi x}{a}\right)\sin\left(\frac{2\pi x}{a}\right) + \sin\left(\frac{2\pi x}{a}\right)\sin\left(\frac{\pi x}{a}\right)\right]^2 dx$$

$$= -\frac{8V_0}{a}\int_0^a \sin^2\left(\frac{\pi x}{a}\right)\sin^2\left(\frac{2\pi x}{a}\right)dx = -\frac{8V_0}{a}\cdot\frac{a}{\pi}\int_0^\pi \sin^2 y\sin^2(2y)\,dy$$

$$= -\frac{8V_0}{\pi}\cdot 4\int_0^\pi \sin^2 y\sin^2 y\cos^2 y\,dy = -\frac{32V_0}{\pi}\int_0^\pi (\sin^4 y - \sin^6 y)\,dy$$

$$= -\frac{32V_0}{\pi}\left(\frac{3\pi}{8} - \frac{5\pi}{16}\right) = \boxed{-2V_0.}$$

---

## Problem 6.4

(a)

$$\langle \psi_m^0 | H | \psi_n^0 \rangle = \frac{2}{a}\alpha \int_0^a \sin\left(\frac{m\pi}{a}x\right) \delta\left(x - \frac{a}{2}\right) \sin\left(\frac{n\pi}{a}x\right)\, dx = \frac{2\alpha}{a}\sin\left(\frac{m\pi}{2}\right)\sin\left(\frac{n\pi}{2}\right),$$

which is zero unless both $m$ and $n$ are odd—in which case it is $\pm 2\alpha/a$. So Eq. 6.15 says

$$E_n^2 = \sum_{m \neq n,\,\text{odd}} \left(\frac{2\alpha}{a}\right)^2 \frac{1}{(E_n^0 - E_m^0)}. \quad \text{But Eq. 2.27 says} \quad E_n^0 = \frac{\pi^2\hbar^2}{2ma^2}n^2, \text{ so}$$

$$\boxed{E_n^2 = \begin{cases} 0, & \text{if } n \text{ is even;} \\ 2m\left(\dfrac{2\alpha}{\pi\hbar}\right)^2 \displaystyle\sum_{m \neq n,\,\text{odd}} \frac{1}{(n^2 - m^2)}, & \text{if } n \text{ is odd.} \end{cases}}$$

To sum the series, note that $\dfrac{1}{(n^2 - m^2)} = \dfrac{1}{2n}\left(\dfrac{1}{m+n} - \dfrac{1}{m-n}\right)$.   Thus,

$$\underline{\text{for } n = 1}: \quad \sum = \frac{1}{2}\sum_{3,5,7,\ldots}\left(\frac{1}{m+1} - \frac{1}{m-1}\right)$$

$$= \frac{1}{2}\left(\frac{1}{4} + \frac{1}{6} + \frac{1}{8} + \cdots - \frac{1}{2} - \frac{1}{4} - \frac{1}{6} - \frac{1}{8}\cdots\right) = \frac{1}{2}\left(-\frac{1}{2}\right) = -\frac{1}{4};$$

$$\underline{\text{for } n = 3}: \quad \sum = \frac{1}{6}\sum_{1,5,7,\ldots}\left(\frac{1}{m+3} - \frac{1}{m-3}\right)$$

$$= \frac{1}{6}\left(\frac{1}{4} + \frac{1}{8} + \frac{1}{10} + \cdots + \frac{1}{2} - \frac{1}{2} - \frac{1}{4} - \frac{1}{6} - \frac{1}{8} - \frac{1}{10}\cdots\right) = \frac{1}{6}\left(-\frac{1}{6}\right) = -\frac{1}{36}.$$

In general, there is perfect cancellation except for the "missing" term $1/2n$ in the first sum, so the total is $\dfrac{1}{2n}\left(-\dfrac{1}{2n}\right) = -\dfrac{1}{(2n)^2}$.   Therefore: $\boxed{E_n^2 = \begin{cases} 0, & \text{if } n \text{ is even;} \\ -2m\left(\alpha/\pi\hbar n\right)^2, & \text{if } n \text{ is odd.} \end{cases}}$

(b)

$$H' = \frac{1}{2}\epsilon k x^2; \quad \langle \psi_m^0 | H' | \psi_n^0 \rangle = \frac{1}{2}\epsilon k \langle m | x^2 | n \rangle. \quad \text{Using Eqs. 2.66 and 2.69:}$$

$$\langle m | x^2 | n \rangle = \frac{\hbar}{2m\omega}\langle m | (a_+^2 + a_+ a_- + a_- a_+ + a_-^2) | n \rangle$$

$$= \frac{\hbar}{2m\omega}\left[\sqrt{(n+1)(n+2)}\langle m | n+2 \rangle + n\langle m | n \rangle + (n+1)\langle m | n \rangle + \sqrt{n(n-1)}\langle m | n-2 \rangle\right].$$

So, for $m \neq n$, $\quad \langle \psi_m^0 | H' | \psi_n^0 \rangle = \left( \frac{1}{2} k\epsilon \right) \left( \frac{\hbar}{2m\omega} \right) \left[ \sqrt{(n+1)(n+2)}\, \delta_{m,n+2} + \sqrt{n(n-1)}\, \delta_{m,n-2} \right]$.

$$E_n^2 = \left( \frac{\epsilon \hbar \omega}{4} \right)^2 \sum_{m \neq n} \frac{\left[ \sqrt{(n+1)(n+2)}\, \delta_{m,n+2} + \sqrt{n(n-1)}\, \delta_{m,n-2} \right]^2}{(n + \frac{1}{2})\hbar\omega - (m + \frac{1}{2})\hbar\omega}$$

$$= \frac{\epsilon^2 \hbar \omega}{16} \sum_{m \neq n} \frac{\left[ (n+1)(n+2)\, \delta_{m,n+2} + n(n-1)\, \delta_{m,n-2} \right]}{(n - m)}$$

$$= \frac{\epsilon^2 \hbar \omega}{16} \left[ \frac{(n+1)(n+2)}{n - (n+2)} + \frac{n(n-1)}{n - (n-2)} \right] = \frac{\epsilon^2 \hbar \omega}{16} \left[ -\frac{1}{2}(n+1)(n+2) + \frac{1}{2}n(n-1) \right]$$

$$= \frac{\epsilon^2 \hbar \omega}{32} \left( -n^2 - 3n - 2 + n^2 - n \right) = \frac{\epsilon^2 \hbar \omega}{32} (-4n - 2) = \boxed{-\epsilon^2 \frac{1}{8} \hbar \omega \left( n + \frac{1}{2} \right)}$$

(which agrees with the $\epsilon^2$ term in the exact solution—Problem 6.2(a)).

---

# Problem 6.5

(a)

$$E_n^1 = \langle \psi_n^0 | H' | \psi_n^0 \rangle = -qE\langle n|x|n \rangle = \boxed{0} \text{ (Problem 2.12).}$$

From Eq. 6.15 and Problem 3.33: $\quad E_n^2 = (qE)^2 \sum_{m \neq n} \frac{|\langle m|x|n \rangle|^2}{(n - m)\hbar\omega}$

$$= \frac{(qE)^2}{\hbar\omega} \frac{\hbar}{2m\omega} \sum_{m \neq n} \frac{\left[ \sqrt{n+1}\, \delta_{m,n+1} + \sqrt{n}\, \delta_{m,n-1} \right]^2}{(n - m)} = \frac{(qE)^2}{2m\omega^2} \sum_{m \neq n} \frac{\left[ (n+1)\, \delta_{m,n+1} + n\, \delta_{m,n-1} \right]}{(n - m)}$$

$$= \frac{(qE)^2}{2m\omega^2} \left[ \frac{(n+1)}{n - (n+1)} + \frac{n}{n - (n-1)} \right] = \frac{(qE)^2}{2m\omega^2} [-(n+1) + n] = \boxed{-\frac{(qE)^2}{2m\omega^2}.}$$

(b) $-\frac{\hbar^2}{2m} \frac{d^2\psi}{dx^2} + \left( \frac{1}{2} m\omega^2 x^2 - qEx \right) \psi = E\psi$. With the suggested change of variables,

$$\left( \frac{1}{2} m\omega^2 x^2 - qEx \right) = \frac{1}{2} m\omega^2 \left[ x' + \left( \frac{qE}{m\omega^2} \right) \right]^2 - qE \left[ x' + \left( \frac{qE}{m\omega^2} \right) \right]$$

$$= \frac{1}{2} m\omega^2 x'^2 + m\omega^2 x' \frac{qE}{m\omega^2} + \frac{1}{2} m\omega^2 \frac{(qE)^2}{m^2\omega^4} - qEx' - \frac{(qE)^2}{m\omega^2} = \frac{1}{2} m\omega^2 x'^2 - \frac{1}{2} \frac{(qE)^2}{m\omega^2}.$$

So the Schrödinger equation says

$$-\frac{\hbar^2}{2m}\frac{d^2\psi}{dx'^2} + \frac{1}{2}m\omega^2 x'^2\psi = \left[E + \frac{1}{2}\frac{(qE)^2}{m\omega^2}\right]\psi,$$

which is the Schrödinger equation for a simple harmonic oscillator, in the variable $x'$. The constant on the right must therefore be $(n+\frac{1}{2})\hbar\omega$, and we conclude that

$$\boxed{E_n = (n+\frac{1}{2})\hbar\omega - \frac{1}{2}\frac{(qE)^2}{m\omega^2}.}$$

The subtracted term is exactly what we got in part (a) using perturbation theory. Evidently all the higher corrections (like the first-order correction) are zero, in this case.

## Problem 6.6

**(a)**

$$\langle\psi_+^0|\psi_-^0\rangle = \langle(\alpha_+\psi_a^0 + \beta_+\psi_b^0)|(\alpha_-\psi_a^0 + \beta_-\psi_b^0)\rangle$$

$$= \alpha_+^*\alpha_-\langle\psi_a^0|\psi_a^0\rangle + \alpha_+^*\beta_-\langle\psi_a^0|\psi_b^0\rangle + \beta_+^*\alpha_-\langle\psi_b^0|\psi_a^0\rangle + \beta_+^*\beta_-\langle\psi_b^0|\psi_b^0\rangle$$

$$= \alpha_+^*\alpha_- + \beta_+^*\beta_-. \quad \text{But Eq. 6.22} \Rightarrow \beta_\pm = \alpha_\pm(E_\pm^1 - W_{aa})/W_{ab}, \quad \text{so}$$

$$\langle\psi_+^0|\psi_-^0\rangle = \alpha_+^*\alpha_-\left[1 + \frac{(E_+^1 - W_{aa})(E_-^1 - W_{aa})}{W_{ab}^*W_{ab}}\right] = \frac{\alpha_+^*\alpha_-}{|W_{ab}|^2}\left[|W_{ab}|^2 + (E_+^1 - W_{aa})(E_-^1 - W_{aa})\right].$$

The term in square brackets is:

$[\,] = E_+^1 E_-^1 - W_{aa}(E_+^1 + E_-^1) + |W_{ab}|^2 + W_{aa}^2.$ But Eq. 6.27 $\Rightarrow E_\pm^1 = \frac{1}{2}[(W_{aa} + W_{bb}) \pm \sqrt{\,}]$, where $\sqrt{\,}$ is shorthand for the square root term. So $E_+^1 + E_-^1 = W_{aa} + W_{bb}$, and

$$E_+^1 E_-^1 = \frac{1}{4}\left[(W_{aa}+W_{bb})^2 - (\sqrt{\,})^2\right] = \frac{1}{4}\left[(W_{aa}+W_{bb})^2 - (W_{aa}-W_{bb})^2 - 4|W_{ab}|^2\right] = W_{aa}W_{bb} - |W_{ab}|^2.$$

Thus $[\,] = W_{aa}W_{bb} - |W_{ab}|^2 - W_{aa}(W_{aa}+W_{bb}) + |W_{ab}|^2 + W_{aa}^2 = 0$, so $\langle\psi_+^0|\psi_-^0\rangle = 0$. QED

**(b)**

$$\langle\psi_+^0|H'|\psi_-^0\rangle = \alpha_+^*\alpha_-\langle\psi_a^0|H'|\psi_a^0\rangle + \alpha_+^*\beta_-\langle\psi_a^0|H'|\psi_b^0\rangle + \beta_+^*\alpha_-\langle\psi_b^0|H'|\psi_a^0\rangle + \beta_+^*\beta_-\langle\psi_b^0|H'|\psi_b^0\rangle$$

$$= \alpha_+^*\alpha_- W_{aa} + \alpha_+^*\beta_- W_{ab} + \beta_+^*\alpha_- W_{ba} + \beta_+^*\beta_- W_{bb}$$

$$= \alpha_+^*\alpha_-\left[W_{aa} + W_{ab}\frac{(E_-^1 - W_{aa})}{W_{ab}} + W_{ba}\frac{(E_+^1 - W_{aa})}{W_{ab}^*} + W_{bb}\frac{(E_+^1 - W_{aa})}{W_{ab}^*}\frac{(E_-^1 - W_{aa})}{W_{ab}}\right]$$

$$= \alpha_+^*\alpha_-\left[W_{aa} + E_-^1 - W_{aa} + E_+^1 - W_{aa} + W_{bb}\frac{(E_+^1 - W_{aa})(E_-^1 - W_{aa})}{|W_{ab}|^2}\right].$$

But we know from (a) that $\dfrac{(E_+^1 - W_{aa})(E_-^1 - W_{aa})}{|W_{ab}|^2} = -1$, so

$$\langle\psi_+^0|H'|\psi_-^0\rangle = \alpha_+^*\alpha_-[E_-^1 + E_+^1 - W_{aa} - W_{bb}] = 0. \quad \text{QED}$$

**(c)**

$$\langle \psi_\pm^0 | H' | \psi_\pm^0 \rangle = \alpha_\pm^* \alpha_\pm \langle \psi_a^0 | H' | \psi_a^0 \rangle + \alpha_\pm^* \beta_\pm \langle \psi_a^0 | H' | \psi_b^0 \rangle + \beta_\pm^* \alpha_\pm \langle \psi_b^0 | H' | \psi_a^0 \rangle + \beta_\pm^* \beta_\pm \langle \psi_b^0 | H' | \psi_b^0 \rangle$$

$$= |\alpha_\pm|^2 \left[ W_{aa} + W_{ab} \frac{(E_\pm^1 - W_{aa})}{W_{ab}} \right] + |\beta_\pm|^2 \left[ W_{ba} \frac{(E_\pm^1 - W_{bb})}{W_{ba}} + W_{bb} \right]$$

(this time I used Eq. 6.24 to express $\alpha$ in terms of $\beta$, in the third term).

$$\therefore \langle \psi_\pm^0 | H' | \psi_\pm^0 \rangle = |\alpha_\pm|^2 (E_\pm^1) + |\beta_\pm|^2 (E_\pm^1) = \left( |\alpha_\pm|^2 + |\beta_\pm|^2 \right) E_\pm^1 = E_\pm^1. \quad \text{QED}$$

---

## Problem 6.7

**(a)** See Problem 2.46.

**(b)** With $a \to n, b \to -n$, we have:

$$W_{aa} = W_{bb} = -\frac{V_0}{L} \int_{-L/2}^{L/2} e^{-x^2/a^2} dx \approx -\frac{V_0}{L} \int_{-\infty}^{\infty} e^{-x^2/a^2} dx = -\frac{V_0}{L} a\sqrt{\pi}.$$

$$W_{ab} = -\frac{V_0}{L} \int_{-L/2}^{L/2} e^{-x^2/a^2} e^{-4\pi n i x/L} dx \approx -\frac{V_0}{L} \int_{-\infty}^{\infty} e^{-(x^2/a^2 + 4\pi n i x/L)} dx = -\frac{V_0}{L} a\sqrt{\pi} e^{-(2\pi n a/L)^2}.$$

(We did this integral in Problem 2.22.) In this case $W_{aa} = W_{bb}$, and $W_{ab}$ is real, so Eq. 6.26 $\Rightarrow$

$$E_\pm^1 = W_{aa} \pm |W_{ab}|, \quad \text{or} \quad \boxed{E_\pm^1 = -\sqrt{\pi} \frac{V_0 a}{L} \left( 1 \mp e^{-(2\pi n a/L)^2} \right).}$$

**(c)** Equation 6.22 $\Rightarrow \beta = \alpha \dfrac{(E_-^1 - W_{aa})}{W_{ab}} = \alpha \left[ \dfrac{\pm \sqrt{\pi}(V_0 a/L) e^{-(2\pi n a/L)^2}}{-\sqrt{\pi}(V_0 a/L) e^{-(2\pi n a/L)^2}} \right] = \mp \alpha.$ Evidently, the "good" linear combinations are:

$$\psi_+ = \alpha \psi_n - \alpha \psi_{-n} = \frac{1}{\sqrt{2}} \frac{1}{\sqrt{L}} \left[ e^{i 2\pi n x/L} - e^{-i 2\pi n x/L} \right] = \boxed{i \sqrt{\frac{2}{L}} \sin \left( \frac{2\pi n x}{L} \right)} \quad \text{and}$$

$$\psi_- = \alpha \psi_n + \alpha \psi_{-n} = \boxed{\sqrt{\frac{2}{L}} \cos \left( \frac{2\pi n x}{L} \right).} \quad \text{Using Eq. 6.9, we have :}$$

$$E_+^1 = \langle \psi_+ | H' | \psi_+ \rangle = \frac{2}{L} (-V_0) \int_{-L/2}^{L/2} e^{-x^2/a^2} \sin^2 \left( \frac{2\pi n x}{L} \right) dx,$$

$$E_-^1 = \langle \psi_- | H' | \psi_- \rangle = \frac{2}{L} (-V_0) \int_{-L/2}^{L/2} e^{-x^2/a^2} \cos^2 \left( \frac{2\pi n x}{L} \right) dx.$$

But $\quad \sin^2\theta = (1 - \cos 2\theta)/2,\quad$ and $\quad \cos^2\theta = (1 + \cos 2\theta)/2$, so

$$E_{\pm}^1 \approx -\frac{V_0}{L}\int_{-\infty}^{\infty} e^{-x^2/a^2}\left[1 \mp \cos\left(\frac{4\pi n x}{L}\right)\right] dx = -\frac{V_0}{L}\left[\int_{-\infty}^{\infty} e^{-x^2/a^2}\,dx \mp \int_{-\infty}^{\infty} e^{-x^2/a^2}\cos\left(\frac{4\pi n x}{L}\right)\,dx\right]$$

$$= -\frac{V_0}{L}\left[\sqrt{\pi}\,a \mp a\sqrt{\pi}e^{-(2\pi na/L)^2}\right] = -\sqrt{\pi}\frac{V_0 a}{L}\left[1 \mp e^{-(2\pi na/L)^2}\right],\quad \text{same as (b).}$$

**(d)** $Af(x) = f(-x)$ (the parity operator). The eigenstates are *even* functions (with eigenvalue $+1$) and *odd* functions (with eigenvalue $-1$). The linear combinations we found in (c) are precisely the odd and even linear combinations of $\psi_n$ and $\psi_{-n}$.

---

## Problem 6.8

<u>Ground state</u> is nondegenerate; Eqs. 6.9 and 6.31 $\Rightarrow$

$$E^1 = \left(\frac{2}{a}\right)^3 a^3 V_0 \iiint_0^a \sin^2\left(\frac{\pi}{a}x\right)\sin^2\left(\frac{\pi}{a}y\right)\sin^2\left(\frac{\pi}{a}z\right)\delta(x - \frac{a}{4})\delta(y - \frac{a}{2})\delta(z - \frac{3a}{4})\,dx\,dy\,dz$$

$$= 8V_0 \sin^2\left(\frac{\pi}{4}\right)\sin^2\left(\frac{\pi}{2}\right)\sin^2\left(\frac{3\pi}{4}\right) = 8V_0\left(\frac{1}{2}\right)(1)\left(\frac{1}{2}\right) = \boxed{2V_0.}$$

<u>First excited states</u> (Eq. 6.34):

$$W_{aa} = 8V_0 \iiint \sin^2\left(\frac{\pi}{a}x\right)\sin^2\left(\frac{\pi}{a}y\right)\sin^2\left(\frac{2\pi}{a}z\right)\delta(x - \frac{a}{4})\delta(y - \frac{a}{2})\delta(z - \frac{3a}{4})\,dx\,dy\,dz$$

$$= 8V_0\left(\frac{1}{2}\right)(1)(1) = 4V_0.$$

$$W_{bb} = 8V_0 \iiint \sin^2\left(\frac{\pi}{a}x\right)\sin^2\left(\frac{2\pi}{a}y\right)\sin^2\left(\frac{\pi}{a}z\right)\delta(x - \frac{a}{4})\delta(y - \frac{a}{2})\delta(z - \frac{3a}{4})\,dx\,dy\,dz$$

$$= 8V_0\left(\frac{1}{2}\right)(0)\left(\frac{1}{2}\right) = 0.$$

$$W_{cc} = 8V_0 \iiint \sin^2\left(\frac{2\pi}{a}x\right)\sin^2\left(\frac{\pi}{a}y\right)\sin^2\left(\frac{\pi}{a}z\right)\delta(x - \frac{a}{4})\delta(y - \frac{a}{2})\delta(z - \frac{3a}{4})\,dx\,dy\,dz$$

$$= 8V_0(1)(1)\left(\frac{1}{2}\right) = 4V_0.$$

$$W_{ab} = 8V_0 \sin^2\left(\frac{\pi}{4}\right)\sin\left(\frac{\pi}{2}\right)\sin(\pi)\sin\left(\frac{3\pi}{2}\right)\sin\left(\frac{3\pi}{4}\right) = 0.$$

$$W_{ac} = 8V_0 \sin\left(\frac{\pi}{4}\right)\sin\left(\frac{\pi}{2}\right)\sin^2\left(\frac{\pi}{2}\right)\sin\left(\frac{3\pi}{2}\right)\sin\left(\frac{3\pi}{4}\right) = 8V_0\left(\frac{1}{\sqrt{2}}\right)(1)(1)(-1)\left(\frac{1}{\sqrt{2}}\right) = -4V_0.$$

$$W_{bc} = 8V_0 \sin\left(\frac{\pi}{4}\right)\sin\left(\frac{\pi}{2}\right)\sin(\pi)\sin\left(\frac{\pi}{2}\right)\sin\left(\frac{3\pi}{4}\right) = 0.$$

$$\mathsf{W} = 4V_0\begin{pmatrix} 1 & 0 & -1 \\ 0 & 0 & 0 \\ -1 & 0 & 1 \end{pmatrix} = 4V_0\mathsf{D}; \quad \det(\mathsf{D}-\lambda) = \begin{vmatrix} (1-\lambda) & 0 & -1 \\ 0 & -\lambda & 0 \\ -1 & 0 & (1-\lambda) \end{vmatrix} = -\lambda(1-\lambda)^2 + \lambda = 0 \quad \Rightarrow$$

$$\lambda = 0, \quad \text{or} \quad (1-\lambda)^2 = 1 \Rightarrow 1-\lambda = \pm 1 \Rightarrow \lambda = 0 \quad \text{or} \quad \lambda = 2.$$

So the first-order corrections to the energies are $\boxed{0,\ 0,\ 8V_0.}$

---

## Problem 6.9

**(a)** $\boxed{\chi_1 = \begin{pmatrix} 1 \\ 0 \\ 0 \end{pmatrix},}$ eigenvalue $\boxed{V_0;}$ $\chi_2 = \begin{pmatrix} 0 \\ 1 \\ 0 \end{pmatrix},$ eigenvalue $\boxed{V_0;}$ $\chi_3 = \begin{pmatrix} 0 \\ 0 \\ 1 \end{pmatrix},$ eigenvalue $\boxed{2V_0.}$

**(b)** Characteristic equation: $\det(\mathsf{H}-\lambda) = \begin{vmatrix} [V_0(1-\epsilon)-\lambda] & 0 & 0 \\ 0 & [V_0-\lambda] & \epsilon V_0 \\ 0 & \epsilon V_0 & [2V_0-\lambda] \end{vmatrix} = 0;$

$$[V_0(1-\epsilon)-\lambda][(V_0-\lambda)(2V_0-\lambda) - (\epsilon V_0)^2] = 0 \Rightarrow \boxed{\lambda_1 = V_0(1-\epsilon).}$$

$$(V_0-\lambda)(2V_0-\lambda) - (\epsilon V_0)^2 = 0 \Rightarrow \lambda^2 - 3V_0\lambda + (2V_0^2 - \epsilon^2 V_0^2) = 0 \Rightarrow$$

$$\lambda = \frac{3V_0 \pm \sqrt{9V_0^2 - 4(2V_0^2 - \epsilon^2 V_0^2)}}{2} = \frac{V_0}{2}\left[3 \pm \sqrt{1+4\epsilon^2}\right] \approx \frac{V_0}{2}\left[3 \pm (1+2\epsilon^2)\right].$$

$$\boxed{\lambda_2 = \frac{V_0}{2}\left(3 - \sqrt{1+4\epsilon^2}\right) \approx V_0(1-\epsilon^2); \quad \lambda_3 = \frac{V_0}{2}\left(3 + \sqrt{1+4\epsilon^2}\right) \approx V_0(2+\epsilon^2).}$$

**(c)**

$$\mathsf{H}' = \epsilon V_0\begin{pmatrix} -1 & 0 & 0 \\ 0 & 0 & 1 \\ 0 & 1 & 0 \end{pmatrix}; \quad E_3^1 = \langle\chi_3|H'|\chi_3\rangle = \epsilon V_0\begin{pmatrix} 0 & 0 & 1 \end{pmatrix}\begin{pmatrix} -1 & 0 & 0 \\ 0 & 0 & 1 \\ 0 & 1 & 0 \end{pmatrix}\begin{pmatrix} 0 \\ 0 \\ 1 \end{pmatrix}$$

$$= \epsilon V_0\begin{pmatrix} 0 & 0 & 1 \end{pmatrix}\begin{pmatrix} 0 \\ 1 \\ 0 \end{pmatrix} = \boxed{0}\ \text{(no first-order correction)}.$$

$$E_3^2 = \sum_{m=1,2}\frac{|\langle\chi_m|H'|\chi_3\rangle|^2}{E_3^0 - E_m^0}; \quad \langle\chi_1|H'|\chi_3\rangle = \epsilon V_0\begin{pmatrix} 1 & 0 & 0 \end{pmatrix}\begin{pmatrix} -1 & 0 & 0 \\ 0 & 0 & 1 \\ 0 & 1 & 0 \end{pmatrix}\begin{pmatrix} 0 \\ 0 \\ 1 \end{pmatrix} = \epsilon V_0\begin{pmatrix} 1 & 0 & 0 \end{pmatrix}\begin{pmatrix} 0 \\ 1 \\ 0 \end{pmatrix} = 0,$$

$$\langle\chi_2|H'|\chi_3\rangle = \epsilon V_0\begin{pmatrix} 0 & 1 & 0 \end{pmatrix}\begin{pmatrix} 0 \\ 0 \\ 1 \end{pmatrix} = \epsilon V_0.$$

$E_3^0 - E_2^0 = 2V_0 - V_0 = V_0.$ So $E_3^2 = (\epsilon V_0)^2/V_0 = \boxed{\epsilon^2 V_0.}$ Through second-order, then,

$$E_3 = E_3^0 + E_3^1 + E_3^2 = 2V_0 + 0 + \epsilon^2 V_0 = V_0(2+\epsilon^2) \quad \text{(same as we got for } \lambda_3 \text{ in (b))}.$$

---

**(d)**

$$W_{aa} = \langle \chi_1 | H' | \chi_1 \rangle = \epsilon V_0 \begin{pmatrix} 1 & 0 & 0 \end{pmatrix} \begin{pmatrix} -1 & 0 & 0 \\ 0 & 0 & 1 \\ 0 & 1 & 0 \end{pmatrix} \begin{pmatrix} 1 \\ 0 \\ 0 \end{pmatrix} = \epsilon V_0 \begin{pmatrix} 1 & 0 & 0 \end{pmatrix} \begin{pmatrix} -1 \\ 0 \\ 0 \end{pmatrix} = -\epsilon V_0.$$

$$W_{bb} = \langle \chi_2 | H' | \chi_2 \rangle = \epsilon V_0 \begin{pmatrix} 0 & 1 & 0 \end{pmatrix} \begin{pmatrix} -1 & 0 & 0 \\ 0 & 0 & 1 \\ 0 & 1 & 0 \end{pmatrix} \begin{pmatrix} 0 \\ 1 \\ 0 \end{pmatrix} = \epsilon V_0 \begin{pmatrix} 0 & 1 & 0 \end{pmatrix} \begin{pmatrix} 0 \\ 0 \\ 1 \end{pmatrix} = 0.$$

$$W_{ab} = \langle \chi_1 | H' | \chi_2 \rangle = \epsilon V_0 \begin{pmatrix} 1 & 0 & 0 \end{pmatrix} \begin{pmatrix} -1 & 0 & 0 \\ 0 & 0 & 1 \\ 0 & 1 & 0 \end{pmatrix} \begin{pmatrix} 0 \\ 1 \\ 0 \end{pmatrix} = \epsilon V_0 \begin{pmatrix} 1 & 0 & 0 \end{pmatrix} \begin{pmatrix} 0 \\ 0 \\ 1 \end{pmatrix} = 0.$$

Plug the expressions for $W_{aa}$, $W_{bb}$, and $W_{ab}$ into Eq. 6.27:

$$E_\pm^1 = \frac{1}{2} \left[ -\epsilon V_0 + 0 \pm \sqrt{\epsilon^2 V_0^2 + 0} \right] = \frac{1}{2}(-\epsilon V_0 \pm \epsilon V_0) = \{0, -\epsilon V_0\}.$$

To first-order, then, $\boxed{E_1 = V_0 - \epsilon V_0, \quad E_2 = V_0,}$ and these are consistent (to first order in $\epsilon$) with what we got in (b).

---

## Problem 6.10

Given a set of orthonornal states $\{\psi_j^0\}$ that are degenerate eigenfunctions of the unperturbed Hamiltonian:

$$H\psi_j^0 = E^0 \psi_j^0, \quad \langle \psi_j^0 | \psi_l^0 \rangle = \delta_{jl},$$

construct the general linear combination,

$$\psi^0 = \sum_{j=1}^{n} \alpha_j \psi_j^0.$$

It too is an eigenfunction of the unperturbed Hamiltonian, with the same eigenvalue:

$$H^0 \psi^0 = \sum_{j=1}^{n} \alpha_j H^0 \psi_j^0 = E^0 \sum_{j=1}^{n} \alpha_j \psi_j^0 = E^0 \psi^0.$$

We want to solve the Schrödinger equation $H\psi = E\psi$ for the perturbed Hamiltonian $H = H^0 + \lambda H'$. Expand the eigenvalues and eigenfunctions as power series in $\lambda$:

$$E = E^0 + \lambda E^1 + \lambda^2 E^2 + \dots, \quad \psi = \psi^0 + \lambda \psi^1 + \lambda^2 \psi^2 + \dots.$$

Plug these into the Schrödinger equation and collect like powers:

$$(H^0 + \lambda H')(\psi^0 + \lambda \psi^1 + \lambda^2 \psi^2 + \dots) = (E^0 + \lambda E^1 + \lambda^2 E^2 + \dots)(\psi^0 + \lambda \psi^1 + \lambda^2 \psi^2 + \dots) \quad \Rightarrow$$

$$H^0 \psi^0 + \lambda(H^0 \psi^1 + H' \psi^0) + \dots = E^0 \psi^0 + \lambda(E^0 \psi^1 + E^1 \psi^0) + \dots$$

The zeroth-order terms cancel; to first order

$$H^0 \psi^1 + H' \psi^0 = E^0 \psi^1 + E^1 \psi^0.$$

Take the inner product with $\psi_j^0$:

$$\langle \psi_j^0 | H^0 \psi^1 \rangle + \langle \psi_j^0 | H' \psi^0 \rangle = E^0 \langle \psi_j^0 | \psi^1 \rangle + E^1 \langle \psi_j^0 | \psi^0 \rangle.$$

But $\langle \psi_j^0 | H^0 \psi^1 \rangle = \langle H^0 \psi_j^0 | \psi^1 \rangle = E^0 \langle \psi_j^0 | \psi^1 \rangle$, so the first terms cancel, leaving

$$\langle \psi_j^0 | H' \psi^0 \rangle = E^1 \langle \psi_j^0 | \psi^0 \rangle.$$

Now use $\psi^0 = \sum_{l=1}^{n} \alpha_l \psi_l^0$, and exploit the orthonormality of $\{\psi_l^0\}$:

$$\sum_{l=1}^{n} \alpha_l \langle \psi_j^0 | H' | \psi_l^0 \rangle = E^1 \sum_{l=1}^{n} \alpha_l \langle \psi_j^0 | \psi_l^0 \rangle = E^1 \alpha_j,$$

or, defining

$$W_{jl} \equiv \langle \psi_j^0 | H' | \psi_l^0 \rangle, \qquad \boxed{\sum_{l=1}^{n} W_{jl} \alpha_l = E^1 \alpha_l.}$$

This (the generalization of Eq. 6.22 for the case of $n$-fold degeneracy) is the eigenvalue equation for the matrix $\mathsf{W}$ (whose $jl^{\text{th}}$ element, in the $\{\psi_j^0\}$ basis, is $W_{jl}$); $E^1$ is the eigenvalue, and the eigenvector (in the $\{\psi_j^0\}$ basis) is $\chi_j = \alpha_j$. *Conclusion:* The first-order corrections to the energy are the eigenvalues of $\mathsf{W}$. QED

---

## Problem 6.11

(a) From Eq. 4.70: $E_n = -\left[ \dfrac{m}{2\hbar^2} \left( \dfrac{e^2}{4\pi\epsilon_0} \right)^2 \right] \dfrac{1}{n^2} = -\dfrac{1}{2} mc^2 \left( \dfrac{1}{\hbar c} \dfrac{e^2}{4\pi\epsilon_0} \right)^2 \dfrac{1}{n^2} = \boxed{-\dfrac{\alpha^2 mc^2}{2n^2}.}$

(b) I have found a wonderful solution—unfortunately, there isn't enough room on this page for the proof.

---

## Problem 6.12

Equation 4.191 $\Rightarrow \langle V \rangle = 2E_n$, for hydrogen. $V = -\dfrac{e^2}{4\pi\epsilon_0} \dfrac{1}{r}$; $E_n = -\left[ \dfrac{m}{2\hbar^2} \left( \dfrac{e^2}{4\pi\epsilon_0} \right)^2 \right] \dfrac{1}{n^2}.$ So

$$-\dfrac{e^2}{4\pi\epsilon_0} \left\langle \dfrac{1}{r} \right\rangle = -2 \left[ \dfrac{m}{2\hbar^2} \left( \dfrac{e^2}{4\pi\epsilon_0} \right)^2 \right] \dfrac{1}{n^2} \quad \Rightarrow \quad \left\langle \dfrac{1}{r} \right\rangle = \left( \dfrac{me^2}{4\pi\epsilon_0 \hbar^2} \right) \dfrac{1}{n^2} = \dfrac{1}{an^2} \quad \text{(Eq. 4.72)}. \text{ QED}$$

---

## Problem 6.13

In Problem 4.43 we found (for $n = 3$, $l = 2$, $m = 1$) that $\quad \langle r^s \rangle = \dfrac{(s+6)!}{6!} \left( \dfrac{3a}{2} \right)^s$.

$\underline{s = 0}$ : $\langle 1 \rangle = \dfrac{6!}{6!}(1) = \boxed{1}$   (of course).   ✓

$\underline{s = -1}$ : $\left\langle \dfrac{1}{r} \right\rangle = \dfrac{5!}{6!} \left( \dfrac{3a}{2} \right)^{-1} = \dfrac{1}{6} \cdot \dfrac{2}{3a} = \boxed{\dfrac{1}{9a}}$   $\left( \text{Eq. 6.55 says } \dfrac{1}{3^2 a} = \dfrac{1}{9a} \right)$.   ✓

$\underline{s = -2}$ : $\left\langle \dfrac{1}{r^2} \right\rangle = \dfrac{4!}{6!} \left( \dfrac{3a}{2} \right)^{-2} = \dfrac{1}{6 \cdot 5} \cdot \dfrac{4}{9a^2} = \boxed{\dfrac{2}{135a^2}}$   $\left( \text{Eq. 6.56 says } \dfrac{1}{(5/2) \cdot 27 \cdot a^2} = \dfrac{2}{135a^2} \right)$.   ✓

$\underline{s = -3}$ : $\left\langle \dfrac{1}{r^3} \right\rangle = \dfrac{3!}{6!} \left( \dfrac{3a}{2} \right)^{-3} = \dfrac{1}{6 \cdot 5 \cdot 4} \cdot \dfrac{8}{27a^3} = \boxed{\dfrac{1}{405a^3}}$   $\left( \text{Eq. 6.64 says } \dfrac{1}{2(5/2)3 \cdot 27 \cdot a^3} = \dfrac{1}{405a^3} \right)$.   ✓

For $s = -7$ (or smaller) the integral does not converge: $\langle 1/r^7 \rangle = \infty$ in this state; this is reflected in the fact that $(-1)! = \infty$.

## Problem 6.14

Equation 6.53 $\Rightarrow E_r^1 = -\dfrac{1}{2mc^2} \left[ E^2 - 2E\langle V \rangle + \langle V^2 \rangle \right]$.   Here   $E = (n + \tfrac{1}{2})\hbar\omega$, $V = \tfrac{1}{2}m\omega^2 x^2$   $\Rightarrow$

$$E_r^1 = -\dfrac{1}{2mc^2} \left[ \left( n + \dfrac{1}{2} \right)^2 \hbar^2\omega^2 - 2\left( n + \dfrac{1}{2} \right)\hbar\omega\dfrac{1}{2}m\omega^2\langle x^2 \rangle + \dfrac{1}{4}m^2\omega^4\langle x^4 \rangle \right].$$

But Problem 2.12   $\Rightarrow$   $\langle x^2 \rangle = (n + \dfrac{1}{2})\dfrac{\hbar}{m\omega}$, so

$$E_r^1 = -\dfrac{1}{2mc^2} \left[ \left( n + \dfrac{1}{2} \right)^2 \hbar^2\omega^2 - \left( n + \dfrac{1}{2} \right)^2 \hbar^2\omega^2 + \dfrac{1}{4}m^2\omega^4\langle x^4 \rangle \right] = -\dfrac{m\omega^4}{8c^2}\langle x^4 \rangle.$$

From Eq. 2.69:   $x^4 = \dfrac{\hbar^2}{4m^2\omega^2}\left( a_+^2 + a_+a_- + a_-a_+ + a_-^2 \right)\left( a_+^2 + a_+a_- + a_-a_+ + a_-^2 \right)$,

$$\langle x^4 \rangle = \dfrac{\hbar^2}{4m^2\omega^2}\langle n| \left( a_+^2a_-^2 + a_+a_-a_+a_- + a_+a_-a_-a_+ + a_-a_+a_+a_- + a_-a_+a_-a_+ + a_-^2a_+^2 \right)|n\rangle.$$

(Note that only terms with equal numbers of raising and lowering operators will survive). Using Eq. 2.66,

$$\langle x^4 \rangle = \dfrac{\hbar^2}{4m^2\omega^2}\langle n| \left[ a_+^2 \left( \sqrt{n(n-1)}\,|n-2\rangle \right) + a_+a_-(n\,|n\rangle) + a_+a_-((n+1)\,|n\rangle) \right.$$

$$+a_-a_+\left(n\left|n\right\rangle\right)+a_-a_+\left((n+1)\left|n\right\rangle\right)+a_-^2\left(\sqrt{(n+1)(n+2)}\left|n+2\right\rangle\right)\Big]$$

$$=\frac{\hbar^2}{4m^2\omega^2}\langle n|\left[\sqrt{n(n-1)}\left(\sqrt{n(n-1)}\left|n\right\rangle\right)+n\left(n\left|n\right\rangle\right)+(n+1)\left(n\left|n\right\rangle\right)\right.$$

$$\left.+n\big((n+1)\left|n\right\rangle\big)+(n+1)\big((n+1)\left|n\right\rangle\big)+\sqrt{(n+1)(n+2)}\left(\sqrt{(n+1)(n+2)}\left|n\right\rangle\right)\right]$$

$$=\frac{\hbar^2}{4m^2\omega^2}\left[n(n-1)+n^2+(n+1)n+n(n+1)+(n+1)^2+(n+1)(n+2)\right]$$

$$=\left(\frac{\hbar}{2m\omega}\right)^2(n^2-n+n^2+n^2+n+n^2+n+n^2+2n+1+n^2+3n+2)=\left(\frac{\hbar}{2m\omega}\right)^2(6n^2+6n+3).$$

$$E_r^1=-\frac{m\omega^4}{8c^2}\cdot\frac{\hbar^2}{4m^2\omega^2}\cdot3(3n^2+2n+1)=\boxed{-\frac{3}{32}\left(\frac{\hbar^2\omega^2}{mc^2}\right)(2n^2+2n+1).}$$

## Problem 6.15

Quoting the Laplacian in spherical coordinates (Eq. 4.13), we have, for states with no dependence on $\theta$ or $\phi$:

$$p^2=-\hbar^2\nabla^2=-\frac{\hbar^2}{r^2}\frac{d}{dr}\left(r^2\frac{d}{dr}\right).$$

*Question:* Is it Hermitian?

Using integration by parts (twice), and test functions $f(r)$ and $g(r)$:

$$\langle f|p^2g\rangle=-\hbar^2\int_0^\infty f\frac{1}{r^2}\frac{d}{dr}\left(r^2\frac{dg}{dr}\right)4\pi r^2\,dr=-4\pi\hbar^2\int_0^\infty f\frac{d}{dr}\left(r^2\frac{dg}{dr}\right)dr$$

$$=-4\pi\hbar^2\left\{r^2f\frac{dg}{dr}\Big|_0^\infty-\int_0^\infty r^2\frac{df}{dr}\frac{dg}{dr}\,dr\right\}$$

$$=-4\pi\hbar^2\left\{r^2f\frac{dg}{dr}\Big|_0^\infty-r^2g\frac{df}{dr}\Big|_0^\infty+\int_0^\infty\frac{d}{dr}\left(r^2\frac{df}{dr}\right)g\,dr\right\}$$

$$=-4\pi\hbar^2\left(r^2f\frac{dg}{dr}-r^2g\frac{df}{dr}\right)\Big|_0^\infty+\langle p^2f|g\rangle.$$

The boundary term at infinity vanishes for functions $f(r)$ and $g(r)$ that go to zero exponentially; the boundary term at zero is killed by the factor $r^2$, as long as the functions (and their derivatives) are finite. So

$$\langle f|p^2g\rangle=\langle p^2f|g\rangle,$$

and hence $p^2$ is Hermitian.

Now we apply the same argument to

$$p^4=\frac{\hbar^4}{r^2}\frac{d}{dr}\left\{r^2\frac{d}{dr}\left[\frac{1}{r^2}\frac{d}{dr}\left(r^2\frac{d}{dr}\right)\right]\right\},$$

integrating by parts *four* times:

$$\langle f|p^4 g\rangle = 4\pi\hbar^4 \int_0^\infty f\frac{d}{dr}\left\{r^2\frac{d}{dr}\left[\frac{1}{r^2}\frac{d}{dr}\left(r^2\frac{dg}{dr}\right)\right]\right\} dr$$

$$= 4\pi\hbar^4\left\{\left.r^2 f\frac{d}{dr}\left[\frac{1}{r^2}\frac{d}{dr}\left(r^2\frac{dg}{dr}\right)\right]\right|_0^\infty - \int_0^\infty r^2\frac{df}{dr}\frac{d}{dr}\left[\frac{1}{r^2}\frac{d}{dr}\left(r^2\frac{dg}{dr}\right)\right] dr\right\}$$

$$= 4\pi\hbar^4\left\{\left[r^2 f\frac{d}{dr}\left[\frac{1}{r^2}\frac{d}{dr}\left(r^2\frac{dg}{dr}\right)\right] - \frac{df}{dr}\frac{d}{dr}\left(r^2\frac{dg}{dr}\right)\right]\Big|_0^\infty + \int_0^\infty \frac{1}{r^2}\frac{d}{dr}\left(r^2\frac{df}{dr}\right)\frac{d}{dr}\left(r^2\frac{dg}{dr}\right) dr\right\}$$

$$= 4\pi\hbar^4\left\{\left[r^2 f\frac{d}{dr}\left[\frac{1}{r^2}\frac{d}{dr}\left(r^2\frac{dg}{dr}\right)\right] - \frac{df}{dr}\frac{d}{dr}\left(r^2\frac{dg}{dr}\right) + \frac{d}{dr}\left(r^2\frac{df}{dr}\right)\frac{dg}{dr}\right]\Big|_0^\infty \right.$$
$$\left. - \int_0^\infty r^2\frac{d}{dr}\left[\frac{1}{r^2}\frac{d}{dr}\left(r^2\frac{df}{dr}\right)\right]\frac{dg}{dr} dr\right\}$$

$$= 4\pi\hbar^4\left\{\left[r^2 f\frac{d}{dr}\left[\frac{1}{r^2}\frac{d}{dr}\left(r^2\frac{dg}{dr}\right)\right] - \frac{df}{dr}\frac{d}{dr}\left(r^2\frac{dg}{dr}\right) + \frac{d}{dr}\left(r^2\frac{df}{dr}\right)\frac{dg}{dr} - r^2 g\frac{d}{dr}\left[\frac{1}{r^2}\frac{d}{dr}\left(r^2\frac{df}{dr}\right)\right]\right]\Big|_0^\infty \right.$$
$$\left. + \int_0^\infty \frac{d}{dr}\left(r^2\frac{d}{dr}\left[\frac{1}{r^2}\frac{d}{dr}\left(r^2\frac{df}{dr}\right)\right]\right) g\, dr\right\}$$

$$= 4\pi\hbar^4\left\{r^2 f\frac{d}{dr}\left[\frac{1}{r^2}\frac{d}{dr}\left(r^2\frac{dg}{dr}\right)\right] - r^2 g\frac{d}{dr}\left[\frac{1}{r^2}\frac{d}{dr}\left(r^2\frac{df}{dr}\right)\right]\right\}\Big|_0^\infty$$
$$- 4\pi\hbar^4\left\{\frac{df}{dr}\frac{d}{dr}\left(r^2\frac{dg}{dr}\right) - \frac{d}{dr}\left(r^2\frac{df}{dr}\right)\frac{dg}{dr}\right\}\Big|_0^\infty + \langle p^4 f|g\rangle$$

This time there are *four* boundary terms to worry about. Infinity is no problem; the trouble comes at $r = 0$. If the functions $f$ and $g$ went to zero at the origin (as they do for states with $l > 0$) we'd be OK, but states with $l = 0$ go like $\exp(-r/na)$. So let's test the boundary terms using

$$f(r) = e^{-r/na}, \qquad g(r) = e^{-r/ma}.$$

In this case

$$r^2\frac{dg}{dr} = -\frac{1}{ma}r^2 e^{-r/ma}$$

$$\frac{d}{dr}\left(r^2\frac{dg}{dr}\right) = \frac{1}{(ma)^2}\left(r^2 - 2mar\right)e^{-r/ma}$$

$$\frac{df}{dr}\frac{d}{dr}\left(r^2\frac{dg}{dr}\right) = -\frac{1}{na}e^{-r/na}\frac{1}{(ma)^2}\left(r^2 - 2mar\right)e^{-r/ma}.$$

This goes to zero as $r \to 0$, so the second pair of boundary terms vanishes—but not the first pair:

$$\frac{1}{r^2}\frac{d}{dr}\left(r^2\frac{dg}{dr}\right) = \frac{1}{(ma)^2}\left(1 - \frac{2ma}{r}\right)e^{-r/ma}$$

$$\frac{d}{dr}\left[\frac{1}{r^2}\frac{d}{dr}\left(r^2\frac{dg}{dr}\right)\right] = \frac{1}{(ma)^3 r^2}\left[2(ma)^2 + 2mar - r^2\right]e^{-r/ma}$$

$$r^2 f\frac{d}{dr}\left[\frac{1}{r^2}\frac{d}{dr}\left(r^2\frac{dg}{dr}\right)\right] = \frac{1}{(ma)^3}\left[2(ma)^2 + 2mar - r^2\right]e^{-r/ma}e^{-r/na}$$

This does *not* vanish as $r \to 0$; rather, it goes to $2/ma$. For these particular states, then,

$$\langle f|p^4 g\rangle = \frac{8\pi\hbar^4}{a}\left(\frac{1}{m} - \frac{1}{n}\right) + \langle p^4 f|g\rangle,$$

or, tacking on the normalization factor,

$$\psi n00 = \frac{1}{\sqrt{\pi}\,(na)^{3/2}}e^{-r/na}, \quad \langle\psi_{n00}|p^4\psi_{m00}\rangle = \frac{8\hbar^4}{a^4}\frac{(n-m)}{(nm)^{5/2}} + \langle p^4\psi_{n00}|\psi_{m00}\rangle,$$

and hence $p^4$ is not Hermitian, for such states.

---

## Problem 6.16

**(a)**

$$[\mathbf{L}\cdot\mathbf{S}, L_x] = [L_xS_x + L_yS_y + L_zS_z, L_x] = S_x\,[L_x, L_x] + S_y\,[L_y, L_x] + S_z\,[L_z, L_x]$$

$$= S_x(0) + S_y(-i\hbar L_z) + S_z(i\hbar L_y) = i\hbar(L_yS_z - L_zS_y) = i\hbar(\mathbf{L}\times\mathbf{S})_x.$$

Same goes for the other two components, so $\boxed{[\mathbf{L}\cdot\mathbf{S}, \mathbf{L}] = i\hbar(\mathbf{L}\times\mathbf{S}).}$

**(b)** $[\mathbf{L}\cdot\mathbf{S}, \mathbf{S}]$ is identical, only with $\mathbf{L}\leftrightarrow\mathbf{S}$: $\boxed{[\mathbf{L}\cdot\mathbf{S}, \mathbf{S}] = i\hbar(\mathbf{S}\times\mathbf{L}).}$

**(c)** $[\mathbf{L}\cdot\mathbf{S}, \mathbf{J}] = [\mathbf{L}\cdot\mathbf{S}, \mathbf{L}] + [\mathbf{L}\cdot\mathbf{S}, \mathbf{S}] = i\hbar(\mathbf{L}\times\mathbf{S} + \mathbf{S}\times\mathbf{L}) = \boxed{0.}$

**(d)** $L^2$ commutes with all components of $\mathbf{L}$ (and $\mathbf{S}$) , so $\boxed{[\mathbf{L}\cdot\mathbf{S}, L^2] = 0.}$

**(e)** Likewise, $\boxed{[\mathbf{L}\cdot\mathbf{S}, S^2] = 0.}$

**(f)** $\left[\mathbf{L}\cdot\mathbf{S}, J^2\right] = \left[\mathbf{L}\cdot\mathbf{S}, L^2\right] + \left[\mathbf{L}\cdot\mathbf{S}, S^2\right] + 2\left[\mathbf{L}\cdot\mathbf{S}, \mathbf{L}\cdot\mathbf{S}\right] = 0 + 0 + 0 \Longrightarrow \boxed{\left[\mathbf{L}\cdot\mathbf{S}, J^2\right] = 0.}$

---

## Problem 6.17

With the plus sign, $j = l + 1/2$ $(l = j - 1/2)$: Eq. 6.57 $\Rightarrow E_r^1 = -\dfrac{(E_n)^2}{2mc^2}\left(\dfrac{4n}{j} - 3\right)$ .

Equation 6.65 $\Rightarrow E_{so}^1 = \dfrac{(E_n)^2}{mc^2}\dfrac{n\left[j(j+1) - (j-\frac{1}{2})(j+\frac{1}{2}) - \frac{3}{4}\right]}{(j-\frac{1}{2})j(j+\frac{1}{2})}$

$$= \frac{(E_n)^2}{mc^2}\frac{n(j^2 + j - j^2 + \frac{1}{4} - \frac{3}{4})}{(j-\frac{1}{2})j(j+\frac{1}{2})} = \frac{(E_n)^2}{mc^2}\frac{n}{j(j+\frac{1}{2})}.$$

$$E_{fs}^1 = E_r^1 + E_{so}^1 = \frac{(E_n)^2}{2mc^2}\left(-\frac{4n}{j} + 3 + \frac{2n}{j(j+\frac{1}{2})}\right)$$

$$= \frac{(E_n)^2}{2mc^2}\left\{3 + \frac{2n}{j(j+\frac{1}{2})}\left[1 - 2\left(j + \frac{1}{2}\right)\right]\right\} = \frac{(E_n)^2}{2mc^2}\left(3 - \frac{4n}{j+\frac{1}{2}}\right).$$

With the minus sign, $j = l - 1/2$ $(l = j + 1/2)$:    Eq. 6.57 $\Rightarrow E_r^1 = -\dfrac{(E_n)^2}{2mc^2}\left(\dfrac{4n}{j+1} - 3\right)$.

Equation 6.65 $\Rightarrow E_{so}^1 = \dfrac{(E_n)^2}{mc^2}\dfrac{n\left[j(j+1) - (j+\frac{1}{2})(j+\frac{3}{2}) - \frac{3}{4}\right]}{(j+\frac{1}{2})(j+1)(j+\frac{3}{2})}$

$$= \dfrac{(E_n)^2}{mc^2}\dfrac{n(j^2 + j - j^2 - 2j - \frac{3}{4} - \frac{3}{4})}{(j+\frac{1}{2})(j+1)(j+\frac{3}{2})} = \dfrac{(E_n)^2}{mc^2}\dfrac{-n}{(j+1)(j+\frac{1}{2})}.$$

$$E_{fs}^1 = \dfrac{(E_n)^2}{2mc^2}\left[-\dfrac{4n}{j+1} - 3 + \dfrac{2n}{(j+1)(j+\frac{1}{2})}\right] = \dfrac{(E_n)^2}{2mc^2}\left\{3 - \dfrac{2n}{(j+1)(j+\frac{1}{2})}\left[1 + 2\left(j+\dfrac{1}{2}\right)\right]\right\}$$

$$= \dfrac{(E_n)^2}{2mc^2}\left(3 - \dfrac{4n}{j+\frac{1}{2}}\right).\quad\text{For both signs, then,}\quad E_{fs}^1 = \dfrac{(E_n)^2}{2mc^2}\left(3 - \dfrac{4n}{j+\frac{1}{2}}\right).\quad\text{QED}$$

---

## Problem 6.18

$E_3^0 - E_2^0 = h\nu = \dfrac{2\pi\hbar c}{\lambda} = E_1\left(\dfrac{1}{9} - \dfrac{1}{4}\right) = -\dfrac{5}{36}E_1 \Rightarrow \lambda = -\dfrac{36}{5}\dfrac{2\pi\hbar c}{E_1};\quad E_1 = -13.6\,\text{eV};$

$\hbar c = 1.97 \times 10^{-11}\,\text{MeV·cm};\quad \lambda = \dfrac{36}{5}\dfrac{(2\pi)(1.97 \times 10^{-11} \times 10^6\,\text{eV}\cdot\text{cm})}{(13.6\,\text{eV})} = 6.55 \times 10^{-5}\,\text{cm} = \boxed{655\,\text{nm.}}$

$\nu = \dfrac{c}{\lambda} = \dfrac{3.00 \times 10^8\,\text{m/s}}{6.55 \times 10^{-7}\,\text{m}} = \boxed{4.58 \times 10^{14}\,\text{Hz.}}\quad\text{Equation 6.66} \Rightarrow E_{fs}^1 = \dfrac{(E_n)^2}{2mc^2}\left(3 - \dfrac{4n}{j+\frac{1}{2}}\right):$

For $n = 2$: $l = 0$ or $l = 1$, so $j = 1/2$ or $3/2$. Thus $n = 2$ splits into *two* levels:

$\underline{j = 1/2}$: $E_2^1 = \dfrac{(E_2)^2}{2mc^2}\left(3 - \dfrac{8}{1}\right) = -\dfrac{5}{2}\dfrac{(E_2)^2}{mc^2} = -\dfrac{5}{2}\left(\dfrac{1}{4}\right)^2\dfrac{(E_1)^2}{mc^2} = -\dfrac{5}{32}\dfrac{(13.6\,\text{eV})^2}{(.511 \times 10^6\,\text{eV})} = -5.66 \times 10^{-5}\text{eV.}$

$\underline{j = 3/2}$: $E_2^1 = \dfrac{(E_2)^2}{2mc^2}\left(3 - \dfrac{8}{2}\right) = -\dfrac{1}{2}\dfrac{(E_2)^2}{mc^2} = -\dfrac{1}{32}(3.62 \times 10^{-4}\,\text{eV}) = -1.13 \times 10^{-5}\text{eV.}$

For $n = 3$: $l = 0, 1$ or $2$, so $j = 1/2, 3/2$ or $5/2$. Thus $n = 3$ splits into *three* levels:

$\underline{j = 1/2}$: $E_3^1 = \dfrac{(E_3)^2}{2mc^2}\left(3 - \dfrac{12}{1}\right) = -9\dfrac{(E_3)^2}{mc^2} = -\dfrac{9}{2}\left(\dfrac{1}{9^2}\right)\dfrac{(E_1)^2}{mc^2} = -\dfrac{1}{18}(3.62 \times 10^{-4}\text{eV}) = -2.01 \times 10^{-5}\text{eV.}$

$\underline{j = 3/2}$: $E_3^1 = \dfrac{(E_3)^2}{2mc^2}\left(3 - \dfrac{12}{2}\right) = -\dfrac{3}{2}\dfrac{(E_3)^2}{mc^2} = -\dfrac{1}{54}(3.62 \times 10^{-4}\,\text{eV}) = -0.67 \times 10^{-5}\,\text{eV.}$

$\underline{j = 5/2}$: $E_3^1 = \dfrac{(E_3)^2}{2mc^2}\left(3 - \dfrac{12}{3}\right) = -\dfrac{1}{2}\dfrac{(E_3)^2}{mc^2} = -\dfrac{1}{162}(3.62 \times 10^{-4}\,\text{eV}) = -0.22 \times 10^{-5}\,\text{eV.}$

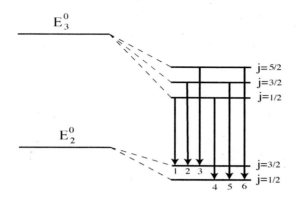

There are *six* transitions here; their energies are $(E_3^0 + E_3^1) - (E_2^0 + E_2^1) = (E_3^0 - E_2^0) + \Delta E$, where $\Delta E \equiv E_3^1 - E_2^1$. Let $\beta \equiv (E_1)^2/mc^2 = 3.62 \times 10^{-4}$ eV. Then:

$$(\tfrac{1}{2} \to \tfrac{3}{2}): \quad \Delta E = \left[ \left( -\frac{1}{18} \right) - \left( -\frac{1}{32} \right) \right] \beta = -\frac{7}{288}\beta = -8.80 \times 10^{-6} \text{ eV}.$$

$$(\tfrac{3}{2} \to \tfrac{3}{2}): \quad \Delta E = \left[ \left( -\frac{1}{54} \right) - \left( -\frac{1}{32} \right) \right] \beta = \frac{11}{864}\beta = 4.61 \times 10^{-6} \text{ eV}.$$

$$(\tfrac{5}{2} \to \tfrac{3}{2}): \quad \Delta E = \left[ \left( -\frac{1}{162} \right) + \left( \frac{1}{32} \right) \right] \beta = \frac{65}{2592}\beta = 9.08 \times 10^{-6} \text{ eV}.$$

$$(\tfrac{1}{2} \to \tfrac{1}{2}): \quad \Delta E = \left[ \left( \frac{5}{32} \right) - \left( \frac{1}{18} \right) \right] \beta = \frac{29}{288}\beta = 36.45 \times 10^{-6} \text{ eV}.$$

$$(\tfrac{3}{2} \to \tfrac{1}{2}): \quad \Delta E = \left[ \left( -\frac{1}{54} \right) + \left( \frac{5}{32} \right) \right] \beta = \frac{119}{864}\beta = 49.86 \times 10^{-6} \text{ eV}.$$

$$(\tfrac{5}{2} \to \tfrac{1}{2}): \quad \Delta E = \left[ \left( -\frac{1}{162} \right) + \left( \frac{5}{32} \right) \right] \beta = \frac{389}{2592}\beta = 54.33 \times 10^{-6} \text{ eV}.$$

*Conclusion:* There are *six* lines; one of them ($\frac{1}{2} \to \frac{3}{2}$) has a frequency *less* than the unperturbed line, the other five have (slightly) *higher* frequencies. In order they are: $\frac{3}{2} \to \frac{3}{2}$; $\frac{5}{2} \to \frac{3}{2}$; $\frac{1}{2} \to \frac{1}{2}$; $\frac{3}{2} \to \frac{1}{2}$; $\frac{5}{2} \to \frac{1}{2}$. The frequency spacings are:

| | | | | |
|---|---|---|---|---|
| $\nu_2 - \nu_1$ | $=$ | $(\Delta E_2 - \Delta E_1)/2\pi\hbar$ | $=$ | $3.23 \times 10^9$ Hz |
| $\nu_3 - \nu_3$ | $=$ | $(\Delta E_3 - \Delta E_2)/2\pi\hbar$ | $=$ | $1.08 \times 10^9$ Hz |
| $\nu_4 - \nu_3$ | $=$ | $(\Delta E_4 - \Delta E_3)/2\pi\hbar$ | $=$ | $6.60 \times 10^9$ Hz |
| $\nu_5 - \nu_4$ | $=$ | $(\Delta E_5 - \Delta E_4)/2\pi\hbar$ | $=$ | $3.23 \times 10^9$ Hz |
| $\nu_6 - \nu_5$ | $=$ | $(\Delta E_6 - \Delta E_5)/2\pi\hbar$ | $=$ | $1.08 \times 10^9$ Hz |

## Problem 6.19

$$\sqrt{\left(j+\frac{1}{2}\right)^2 - \alpha^2} = \left(j+\frac{1}{2}\right)\sqrt{1-\left(\frac{\alpha}{j+\frac{1}{2}}\right)^2} \approx \left(j+\frac{1}{2}\right)\left[1-\frac{1}{2}\left(\frac{\alpha}{j+\frac{1}{2}}\right)^2\right] = \left(j+\frac{1}{2}\right) - \frac{\alpha^2}{2(j+\frac{1}{2})}.$$

$$\frac{\alpha}{n-(j+\frac{1}{2})+\sqrt{\left(j+\frac{1}{2}\right)^2 - \alpha^2}} \approx \frac{\alpha}{n-(j+\frac{1}{2})+(j+\frac{1}{2})-\frac{\alpha^2}{2(j+\frac{1}{2})}} = \frac{\alpha}{n-\frac{\alpha^2}{2(j+\frac{1}{2})}}$$

$$= \frac{\alpha}{n\left[1-\frac{\alpha^2}{2n(j+\frac{1}{2})}\right]} \approx \frac{\alpha}{n}\left[1+\frac{\alpha^2}{2n(j+\frac{1}{2})}\right].$$

$$\left[1+\left(\frac{\alpha}{n-(j+\frac{1}{2})+\sqrt{\left(j+\frac{1}{2}\right)^2 - \alpha^2}}\right)^2\right]^{-1/2} \approx \left[1+\frac{\alpha^2}{n^2}\left(1+\frac{\alpha^2}{n(j+\frac{1}{2})}\right)\right]^{-1/2}$$

$$\approx 1 - \frac{1}{2}\frac{\alpha^2}{n^2}\left(1+\frac{\alpha^2}{n(j+\frac{1}{2})}\right) + \frac{3}{8}\frac{\alpha^4}{n^4} = 1 - \frac{\alpha^2}{2n^2} + \frac{\alpha^4}{2n^4}\left(\frac{-n}{j+\frac{1}{2}}+\frac{3}{4}\right).$$

$$E_{nj} \approx mc^2\left[1 - \frac{\alpha^2}{2n^2} + \frac{\alpha^4}{2n^4}\left(\frac{-n}{j+\frac{1}{2}}+\frac{3}{4}\right) - 1\right] = -\frac{\alpha^2 mc^2}{2n^2}\left[1 + \frac{\alpha^2}{n^2}\left(\frac{n}{j+\frac{1}{2}}-\frac{3}{4}\right)\right]$$

$$= -\frac{13.6\,\text{eV}}{n^2}\left[1+\frac{\alpha^2}{n^2}\left(\frac{n}{j+\frac{1}{2}}-\frac{3}{4}\right)\right], \quad \text{confirming Eq. 6.67.}$$

---

## Problem 6.20

Equation $6.59 \Rightarrow \mathbf{B} = \frac{1}{4\pi\epsilon_0}\frac{e}{mc^2 r^3}\mathbf{L}.$   Say $L = \hbar$, $r = a$; then

$$B = \frac{1}{4\pi\epsilon_0}\frac{e\hbar}{mc^2 a^3}$$

$$= \frac{(1.60 \times 10^{-19}\,\text{C})(1.05 \times 10^{-34}\,\text{J}\cdot\text{s})}{4\pi\left(8.9 \times 10^{-12}\,\text{C}^2/\text{N}\cdot\text{m}^2\right)(9.1 \times 10^{-31}\,\text{kg})(3 \times 10^8\,\text{m/s})^2(0.53 \times 10^{-10}\,\text{m})^3} = \boxed{12\,\text{T.}}$$

So a "strong" Zeeman field is $B_{\text{ext}} \gg 10$ T, and a "weak" one is $B_{\text{ext}} \ll 10$ T. Incidentally, the earth's field $(10^{-4}$ T) is definitely *weak*.

---

## Problem 6.21

For $n = 2$, $l = 0$ ($j = 1/2$) or $l = 1$ ($j = 1/2$ or $3/2$). The eight states are:

$$\left.\begin{array}{l} |1\rangle = |2\ 0\ \tfrac{1}{2}\ \tfrac{1}{2}\rangle \\[2mm] |2\rangle = |2\ 0\ \tfrac{1}{2}\ -\tfrac{1}{2}\rangle \end{array}\right\} g_J = \left[1 + \frac{(1/2)(3/2) + (3/4)}{2(1/2)(3/2)}\right] = 1 + \frac{3/2}{3/2} = 2.$$

$$\left.\begin{array}{l} |3\rangle = |2\ 1\ \tfrac{1}{2}\ \tfrac{1}{2}\rangle \\[2mm] |4\rangle = |2\ 1\ \tfrac{1}{2}\ -\tfrac{1}{2}\rangle \end{array}\right\} g_J = \left[1 + \frac{(1/2)(3/2) - (1)(2) + (3/4)}{2(1/2)(3/2)}\right] = 1 + \frac{-1/2}{3/2} = 2/3.$$

In these four cases, $E_{nj} = -\dfrac{13.6\ \text{eV}}{4}\left[1 + \dfrac{\alpha^2}{4}\left(\dfrac{2}{1} - \dfrac{3}{4}\right)\right] = -3.4\ \text{eV}\left(1 + \dfrac{5}{16}\alpha^2\right).$

$$\left.\begin{array}{l} |5\rangle = |2\ 1\ \tfrac{3}{2}\ \tfrac{3}{2}\rangle \\[2mm] |6\rangle = |2\ 1\ \tfrac{3}{2}\ \tfrac{1}{2}\rangle \\[2mm] |7\rangle = |2\ 1\ \tfrac{3}{2}\ -\tfrac{1}{2}\rangle \\[2mm] |8\rangle = |2\ 1\ \tfrac{3}{2}\ -\tfrac{3}{2}\rangle \end{array}\right\} g_J = \left[1 + \frac{(3/2)(5/2) - (1)(2) + (3/4)}{2(3/2)(5/2)}\right] = 1 + \frac{5/2}{15/2} = 4/3.$$

In these four cases, $E_{nj} = -3.4\ \text{eV}\left[1 + \dfrac{\alpha^2}{4}\left(\dfrac{2}{2} - \dfrac{3}{4}\right)\right] = -3.4\ \text{eV}\left(1 + \dfrac{1}{16}\alpha^2\right).$

The energies are:

$$\boxed{\begin{array}{l} E_1 = -3.4\ \text{eV}\ \left(1 + \tfrac{5}{16}\alpha^2\right) + \mu_B B_{\text{ext}}. \\[3mm] E_2 = -3.4\ \text{eV}\ \left(1 + \tfrac{5}{16}\alpha^2\right) - \mu_B B_{\text{ext}}. \\[3mm] E_3 = -3.4\ \text{eV}\ \left(1 + \tfrac{5}{16}\alpha^2\right) + \tfrac{1}{3}\mu_B B_{\text{ext}}. \\[3mm] E_4 = -3.4\ \text{eV}\ \left(1 + \tfrac{5}{16}\alpha^2\right) - \tfrac{1}{3}\mu_B B_{\text{ext}}. \\[3mm] E_5 = -3.4\ \text{eV}\ \left(1 + \tfrac{1}{16}\alpha^2\right) + 2\mu_B B_{\text{ext}}. \\[3mm] E_6 = -3.4\ \text{eV}\ \left(1 + \tfrac{1}{16}\alpha^2\right) + \tfrac{2}{3}\mu_B B_{\text{ext}}. \\[3mm] E_7 = -3.4\ \text{eV}\ \left(1 + \tfrac{1}{16}\alpha^2\right) - \tfrac{2}{3}\mu_B B_{\text{ext}}. \\[3mm] E_8 = -3.4\ \text{eV}\ \left(1 + \tfrac{1}{16}\alpha^2\right) - 2\mu_B B_{\text{ext}}. \end{array}}$$

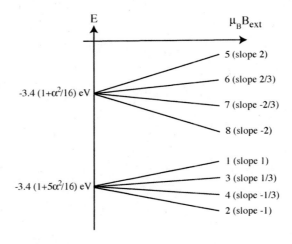

## Problem 6.22

$$E_{\text{fs}}^1 = \langle nlm_lm_s|(H_r' + H_{\text{so}}')|nlm_lm_s\rangle = -\frac{E_n^2}{2mc^2}\left[\frac{4n}{l+1/2} - 3\right] + \frac{e^2}{8\pi\epsilon_0 m^2 c^2}\frac{\hbar^2 m_l m_s}{l(l+1/2)(l+1)n^3 a^3}.$$

$$\text{Now} \begin{cases} \dfrac{2E_n^2}{mc^2} = \left(-\dfrac{2E_1}{mc^2}\right)\left(-\dfrac{E_1}{n^4}\right) = \dfrac{\alpha^2}{n^4}(13.6 \text{ eV}). \quad \text{(Problem 6.11.)} \\[2mm] \dfrac{e^2\hbar^2}{8\pi\epsilon_0 m^2 c^2 a^3} = \dfrac{e^2\hbar^2(me^2)^3}{2\cdot 4\pi\epsilon_0 m^2 c^2(4\pi\epsilon_0\hbar^2)^3} = \left[\dfrac{m}{2\hbar^2}\left(\dfrac{e^2}{4\pi\epsilon_0}\right)^2\right]\left(\dfrac{e^2}{4\pi\epsilon_0\hbar c}\right)^2 = \alpha^2(13.6 \text{ eV}). \end{cases}$$

$$E_{\text{fs}}^1 = \frac{13.6 \text{ eV}}{n^3}\alpha^2\left\{-\frac{1}{(l+1/2)} + \frac{3}{4n} + \frac{m_l m_s}{l(l+1/2)(l+1)}\right\} = \frac{13.6 \text{ eV}}{n^3}\alpha^2\left\{\frac{3}{4n} - \frac{l(l+1) - m_l m_s}{l(l+1/2)(l+1)}\right\}. \quad \text{QED}$$

## Problem 6.23

The Bohr energy is the same for all of them: $E_2 = -13.6 \text{ eV}/2^2 = -3.4 \text{ eV}$. The Zeeman contribution is the second term in Eq. 6.79: $\mu_B B_{\text{ext}}(m_l + 2m_s)$. The fine structure is given by Eq. 6.82: $E_{\text{fs}}^1 = (13.6 \text{ eV}/8)\alpha^2\{\cdots\} = (1.7 \text{ eV})\alpha^2\{\cdots\}$. In the table below I record the 8 states, the value of $(m_l + 2m_s)$, the value of $\{\cdots\} \equiv \frac{3}{8} - \left[\frac{l(l+1) - m_l m_s}{l(l+1/2)(l+1)}\right]$, and (in the last column) the total energy, $-3.4 \text{ eV}\left[1 - (\alpha^2/2)\{\cdots\}\right] + (m_l + 2m_s)\mu_B B_{\text{ext}}$.

| State $= |nlm_lm_s\rangle$ | $(m_l + 2m_s)$ | $\{\cdots\}$ | Total Energy |
|---|---|---|---|
| $|1\rangle = |2\,0\,0\,\tfrac{1}{2}\rangle$ | $1$ | $-5/8$ | $-3.4 \text{ eV}\left[1 + (5/16)\alpha^2\right] + \mu_B B_{\text{ext}}$ |
| $|2\rangle = |2\,0\,0\,-\tfrac{1}{2}\rangle$ | $-1$ | $-5/8$ | $-3.4 \text{ eV}\left[1 + (5/16)\alpha^2\right] - \mu_B B_{\text{ext}}$ |
| $|3\rangle = |2\,1\,1\,\tfrac{1}{2}\rangle$ | $2$ | $-1/8$ | $-3.4 \text{ eV}\left[1 + (1/16)\alpha^2\right] + 2\mu_B B_{\text{ext}}$ |
| $|4\rangle = |2\,1\,-1\,-\tfrac{1}{2}\rangle$ | $-2$ | $-1/8$ | $-3.4 \text{ eV}\left[1 + (1/16)\alpha^2\right] - 2\mu_B B_{\text{ext}}$ |
| $|5\rangle = |2\,1\,0\,\tfrac{1}{2}\rangle$ | $1$ | $-7/24$ | $-3.4 \text{ eV}\left[1 + (7/48)\alpha^2\right] + \mu_B B_{\text{ext}}$ |
| $|6\rangle = |2\,1\,0\,-\tfrac{1}{2}\rangle$ | $-1$ | $-7/24$ | $-3.4 \text{ eV}\left[1 + (7/48)\alpha^2\right] - \mu_B B_{\text{ext}}$ |
| $|7\rangle = |2\,1\,1\,-\tfrac{1}{2}\rangle$ | $0$ | $-11/24$ | $-3.4 \text{ eV}\left[1 + (11/48)\alpha^2\right]$ |
| $|8\rangle = |2\,1\,-1\,\tfrac{1}{2}\rangle$ | $0$ | $-11/24$ | $-3.4 \text{ eV}\left[1 + (11/48)\alpha^2\right]$ |

Ignoring fine structure there are ⎡five⎤ distinct levels—corresponding to the possible values of $(m_l + 2m_s)$:

$$\boxed{2 \quad (d = 1); \ 1 \quad (d = 2); \ 0 \quad (d = 2); \ -1 \quad (d = 2); \ -2 \quad (d = 1).}$$

---

## Problem 6.24

Equation 6.72 $\Rightarrow E_z^1 = \dfrac{e}{2m}\mathbf{B}_{\text{ext}} \cdot \langle \mathbf{L} + 2\mathbf{S} \rangle = \dfrac{e}{2m} B_{\text{ext}} 2m_s\hbar = 2m_s\mu_B B_{\text{ext}}$ (same as the Zeeman term in Eq. 6.79,

with $m_l = 0$). Equation 6.67 $\Rightarrow E_{nj} = -\dfrac{13.6\text{ eV}}{n^2}\left[1 + \dfrac{\alpha^2}{n^2}\left(n - \dfrac{3}{4}\right)\right]$ (since $j = 1/2$). So the total energy is

$$\boxed{E = -\dfrac{13.6\text{ eV}}{n^2}\left[1 + \dfrac{\alpha^2}{n^2}\left(n - \dfrac{3}{4}\right)\right] + 2m_s\mu_B B_{\text{ext}}.}$$

Fine structure is the $\alpha^2$ term: $E_{\text{fs}}^1 = -\dfrac{13.6\text{ eV}}{n^4}\alpha^2\left(n - \dfrac{3}{4}\right) = \dfrac{13.6\text{ eV}}{n^3}\alpha^2\left(\dfrac{3}{4n} - 1\right)$, which is the same as

Eq. 6.82, with the term in square brackets set equal to 1. QED

---

## Problem 6.25

Equation 6.66 $\Rightarrow E_{\text{fs}}^1 = \dfrac{E_2^2}{2mc^2}\left(3 - \dfrac{8}{j + 1/2}\right) = \dfrac{E_1^2}{32mc^2}\left(3 - \dfrac{8}{j + 1/2}\right); \quad \dfrac{E_1}{mc^2} = -\dfrac{\alpha^2}{2}$ (Problem 6.11), so

$$E_{\text{fs}}^1 = -\dfrac{E_1}{32}\left(\dfrac{\alpha^2}{2}\right)\left(3 - \dfrac{8}{j + 1/2}\right) = \dfrac{13.6\text{ eV}}{64}\alpha^2\left(3 - \dfrac{8}{j + 1/2}\right) = \gamma\left(3 - \dfrac{8}{j + 1/2}\right).$$

For $j = 1/2$ $(\psi_1, \psi_2, \psi_6, \psi_8)$, $H_{\text{fs}}^1 = \gamma(3 - 8) = -5\gamma$. For $j = 3/2$ $(\psi_3, \psi_4, \psi_5, \psi_7)$, $H_{\text{fs}}^1 = \gamma\left(3 - \dfrac{8}{2}\right) = -\gamma$.

This confirms all the $\gamma$ terms in $-\mathbf{W}$ (p. 281). Meanwhile, $H_z' = (e/2m)B_{\text{ext}}(L_z + 2S_z)$ (Eq. 6.71); $\psi_1, \psi_2, \psi_3, \psi_4$ are eigenstates of $L_z$ and $S_z$; for these there are only diagonal elements:

$$\langle H_z' \rangle = \dfrac{e\hbar}{2m}B_{\text{ext}}(m_l + 2m_s) = (m_l + 2m_s)\beta; \quad \langle H_z' \rangle_{11} = \beta; \quad \langle H_z' \rangle_{22} = -\beta; \quad \langle H_z' \rangle_{33} = 2\beta; \quad \langle H_z' \rangle_{44} = -2\beta.$$

This confirms the upper left corner of $-\mathbf{W}$. Finally:

$$\left.\begin{array}{l} (L_z + 2S_z)|\psi_5\rangle = +\hbar\sqrt{\tfrac{2}{3}}|1\ 0\rangle|\tfrac{1}{2}\ \tfrac{1}{2}\rangle \\[4pt] (L_z + 2S_z)|\psi_6\rangle = -\hbar\sqrt{\tfrac{1}{3}}|1\ 0\rangle|\tfrac{1}{2}\ \tfrac{1}{2}\rangle \\[4pt] (L_z + 2S_z)|\psi_7\rangle = -\hbar\sqrt{\tfrac{2}{3}}|1\ 0\rangle|\tfrac{1}{2}\ -\tfrac{1}{2}\rangle \\[4pt] (L_z + 2S_z)|\psi_8\rangle = -\hbar\sqrt{\tfrac{1}{3}}|1\ 0\rangle|\tfrac{1}{2}\ -\tfrac{1}{2}\rangle \end{array}\right\} \text{ so } \begin{array}{l} \langle H_z' \rangle_{55} = (2/3)\beta, \\ \langle H_z' \rangle_{66} = (1/3)\beta, \\ \langle H_z' \rangle_{77} = -(2/3)\beta, \\ \langle H_z' \rangle_{88} = -(1/3)\beta, \\ \langle H_z' \rangle_{56} = \langle H_z' \rangle_{65} = -(\sqrt{2}/3)\beta, \\ \langle H_z' \rangle_{78} = \langle H_z' \rangle_{87} = -(\sqrt{2}/3)\beta, \end{array}$$

which confirms the remaining elements.

---

## Problem 6.26

There are eighteen $n = 3$ states (in general, $2n^2$).

### WEAK FIELD

Equation 6.67 $\Rightarrow E_{3j} = -\dfrac{13.6\,\text{eV}}{9}\left[1 + \dfrac{\alpha^2}{9}\left(\dfrac{3}{j+1/2} - \dfrac{3}{4}\right)\right] = -1.51\,\text{eV}\left[1 + \dfrac{\alpha^2}{3}\left(\dfrac{1}{j+1/2} - \dfrac{1}{4}\right)\right].$

Equation 6.76 $\Rightarrow E_z^1 = g_J m_j \mu_B B_{\text{ext}}.$

| State $\lvert 3\ l\ j\ m_j\rangle$ | | $g_J$(Eq. 6.75) | $\frac{1}{3}\left(\frac{1}{j+1/2} - \frac{1}{4}\right)$ | Total Energy |
|---|---|---|---|---|
| $l=0,\ j=1/2$ | $\lvert 3\ 0\ \frac{1}{2}\ \frac{1}{2}\rangle$ | 2 | 1/4 | $-1.51\,\text{eV}\left(1 + \frac{\alpha^2}{4}\right) + \mu_B B_{\text{ext}}$ |
| $l=0,\ j=1/2$ | $\lvert 3\ 0\ \frac{1}{2}\ -\frac{1}{2}\rangle$ | 2 | 1/4 | $-1.51\,\text{eV}\left(1 + \frac{\alpha^2}{4}\right) - \mu_B B_{\text{ext}}$ |
| $l=1,\ j=1/2$ | $\lvert 3\ 1\ \frac{1}{2}\ \frac{1}{2}\rangle$ | 2/3 | 1/4 | $-1.51\,\text{eV}\left(1 + \frac{\alpha^2}{4}\right) + \frac{1}{3}\mu_B B_{\text{ext}}$ |
| $l=1,\ j=1/2$ | $\lvert 3\ 1\ \frac{1}{2}\ -\frac{1}{2}\rangle$ | 2/3 | 1/4 | $-1.51\,\text{eV}\left(1 + \frac{\alpha^2}{4}\right) - \frac{1}{3}\mu_B B_{\text{ext}}$ |
| $l=1,\ j=3/2$ | $\lvert 3\ 1\ \frac{3}{2}\ \frac{3}{2}\rangle$ | 4/3 | 1/12 | $-1.51\,\text{eV}\left(1 + \frac{\alpha^2}{12}\right) + 2\mu_B B_{\text{ext}}$ |
| $l=1,\ j=3/2$ | $\lvert 3\ 1\ \frac{3}{2}\ \frac{1}{2}\rangle$ | 4/3 | 1/12 | $-1.51\,\text{eV}\left(1 + \frac{\alpha^2}{12}\right) + \frac{2}{3}\mu_B B_{\text{ext}}$ |
| $l=1,\ j=3/2$ | $\lvert 3\ 1\ \frac{3}{2}\ -\frac{1}{2}\rangle$ | 4/3 | 1/12 | $-1.51\,\text{eV}\left(1 + \frac{\alpha^2}{12}\right) - \frac{2}{3}\mu_B B_{\text{ext}}$ |
| $l=1,\ j=3/2$ | $\lvert 3\ 1\ \frac{3}{2}\ -\frac{3}{2}\rangle$ | 4/3 | 1/12 | $-1.51\,\text{eV}\left(1 + \frac{\alpha^2}{12}\right) - 2\mu_B B_{\text{ext}}$ |
| $l=2,\ j=3/2$ | $\lvert 3\ 2\ \frac{3}{2}\ \frac{3}{2}\rangle$ | 4/5 | 1/12 | $-1.51\,\text{eV}\left(1 + \frac{\alpha^2}{12}\right) + \frac{6}{5}\mu_B B_{\text{ext}}$ |
| $l=2,\ j=3/2$ | $\lvert 3\ 2\ \frac{3}{2}\ \frac{1}{2}\rangle$ | 4/5 | 1/12 | $-1.51\,\text{eV}\left(1 + \frac{\alpha^2}{12}\right) + \frac{2}{5}\mu_B B_{\text{ext}}$ |
| $l=2,\ j=3/2$ | $\lvert 3\ 2\ \frac{3}{2}\ -\frac{1}{2}\rangle$ | 4/5 | 1/12 | $-1.51\,\text{eV}\left(1 + \frac{\alpha^2}{12}\right) - \frac{2}{5}\mu_B B_{\text{ext}}$ |
| $l=2,\ j=3/2$ | $\lvert 3\ 2\ \frac{3}{2}\ -\frac{3}{2}\rangle$ | 4/5 | 1/12 | $-1.51\,\text{eV}\left(1 + \frac{\alpha^2}{12}\right) - \frac{6}{5}\mu_B B_{\text{ext}}$ |
| $l=2,\ j=5/2$ | $\lvert 3\ 2\ \frac{5}{2}\ \frac{5}{2}\rangle$ | 6/5 | 1/36 | $-1.51\,\text{eV}\left(1 + \frac{\alpha^2}{36}\right) + 3\mu_B B_{\text{ext}}$ |
| $l=2,\ j=5/2$ | $\lvert 3\ 2\ \frac{5}{2}\ \frac{3}{2}\rangle$ | 6/5 | 1/36 | $-1.51\,\text{eV}\left(1 + \frac{\alpha^2}{36}\right) + \frac{9}{5}\mu_B B_{\text{ext}}$ |
| $l=2,\ j=5/2$ | $\lvert 3\ 2\ \frac{5}{2}\ \frac{1}{2}\rangle$ | 6/5 | 1/36 | $-1.51\,\text{eV}\left(1 + \frac{\alpha^2}{36}\right) + \frac{3}{5}\mu_B B_{\text{ext}}$ |
| $l=2,\ j=5/2$ | $\lvert 3\ 2\ \frac{5}{2}\ -\frac{1}{2}\rangle$ | 6/5 | 1/36 | $-1.51\,\text{eV}\left(1 + \frac{\alpha^2}{36}\right) - \frac{3}{5}\mu_B B_{\text{ext}}$ |
| $l=2,\ j=5/2$ | $\lvert 3\ 2\ \frac{5}{2}\ -\frac{3}{2}\rangle$ | 6/5 | 1/36 | $-1.51\,\text{eV}\left(1 + \frac{\alpha^2}{36}\right) - \frac{9}{5}\mu_B B_{\text{ext}}$ |
| $l=2,\ j=5/2$ | $\lvert 3\ 2\ \frac{5}{2}\ -\frac{5}{2}\rangle$ | 6/5 | 1/36 | $-1.51\,\text{eV}\left(1 + \frac{\alpha^2}{36}\right) - 3\mu_B B_{\text{ext}}$ |

### STRONG FIELD

Equation 6.79 $\Rightarrow -1.51\,\text{eV} + (m_l + 2m_s)\mu_B B_{\text{ext}};$

Equation 6.82 $\Rightarrow \dfrac{13.6\,\text{eV}}{27}\alpha^2\left\{\dfrac{1}{4} - \left[\dfrac{l(l+1) - m_l m_s}{l(l+1/2)(l+1)}\right]\right\} = -1.51\,\text{eV}\dfrac{\alpha^2}{3}\left\{\left[\dfrac{l(l+1) - m_l m_s}{l(l+1/2)(l+1)}\right] - \dfrac{1}{4}\right\}.$

$$E_{\text{tot}} = -1.51 \text{ eV}(1 + \alpha^2 A) + (m_l + 2m_s)\mu_B B_{\text{ext}}, \text{ where } A \equiv \frac{1}{3}\left\{\left[\frac{l(l+1) - m_l m_s}{l(l+1/2)(l+1)} - \frac{1}{4}\right]\right\}.$$

These terms are given in the table below:

| State $\lvert n\, l\, m_l\, m_s\rangle$ | | $(m_l + 2m_s)$ | $A$ | Total Energy |
|---|---|---|---|---|
| $l = 0$ | $\lvert 3\ 0\ 0\ \frac{1}{2}\rangle$ | $1$ | $1/4$ | $-1.51 \text{ eV}\left(1 + \frac{\alpha^2}{4}\right) + \mu_B B_{\text{ext}}$ |
| $l = 0$ | $\lvert 3\ 0\ 0\ -\frac{1}{2}\rangle$ | $-1$ | $1/4$ | $-1.51 \text{ eV}\left(1 + \frac{\alpha^2}{4}\right) - \mu_B B_{\text{ext}}$ |
| $l = 1$ | $\lvert 3\ 1\ 1\ \frac{1}{2}\rangle$ | $2$ | $1/12$ | $-1.51 \text{ eV}\left(1 + \frac{\alpha^2}{12}\right) + 2\mu_B B_{\text{ext}}$ |
| $l = 1$ | $\lvert 3\ 1\ -1\ -\frac{1}{2}\rangle$ | $-2$ | $1/12$ | $-1.51 \text{ eV}\left(1 + \frac{\alpha^2}{12}\right) - 2\mu_B B_{\text{ext}}$ |
| $l = 1$ | $\lvert 3\ 1\ 0\ \frac{1}{2}\rangle$ | $1$ | $5/36$ | $-1.51 \text{ eV}\left(1 + \frac{5\alpha^2}{36}\right) + \mu_B B_{\text{ext}}$ |
| $l = 1$ | $\lvert 3\ 1\ 0\ -\frac{1}{2}\rangle$ | $-1$ | $5/36$ | $-1.51 \text{ eV}\left(1 + \frac{5\alpha^2}{36}\right) - \mu_B B_{\text{ext}}$ |
| $l = 1$ | $\lvert 3\ 1\ -1\ \frac{1}{2}\rangle$ | $0$ | $7/36$ | $-1.51 \text{ eV}\left(1 + \frac{7\alpha^2}{36}\right)$ |
| $l = 1$ | $\lvert 3\ 1\ 1\ -\frac{1}{2}\rangle$ | $0$ | $7/36$ | $-1.51 \text{ eV}\left(1 + \frac{7\alpha^2}{36}\right)$ |
| $l = 2$ | $\lvert 3\ 2\ 2\ \frac{1}{2}\rangle$ | $3$ | $1/36$ | $-1.51 \text{ eV}\left(1 + \frac{\alpha^2}{36}\right) + 3\mu_B B_{\text{ext}}$ |
| $l = 2$ | $\lvert 3\ 2\ -2\ -\frac{1}{2}\rangle$ | $-3$ | $1/36$ | $-1.51 \text{ eV}\left(1 + \frac{\alpha^2}{36}\right) - 3\mu_B B_{\text{ext}}$ |
| $l = 2$ | $\lvert 3\ 2\ 1\ \frac{1}{2}\rangle$ | $2$ | $7/180$ | $-1.51 \text{ eV}\left(1 + \frac{7\alpha^2}{180}\right) + 2\mu_B B_{\text{ext}}$ |
| $l = 2$ | $\lvert 3\ 2\ -1\ -\frac{1}{2}\rangle$ | $-2$ | $7/180$ | $-1.51 \text{ eV}\left(1 + \frac{7\alpha^2}{180}\right) - 2\mu_B B_{\text{ext}}$ |
| $l = 2$ | $\lvert 3\ 2\ 0\ \frac{1}{2}\rangle$ | $1$ | $1/20$ | $-1.51 \text{ eV}\left(1 + \frac{\alpha^2}{20}\right) + \mu_B B_{\text{ext}}$ |
| $l = 2$ | $\lvert 3\ 2\ 0\ -\frac{1}{2}\rangle$ | $-1$ | $1/20$ | $-1.51 \text{ eV}\left(1 + \frac{\alpha^2}{20}\right) - \mu_B B_{\text{ext}}$ |
| $l = 2$ | $\lvert 3\ 2\ -1\ \frac{1}{2}\rangle$ | $0$ | $11/180$ | $-1.51 \text{ eV}\left(1 + \frac{11\alpha^2}{180}\right)$ |
| $l = 2$ | $\lvert 3\ 2\ 1\ -\frac{1}{2}\rangle$ | $0$ | $11/180$ | $-1.51 \text{ eV}\left(1 + \frac{11\alpha^2}{180}\right)$ |
| $l = 2$ | $\lvert 3\ 2\ -2\ \frac{1}{2}\rangle$ | $-1$ | $13/180$ | $-1.51 \text{ eV}\left(1 + \frac{13\alpha^2}{180}\right) - \mu_B B_{\text{ext}}$ |
| $l = 2$ | $\lvert 3\ 2\ 2\ -\frac{1}{2}\rangle$ | $1$ | $13/180$ | $-1.51 \text{ eV}\left(1 + \frac{13\alpha^2}{180}\right) + \mu_B B_{\text{ext}}$ |

### INTERMEDIATE FIELD

As in the book, I'll use the basis $\lvert n\, l\, j\, m_j\rangle$ (same as for weak field); then the fine structure matrix elements are diagonal: Eq. 6.66 $\Rightarrow$

$$E_{\text{fs}}^1 = \frac{E_3^2}{2mc^2}\left(3 - \frac{12}{j + 1/2}\right) = \frac{E_1^2}{54mc^2}\left(1 - \frac{4}{j + 1/2}\right) = -\frac{E_1\alpha^2}{108}\left(1 - \frac{4}{j + 1/2}\right) = 3\gamma\left(1 - \frac{4}{j + 1/2}\right),$$

$$\gamma \equiv \frac{13.6 \text{ eV}}{324}\alpha^2. \quad \text{For } j = 1/2, E_{\text{fs}}^1 = -9\gamma; \text{ for } j = 3/2, E_{\text{fs}}^1 = -3\gamma; \text{ for } j = 5/2, E_{\text{fs}}^1 = -\gamma.$$

The Zeeman Hamiltonian is Eq. 6.71: $H_z' = \frac{1}{\hbar}(L_z + 2S_z)\mu_B B_{\text{ext}}$. The first eight states ($l = 0$ and $l = 1$) are the same as before (p. 281), so the $\beta$ terms in $\mathsf{W}$ are unchanged; recording just the non-zero blocks of $-\mathsf{W}$:

$$(9\gamma - \beta), (9\gamma + \beta), (3\gamma - 2\beta), (3\gamma + 2\beta), \begin{pmatrix} (3\gamma - \frac{2}{3}\beta) & \frac{\sqrt{2}}{3}\beta \\ \frac{\sqrt{2}}{3}\beta & (9\gamma - \frac{1}{3}\beta) \end{pmatrix}, \begin{pmatrix} (3\gamma + \frac{2}{3}\beta) & \frac{\sqrt{2}}{3}\beta \\ \frac{\sqrt{2}}{3}\beta & (9\gamma + \frac{1}{3}\beta) \end{pmatrix}.$$

The other 10 states ($l = 2$) must first be decomposed into eigenstates of $L_z$ and $S_z$:

$$|\tfrac{5}{2}\,\tfrac{5}{2}\rangle \;\; = |2\,2\rangle|\tfrac{1}{2}\,\tfrac{1}{2}\rangle \qquad \Longrightarrow (\gamma - 3\beta)$$

$$|\tfrac{5}{2}\,-\tfrac{5}{2}\rangle = |2\,-2\rangle|\tfrac{1}{2}\,-\tfrac{1}{2}\rangle \Longrightarrow (\gamma + 3\beta)$$

$$\left.\begin{array}{l}|\tfrac{5}{2}\,\tfrac{3}{2}\rangle = \sqrt{\tfrac{1}{5}}|2\,2\rangle|\tfrac{1}{2}\,-\tfrac{1}{2}\rangle + \sqrt{\tfrac{4}{5}}|2\,1\rangle|\tfrac{1}{2}\,\tfrac{1}{2}\rangle \\[2mm] |\tfrac{3}{2}\,\tfrac{3}{2}\rangle = \sqrt{\tfrac{4}{5}}|2\,2\rangle|\tfrac{1}{2}\,-\tfrac{1}{2}\rangle - \sqrt{\tfrac{1}{5}}|2\,1\rangle|\tfrac{1}{2}\,\tfrac{1}{2}\rangle\end{array}\right\} \Longrightarrow \begin{pmatrix} (\gamma - \tfrac{9}{5}\beta) & \tfrac{2}{5}\beta \\[2mm] \tfrac{2}{5}\beta & (3\gamma - \tfrac{6}{5}\beta) \end{pmatrix}$$

$$\left.\begin{array}{l}|\tfrac{5}{2}\,\tfrac{1}{2}\rangle = \sqrt{\tfrac{2}{5}}|2\,1\rangle|\tfrac{1}{2}\,-\tfrac{1}{2}\rangle + \sqrt{\tfrac{3}{5}}|2\,0\rangle|\tfrac{1}{2}\,\tfrac{1}{2}\rangle \\[2mm] |\tfrac{3}{2}\,\tfrac{1}{2}\rangle = \sqrt{\tfrac{3}{5}}|2\,1\rangle|\tfrac{1}{2}\,-\tfrac{1}{2}\rangle - \sqrt{\tfrac{2}{5}}|2\,0\rangle|\tfrac{1}{2}\,\tfrac{1}{2}\rangle\end{array}\right\} \Longrightarrow \begin{pmatrix} (\gamma - \tfrac{3}{5}\beta) & \tfrac{\sqrt{6}}{5}\beta \\[2mm] \tfrac{\sqrt{6}}{5}\beta & (3\gamma - \tfrac{2}{5}\beta) \end{pmatrix}$$

$$\left.\begin{array}{l}|\tfrac{5}{2}\,-\tfrac{1}{2}\rangle = \sqrt{\tfrac{3}{5}}|2\,0\rangle|\tfrac{1}{2}\,-\tfrac{1}{2}\rangle + \sqrt{\tfrac{2}{5}}|2\,-1\rangle|\tfrac{1}{2}\,\tfrac{1}{2}\rangle \\[2mm] |\tfrac{3}{2}\,-\tfrac{1}{2}\rangle = \sqrt{\tfrac{2}{5}}|2\,0\rangle|\tfrac{1}{2}\,-\tfrac{1}{2}\rangle - \sqrt{\tfrac{3}{5}}|2\,-1\rangle|\tfrac{1}{2}\,\tfrac{1}{2}\rangle\end{array}\right\} \Longrightarrow \begin{pmatrix} (\gamma + \tfrac{3}{5}\beta) & \tfrac{\sqrt{6}}{5}\beta \\[2mm] \tfrac{\sqrt{6}}{5}\beta & (3\gamma + \tfrac{2}{5}\beta) \end{pmatrix}$$

$$\left.\begin{array}{l}|\tfrac{5}{2}\,-\tfrac{3}{2}\rangle = \sqrt{\tfrac{4}{5}}|2\,-1\rangle|\tfrac{1}{2}\,-\tfrac{1}{2}\rangle + \sqrt{\tfrac{1}{5}}|2\,-2\rangle|\tfrac{1}{2}\,\tfrac{1}{2}\rangle \\[2mm] |\tfrac{3}{2}\,-\tfrac{3}{2}\rangle = \sqrt{\tfrac{1}{5}}|2\,-1\rangle|\tfrac{1}{2}\,-\tfrac{1}{2}\rangle - \sqrt{\tfrac{4}{5}}|2\,-2\rangle|\tfrac{1}{2}\,\tfrac{1}{2}\rangle\end{array}\right\} \Longrightarrow \begin{pmatrix} (\gamma + \tfrac{9}{5}\beta) & \tfrac{2}{5}\beta \\[2mm] \tfrac{2}{5}\beta & (3\gamma + \tfrac{6}{5}\beta) \end{pmatrix}$$

[*Sample Calculation:* For the last two, letting $Q \equiv \tfrac{1}{\hbar}(L_z + 2S_z)$, we have

$$Q|\tfrac{5}{2}\,-\tfrac{3}{2}\rangle = -2\sqrt{\tfrac{4}{5}}|2\,-1\rangle|\tfrac{1}{2}\,-\tfrac{1}{2}\rangle - \sqrt{\tfrac{1}{5}}|2\,-2\rangle|\tfrac{1}{2}\,\tfrac{1}{2}\rangle;$$

$$Q|\tfrac{3}{2}\,-\tfrac{3}{2}\rangle = -2\sqrt{\tfrac{1}{5}}|2\,-1\rangle|\tfrac{1}{2}\,-\tfrac{1}{2}\rangle + \sqrt{\tfrac{4}{5}}|2\,-2\rangle|\tfrac{1}{2}\,\tfrac{1}{2}\rangle.$$

$$\langle\tfrac{5}{2}\,-\tfrac{3}{2}|Q|\tfrac{5}{2}\,-\tfrac{3}{2}\rangle = (-2)\tfrac{4}{5} - \tfrac{1}{5} = -\tfrac{9}{5}; \quad \langle\tfrac{3}{2}\,-\tfrac{3}{2}|Q|\tfrac{3}{2}\,-\tfrac{3}{2}\rangle = (-2)\tfrac{1}{5} - \tfrac{4}{5} = -\tfrac{6}{5};$$

$$\langle\tfrac{5}{2}\,-\tfrac{3}{2}|Q|\tfrac{3}{2}\,-\tfrac{3}{2}\rangle = -2\sqrt{\tfrac{4}{5}}\sqrt{\tfrac{1}{5}} + \sqrt{\tfrac{1}{5}}\sqrt{\tfrac{4}{5}} = -\tfrac{4}{5} + \tfrac{2}{5} = -\tfrac{2}{5} = \langle\tfrac{3}{2}\,-\tfrac{3}{2}|Q|\tfrac{5}{2}\,-\tfrac{3}{2}\rangle.]$$

So the $18 \times 18$ matrix $-\mathbf{W}$ splits into six $1 \times 1$ blocks and six $2 \times 2$ blocks. We need the eigenvalues of the $2 \times 2$ blocks. This means solving 3 characteristic equations (the other 3 are obtained trivially by changing the sign of $\beta$):

$$\left(3\gamma - \tfrac{2}{3}\beta - \lambda\right)\left(9\gamma - \tfrac{1}{3}\beta - \lambda\right) - \tfrac{2}{9}\beta^2 = 0 \Longrightarrow \lambda^2 + \lambda(\beta - 12\gamma) + \gamma(27\gamma - 7\beta) = 0.$$

$$\left(\gamma - \tfrac{9}{5}\beta - \lambda\right)\left(3\gamma - \tfrac{6}{5}\beta - \lambda\right) - \tfrac{4}{25}\beta^2 = 0 \Longrightarrow \lambda^2 + \lambda(3\beta - 4\gamma) + \gamma\left(3\gamma^2 - \tfrac{33}{5}\gamma\beta + 2\beta^2\right) = 0.$$

$$\left(\gamma - \tfrac{3}{5}\beta - \lambda\right)\left(3\gamma - \tfrac{2}{5}\beta - \lambda\right) - \tfrac{6}{25}\beta^2 = 0 \Longrightarrow \lambda^2 + \lambda(\beta - 4\gamma) + \gamma\left(3\gamma - \tfrac{11}{5}\beta\right) = 0.$$

The solutions are:

$$\lambda = -\beta/2 + 6\gamma \pm \sqrt{(\beta/2)^2 + \beta\gamma + 9\gamma^2}$$

$$\lambda = -3\beta/2 + 2\gamma \pm \sqrt{(\beta/2)^2 + \tfrac{3}{5}\beta\gamma + \gamma^2} \quad \Rightarrow$$

$$\lambda = -\beta/2 + 2\gamma \pm \sqrt{(\beta/2)^2 + \tfrac{1}{5}\beta\gamma + \gamma^2}$$

$$\begin{aligned}
\epsilon_1 &= E_3 - 9\gamma + \beta \\
\epsilon_2 &= E_3 - 3\gamma + 2\beta \\
\epsilon_3 &= E_3 - \gamma + 3\beta \\
\epsilon_4 &= E_3 - 6\gamma + \beta/2 + \sqrt{9\gamma^2 + \beta\gamma + \beta^2/4} \\
\epsilon_5 &= E_3 - 6\gamma + \beta/2 - \sqrt{9\gamma^2 + \beta\gamma + \beta^2/4} \\
\epsilon_6 &= E_3 - 2\gamma + 3\beta/2 + \sqrt{\gamma^2 + \tfrac{3}{5}\beta\gamma + \beta^2/4} \\
\epsilon_7 &= E_3 - 2\gamma + 3\beta/2 - \sqrt{\gamma^2 + \tfrac{3}{5}\beta\gamma + \beta^2/4} \\
\epsilon_8 &= E_3 - 2\gamma + \beta/2 + \sqrt{\gamma^2 + \tfrac{1}{5}\beta\gamma + \beta^2/4} \\
\epsilon_9 &= E_3 - 2\gamma + \beta/2 - \sqrt{\gamma^2 + \tfrac{1}{5}\beta\gamma + \beta^2/4}
\end{aligned}$$

(The other 9 $\epsilon$'s are the same, but with $\beta \to -\beta$.) Here $\gamma = \frac{13.6 \text{ eV}}{324}\alpha^2$, and $\beta = \mu_B B_{\text{ext}}$.

In the weak-field limit ($\beta \ll \gamma$):

$$\epsilon_4 \approx E_3 - 6\gamma + \beta/2 + 3\gamma\sqrt{1 + \beta/9\gamma} \approx E_3 - 6\gamma + \beta/2 + 3\gamma(1 + \beta/18\gamma) = E_3 - 3\gamma + \frac{2}{3}\beta.$$

$$\epsilon_5 \approx E_3 - 6\gamma + \beta/2 - 3\gamma(1 + \beta/18\gamma) = E_3 - 9\gamma + \frac{1}{3}\beta.$$

$$\epsilon_6 \approx E_3 - 2\gamma + 3\beta/2 + \gamma(1 + 3\beta/10\gamma) = E_3 - \gamma + \frac{9}{5}\beta.$$

$$\epsilon_7 \approx E_3 - 2\gamma + 3\beta/2 - \gamma(1 + 3\beta/10\gamma) = E_3 - 3\gamma + \frac{6}{5}\beta.$$

$$\epsilon_8 \approx E_3 - 2\gamma + \beta/2 + \gamma(1 + \beta/10\gamma) = E_3 - \gamma + \frac{3}{5}\beta.$$

$$\epsilon_9 \approx E_3 - 2\gamma + \beta/2 - \gamma(1 + \beta/10\gamma) = E_3 - 3\gamma + \frac{2}{5}\beta.$$

Noting that $\gamma = -(E_3/36)\alpha^2 = \frac{1.51 \text{ eV}}{36}\alpha^2$, we see that the weak field energies are recovered as in the first table.

In the strong-field limit ($\beta \gg \gamma$):

$$\epsilon_4 \approx E_3 - 6\gamma + \beta/2 + \beta/2\sqrt{1 + 4\gamma/\beta} \approx E_3 - 6\gamma + \beta/2 + \beta/2(1 + 2\gamma/\beta) = E_3 - 5\gamma + \beta.$$

$$\epsilon_5 \approx E_3 - 6\gamma + \beta/2 - \beta/2(1 + 2\gamma/\beta) = E_3 - 7\gamma.$$

$$\epsilon_6 \approx E_3 - 2\gamma + 3\beta/2 + \beta/2(1 + 6\gamma/5\beta) = E_3 - \frac{7}{5}\gamma + 2\beta.$$

$$\epsilon_7 \approx E_3 - 2\gamma + 3\beta/2 - \beta/2(1 + 6\gamma/5\beta) = E_3 - \frac{13}{5}\gamma + \beta.$$

$$\epsilon_8 \approx E_3 - 2\gamma + \beta/2 + \beta/2(1 + 2\gamma/5\beta) = E_3 - \frac{9}{5}\gamma + \beta.$$

$$\epsilon_9 \approx E_3 - 2\gamma + \beta/2 - \beta/2(1 + 2\gamma/5\beta) = E_3 - \frac{11}{5}\gamma.$$

Again, these reproduce the strong-field results in the second table.

In the figure below each line is labeled by the level number and (in parentheses) the starting and ending slope; for each line there is a corresponding one starting from the same point but sloping *down*.

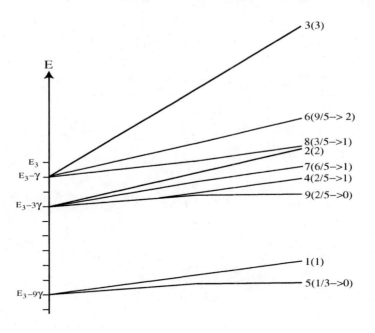

## Problem 6.27

$$I \equiv \int (\mathbf{a} \cdot \hat{r})(\mathbf{b} \cdot \hat{r}) \sin\theta \, d\theta \, d\phi$$

$$= \int (a_x \sin\theta \cos\phi + a_y \sin\theta \sin\phi + a_z \cos\theta)(b_x \sin\theta \cos\phi + b_y \sin\theta \sin\phi + b_z \cos\theta) \sin\theta \, d\theta \, d\phi.$$

But $\displaystyle\int_0^{2\pi} \sin\phi \, d\phi = \int_0^{2\pi} \cos\phi \, d\phi = \int_0^{2\pi} \sin\phi \cos\phi \, d\phi = 0$, so only three terms survive :

$$I = \int (a_x b_x \sin^2\theta \cos^2\phi + a_y b_y \sin^2\theta \sin^2\phi + a_z b_z \cos^2\theta) \sin\theta \, d\theta \, d\phi.$$

But $\displaystyle\int_0^{2\pi} \sin^2\phi \, d\phi = \int_0^{2\pi} \cos^2\phi \, d\phi = \pi, \quad \int_0^{2\pi} d\phi = 2\pi$, so

$$I = \int_0^{\pi} \left[ \pi(a_x b_x + a_y b_y)\sin^2\theta + 2\pi a_z b_z \cos^2\theta \right] \sin\theta \, d\theta. \quad \text{But } \int_0^{\pi} \sin^3\theta \, d\theta = \frac{4}{3}, \int_0^{\pi} \cos^2\theta \sin\theta \, d\theta = \frac{2}{3},$$

so $\quad I = \pi(a_x b_x + a_y b_y)\dfrac{4}{3} + 2\pi a_z b_z \dfrac{2}{3} = \dfrac{4\pi}{3}(a_x b_x + a_y b_y + a_z b_z) = \dfrac{4\pi}{3}(\mathbf{a} \cdot \mathbf{b}).$ QED

[Alternatively, noting that $I$ has to be a *scalar* bilinear in $\mathbf{a}$ and $\mathbf{b}$, we know immediately that $I = A(\mathbf{a} \cdot \mathbf{b})$, where $A$ is some constant (same for all $\mathbf{a}$ and $\mathbf{b}$). To determine $A$, pick $\mathbf{a} = \mathbf{b} = \hat{k}$; then $I = A = \int \cos^2\theta \sin\theta \, d\theta \, d\phi = 4\pi/3$.]

For states with $l = 0$, the wave function is independent of $\theta$ and $\phi$ ($Y_0^0 = 1/\sqrt{4\pi}$), so

$$\left\langle \frac{3(\mathbf{S}_p \cdot \hat{r})(\mathbf{S}_e \cdot \hat{r}) - \mathbf{S}_p \cdot \mathbf{S}_e}{r^3} \right\rangle = \left\{ \int_0^{\infty} \frac{1}{r^3} |\psi(r)|^2 r^2 dr \right\} \int [3(\mathbf{S}_p \cdot \hat{r})(\mathbf{S}_e \cdot \hat{r})] \sin\theta \, d\theta \, d\phi.$$

The first angular integral is $3(4\pi/3)(\mathbf{S}_p \cdot \mathbf{S}_e) = 4\pi(\mathbf{S}_p \cdot \mathbf{S}_e)$, while the second is $-(\mathbf{S}_p \cdot \mathbf{S}_e)\int \sin\theta\,d\theta\,d\phi = -4\pi(\mathbf{S}_p \cdot \mathbf{S}_e)$, so the two cancel, and the result is zero. QED [Actually, there is a little sleight-of-hand here, since for $l = 0$, $\psi \to$ constant as $r \to 0$, and hence the radial integral diverges logarithmically at the origin. Technically, the first term in Eq. 6.86 is the field outside an infinitesimal *sphere*; the delta-function gives the field *inside*. For this reason it is correct to do the angular integral first (getting zero) and not worry about the radial integral.]

---

## Problem 6.28

From Eq. 6.89 we see that $\Delta E \propto \left(\dfrac{g}{m_p m_e a^3}\right)$; we want reduced mass in $a$, but *not* in $m_p m_e$ (which come from Eq. 6.85); the notation in Eq. 6.93 obscures this point.

**(a)** $g$ and $m_p$ are unchanged; $m_e \to m_\mu = 207 m_e$, and $a \to a_\mu$. From Eq. 4.72, $a \propto 1/m$, so

$$\frac{a}{a_\mu} = \frac{m_\mu(\text{reduced})}{m_e} = \frac{m_\mu m_p}{m_\mu + m_p} \cdot \frac{1}{m_e} = \frac{207}{1 + 207(m_e/m_p)} = \frac{207}{1 + 207\frac{(9.11\times10^{-31})}{1.67\times10^{-27}}} = \frac{207}{1.11} = 186.$$

$$\Delta E = (5.88 \times 10^{-6}\text{ eV})\,(1/207)\,(186)^3 = \boxed{0.183\text{ eV.}}$$

**(b)** $g : 5.59 \to 2$; $\quad m_p \to m_e$; $\quad \dfrac{a}{a_p} = \dfrac{m_p(\text{reduced})}{m_e} = \dfrac{m_e^2}{m_e + m_e} \cdot \dfrac{1}{m_e} = \dfrac{1}{2}$.

$$\Delta E = (5.88 \times 10^{-6}\text{ eV}) \left(\frac{2}{5.59}\right) \left(\frac{1.67 \times 10^{-27}}{9.11 \times 10^{-31}}\right) \left(\frac{1}{2}\right)^3 = \boxed{4.82 \times 10^{-4}\text{ eV.}}$$

**(c)** $g : 5.59 \to 2$; $\quad m_p \to m_\mu$; $\quad \dfrac{a}{a_m} = \dfrac{m_m(\text{reduced})}{m_e} = \dfrac{m_e m_\mu}{m_e + m_\mu} \cdot \dfrac{1}{m_e} = \dfrac{207}{208}$.

$$\Delta E = (5.88 \times 10^{-6}) \left(\frac{2}{5.59}\right) \left(\frac{1.67 \times 10^{-27}}{(207)(9.11 \times 10^{-31})}\right) \left(\frac{207}{208}\right)^3 = \boxed{1.84 \times 10^{-5}\text{ eV.}}$$

---

## Problem 6.29

Use perturbation theory:

$$H' = -\frac{e^2}{4\pi\epsilon_0}\left(\frac{1}{b} - \frac{1}{r}\right), \quad \text{for} \quad 0 < r < b. \quad \Delta E = \langle\psi|H'|\psi\rangle, \quad \text{with} \quad \psi \equiv \frac{1}{\sqrt{\pi a^3}}e^{-r/a}.$$

$$\Delta E = -\frac{e^2}{4\pi\epsilon_0}\frac{1}{\pi a^3}4\pi \int_0^b \left(\frac{1}{b} - \frac{1}{r}\right)e^{-2r/a}r^2\,dr = -\frac{e^2}{\pi\epsilon_0 a^3}\left(\frac{1}{b}\int_0^b r^2 e^{-2r/a}\,dr - \int_0^b r e^{-2r/a}\,dr\right)$$

$$= -\frac{e^2}{\pi\epsilon_0 a^3}\left\{\frac{1}{b}\left[-\frac{a}{2}r^2 e^{-2r/a} + a\left(\frac{a}{2}\right)^2 e^{-2r/a}\left(-\frac{2r}{a} - 1\right)\right] - \left[\left(\frac{a}{2}\right)^2 e^{-2r/a}\left(-\frac{2r}{a} - 1\right)\right]\right\}\Bigg|_0^b$$

$$= -\frac{e^2}{\pi\epsilon_0 a^3}\left[-\frac{a}{2b}b^2 e^{-2b/a} + \frac{a^3}{4b}e^{-2b/a}\left(-\frac{2b}{a} - 1\right) - \frac{a^2}{4}e^{-2b/a}\left(-\frac{2b}{a} - 1\right) + \frac{a^3}{4b} - \frac{a^2}{4}\right]$$

$$= -\frac{e^2}{\pi\epsilon_0 a^3}\left[e^{-2b/a}\left(-\frac{ab}{2} - \frac{a^2}{2} - \frac{a^3}{4b} + \frac{ab}{2} + \frac{a^2}{4}\right) + \frac{a^2}{4}\left(\frac{a}{b} - 1\right)\right]$$

$$= -\frac{e^2}{\pi\epsilon_0 a^3}\left[e^{-2b/a}\left(-\frac{a^2}{4}\right)\left(\frac{a}{b} + 1\right) + \frac{a^2}{4}\left(\frac{a}{b} - 1\right)\right] = \frac{e^2}{4\pi\epsilon_0 a}\left[\left(1 - \frac{a}{b}\right) + \left(1 + \frac{a}{b}\right)e^{-2b/a}\right].$$

---

Let $+2b/a = \epsilon$ (very small). Then the term in square brackets is:

$$\left(1 - \frac{2}{\epsilon}\right) + \left(1 + \frac{2}{\epsilon}\right)\left(1 - \epsilon + \frac{\epsilon^2}{2} - \frac{\epsilon^3}{6} + \cdots\right)$$

$$= \not{1} - \frac{\not{2}}{\epsilon} + \not{1} + \frac{\not{2}}{\epsilon} - \not{\epsilon} - \not{2} + \frac{\epsilon^2}{2} + \not{\epsilon} - \frac{\epsilon^3}{6} - \frac{\epsilon^2}{3} + (\ )\epsilon^3 + \cdots = \frac{\epsilon^2}{6} + (\ )\epsilon^3 + (\ )\epsilon^4 \cdots$$

To leading order, then, $\Delta E = \frac{e^2}{4\pi\epsilon_0} \frac{1}{a} \frac{4b^2}{6a^2}$.

$$E = E_1 = -\frac{me^4}{2(4\pi\epsilon_0)^2\hbar^2}; \quad a = \frac{4\pi\epsilon_0\hbar^2}{me^2}; \quad \text{so} \quad Ea = -\frac{e^2}{2(4\pi\epsilon_0)}.$$

$$\frac{\Delta E}{E} = \frac{e^2}{4\pi\epsilon_0}\left(-\frac{2(4\pi\epsilon_0)}{e^2}\right)\frac{2b^2}{3a^2} = \boxed{-\frac{4}{3}\left(\frac{b}{a}\right)^2}.$$

Putting in $a = 5 \times 10^{-11}$ m:

$$\frac{\Delta E}{E} = -\frac{4}{3}\left(\frac{10^{-15}}{5 \times 10^{-11}}\right) = -\frac{16}{3} \times 10^{-10} \approx \boxed{-5 \times 10^{-10}.}$$

By contrast, $\begin{cases} \text{fine structure:} & \Delta E/E \approx \alpha^2 = (1/137)^2 = 5 \times 10^{-5}, \\ \text{hyperfine structure:} & \Delta E/E \approx (m_e/m_p)\alpha^2 = (1/1800)(1/137)^2 = 3 \times 10^{-8}. \end{cases}$

So the correction for the finite size of the nucleus is *much* smaller (about 1% of hyperfine).

---

## Problem 6.30

(a) In terms of the one-dimensional harmonic oscillator states $\{\psi_n(x)\}$, the unperturbed ground state is

$$|0\rangle = \psi_0(x)\psi_0(y)\psi_0(z).$$

$$E_0^1 = \langle 0|H'|0\rangle = \langle\psi_0(x)\psi_0(y)\psi_0(z)|\lambda x^2 yz|\psi_0(x)\psi_0(y)\psi_0(z)\rangle = \lambda\langle x^2\rangle_0\langle y\rangle_0\langle z\rangle_0.$$

But $\langle y\rangle_0 = \langle z\rangle_0 = 0$. So there is *no* change, in first order.

(b) The (triply degenerate) first excited states are

$$\begin{cases} |1\rangle = \psi_0(x)\psi_0(y)\psi_1(z) \\ |2\rangle = \psi_0(x)\psi_1(y)\psi_0(z) \\ |3\rangle = \psi_1(x)\psi_0(y)\psi_0(z) \end{cases}$$

In this basis the perturbation matrix is $\quad W_{ij} = \langle i|H'|j\rangle, \quad i = 1, 2, 3.$

$$\langle 1|H'|1\rangle = \langle\psi_0(x)\psi_0(y)\psi_1(z)|\lambda x^2 yz|\psi_0(x)\psi_0(y)\psi_1(z)\rangle = \lambda\langle x^2\rangle_0\langle y\rangle_0\langle z\rangle_1 = 0,$$

$$\langle 2|H'|2\rangle = \langle\psi_0(x)\psi_1(y)\psi_0(z)|\lambda x^2 yz|\psi_0(x)\psi_1(y)\psi_0(z)\rangle = \lambda\langle x^2\rangle_0\langle y\rangle_1\langle z\rangle_0 = 0,$$

$$\langle 3|H'|3\rangle = \langle\psi_1(x)\psi_0(y)\psi_0(z)|\lambda x^2 yz|\psi_1(x)\psi_0(y)\psi_0(z)\rangle = \lambda\langle x^2\rangle_1\langle y\rangle_0\langle z\rangle_0 = 0,$$

$$\langle 1|H'|2\rangle = \langle\psi_0(x)\psi_0(y)\psi_1(z)|\lambda x^2 yz|\psi_0(x)\psi_1(y)\psi_0(z)\rangle = \lambda\langle x^2\rangle_0\langle 0|y|1\rangle\langle 1|z|0\rangle$$

$$= \lambda\frac{\hbar}{2m\omega}|\langle 0|x|1\rangle|^2 = \lambda\left(\frac{\hbar}{2m\omega}\right)^2 \quad \text{[using Problems 2.11 and 3.33].}$$

$$\langle 1|H'|3\rangle = \langle\psi_0(x)\psi_0(y)\psi_1(z)|\lambda x^2 yz|\psi_1(x)\psi_0(y)\psi_0(z)\rangle = \lambda\langle 0|x^2|1\rangle\langle y\rangle_0\langle 1|z|0\rangle = 0,$$

$$\langle 2|H'|3\rangle = \langle\psi_0(x)\psi_1(y)\psi_0(z)|\lambda x^2 yz|\psi_1(x)\psi_0(y)\psi_0(z)\rangle = \lambda\langle 0|x^2|1\rangle\langle 1|y|0\rangle_0\langle z\rangle_0 = 0.$$

$$W = \begin{pmatrix} 0 & a & 0 \\ a & 0 & 0 \\ 0 & 0 & 0 \end{pmatrix}, \quad \text{where} \quad a \equiv \lambda \left( \frac{\hbar}{2m\omega} \right)^2.$$

Eigenvalues of W : $\begin{vmatrix} -E & a & 0 \\ a & -E & 0 \\ 0 & 0 & -E \end{vmatrix} = -E^3 + Ea^2 = 0 \Rightarrow E = \{0, \pm a\} = \boxed{0, \ \pm\lambda \left( \frac{\hbar}{2m\omega} \right)^2}.$

## Problem 6.31

(a) The first term is the nucleus/nucleus interaction, the second is the interaction between the nucleus of atom 2 and the electron in atom 1, the third is between nucleus 1 and electron 2, and the last term is the interaction between the electrons.

$$\frac{1}{R - x} = \frac{1}{R} \left( 1 - \frac{x}{R} \right)^{-1} = \frac{1}{R} \left[ 1 + \left( \frac{x}{R} \right) + \left( \frac{x}{R} \right)^2 + \dots \right],$$

so

$$H' \cong \frac{1}{4\pi\epsilon_0} \frac{e^2}{R} \left\{ 1 - \left[ 1 + \left( \frac{x_1}{R} \right) + \left( \frac{x_1}{R} \right)^2 \right] - \left[ 1 - \left( \frac{x_2}{R} \right) + \left( \frac{x_2}{R} \right)^2 \right] + \left[ 1 + \left( \frac{x_1 - x_2}{R} \right) + \left( \frac{x_1 - x_2}{R} \right)^2 \right] \right\}$$

$$\approx \frac{1}{4\pi\epsilon_0} \frac{e^2}{R} \left( \frac{-2x_1 x_2}{R^2} \right) = -\frac{e^2 x_1 x_2}{2\pi\epsilon_0 R^3}. \quad \checkmark$$

(b) Expanding Eq. 6.99:

$$H = \frac{1}{2m} \left( p_+^2 + p_-^2 \right) + \frac{1}{2} k \left( x_+^2 + x_-^2 \right) - \frac{e^2}{4\pi\epsilon_0 R^3} \left( x_+^2 - x_-^2 \right)$$

$$= \frac{1}{2m} \left( p_1^2 + p_2^2 \right) + \frac{1}{2} k \left( x_1^2 + x_2^2 \right) - \frac{e^2}{4\pi\epsilon_0 R^3} (2x_1 x_2) = H^0 + H' \quad \text{(Eqs. 6.96 and 6.98)}.$$

(c)

$$\omega_\pm = \sqrt{\frac{k}{m}} \left( 1 \mp \frac{e^2}{2\pi\epsilon_0 R^3 k} \right)^{1/2} \cong \omega_0 \left[ 1 \mp \frac{1}{2} \left( \frac{e^2}{2\pi\epsilon_0 R^3 m\omega_0^2} \right) - \frac{1}{8} \left( \frac{e^2}{2\pi\epsilon_0 R^3 m\omega_0^2} \right)^2 + \dots \right].$$

$$\Delta V \cong \frac{1}{2} \hbar\omega_0 \left[ 1 - \frac{1}{2} \left( \frac{e^2}{2\pi\epsilon_0 R^3 m\omega_0^2} \right) - \frac{1}{8} \left( \frac{e^2}{2\pi\epsilon_0 R^3 m\omega_0^2} \right)^2 + \right.$$

$$\left. 1 + \frac{1}{2} \left( \frac{e^2}{2\pi\epsilon_0 R^3 m\omega_0^2} \right) - \frac{1}{8} \left( \frac{e^2}{2\pi\epsilon_0 R^3 m\omega_0^2} \right)^2 \right] - \hbar\omega_0$$

$$= \frac{1}{2} \hbar\omega_0 \left( -\frac{1}{4} \right) \left( \frac{e^2}{2\pi\epsilon_0 R^3 m\omega_0^2} \right)^2 = -\frac{1}{8} \frac{\hbar}{m^2 \omega_0^3} \left( \frac{e^2}{2\pi\epsilon_0} \right)^2 \frac{1}{R^6}. \quad \checkmark$$

(d) In first order:

$$E_0^1 = \langle 0 | H' | 0 \rangle = -\frac{e^2}{2\pi\epsilon_0 R^3} \langle \psi_0(x_1)\psi_0(x_2) | x_1 x_2 | \psi_0(x_1)\psi_0(x_2) \rangle = -\frac{e^2}{2\pi\epsilon_0 R^3} \langle x \rangle_0 \langle x \rangle_0 = 0.$$

In second order:

$$E_0^2 = \sum_{n=1}^{\infty} \frac{|\langle\psi_n|H'|\psi_0\rangle|^2}{E_0 - E_n}. \quad \text{Here} \quad |\psi_0\rangle = |0\rangle|0\rangle, \quad |\psi_n\rangle = |n_1\rangle|n_2\rangle, \quad \text{so}$$

$$= \left(\frac{e^2}{2\pi\epsilon_0 R^3}\right)^2 \sum_{n_1=1}^{\infty}\sum_{n_2=1}^{\infty} \frac{|\langle n_1|x_1|0\rangle|^2\,|\langle n_2|x_2|0\rangle|^2}{E_{0,0} - E_{n_1,n_2}} \quad \text{[use Problem 3.33]}$$

$$= \left(\frac{e^2}{2\pi\epsilon_0 R^3}\right)^2 \frac{|\langle 1|x|0\rangle|^2\,|\langle 1|x|0\rangle|^2}{(\frac{1}{2}\hbar\omega_0 + \frac{1}{2}\hbar\omega_0) - (\frac{3}{2}\hbar\omega_0 + \frac{3}{2}\hbar\omega_0)} \quad \text{[zero unless } n_1 = n_2 = 1]$$

$$= \left(\frac{e^2}{2\pi\epsilon_0 R^3}\right)^2 \left(-\frac{1}{2\hbar\omega_0}\right)\left(\frac{\hbar}{2m\omega_0}\right)^2 = -\frac{\hbar}{8m^2\omega_0^3}\left(\frac{e^2}{2\pi\epsilon_0}\right)^2\frac{1}{R^6}. \quad \checkmark$$

## Problem 6.32

(a) Let the unperturbed Hamiltonian be $H(\lambda_0)$, for some fixed value $\lambda_0$. Now tweak $\lambda$ to $\lambda_0 + d\lambda$. The perturbing Hamiltonian is $H' = H(\lambda_0 + d\lambda) - H(\lambda_0) = (\partial H/\partial\lambda)\,d\lambda$ (derivative evaluated at $\lambda_0$).

The change in energy is given by Eq. 6.9:

$$dE_n = E_n^1 = \langle\psi_n^0|H'|\psi_n^0\rangle = \langle\psi_n|\frac{\partial H}{\partial\lambda}|\psi_n\rangle\,d\lambda \text{ (all evaluated at } \lambda_0); \quad \text{so} \quad \frac{\partial E_n}{\partial\lambda} = \langle\psi_n|\frac{\partial H}{\partial\lambda}|\psi_n\rangle.$$

[*Note:* Even though we used perturbation theory, the result is exact, since all we needed (to calculate the derivative) was the *infinitesimal* change in $E_n$.]

(b) $E_n = (n + \frac{1}{2})\hbar\omega; \quad H = -\frac{\hbar^2}{2m}\frac{d^2}{dx^2} + \frac{1}{2}m\omega^2 x^2.$

(i)

$$\frac{\partial E_n}{\partial\omega} = (n + \frac{1}{2})\hbar; \quad \frac{\partial H}{\partial\omega} = m\omega x^2; \quad \text{so F-H} \Rightarrow (n + \frac{1}{2})\hbar = \langle n|m\omega x^2|n\rangle. \quad \text{But}$$

$$V = \frac{1}{2}m\omega^2 x^2, \quad \text{so} \quad \langle V\rangle = \langle n|\frac{1}{2}m\omega^2 x^2|n\rangle = \frac{1}{2}\omega(n + \frac{1}{2})\hbar; \quad \boxed{\langle V\rangle = \frac{1}{2}(n + \frac{1}{2})\hbar\omega.}$$

(ii)

$$\frac{\partial E_n}{\partial\hbar} = (n + \frac{1}{2})\omega; \quad \frac{\partial H}{\partial\hbar} = -\frac{\hbar}{m}\frac{d^2}{dx^2} = \frac{2}{\hbar}\left(-\frac{\hbar^2}{2m}\frac{d^2}{dx^2}\right) = \frac{2}{\hbar}T;$$

$$\text{so F-H} \Rightarrow (n + \frac{1}{2})\omega = \frac{2}{\hbar}\langle n|T|n\rangle, \quad \text{or} \quad \boxed{\langle T\rangle = \frac{1}{2}(n + \frac{1}{2})\hbar\omega.}$$

(iii)

$$\frac{\partial E_n}{\partial m} = 0; \quad \frac{\partial H}{\partial m} = \frac{\hbar^2}{2m^2}\frac{d^2}{dx^2} + \frac{1}{2}\omega^2 x^2 = -\frac{1}{m}\left(-\frac{\hbar^2}{2m}\frac{d^2}{dx^2}\right) + \frac{1}{m}\left(\frac{1}{2}m\omega^2 x^2\right) = -\frac{1}{m}T + \frac{1}{m}V.$$

So F-H $\Rightarrow 0 = -\frac{1}{m}\langle T\rangle + \frac{1}{m}\langle V\rangle$, or $\boxed{\langle T\rangle = \langle V\rangle.}$ These results are consistent with what we found in Problems 2.12 and 3.31.

## Problem 6.33

(a)

$$\frac{\partial E_n}{\partial e} = -\frac{4me^3}{32\pi^2\epsilon_0^2\hbar^2(j_{max}+l+1)^2} = \frac{4}{e}E_n; \quad \frac{\partial H}{\partial e} = -\frac{2e}{4\pi\epsilon_0}\frac{1}{r}. \quad \text{So the F-H theorem says:}$$

$$\frac{4}{e}E_n = -\frac{e}{2\pi\epsilon_0}\left\langle\frac{1}{r}\right\rangle, \quad \text{or} \quad \left\langle\frac{1}{r}\right\rangle = -\frac{8\pi\epsilon_0}{e^2}E_n = -\frac{8\pi\epsilon_0 E_1}{e^2n^2} = -\frac{8\pi\epsilon_0}{e^2}\left[-\frac{m}{2\hbar^2}\left(\frac{e^2}{4\pi\epsilon_0}\right)^2\right]\frac{1}{n^2} = \frac{e^2m}{4\pi\epsilon_0\hbar^2}\frac{1}{n^2}.$$

But $\quad \dfrac{4\pi\epsilon_0\hbar^2}{me^2} = a \;$ (by Eq. 4.72), so $\quad \boxed{\left\langle\dfrac{1}{r}\right\rangle = \dfrac{1}{n^2a}.} \quad$ (Agrees with Eq. 6.55.)

(b)

$$\frac{\partial E_n}{\partial l} = \frac{2me^4}{32\pi^2\epsilon_0^2\hbar^2(j_{max}+l+1)^3} = -\frac{2E_n}{n}; \quad \frac{\partial H}{\partial l} = \frac{\hbar^2}{2mr^2}(2l+1); \quad \text{so F-H says}$$

$$-\frac{2E_n}{n} = \frac{\hbar^2(2l+1)}{2m}\left\langle\frac{1}{r^2}\right\rangle, \quad \text{or} \quad \left\langle\frac{1}{r^2}\right\rangle = -\frac{4mE_n}{n(2l+1)\hbar^2} = -\frac{4mE_1}{n^3(2l+1)\hbar^2}.$$

But $\quad -\dfrac{4mE_1}{\hbar^2} = \dfrac{2}{a^2}, \quad \text{so} \quad \boxed{\left\langle\dfrac{1}{r^2}\right\rangle = \dfrac{1}{n^3(l+\frac{1}{2})a^2}.} \quad$ (Agrees with Eq. 6.56.)

---

## Problem 6.34

Equation 4.53 $\Rightarrow u'' = \left[\dfrac{l(l+1)}{r^2} - \dfrac{2mE_n}{\hbar^2} - \dfrac{2m}{\hbar^2}\left(\dfrac{e^2}{4\pi\epsilon_0}\right)\dfrac{1}{r}\right]u.$

But $\quad \dfrac{me^2}{4\pi\epsilon_0\hbar^2} = \dfrac{1}{a} \;$ (Eq. 4.72), and $\quad -\dfrac{2mE_n}{\hbar^2} = \dfrac{2m}{\hbar^2}\dfrac{m}{2\hbar^2}\left(\dfrac{e^2}{4\pi\epsilon_0}\right)^2\dfrac{1}{n^2} = \dfrac{1}{a^2n^2}. \quad$ So

★ $\quad u'' = \left[\dfrac{l(l+1)}{r^2} - \dfrac{2}{ar} + \dfrac{1}{n^2a^2}\right]u.$

$\therefore \displaystyle\int(ur^su'')\,dr = \int ur^s\left[\dfrac{l(l+1)}{r^2} - \dfrac{2}{ar} + \dfrac{1}{n^2a^2}\right]u\,dr = l(l+1)\langle r^{s-2}\rangle - \dfrac{2}{a}\langle r^{s-1}\rangle + \dfrac{1}{n^2a^2}\langle r^s\rangle$

♦ $\quad = -\displaystyle\int\dfrac{d}{dr}(ur^s)u'\,dr = -\int(u'r^su')\,dr - s\int(ur^{s-1}u')\,dr.$

<u>Lemma 1</u>: $\int (u r^s u')\, dr = -\int \frac{d}{dr}(u r^s) u \, dr = -\int (u' r^s u)\, dr - s\int u r^{s-1} u \, dr \quad \Rightarrow$

$$2\int (u r^s u')\, dr = -s\langle r^{s-1}\rangle, \quad \text{or} \quad \int (u r^s u')\, dr = -\frac{s}{2}\langle r^{s-1}\rangle.$$

<u>Lemma 2</u>: $\int (u'' r^{s+1} u')\, dr = -\int u' \frac{d}{dr}(r^{s+1} u')\, dr = -(s+1)\int (u' r^s u')\, dr - \int (u' r^{s+1} u'')\, dr.$

$$2\int (u'' r^{s+1} u')\, dr = -(s+1)\int (u' r^s u')\, dr, \quad \text{or:} \quad \int (u' r^s u')\, dr = -\frac{2}{s+1}\int (u'' r^{s+1} u')\, dr.$$

<u>Lemma 3</u>: Use ★ in Lemma 2, and exploit Lemma 1:

$$\begin{aligned}
\int (u' r^s u')\, dr &= -\frac{2}{s+1}\int \left[\frac{l(l+1)}{r^2} - \frac{2}{ar} + \frac{1}{n^2 a^2}\right](u r^{s+1} u')\, dr \\
&= -\frac{2}{s+1}\left[l(l+1)\int (u r^{s-1} u')\, dr - \frac{2}{a}\int (u r^s u')\, dr + \frac{1}{n^2 a^2}\int (u r^{s+1} u')\, dr\right] \\
&= -\frac{2}{s+1}\left[l(l+1)\left(-\frac{s-1}{2}\langle r^{s-2}\rangle\right) - \frac{2}{a}\left(-\frac{s}{2}\langle r^{s-1}\rangle\right) + \frac{1}{n^2 a^2}\left(-\frac{s+1}{2}\langle r^s\rangle\right)\right] \\
&= l(l+1)\left(\frac{s-1}{s+1}\right)\langle r^{s-2}\rangle - \frac{2}{a}\left(\frac{s}{s+1}\right)\langle r^{s-1}\rangle + \frac{1}{n^2 a^2}\langle r^s\rangle.
\end{aligned}$$

Plug Lemmas 1 and 3 into ♦:

$$\begin{aligned}
&l(l+1)\langle r^{s-2}\rangle - \frac{2}{a}\langle r^{s-1}\rangle + \frac{1}{n^2 a^2}\langle r^s\rangle \\
&\quad = -l(l+1)\left(\frac{s-1}{s+1}\right)\langle r^{s-2}\rangle + \frac{2}{a}\left(\frac{s}{s+1}\right)\langle r^{s-1}\rangle - \frac{1}{n^2 a^2}\langle r^s\rangle + \frac{s(s-1)}{2}\langle r^{s-2}\rangle.
\end{aligned}$$

$$\frac{2}{n^2 a^2}\langle r^s\rangle - \frac{2}{a}\underbrace{\left[1 + \frac{s}{s+1}\right]}_{\frac{2s+1}{s+1}}\langle r^{s-1}\rangle + \left\{l(l+1)\underbrace{\left[1 + \frac{s-1}{s+1}\right]}_{\frac{2s}{s+1}} - \frac{s(s-1)}{2}\right\}\langle r^{s-2}\rangle = 0.$$

$$\frac{2(s+1)}{n^2 a^2}\langle r^s\rangle - \frac{2}{a}(2s+1)\langle r^{s-1}\rangle + 2s\left[l^2 + l - \frac{(s^2-1)}{4}\right]\langle r^{s-2}\rangle = 0, \quad \text{or, finally,}$$

$$\frac{(s+1)}{n^2}\langle r^s\rangle - a(2s+1)\langle r^{s-1}\rangle + \frac{sa^2}{4}(\underbrace{4l^2 + 4l + 1}_{(2l+1)^2} - s^2)\langle r^{s-2}\rangle = 0. \quad \text{QED}$$

## Problem 6.35

**(a)**

$$\frac{1}{n^2}\langle 1\rangle - a\left\langle\frac{1}{r}\right\rangle + 0 = 0 \Rightarrow \boxed{\left\langle\frac{1}{r}\right\rangle = \frac{1}{n^2 a}}.$$

$$\frac{2}{n^2}\langle r\rangle - 3a\langle 1\rangle + \frac{1}{4}\left[(2l+1)^2 - 1\right]a^2\left\langle\frac{1}{r}\right\rangle = 0 \Rightarrow \frac{2}{n^2}\langle r\rangle = 3a - l(l+1)a^2\frac{1}{n^2 a} = \frac{a}{n^2}\left[3n^2 - l(l+1)\right].$$

$$\boxed{\langle r\rangle = \frac{a}{2}\left[3n^2 - l(l+1)\right].}$$

$$\frac{3}{n^2}\langle r^2\rangle - 5a\langle r\rangle + \frac{1}{2}\left[(2l+1)^2 - 4\right]a^2 = 0 \Rightarrow \frac{3}{n^2}\langle r^2\rangle = 5a\frac{a}{2}\left[3n^2 - l(l+1)\right] - \frac{a^2}{2}\left[(2l+1)^2 - 4\right]$$

$$\frac{3}{n^2}\langle r^2\rangle = \frac{a^2}{2}\left[15n^2 - 5l(l+1) - 4l(l+1) - 1 + 4\right] = \frac{a^2}{2}\left[15n^2 - 9l(l+1) + 3\right]$$

$$= \frac{3a^2}{2}\left[5n^2 - 3l(l+1) + 1\right]; \quad \boxed{\langle r^2\rangle = \frac{n^2 a^2}{2}\left[5n^2 - 3l(l+1) + 1\right].}$$

$$\frac{4}{n^2}\langle r^3\rangle - 7a\langle r^2\rangle + \frac{3}{4}\left[(2l+1)^2 - 9\right]a^2\langle r\rangle = 0 \Longrightarrow$$

$$\frac{4}{n^2}\langle r^3\rangle = 7a\frac{n^2 a^2}{2}\left[5n^2 - 3l(l+1) + 1\right] - \frac{3}{4}\left[4l(l+1) - 8\right]a^2\frac{a}{2}\left[3n^2 - l(l+1)\right]$$

$$= \frac{a^3}{2}\left\{35n^4 - 21l(l+1)n^2 + 7n^2 - \left[3l(l+1) - 6\right]\left[3n^2 - l(l+1)\right]\right\}$$

$$= \frac{a^3}{2}\left[35n^4 - 21l(l+1)n^2 + 7n^2 - 9l(l+1)n^2 + 3l^2(l+1)^2 + 18n^2 - 6l(l+1)\right]$$

$$= \frac{a^3}{2}\left[35n^4 + 25n^2 - 30l(l+1)n^2 + 3l^2(l+1)^2 - 6l(l+1)\right].$$

$$\boxed{\langle r^3\rangle = \frac{n^2 a^3}{8}\left[35n^4 + 25n^2 - 30l(l+1)n^2 + 3l^2(l+1)^2 - 6l(l+1)\right].}$$

**(b)**

$$0 + a\left\langle\frac{1}{r^2}\right\rangle - \frac{1}{4}\left[(2l+1)^2 - 1\right]a^2\left\langle\frac{1}{r^3}\right\rangle = 0 \Rightarrow \boxed{\left\langle\frac{1}{r^2}\right\rangle = al(l+1)\left\langle\frac{1}{r^3}\right\rangle.}$$

**(c)**

$$al(l+1)\left\langle\frac{1}{r^3}\right\rangle = \frac{1}{(l+1/2)n^3 a^2} \Rightarrow \boxed{\left\langle\frac{1}{r^3}\right\rangle = \frac{1}{l(l+1/2)(l+1)n^3 a^3}.} \quad \text{Agrees with Eq. 6.64.}$$

## Problem 6.36

**(a)**

$$|100\rangle = \frac{1}{\sqrt{\pi a^3}}e^{-r/a} \text{ (Eq. 4.80)}, \quad E_s^1 = \langle 100|H'|100\rangle = eE_{\text{ext}}\frac{1}{\pi a^3}\int e^{-2r/a}(r\cos\theta)r^2\sin\theta\, dr\, d\theta\, d\phi.$$

But the $\theta$ integral is zero: $\displaystyle\int_0^\pi \cos\theta\sin\theta\, d\theta = \left.\frac{\sin^2\theta}{2}\right|_0^\pi = 0.$ So $E_s^1 = 0.$ QED

**(b)** From Problem 4.11:
$$\begin{cases} |1\rangle = \psi_{200} = \dfrac{1}{\sqrt{2\pi a}}\dfrac{1}{2a}\left(1-\dfrac{r}{2a}\right)e^{-r/2a} \\[2mm] |2\rangle = \psi_{211} = -\dfrac{1}{\sqrt{\pi a}}\dfrac{1}{8a^2}re^{-r/2a}\sin\theta e^{i\phi} \\[2mm] |3\rangle = \psi_{210} = \dfrac{1}{\sqrt{2\pi a}}\dfrac{1}{4a^2}re^{-r/2a}\cos\theta \\[2mm] |4\rangle = \psi_{21-1} = \dfrac{1}{\sqrt{\pi a}}\dfrac{1}{8a^2}re^{-r/2a}\sin\theta e^{-i\phi} \end{cases}$$

$$\left.\begin{aligned}
\langle 1|H_s'|1\rangle &= \{\dots\}\int_0^\pi \cos\theta\sin\theta\, d\theta = 0 \\[1mm]
\langle 2|H_s'|2\rangle &= \{\dots\}\int_0^\pi \sin^2\theta\cos\theta\sin\theta\, d\theta = 0 \\[1mm]
\langle 3|H_s'|3\rangle &= \{\dots\}\int_0^\pi \cos^2\theta\cos\theta\sin\theta\, d\theta = 0 \\[1mm]
\langle 4|H_s'|4\rangle &= \{\dots\}\int_0^\pi \sin^2\theta\cos\theta\sin\theta\, d\theta = 0 \\[1mm]
\langle 1|H_s'|2\rangle &= \{\dots\}\int_0^{2\pi} e^{i\phi}\, d\phi = 0 \\[1mm]
\langle 1|H_s'|4\rangle &= \{\dots\}\int_0^{2\pi} e^{-i\phi}\, d\phi = 0 \\[1mm]
\langle 2|H_s'|3\rangle &= \{\dots\}\int_0^{2\pi} e^{-i\phi}\, d\phi = 0 \\[1mm]
\langle 2|H_s'|4\rangle &= \{\dots\}\int_0^{2\pi} e^{-2i\phi}\, d\phi = 0 \\[1mm]
\langle 3|H_s'|4\rangle &= \{\dots\}\int_0^{2\pi} e^{-i\phi}\, d\phi = 0
\end{aligned}\right\}$$

All matrix elements of $H_s'$ are zero except $\langle 1|H_s'|3\rangle$ and $\langle 3|H_s'|1\rangle$ (which are complex conjugates, so only one needs to be evaluated).

$$\begin{aligned}
\langle 1|H_s'|3\rangle &= eE_{\text{ext}}\frac{1}{\sqrt{2\pi a}}\frac{1}{2a}\frac{1}{\sqrt{2\pi a}}\frac{1}{4a^2}\int\left(1-\frac{r}{2a}\right)e^{-r/2a}re^{-r/2a}\cos\theta(r\cos\theta)r^2\sin\theta\, dr\, d\theta\, d\phi \\[2mm]
&= \frac{eE_{\text{ext}}}{2\pi a 8a^3}(2\pi)\left[\int_0^\pi \cos^2\theta\sin\theta\, d\theta\right]\int_0^\infty\left(1-\frac{r}{2a}\right)e^{-r/a}r^4\, dr \\[2mm]
&= \frac{eE_{\text{ext}}}{8a^4}\frac{2}{3}\left\{\int_0^\infty r^4 e^{-r/a}\, dr - \frac{1}{2a}\int_0^\infty r^5 e^{-r/a}\, dr\right\} = \frac{eE_{\text{ext}}}{12a^4}\left(4!a^5 - \frac{1}{2a}5!a^6\right) \\[2mm]
&= \frac{eE_{\text{ext}}}{12a^4}24a^5\left(1-\frac{5}{2}\right) = eaE_{\text{ext}}(-3) = -3aeE_{\text{ext}}.
\end{aligned}$$

$$\mathbf{W} = -3aeE_{\text{ext}}\begin{pmatrix} 0 & 0 & 1 & 0 \\ 0 & 0 & 0 & 0 \\ 1 & 0 & 0 & 0 \\ 0 & 0 & 0 & 0 \end{pmatrix}.$$

We need the eigenvalues of this matrix. The characteristic equation is:

$$\begin{vmatrix} -\lambda & 0 & 1 & 0 \\ 0 & -\lambda & 0 & 0 \\ 1 & 0 & -\lambda & 0 \\ 0 & 0 & 0 & -\lambda \end{vmatrix} = -\lambda \begin{vmatrix} -\lambda & 0 & 0 \\ 0 & -\lambda & 0 \\ 0 & 0 & -\lambda \end{vmatrix} + \begin{vmatrix} 0 & -\lambda & 0 \\ 1 & 0 & 0 \\ 0 & 0 & -\lambda \end{vmatrix} = -\lambda(-\lambda)^3 + (-\lambda^2) = \lambda^2(\lambda^2 - 1) = 0.$$

The eigenvalues are 0, 0, 1, and $-1$, so the perturbed energies are

$$\boxed{E_2, \ E_2, \ E_2 + 3aeE_{\text{ext}}, \ E_2 - 3aeE_{\text{ext}}. \quad \text{Three levels.}}$$

(c) The eigenvectors with eigenvalue 0 are $|2\rangle = \begin{pmatrix} 0 \\ 1 \\ 0 \\ 0 \end{pmatrix}$ and $|4\rangle = \begin{pmatrix} 0 \\ 0 \\ 0 \\ 1 \end{pmatrix}$; the eigenvectors with eigenvalues $\pm 1$

are $|\pm\rangle \equiv \dfrac{1}{\sqrt{2}}\begin{pmatrix} 1 \\ 0 \\ \pm 1 \\ 0 \end{pmatrix}$. So the "good" states are $\boxed{\psi_{211}, \ \psi_{21-1}, \ \dfrac{1}{\sqrt{2}}(\psi_{200} + \psi_{210}), \ \dfrac{1}{\sqrt{2}}(\psi_{200} - \psi_{210}).}$

$$\langle \mathbf{p}_e\rangle_4 = -e\frac{1}{\pi a}\frac{1}{64a^4}\int r^2 e^{-r/a}\sin^2\theta\left[r\sin\theta\cos\phi\,\hat{i} + r\sin\theta\sin\phi\,\hat{j} + r\cos\theta\,\hat{k}\right]r^2\sin\theta\,dr\,d\theta\,d\phi.$$

But $\displaystyle\int_0^{2\pi}\cos\phi\,d\phi = \int_0^{2\pi}\sin\phi\,d\phi = 0, \quad \int_0^\pi \sin^3\theta\cos\theta\,d\theta = \left.\frac{\sin^4\theta}{4}\right|_0^\pi = 0, \quad$ so

$$\boxed{\langle \mathbf{p}_e\rangle_4 = 0. \quad \text{Likewise} \quad \langle \mathbf{p}_e\rangle_2 = 0.}$$

$$\langle \mathbf{p}_e\rangle_\pm = -\frac{1}{2}e\int(\psi_1 \pm \psi_3)^2(\mathbf{r})r^2\sin\theta\,dr\,d\theta\,d\phi$$
$$= -\frac{1}{2}e\frac{1}{2\pi a}\frac{1}{4a^2}\int\left[\left(1 - \frac{r}{2a}\right) \pm \frac{r}{2a}\cos\theta\right]^2 e^{-r/a}r(\sin\theta\cos\phi\,\hat{i} + \sin\theta\sin\phi\,\hat{j} + \cos\theta\,\hat{k})r^2\sin\theta\,dr\,d\theta\,d\phi$$
$$= -\frac{e}{2}\frac{\hat{k}}{2\pi a}\frac{1}{4a^2}2\pi\int\left[\left(1 - \frac{r}{2a}\right) \pm \frac{r}{2a}\cos\theta\right]^2 r^3 e^{-r/a}\cos\theta\sin\theta\,dr\,d\theta.$$

But $\int_0^\pi \cos\theta\sin\theta\,d\theta = \int_0^\pi \cos^3\theta\sin\theta\,d\theta = 0$, so only the cross-term survives:

$$\langle \mathbf{p}_e\rangle_\pm = -\frac{e}{8a^3}\hat{k}\left(\pm\frac{1}{a}\right)\int\left(1 - \frac{r}{2a}\right)r\cos\theta\,r^3 e^{-r/a}\cos\theta\sin\theta\,dr\,d\theta$$
$$= \mp\left(\frac{e}{8a^4}\hat{k}\right)\left[\int_0^\pi \cos^2\theta\sin\theta\,d\theta\right]\int_0^\infty\left(1 - \frac{r}{2a}\right)r^4 e^{-r/a}dr = \mp\left(\frac{e}{8a^4}\hat{k}\right)\frac{2}{3}\left[4!a^5 - \frac{1}{2a}5!a^6\right]$$
$$= \mp e\hat{k}\left(\frac{1}{12a^4}\right)24a^5\left(1 - \frac{5}{2}\right) = \boxed{\pm 3ae\hat{k}.}$$

## Problem 6.37

(a) The nine states are:

$$\begin{cases} \underline{l=0}: |3\,0\,0\rangle & = R_{30}Y_0^0 \\ \underline{l=1}: |3\,1\,1\rangle & = R_{31}Y_1^1 \\ \phantom{l=1:} |3\,1\,0\rangle & = R_{31}Y_1^0 \\ \phantom{l=1:} |3\,1-1\rangle & = R_{31}Y_1^{-1} \\ \underline{l=2}: |3\,2\,2\rangle & = R_{32}Y_2^2 \\ \phantom{l=2:} |3\,2\,1\rangle & = R_{32}Y_2^1 \\ \phantom{l=2:} |3\,2\,0\rangle & = R_{32}Y_2^0 \\ \phantom{l=2:} |3\,2-1\rangle & = R_{32}Y_2^{-1} \\ \phantom{l=2:} |3\,2-2\rangle & = R_{32}Y_2^{-2} \end{cases}$$

$H'_s$ contains no $\phi$ dependence, so the $\phi$ integral will be:

$$\langle n\,l\,m|H'_s|n'\,l'\,m'\rangle = \{\cdots\} \int_0^{2\pi} e^{-im\phi}e^{im'\phi}\,d\phi, \quad \text{which is zero unless} \quad m'=m.$$

For diagonal elements: $\langle n\,l\,m|H'_s|n\,l\,m\rangle = \{\cdots\}\int_0^\pi [P_l^m(\cos\theta)]^2\cos\theta\sin\theta\,d\theta$. But (p. 137 in the text) $P_l^m$ is a polynomial (even or odd) in $\cos\theta$, multiplied (if $m$ is odd) by $\sin\theta$. Since $\sin^2\theta = 1 - \cos^2\theta$, $[P_l^m(\cos\theta)]^2$ is a polynomial in even powers of $\cos\theta$. So the $\theta$ integral is of the form

$$\int_0^\pi (\cos\theta)^{2j+1}\sin\theta\,d\theta = -\frac{(\cos\theta)^{2j+2}}{(2j+2)}\bigg|_0^\pi = 0. \quad \textit{All diagonal elements are zero.}$$

There remain just 4 elements to calculate:

$$m = m' = 0: \langle 3\,0\,0|H'_s|3\,1\,0\rangle, \; \langle 3\,0\,0|H'_s|3\,2\,0\rangle, \; \langle 3\,1\,0|H'_s|3\,2\,0\rangle; \; m = m' = \pm 1: \langle 3\,1\pm 1|H'_s|3\,2\pm 1\rangle.$$

$$\langle 3\,0\,0|H'_s|3\,1\,0\rangle = eE_{\text{ext}}\int R_{30}R_{31}r^3 dr \int Y_0^0 Y_1^0 \cos\theta\sin\theta\,d\theta\,d\phi. \quad \text{From Table 4.7}:$$

$$\int R_{30}R_{31}r^3\,dr = \frac{2}{\sqrt{27}}\frac{1}{a^{3/2}}\frac{8}{27\sqrt6}\frac{1}{a^{3/2}}\frac{1}{a}\int\left(1 - \frac{2r}{3a} + \frac{2r^2}{27a^2}\right)e^{-r/3a}\left(1 - \frac{r}{6a}\right)re^{-r/3a}r^3\,dr.$$

Let $x \equiv 2r/3a$:

$$\int R_{30}R_{31}r^3\,dr = \frac{2^4}{3^5\sqrt2 a^4}\left(\frac{3a}{2}\right)^5\int_0^\infty\left(1 - x + \frac{x^2}{6}\right)\left(1 - \frac{x}{4}\right)x^4 e^{-x}dx$$

$$= \frac{a}{2\sqrt2}\int_0^\infty\left(1 - \frac54 x + \frac{5}{12}x^2 - \frac{1}{24}x^3\right)x^4 e^{-x}dx = \frac{a}{2\sqrt2}\left(4! - \frac54 5! + \frac{5}{12}6! - \frac{1}{24}7!\right)$$

$$= -9\sqrt2 a.$$

$$\int Y_0^0 Y_1^0 \cos\theta\sin\theta\,d\theta\,d\phi = \frac{1}{\sqrt{4\pi}}\sqrt{\frac{3}{4\pi}}\int\cos\theta\cos\theta\sin\theta\,d\theta\,d\phi = \frac{\sqrt3}{4\pi}2\pi\int_0^\pi\cos^3\theta\sin\theta\,d\theta = \frac{\sqrt3}{2}\frac23 = \frac{\sqrt3}{3}.$$

$$\langle 3\,0\,0|H'_s|3\,1\,0\rangle = eE_{\text{ext}}(-9\sqrt2 a)\left(\frac{\sqrt3}{3}\right) = \boxed{-3\sqrt6\,aeE_{\text{ext}}.}$$

$$\langle 3\,0\,0|H'_s|3\,2\,0\rangle = eE_{\text{ext}}\int R_{30}R_{31}r^3 dr \int Y_0^0 Y_2^0 \cos\theta\sin\theta\,d\theta\,d\phi.$$

$$\int Y_0^0 Y_2^0 \cos\theta \sin\theta \, d\theta \, d\phi = \frac{1}{\sqrt{4\pi}} \sqrt{\frac{5}{16\pi}} \int (3\cos^2\theta - 1)\cos\theta \sin\theta \, d\theta \, d\phi = 0. \quad \boxed{\langle 3\,0\,0\, |H_s'|3\,2\,0\rangle = 0.}$$

$$\langle 3\,1\,0|H_s'|3\,2\,0\rangle = eE_{\text{ext}} \int R_{31} R_{32} r^3 dr \int Y_1^0 Y_2^0 \cos\theta \sin\theta \, d\theta \, d\phi.$$

$$\int R_{31} R_{32} r^3 dr = \frac{8}{27\sqrt{6}} \frac{1}{a^{3/2}} \frac{1}{a} \frac{4}{81\sqrt{30}} \frac{1}{a^{3/2}} \frac{1}{a^2} \int \left(1 - \frac{r}{6a}\right) r e^{-r/3a} r^2 e^{-r/3a} r^3 dr$$

$$= \frac{2^4}{3^8 \sqrt{5} a^6} \left(\frac{3a}{2}\right)^7 \int_0^\infty \left(1 - \frac{x}{4}\right) x^6 e^{-x} dx = \frac{a}{24\sqrt{5}} \left(6! - \frac{1}{4} 7!\right) = -\frac{9\sqrt{5}}{2} a.$$

$$\int Y_1^0 Y_2^0 \sin\theta \cos\theta \, d\theta \, d\phi = \sqrt{\frac{3}{4\pi}} \sqrt{\frac{5}{16\pi}} \int \cos\theta (3\cos^2\theta - 1)\cos\theta \sin\theta \, d\theta \, d\phi$$

$$= \frac{\sqrt{15}}{8\pi} 2\pi \int_0^\pi (3\cos^4\theta - \cos^2\theta)\sin\theta \, d\theta = \frac{\sqrt{15}}{4}\left[-\frac{3}{5}\cos^5\theta + \frac{1}{3}\cos^3\theta\right]\Big|_0^\pi = \frac{2}{\sqrt{15}}.$$

$$\langle 3\,1\,0|H_s'|3\,2\,0\rangle = eE_{\text{ext}}\left(-\frac{9\sqrt{5}}{2}a\right)\left(\frac{2}{\sqrt{15}}\right) = \boxed{-3\sqrt{3}\,aeE_{\text{ext}}.}$$

$$\langle 3\,1 \pm 1|H_s'|3\,2 \pm 1\rangle = eE_{\text{ext}} \int R_{31} R_{32} r^3 dr \int \left(Y_1^{\pm 1}\right)^* Y_2^{\pm 1} \cos\theta \sin\theta \, d\theta \, d\phi.$$

$$\int \left(Y_1^{\pm 1}\right)^* Y_2^{\pm 1} \cos\theta \sin\theta \, d\theta \, d\phi = \left(\mp\sqrt{\frac{3}{8\pi}}\right)\left(\mp\sqrt{\frac{15}{8\pi}}\right) \int \sin\theta e^{\mp i\phi} \sin\theta \cos\theta e^{\pm i\phi} \cos\theta \sin\theta \, d\theta \, d\phi$$

$$= \frac{3\sqrt{5}}{8\pi} 2\pi \int_0^\pi \cos^2\theta (1 - \cos^2\theta)\sin\theta \, d\theta = \frac{3}{4}\sqrt{5}\left(-\frac{\cos^3\theta}{3} + \frac{\cos^5\theta}{5}\right)\Big|_0^\pi$$

$$= \frac{1}{\sqrt{5}}.$$

$$\langle 3\,1 \pm 1|H_s'|3\,2 \pm 1\rangle = eE_{\text{ext}}\left(-9\frac{\sqrt{5}}{2}a\right)\left(\frac{1}{\sqrt{5}}\right) = \boxed{-\frac{9}{2}aeE_{\text{ext}}.}$$

Thus the matrix representing $H_s'$ is (all empty boxes are zero; all numbers multiplied by $-aeE_{\text{ext}}$):

**(b)** The perturbing matrix (below) breaks into a 3×3 block, two 2 × 2 blocks, and two 1 × 1 blocks, so we can work out the eigenvalues in each block separately.

$$\underline{3 \times 3}: \quad 3\sqrt{3}\begin{pmatrix} 0 & \sqrt{2} & 0 \\ \sqrt{2} & 0 & 1 \\ 0 & 1 & 0 \end{pmatrix}; \quad \begin{vmatrix} -\lambda & \sqrt{2} & 0 \\ \sqrt{2} & -\lambda & 1 \\ 0 & 1 & -\lambda \end{vmatrix} = -\lambda^3 + \lambda + 2\lambda = -\lambda(\lambda^2 - 3) = 0;$$

$$\lambda = 0, \pm\sqrt{3} \quad \Rightarrow \quad E_1^1 = 0, \ E_2^1 = 9aeE_{\text{ext}}, \ E_3^1 = -9aeE_{\text{ext}}.$$

$$\underline{2 \times 2}: \quad \frac{9}{2}\begin{pmatrix} 0 & 1 \\ 1 & 0 \end{pmatrix}; \quad \begin{vmatrix} -\lambda & 1 \\ 1 & -\lambda \end{vmatrix} = \lambda^2 - 1 = 0 \Rightarrow \lambda = \pm 1.$$

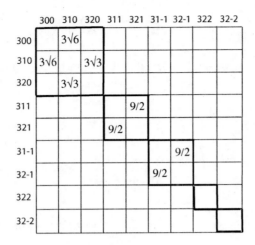

$E_4^1 = \dfrac{9}{2}aeE_{\text{ext}}, \; E_5^1 = -\dfrac{9}{2}aeE_{\text{ext}}.$    From the other $2\times 2$ we get $E_6^1 = E_4^1$, $E_7^1 = E_5^1$, and from the $1\times 1$'s we

get $E_8^1 = E_9^1 = 0$. Thus the perturbations to the energy ($E_3$) are:

$$\boxed{\begin{array}{ll} 0 & \text{(degeneracy 3)} \\ (9/2)aeE_{\text{ext}} & \text{(degeneracy 2)} \\ -(9/2)aeE_{\text{ext}} & \text{(degeneracy 2)} \\ 9aeE_{\text{ext}} & \text{(degeneracy 1)} \\ -9aeE_{\text{ext}} & \text{(degeneracy 1)} \end{array}}$$

## Problem 6.38

Equation $6.89 \Rightarrow E_{\text{hf}}^1 = \dfrac{\mu_0 g_d e^2}{3\pi m_d m_e a^3}\langle \mathbf{S}_d \cdot \mathbf{S}_e\rangle$;   Eq. $6.91 \Rightarrow \mathbf{S}_d \cdot \mathbf{S}_e = \dfrac{1}{2}(S^2 - S_e^2 - S_d^2).$

Electron has spin $\frac{1}{2}$, so $S_e^2 = \frac{1}{2}\left(\frac{3}{2}\right)\hbar^2 = \frac{3}{4}\hbar^2$; deuteron has spin 1, so $S_d^2 = 1(2)\hbar^2 = 2\hbar^2$.
Total spin could be $\frac{3}{2}$ [in which case $S^2 = \frac{3}{2}\left(\frac{5}{2}\right)\hbar^2 = \frac{15}{4}\hbar^2$] or $\frac{1}{2}$ [in which case $S^2 = \frac{3}{4}\hbar^2$].   Thus

$$\langle \mathbf{S}_d \cdot \mathbf{S}_e\rangle = \left\{ \begin{array}{l} \frac{1}{2}\left(\frac{15}{4}\hbar^2 - \frac{3}{4}\hbar^2 - 2\hbar^2\right) = \frac{1}{2}\hbar^2 \\[4pt] \frac{1}{2}\left(\frac{3}{4}\hbar^2 - \frac{3}{4}\hbar^2 - 2\hbar^2\right) \; = -\hbar^2 \end{array} \right\}; \; \text{the difference is } \frac{3}{2}\hbar^2, \text{ so } \quad \Delta E = \dfrac{\mu_0 g_d e^2\hbar^2}{2\pi m_d m_e a^3}.$$

But   $\mu_0\epsilon_0 = \dfrac{1}{c^2} \Rightarrow \mu_0 = \dfrac{1}{\epsilon_0 c^2}$,   so   $\Delta E = \dfrac{2g_d e^2\hbar^2}{4\pi\epsilon_0 m_d m_e c^2 a^3} = \dfrac{2g_d \hbar^4}{m_d m_e^2 c^2 a^4} = \dfrac{3}{2}\dfrac{g_d}{g_p}\dfrac{m_p}{m_d}\Delta E_{\text{hydrogen}}$ (Eq. 6.98).

Now, $\lambda = \dfrac{c}{\nu} = \dfrac{ch}{\Delta E}$,   so   $\lambda_d = \dfrac{2}{3}\dfrac{g_p}{g_d}\dfrac{m_d}{m_p}\lambda_h$, and since $m_d = 2m_p$, $\lambda_d = \dfrac{4}{3}\left(\dfrac{5.59}{1.71}\right)(21\text{ cm}) = \boxed{92\text{ cm.}}$

## Problem 6.39

**(a)** The potential energy of the electron (charge $-e$) at $(x, y, z)$ due to $q$'s at $x = \pm d$ alone is:

$$V = -\dfrac{eq}{4\pi\epsilon_0}\left[\dfrac{1}{\sqrt{(x+d)^2 + y^2 + z^2}} + \dfrac{1}{\sqrt{(x-d)^2 + y^2 + z^2}}\right].$$   Expanding (with $d \gg x, y, z$):

$$\frac{1}{\sqrt{(x \pm d)^2 + y^2 + z^2}} = (x^2 \pm 2dx + d^2 + y^2 + z^2)^{-1/2} = (d^2 \pm 2dx + r^2)^{-1/2} = \frac{1}{d}\left(1 \pm \frac{2x}{d} + \frac{r^2}{d^2}\right)^{-1/2}$$

$$\approx \frac{1}{d}\left(1 \mp \frac{x}{d} - \frac{r^2}{2d^2} + \frac{3}{8}\frac{4x^2}{d^2}\right) = \frac{1}{d}\left[1 \mp \frac{x}{d} + \frac{1}{2d^2}(3x^2 - r^2)\right].$$

$$V = -\frac{eq}{4\pi\epsilon_0 d}\left[1 - \frac{x}{d} + \frac{1}{2d^2}(3x^2 - r^2) + 1 + \frac{x}{d} + \frac{1}{2d^2}(3x^2 - r^2)\right] = -\frac{2eq}{4\pi\epsilon_0 d} - \frac{eq}{4\pi\epsilon_0 d^3}(3x^2 - r^2)$$

$$= 2\beta d^2 + 3\beta x^2 - \beta r^2, \quad \text{where} \quad \beta \equiv -\frac{e}{4\pi\epsilon_0}\frac{q}{d^3}.$$

Thus with all six charges in place

$$H' = 2(\beta_1 d_1^2 + \beta_2 d_2^2 + \beta_3 d_3^2) + 3(\beta_1 x^2 + \beta_2 y^2 + \beta_3 z^2) - r^2(\beta_1 + \beta_2 + \beta_3). \quad \text{QED}$$

(b) $\langle 1\,0\,0|H'|1\,0\,0\rangle = \dfrac{1}{\pi a^3}\displaystyle\int e^{-2r/a}H' r^2 \sin\theta\, dr\, d\theta\, d\phi$

$$= V_0 + \frac{3}{\pi a^3}\int e^{-2r/a}(\beta_1 x^2 + \beta_2 y^2 + \beta_3 z^2)r^2 \sin\theta\, dr\, d\theta\, d\phi - \frac{(\beta_1 + \beta_2 + \beta_3)}{\pi a^3}\int r^2 e^{-2r/a}r^2 \sin\theta\, dr\, d\theta\, d\phi.$$

$$I_1 \equiv \int r^2 e^{-2r/a}r^2 \sin\theta\, dr\, d\theta\, d\phi = 4\pi\int_0^\infty r^4 e^{-2r/a}\, dr = 4\pi 4!\left(\frac{a}{2}\right)^5 = 3\pi a^5.$$

$$I_2 \equiv \int e^{-2r/a}(\beta_1 x^2 + \beta_2 y^2 + \beta_3 z^2)r^2 \sin\theta\, dr\, d\theta\, d\phi$$

$$= \int r^4 e^{-2r/a}(\beta_1 \sin^2\theta \cos^2\phi + \beta_2 \sin^2\theta \sin^2\phi + \beta_3 \cos^2\theta)\sin\theta\, dr\, d\theta\, d\phi.$$

$$\text{But} \quad \int_0^{2\pi}\cos^2\phi\, d\phi = \int_0^{2\pi}\sin^2\phi\, d\phi = \pi, \quad \int_0^{2\pi}d\phi = 2\pi. \quad \text{So}$$

$$= \int_0^\infty r^4 e^{-2r/a}\, dr \int_0^\pi \left[\pi(\beta_1 + \beta_2)\sin^2\theta + 2\pi\beta_3 \cos^2\theta\right]\sin\theta\, d\theta.$$

$$\text{But} \quad \int_0^\pi \sin^3\theta\, d\theta = \frac{4}{3}, \quad \int_0^\pi \cos^2\theta \sin\theta\, d\theta = \frac{2}{3}. \quad \text{So}$$

$$= 4!\left(\frac{a}{2}\right)^5\left[\frac{4\pi}{3}(\beta_1 + \beta_2) + \frac{4\pi}{3}\beta_3\right] = \pi a^5(\beta_1 + \beta_2 + \beta_3).$$

$$\langle 1\,0\,0|H'|1\,0\,0\rangle = V_0 + \frac{3}{\pi a^3}\pi a^5(\beta_1 + \beta_2 + \beta_3) - \frac{(\beta_1 + \beta_2 + \beta_3)}{\pi a^3}3\pi a^5 = \boxed{V_0.}$$

(c) The four states are $\begin{cases} |2\,0\,0\rangle &= R_{20}Y_0^0 \\ |2\,1\,1\rangle &= R_{21}Y_1^1 \\ |2\,1-1\rangle &= R_{21}Y_1^{-1} \\ |2\,1\,0\rangle &= R_{21}Y_1^0 \end{cases}$ (functional forms in Problem 4.11).

<u>Diagonal elements:</u> $\langle n\,l\,m|H'|n\,l\,m\rangle = V_0 + 3\left(\beta_1\langle x^2\rangle + \beta_2\langle y^2\rangle + \beta_3\langle z^2\rangle\right) - (\beta_1 + \beta_2 + \beta_3)\langle r^2\rangle.$

For $|200\rangle$, $\langle x^2 \rangle = \langle y^2 \rangle = \langle z^2 \rangle = \frac{1}{3}\langle r^2 \rangle$ ($Y_0^0$ does not depend on $\phi, \theta$; this state has spherical symmetry), so $\boxed{\langle 200|H'|200\rangle = V_0.}$    (I could have used the same argument in (b).)

From Problem 6.35(a),   $\langle r^2 \rangle = \dfrac{n^2 a^2}{2}\left[5n^2 - 3l(l+1) + 1\right]$, so for $n = 2, l = 1$:   $\langle r^2 \rangle = 30a^2$. Moreover, since $\langle x^2 \rangle = \{\ldots\}\displaystyle\int_0^{2\pi} \cos^2\phi\,d\phi = \{\ldots\}\int_0^{2\pi} \sin^2\phi\,d\phi = \langle y^2 \rangle$, and $\langle x^2 \rangle + \langle y^2 \rangle + \langle z^2 \rangle = \langle r^2 \rangle$, it follows that $\langle x^2 \rangle = \langle y^2 \rangle = \dfrac{1}{2}(\langle r^2 \rangle - \langle z^2 \rangle) = 15a^2 - \dfrac{1}{2}\langle z^2 \rangle$.   So all we need to calculate is $\langle z^2 \rangle$.

$$\langle 210|z^2|210\rangle = \frac{1}{2\pi a}\frac{1}{16a^4}\int r^2 e^{-r/a}\cos^2\theta(r^2\cos^2\theta)r^2\sin\theta\,dr\,d\theta\,d\phi$$

$$= \frac{1}{16a^5}\int_0^\infty r^6 e^{-r/a}\,dr\int_0^\pi \cos^4\theta\sin\theta\,d\theta = \frac{1}{16a^5}6!a^7\frac{2}{5} = 18a^2; \quad \langle x^2 \rangle = \langle y^2 \rangle = 15a^2 - 9a^2 = 6a^2.$$

$$\langle 210|H'|210\rangle = V_0 + 3(6a^2\beta_1 + 6a^2\beta_2 + 18a^2\beta_3) - 30a^2(\beta_1 + \beta_2 + \beta_3)$$
$$= \boxed{V_0 - 12a^2(\beta_1 + \beta_2 + \beta_3) + 36a^2\beta_3.}$$

$$\langle 21\pm1|z^2|21\pm1\rangle = \frac{1}{\pi a}\frac{1}{64a^4}\int r^2 e^{-r/a}\sin^2\theta(r^2\cos^2\theta)r^2\sin\theta\,dr\,d\theta\,d\phi$$

$$= \frac{1}{32a^5}\int_0^\infty r^6 e^{-r/a}\,dr\int_0^\pi(1-\cos^2\theta)\cos^2\theta\sin\theta\,d\theta = \frac{1}{32a^5}6!a^7\left(\frac{2}{3} - \frac{2}{5}\right) = 6a^2;$$

$$\langle x^2 \rangle = \langle y^2 \rangle = 15a^2 - 3a^2 = 12a^2.$$

$$\langle 21\pm1|H'|21\pm1\rangle = V_0 + 3(12a^2\beta_1 + 12a^2\beta_2 + 6a^2\beta_3) - 30a^2(\beta_1 + \beta_2 + \beta_3)$$
$$= \boxed{V_0 + 6a^2(\beta_1 + \beta_2 + \beta_3) - 18a^2\beta_3.}$$

Off-diagonal elements:   We need $\langle 200|H'|210\rangle$, $\langle 200|H'|21\pm1\rangle$, $\langle 210|H'|21\pm1\rangle$, and $\langle 21-1|H'|211\rangle$. Now $\langle nlm|V_0|n'l'm'\rangle = 0$, by orthogonality, and $\langle nlm|r^2|n'l'm'\rangle = 0$, by orthogonality of $Y_l^m$, so all we need are the matrix elements of $x^2$ and $y^2$ ($\langle|z^2|\rangle = -\langle|x^2|\rangle - \langle|y^2|\rangle$). For $\langle 200|x^2|21\pm1\rangle$ and $\langle 210|x^2|21\pm1\rangle$ the $\phi$ integral is $\int_0^{2\pi}\cos^2\phi e^{\pm i\phi}\,d\phi = \int_0^{2\pi}\cos^3\phi\,d\phi \pm i\int_0^{2\pi}\cos^2\phi\sin\phi\,d\phi = 0$, and the same goes for $y^2$. So $\boxed{\langle 200|H'|21\pm1\rangle = \langle 210|H'|21\pm1\rangle = 0.}$

For $\langle 200|x^2|210\rangle$ and $\langle 200|y^2|210\rangle$ the $\theta$ integral is $\int_0^\pi \cos\theta(\sin^2\theta)\sin\theta\,d\theta = \left.\sin^4\theta/4\right|_0^\pi = 0$, so $\boxed{\langle 200|H'|210\rangle = 0.}$   Finally:

$$\langle 21-1|x^2|211\rangle = -\frac{1}{\pi a}\frac{1}{64a^4}\int r^2 e^{-r/a}\sin^2\theta e^{2i\phi}(r^2\sin^2\theta\cos^2\phi)r^2\sin\theta\,dr\,d\theta\,d\phi$$

$$= -\frac{1}{64\pi a^5}\underbrace{\int_0^\infty r^6 e^{-r/a}\,dr}_{6!a^7}\underbrace{\int_0^\pi \sin^5\theta\,d\theta}_{16/15}\underbrace{\int_0^{2\pi} e^{2i\phi}\cos^2\phi\,d\phi}_{\pi/2}$$

$$= -\frac{1}{64\pi a^5}6!a^7\frac{16}{15}\frac{\pi}{2} = -6a^2.$$

For $y^2$, the $\phi$ integral is $\int_0^{2\pi} e^{2i\phi} \sin^2 \phi \, d\phi = -\pi/2$, so $\langle 2\,1\,-1|y^2|2\,1\,1\rangle = 6a^2$, and $\langle 2\,1-1|z^2|2\,1\,1\rangle = 0$.

$$\langle 2\,1-1|H'|2\,1\,1\rangle = 3\left[\beta_1(-6a^2) + \beta_2(6a^2)\right] = \boxed{-18a^2(\beta_1 - \beta_2).}$$

The perturbation matrix is:

|         | 2 0 0 | 2 1 0 | 2 1 1 | 2 1 -1 |
|---------|-------|-------|-------|--------|
| 2 0 0   | $V_0$ | 0     | 0     | 0      |
| 2 1 0   | 0     | $V_0 - 12a^2(\beta_1 + \beta_2) + 24a^2\beta_3$ | 0 | 0 |
| 2 1 1   | 0     | 0     | $V_0 + 6a^2(\beta_1 + \beta_2) - 12a^2\beta_3$ | $-18a^2(\beta_1 - \beta_2)$ |
| 2 1 -1  | 0     | 0     | $-18a^2(\beta_1 - \beta_2)$ | $V_0 + 6a^2(\beta_1 + \beta_2) - 12a^2\beta_3$ |

The $2\times2$ block has the form $\begin{pmatrix} A & B \\ B & A \end{pmatrix}$; its characteristic equation is $(A-\lambda)^2 - B^2 = 0$, so $A - \lambda = \pm B$, or

$$\lambda = A \mp B = V_0 + 6a^2(\beta_1 + \beta_2) - 12a^2\beta_3 \pm 18a^2(\beta_1 - \beta_2) = \begin{cases} V_0 + 24a^2\beta_1 - 12a^2\beta_2 - 12a^2\beta_3, \\ V_0 - 12a^2\beta_1 + 24a^2\beta_2 - 12a^2\beta_3. \end{cases}$$

The first-order corrections to the energy $(E_2)$ are therefore: $\boxed{\begin{aligned} \epsilon_1 &= V_0 \\ \epsilon_2 &= V_0 - 12a^2(\beta_1 + \beta_2 - 2\beta_3) \\ \epsilon_3 &= V_0 - 12a^2(-2\beta_1 + \beta_2 + \beta_3) \\ \epsilon_4 &= V_0 - 12a^2(\beta_1 - 2\beta_2 + \beta_3) \end{aligned}}$

(i) If $\beta_1 = \beta_2 = \beta_3$, then $\epsilon_1 = \epsilon_2 = \epsilon_3 = \epsilon_4 = V_0$: $\boxed{\text{one level}}$ (still 4-fold degenerate).

(ii) If $\beta_1 = \beta_2 \neq \beta_3$, then $\epsilon_1 = V_0$, $\epsilon_2 = V_0 - 24a^2(\beta_1 - \beta_3)$, $\epsilon_3 = \epsilon_4 = V_0 + 12a^2(\beta_1 - \beta_3)$: $\boxed{\text{three levels}}$ (one remains doubly degenerate).

(iii) If all three $\beta$'s are different, there are $\boxed{\text{four levels}}$ (no remaining degeneracy).

---

## Problem 6.40

**(a)** (i) Equation 6.10:     $(H^0 - E_0^0)\psi_0^1 = -(H' - E_0^1)\psi_0^0$.

$$H^0 = -\frac{\hbar^2}{2m}\nabla^2 - \frac{e^2}{4\pi\epsilon_0}\frac{1}{r} = -\frac{\hbar^2}{2m}\left(\nabla^2 + \frac{2}{ar}\right), \quad \text{since} \quad a = \frac{4\pi\epsilon_0\hbar^2}{me^2}.$$

$$E_0^0 = -\frac{\hbar^2}{2ma^2}.$$

$$H' = eE_{\text{ext}}r\cos\theta; \quad E_0^1 = 0 \quad (\text{Problem 6.36(a)}).$$

$$\psi_0^0 = \frac{1}{\sqrt{\pi a^3}}e^{-r/a}; \quad \psi_0^1 = f(r)e^{-r/a}\cos\theta.$$

Equation 4.13 $\Rightarrow$

$$
\begin{aligned}
\nabla^2 \psi_0^1 &= \frac{\cos\theta}{r^2}\frac{d}{dr}\left[r^2\frac{d}{dr}\left(fe^{-r/a}\right)\right] + \frac{fe^{-r/a}}{r^2\sin\theta}\frac{d}{d\theta}\left[\sin\theta\frac{d}{d\theta}(\cos\theta)\right] \\
&= \frac{\cos\theta}{r^2}\frac{d}{dr}\left[r^2\left(f'-\frac{1}{a}f\right)e^{-r/a}\right] + \frac{fe^{-r/a}}{r^2\sin\theta}\frac{d}{d\theta}\left[-\sin^2\theta\right] \\
&= \frac{\cos\theta}{r^2}\left[2r\left(f'-\frac{1}{a}f\right)e^{-r/a} + r^2\left(f''-\frac{2}{a}f'+\frac{1}{a^2}f\right)e^{-r/a}\right] - \frac{2\cos\theta}{r^2}fe^{-r/a} \\
&= \cos\theta e^{-r/a}\left[\left(f''-\frac{2}{a}f'+\frac{1}{a^2}f\right) + 2\left(f'-\frac{1}{a}f\right)\frac{1}{r} - 2f\frac{1}{r^2}\right].
\end{aligned}
$$

Plug this into Eq. 6.10:

$$
-\frac{\hbar^2}{2m}\cos\theta e^{-r/a}\left[\left(f''-\frac{2}{a}f'+\frac{1}{a^2}f\right) + 2\left(f'-\frac{1}{a}f\right)\frac{1}{r} - 2f\frac{1}{r^2} + 2f\frac{1}{a}\frac{1}{r} - f\frac{1}{a^2}\right] = -eE_{\text{ext}}r\cos\theta\frac{1}{\sqrt{\pi a^3}}e^{-r/a},
$$

$\blacklozenge$ $\quad \left(f''-\frac{2}{a}f'\right) + 2f'\frac{1}{r} - 2f\frac{1}{r^2} = \left(\frac{2meE_{\text{ext}}}{\hbar^2\sqrt{\pi a^3}}\right)r = \frac{4\gamma}{a}r,\quad$ where $\quad\boxed{\gamma \equiv \dfrac{meE_{\text{ext}}}{2\hbar^2\sqrt{\pi a}}.}$

Now let $\quad f(r) = A + Br + Cr^2,\quad$ so $\quad f' = B + 2Cr\quad$ and $\quad f'' = 2C.\quad$ Then

$$
2C - \frac{2}{a}(B + 2Cr) + \frac{2}{r}(B + 2Cr) - \frac{2}{r^2}(A + Br + Cr^2) = \frac{4\gamma}{a}r.
$$

Collecting like powers of $r$:

$r^{-2}:\quad A = 0.$
$r^{-1}:\quad 2B - 2B = 0\quad$ (automatic).
$r^0:\quad 2C - 2B/a + 4C - 2C = 0 \Rightarrow B = 2aC.$
$r^1:\quad -4C/a = 4\gamma/a \Rightarrow C = -\gamma.$

Evidently the function suggested *does* satisfy Eq. 6.10, with the coefficients $\boxed{A = 0,\ B = -2a\gamma,\ C = -\gamma;}$ the second-order correction to the wave function is

$$
\psi_0^1 = -\gamma r(r + 2a)e^{-r/a}\cos\theta.
$$

(ii) Equation 6.11 says, in this case:

$$
\begin{aligned}
E_0^2 &= \langle\psi_0^0|H'|\psi_0^1\rangle = -\frac{1}{\sqrt{\pi a^3}}\frac{meE_{\text{ext}}}{2\hbar^2\sqrt{\pi a}}eE_{\text{ext}}\int e^{-r/a}(r\cos\theta)r(r+2a)e^{-r/a}\cos\theta\, r^2\sin\theta\,dr\,d\theta\,d\phi \\
&= -\frac{m(eE_{\text{ext}})^2}{2\pi a^2\hbar^2}2\pi\int_0^\infty r^4(r+2a)e^{-2r/a}dr\int_0^\pi \cos^2\theta\sin\theta\,d\theta \\
&= -m\left(\frac{eE_{\text{ext}}}{a\hbar}\right)^2\left[5!\left(\frac{a}{2}\right)^6 + 2a\,4!\left(\frac{a}{2}\right)^5\right]\left(-\frac{\cos^3\theta}{3}\right)\Big|_0^\pi \\
&= -m\left(\frac{eE_{\text{ext}}}{a\hbar}\right)^2\left(\frac{27}{8}a^6\right)\frac{2}{3} = \boxed{-m\left(\frac{3eE_{\text{ext}}a^2}{2\hbar}\right)^2.}
\end{aligned}
$$

**(b)** (i) This is the same as (a) [note that $E_0^1 = 0$, as before, since $\psi_0^0$ is spherically symmetric, so $\langle \cos\theta \rangle = 0$] except for the $r$-dependence of $H'$. So Eq. ♦ $\Rightarrow$

$$f'' + 2f'\left(\frac{1}{r} - \frac{1}{a}\right) - 2f\frac{1}{r^2} = -\left(\frac{2mep}{4\pi\epsilon_0\hbar^2\sqrt{\pi a^3}}\right)\frac{1}{r^2} = -\frac{2\beta}{r^2}, \quad \text{where} \quad \boxed{\beta \equiv \frac{mep}{4\pi\epsilon_0\hbar^2\sqrt{\pi a^3}}.}$$

The solution this time it obvious: $f(r) = \beta$ (constant). [For the *general* solution we would add the general solution to the homogeneous equation (right side set equal to zero), but this would simply reproduce the unperturbed ground state, $\psi_0^0$, which we exclude—see p. 253.] So

$$\boxed{\psi_0^1 = \beta e^{-r/a}\cos\theta.}$$

(ii) The electric dipole moment of the electron is

$$\langle p_e \rangle = \langle -er\cos\theta \rangle = -e\langle \psi_0^0 + \psi_0^1 | r\cos\theta | \psi_0^0 + \psi_0^1 \rangle = -e\left(\langle \psi_0^0 | r\cos\theta | \psi_0^0 \rangle + 2\langle \psi_0^0 | r\cos\theta | \psi_0^1 \rangle + \langle \psi_0^1 | r\cos\theta | \psi_0^1 \rangle\right).$$

But the first term is zero, and the third is higher order, so

$$\langle p_e \rangle = -2e\frac{1}{\sqrt{\pi a^3}}\beta\int e^{-r/a}(r\cos\theta)e^{-r/a}\cos\theta\, r^2\sin\theta\, dr\, d\theta\, d\phi$$

$$= -2e\left(\frac{mep}{4\pi\epsilon_0\hbar^2\pi a^3}\right)2\pi\int_0^\infty r^3 e^{-2r/a}dr\int_0^\pi \cos^2\theta\sin\theta\, d\theta = -\left(\frac{me^2p}{\epsilon_0\hbar^2\pi a^3}\right)\left[3!\left(\frac{a}{2}\right)^4\right]\left(\frac{2}{3}\right)$$

$$= -\left(\frac{me^2p}{\epsilon_0\hbar^2\pi a^3}\right)\left(\frac{3a^4}{8}\right)\left(\frac{2}{3}\right) = -\left(\frac{me^2pa}{4\pi\epsilon_0\hbar^2}\right) = \boxed{-p.}$$

Evidently the dipole moment associated with the perturbation of the electron cloud cancels the dipole moment of the nucleus, and the total dipole moment of the atom is zero.

(iii) The first-order correction is zero (as noted in (i)). The second-order correction is

$$E_0^2 = \langle \psi_0^0 | H' | \psi_0^1 \rangle = \frac{1}{\sqrt{\pi a^3}}\left(-\frac{ep}{4\pi\epsilon_0}\right)\left(\frac{mep}{4\pi\epsilon_0\hbar^2\sqrt{\pi a^3}}\right)\int e^{-r/a}\left(\frac{\cos\theta}{r^2}\right)e^{-r/a}\cos\theta\, r^2\sin\theta\, dr\, d\theta\, d\phi$$

$$= -m\frac{(ep)^2}{(4\pi\epsilon_0)^2\hbar^2\pi a^3}2\pi\int_0^\infty e^{-2r/a}dr\int_0^\pi \cos^2\theta\sin\theta\, d\theta = -2m\frac{(ep)^2}{(4\pi\epsilon_0)^2\hbar^2 a^3}\left(\frac{a}{2}\right)\left(\frac{2}{3}\right)$$

$$= \frac{4}{3}\left(-\frac{me^4}{2(4\pi\epsilon_0)^2\hbar^2}\right)\frac{p^2}{e^2a^2} = \boxed{\frac{4}{3}\left(\frac{p}{ea}\right)^2 E_1.}$$

# Chapter 7

# The Variational Principle

## Problem 7.1

(a)

$$\langle V \rangle = 2\alpha A^2 \int_0^\infty x e^{-2bx^2} dx = 2\alpha A^2 \left( -\frac{1}{4b} e^{-2bx^2} \right) \Big|_0^\infty = \frac{\alpha A^2}{2b} = \frac{\alpha}{2b} \sqrt{\frac{2b}{\pi}} = \frac{\alpha}{\sqrt{2b\pi}}.$$

$$\langle H \rangle = \frac{\hbar^2 b}{2m} + \frac{\alpha}{\sqrt{2\pi b}}. \quad \frac{\partial \langle H \rangle}{\partial b} = \frac{\hbar^2}{2m} - \frac{1}{2} \frac{\alpha}{\sqrt{2\pi}} b^{-3/2} = 0 \implies b^{3/2} = \frac{\alpha}{\sqrt{2\pi}} \frac{m}{\hbar^2}; \ b = \left( \frac{m\alpha}{\sqrt{2\pi}\hbar^2} \right)^{2/3}.$$

$$\langle H \rangle_{\min} = \frac{\hbar^2}{2m} \left( \frac{m\alpha}{\sqrt{2\pi}\hbar^2} \right)^{2/3} + \frac{\alpha}{\sqrt{2\pi}} \left( \frac{\sqrt{2\pi}\hbar^2}{m\alpha} \right)^{1/3} = \frac{\alpha^{2/3}\hbar^{2/3}}{m^{1/3}(2\pi)^{1/3}} \left( \frac{1}{2} + 1 \right) = \boxed{\frac{3}{2} \left( \frac{\alpha^2 \hbar^2}{2\pi m} \right)^{1/3}}.$$

(b)

$$\langle V \rangle = 2\alpha A^2 \int_0^\infty x^4 e^{-2bx^2} dx = 2\alpha A^2 \frac{3}{8(2b)^2} \sqrt{\frac{\pi}{2b}} = \frac{3\alpha}{16b^2} \sqrt{\frac{\pi}{2b}} \sqrt{\frac{2b}{\pi}} = \frac{3\alpha}{16b^2}.$$

$$\langle H \rangle = \frac{\hbar^2 b}{2m} + \frac{3\alpha}{16b^2}. \quad \frac{\partial \langle H \rangle}{\partial b} = \frac{\hbar^2}{2m} - \frac{3\alpha}{8b^3} = 0 \implies b^3 = \frac{3\alpha m}{4\hbar^2}; \ b = \left( \frac{3\alpha m}{4\hbar^2} \right)^{1/3}.$$

$$\langle H \rangle_{\min} = \frac{\hbar^2}{2m} \left( \frac{3\alpha m}{4\hbar^2} \right)^{1/3} + \frac{3\alpha}{16} \left( \frac{4\hbar^2}{3\alpha m} \right)^{2/3} = \frac{\alpha^{1/3}\hbar^{4/3}}{m^{2/3}} 3^{1/3} 4^{-1/3} \left( \frac{1}{2} + \frac{1}{4} \right) = \boxed{\frac{3}{4} \left( \frac{3\alpha\hbar^4}{4m^2} \right)^{1/3}}.$$

## Problem 7.2

Normalize:   $1 = 2|A|^2 \int_0^\infty \frac{1}{(x^2 + b^2)^2} dx = 2|A|^2 \frac{\pi}{4b^3} = \frac{\pi}{2b^3} |A|^2. \quad A = \sqrt{\frac{2b^3}{\pi}}.$

Kinetic Energy: $\langle T \rangle = -\dfrac{\hbar^2}{2m}|A|^2 \displaystyle\int_{-\infty}^{\infty} \dfrac{1}{(x^2+b^2)} \dfrac{d^2}{dx^2}\left(\dfrac{1}{(x^2+b^2)}\right)dx.$

But $\dfrac{d^2}{dx^2}\left(\dfrac{1}{(x^2+b^2)}\right) = \dfrac{d}{dx}\left(\dfrac{-2x}{(x^2+b^2)^2}\right) = \dfrac{-2}{(x^2+b^2)^2} + 2x\dfrac{4x}{(x^2+b^2)^3} = \dfrac{2(3x^2-b^2)}{(x^2+b^2)^3},$ so

$$\langle T \rangle = -\dfrac{\hbar^2}{2m}\dfrac{2b^3}{\pi}\int_0^{\infty}\dfrac{(3x^2-b^2)}{(x^2+b^2)^4}dx = -\dfrac{4\hbar^2 b^3}{\pi m}\left[3\int_0^{\infty}\dfrac{1}{(x^2+b^2)^3}dx - 4b^2\int_0^{\infty}\dfrac{1}{(x^2+b^2)^4}dx\right]$$

$$= -\dfrac{4\hbar^2 b^3}{\pi m}\left[3\dfrac{3\pi}{16b^5} - 4b^2\dfrac{5\pi}{32b^7}\right] = \dfrac{\hbar^2}{4mb^2}.$$

Potential Energy: $\langle V \rangle = \dfrac{1}{2}m\omega^2|A|^2 \, 2\displaystyle\int_0^{\infty}\dfrac{x^2}{(x^2+b^2)^2}dx = m\omega^2\dfrac{2b^3}{\pi}\dfrac{\pi}{4b} = \dfrac{1}{2}m\omega^2 b^2.$

$\langle H \rangle = \dfrac{\hbar^2}{4mb^2} + \dfrac{1}{2}m\omega^2 b^2.$  $\dfrac{\partial\langle H\rangle}{\partial b} = -\dfrac{\hbar^2}{2mb^3} + m\omega^2 b = 0 \Longrightarrow b^4 = \dfrac{\hbar^2}{2m^2\omega^2} \Longrightarrow b^2 = \dfrac{1}{\sqrt{2}}\dfrac{\hbar}{m\omega}.$

$$\langle H \rangle_{\min} = \dfrac{\hbar^2}{4m}\dfrac{\sqrt{2}m\omega}{\hbar} + \dfrac{1}{2}m\omega^2\dfrac{1}{\sqrt{2}}\dfrac{\hbar}{m\omega} = \hbar\omega\left(\dfrac{\sqrt{2}}{4} + \dfrac{1}{2\sqrt{2}}\right) = \boxed{\dfrac{\sqrt{2}}{2}\hbar\omega} = 0.707\,\hbar\omega > \dfrac{1}{2}\hbar\omega. \quad \checkmark$$

---

## Problem 7.3

$$\psi(x) = \begin{cases} A(x+a/2), & (-a/2 < x < 0), \\ A(a/2-x), & (0 < x < a/2), \\ 0, & (\text{otherwise}). \end{cases}$$

$1 = |A|^2 2\displaystyle\int_0^{a/2}\left(\dfrac{a}{2}-x\right)^2 dx = -2|A|^2\dfrac{1}{3}\left(\dfrac{a}{2}-x\right)^3\Big|_0^{a/2} = \dfrac{2}{3}|A|^2\left(\dfrac{a}{3}\right)^3 = \dfrac{a^3}{12}|A|^2;$  $A = \sqrt{\dfrac{12}{a^3}}$  (as before).

$$\dfrac{d\psi}{dx} = \begin{cases} A, & (-a/2 < x < 0), \\ -A, & (0 < x < a/2), \\ 0, & (\text{otherwise}). \end{cases} \qquad \dfrac{d^2\psi}{dx^2} = A\delta\left(x+\dfrac{a}{2}\right) - 2A\delta(x) + A\delta\left(x-\dfrac{a}{2}\right).$$

$$\langle T \rangle = -\dfrac{\hbar^2}{2m}\int\psi\left[A\delta\left(x+\dfrac{a}{2}\right) - 2A\delta(x) + A\delta\left(x-\dfrac{a}{2}\right)\right]dx = \dfrac{\hbar^2}{2m}2A\psi(0) = \dfrac{\hbar^2}{m}A^2\dfrac{a}{2}$$

$$= \dfrac{\hbar^2 a}{2m}\dfrac{12}{a^3} = 6\dfrac{\hbar^2}{ma^2} \quad (\text{as before}).$$

$\langle V \rangle = -\alpha\displaystyle\int|\psi|^2\delta(x)\,dx = -\alpha|\psi(0)|^2 = -\alpha A^2\left(\dfrac{a}{2}\right)^2 = -3\dfrac{\alpha}{a}.$  $\langle H \rangle = \langle T \rangle + \langle V \rangle = 6\dfrac{\hbar^2}{ma^2} - 3\dfrac{\alpha}{a}.$

$$\dfrac{\partial}{\partial a}\langle H \rangle = -12\dfrac{\hbar^2}{ma^3} + 3\dfrac{\alpha}{a^2} = 0 \Rightarrow a = 4\dfrac{\hbar^2}{m\alpha}.$$

$$\langle H \rangle_{\min} = 6\dfrac{\hbar^2}{m}\left(\dfrac{m\alpha}{4\hbar^2}\right)^2 - 3\alpha\left(\dfrac{m\alpha}{4\hbar^2}\right) = \dfrac{m\alpha^2}{\hbar^2}\left(\dfrac{3}{8} - \dfrac{3}{4}\right) = \boxed{-\dfrac{3m\alpha^2}{8\hbar^2}} > -\dfrac{m\alpha^2}{2\hbar^2}. \quad \checkmark$$

---

## Problem 7.4

(a) Follow the proof in §7.1: $\psi = \sum_{n=1}^{\infty} c_n \psi_n$, where $\psi_1$ is the ground state. Since $\langle \psi_1 | \psi \rangle = 0$, we have:

$\sum_{n=1}^{\infty} c_n \langle \psi_1 | \psi \rangle = c_1 = 0$; the coefficient of the ground state is zero. So

$$\langle H \rangle = \sum_{n=2}^{\infty} E_n |c_n|^2 \geq E_{\text{fe}} \sum_{n=2}^{\infty} |c_n|^2 = E_{\text{fe}}, \text{ since } E_n \geq E_{\text{fe}} \text{ for all } n \text{ except } 1.$$

(b)

$$1 = |A|^2 \int_{-\infty}^{\infty} x^2 e^{-2bx^2} dx = |A|^2 2 \frac{1}{8b} \sqrt{\frac{\pi}{2b}} \implies |A|^2 = 4b \sqrt{\frac{2b}{\pi}}.$$

$$\langle T \rangle = -\frac{\hbar^2}{2m} |A|^2 \int_{-\infty}^{\infty} x e^{-bx^2} \frac{d^2}{dx^2} \left( x e^{-bx^2} \right) dx$$

$$\frac{d^2}{dx^2} \left( x e^{-bx^2} \right) = \frac{d}{dx} \left( e^{-bx^2} - 2bx^2 e^{-bx^2} \right) = -2bx e^{-bx^2} - 4bx e^{-bx^2} + 4b^2 x^3 e^{-bx^2}$$

$$\langle T \rangle = -\frac{\hbar^2}{2m} 4b \sqrt{\frac{2b}{\pi}} 2 \int_{0}^{\infty} \left( -6bx^2 + 4b^2 x^4 \right) e^{-2bx^2} dx = -\frac{2\hbar^2 b}{m} \sqrt{\frac{2b}{\pi}} 2 \left[ -6b \frac{1}{8b} \sqrt{\frac{\pi}{2b}} + 4b^2 \frac{3}{32b^2} \sqrt{\frac{\pi}{2b}} \right]$$

$$= -\frac{4\hbar^2 b}{m} \left( -\frac{3}{4} + \frac{3}{8} \right) = \frac{3\hbar^2 b}{2m}.$$

$$\langle V \rangle = \frac{1}{2} m\omega^2 |A|^2 \int_{-\infty}^{\infty} x^2 e^{-2bx^2} x^2 dx = \frac{1}{2} m\omega^2 4b \sqrt{\frac{2b}{\pi}} 2 \frac{3}{32b^2} \sqrt{\frac{\pi}{2b}} = \frac{3m\omega^2}{8b}.$$

$$\langle H \rangle = \frac{3\hbar^2 b}{2m} + \frac{3m\omega}{8b}; \quad \frac{\partial \langle H \rangle}{\partial b} = \frac{3\hbar^2}{2m} - \frac{3m\omega^2}{8b^2} = 0 \implies b^2 = \frac{m^2 \omega^2}{4\hbar^2} \implies b = \frac{m\omega}{2\hbar}.$$

$$\langle H \rangle_{\text{min}} = \frac{3\hbar^2}{2m} \frac{m\omega}{2\hbar} + \frac{3m\omega^2}{8} \frac{2\hbar}{m\omega} = \hbar\omega \left( \frac{3}{4} + \frac{3}{4} \right) = \boxed{\frac{3}{2}\hbar\omega.}$$

This is *exact*, since the trial wave function is in the form of the true first excited state.

---

## Problem 7.5

(a) Use the unperturbed ground state $(\psi_{\text{gs}}^0)$ as the trial wave function. The variational principle says $\langle \psi_{\text{gs}}^0 | H | \psi_{\text{gs}}^0 \rangle \geq E_{\text{gs}}^0$. But $H = H^0 + H'$, so $\langle \psi_{\text{gs}}^0 | H | \psi_{\text{gs}}^0 \rangle = \langle \psi_{\text{gs}}^0 | H^0 | \psi_{\text{gs}}^0 \rangle + \langle \psi_{\text{gs}}^0 | H' | \psi_{\text{gs}}^0 \rangle$. But $\langle \psi_{\text{gs}}^0 | H^0 | \psi_{\text{gs}}^0 \rangle = E_{\text{gs}}^0$ (the unperturbed ground state energy), and $\langle \psi_{\text{gs}}^0 | H' | \psi_{\text{gs}}^0 \rangle$ is precisely the first order correction to the ground state energy (Eq. 6.9), so $E_{\text{gs}}^0 + E_{\text{gs}}^1 \geq E_{\text{gs}}$. QED

(b) The second order correction $(E_{\text{gs}}^2)$ is $E_{\text{gs}}^2 = \sum_{m \neq \text{gs}} \frac{|\langle \psi_m^0 | H' | \psi_{\text{gs}}^0 \rangle|^2}{E_{\text{gs}}^0 - E_m^0}$. But the numerator is clearly *positive*, and the denominator is always negative (since $E_{\text{gs}}^0 < E_m^0$ for all $m$), so $E_{\text{gs}}^2$ is *negative*.

---

## Problem 7.6

He$^+$ is a hydrogenic ion (see Problem 4.16); its ground state energy is $(2)^2(-13.6 \text{ eV})$, or $-54.4$ eV. It takes $79.0 - 54.4 = \boxed{24.6 \text{ eV}}$ to remove one electron.

## Problem 7.7

I'll do the general case of a nucleus with $Z_0$ protons. Ignoring electron-electron repulsion altogether gives

$$\psi_0 = \frac{Z_0^3}{\pi a^3} e^{-Z_0(r_1+r_2)/a}, \quad \text{(generalizing Eq. 7.17)}$$

and the energy is $2Z_0^2 E_1$. $\langle V_{ee} \rangle$ goes like $1/a$ (Eqs. 7.20 and 7.25), so the generalization of Eq. 7.25 is $\langle V_{ee} \rangle = -\frac{5}{4} Z_0 E_1$, and the generalization of Eq. 7.26 is $\langle H \rangle = (2Z_0^2 - \frac{5}{4} Z_0) E_1$.

If we include shielding, the only change is that $(Z-2)$ in Eqs. 7.28, 7.29, and 7.32 is replaced by $(Z - Z_0)$. Thus Eq. 7.32 generalizes to

$$\langle H \rangle = \left[ 2Z^2 - 4Z(Z - Z_0) - \frac{5}{4} Z \right] E_1 = \left[ -2Z^2 + 4ZZ_0 - \frac{5}{4} Z \right] E_1.$$

$$\frac{\partial \langle H \rangle}{\partial Z} = \left[ -4Z + 4Z_0 - \frac{5}{4} \right] E_1 = 0 \implies \boxed{Z = Z_0 - \frac{5}{16}}.$$

$$\langle H \rangle_{\min} = \left[ -2 \left( Z_0 - \frac{5}{16} \right)^2 + 4 \left( Z_0 - \frac{5}{16} \right) Z_0 - \frac{5}{4} \left( Z_0 - \frac{5}{16} \right) \right] E_1$$

$$= \left( -2Z_0^2 + \frac{5}{4} Z_0 - \frac{25}{128} + 4Z_0^2 - \frac{5}{4} Z_0 - \frac{5}{4} Z_0 + \frac{25}{64} \right) E_1$$

$$= \boxed{\left( 2Z_0^2 - \frac{5}{4} Z_0 + \frac{25}{128} \right) E_1} = \frac{(16Z_0 - 5)^2}{128} E_1,$$

generalizing Eq. 7.34. The first term is the naive estimate ignoring electron-electron repulsion altogether; the second term is $\langle V_{ee} \rangle$ in the unscreened state, and the third term is the effect of screening.

$\underline{Z_0 = 1 \text{ (H}^-\text{)}:}$ $Z = 1 - \dfrac{5}{16} = \boxed{\dfrac{11}{16} = 0.688.}$ The effective nuclear charge is less than 1, as expected.

$$\langle H \rangle_{\min} = \frac{11^2}{128} E_1 = \boxed{\frac{121}{128} E_1 = -12.9 \text{ eV}.}$$

$\underline{Z_0 = 2 \text{ (He)}:}$ $Z = 2 - \dfrac{5}{16} = \dfrac{27}{16} = 1.69$ (as before); $\langle H \rangle_{\min} = \dfrac{27^2}{128} E_1 = \dfrac{729}{128} E_1 = -77.5$ eV.

$\underline{Z_0 = 3 \text{ (Li}^+\text{)}:}$ $Z = 3 - \dfrac{5}{16} = \boxed{\dfrac{43}{16} = 2.69}$ (somewhat less than 3); $\langle H \rangle_{\min} = \dfrac{43^2}{128} E_1 = \boxed{\dfrac{1849}{128} E_1 = -196 \text{ eV}.}$

## Problem 7.8

$$D = a\langle \psi_0(r_1) \left| \frac{1}{r_2} \right| \psi_0(r_1) \rangle = a\langle \psi_0(r_2) \left| \frac{1}{r_1} \right| \psi_0(r_2) \rangle = a\frac{1}{\pi a^3} \int e^{-2r_2/a} \frac{1}{r_1} d^3r$$

$$= \frac{1}{\pi a^3} \int e^{-\frac{2}{a}\sqrt{r^2 + R^2 - 2rR\cos\theta}} \frac{1}{r} r^2 \sin\theta \, dr \, d\theta \, d\phi = \frac{2\pi}{\pi a^3} \int_0^\infty r \left[ \int_0^\pi e^{-\frac{2}{a}\sqrt{r^2+R^2-2rR\cos\theta}} \sin\theta \, d\theta \right] dr.$$

$$[\ldots] = \frac{1}{rR} \int_{|r-R|}^{r+R} e^{-2y/a} y \, dy = -\frac{a}{2rR} \left[ e^{-2(r+R)/a} \left( r + R + \frac{a}{2} \right) - e^{-2|r-R|/a} \left( |r-R| + \frac{a}{2} \right) \right]$$

$$D = \frac{2}{a^2} \left( -\frac{a}{2R} \right) \left[ e^{-2R/a} \int_0^\infty e^{-2r/a} \left( r + R + \frac{a}{2} \right) dr \right.$$

$$\left. - e^{-2R/a} \int_0^R e^{2R/a} \left( R - r + \frac{a}{2} \right) dr - e^{2R/a} \int_R^\infty e^{-2r/a} \left( r - R + \frac{a}{2} \right) dr \right]$$

$$= -\frac{1}{aR} \left\{ e^{-2R/a} \left[ \left( \frac{a}{2} \right)^2 + \left( R + \frac{a}{2} \right) \left( \frac{a}{2} \right) \right] - e^{-2R/a} \left( R + \frac{a}{2} \right) \left( \frac{a}{2} e^{2r/a} \right) \Big|_0^R \right.$$

$$\left. + e^{-2R/a} \left( \frac{a}{2} \right)^2 e^{2r/a} \left( \frac{2r}{a} - 1 \right) \Big|_0^R - e^{2R/a} \left( -R + \frac{a}{2} \right) \left( -\frac{a}{2} e^{-2r/a} \right) \Big|_R^\infty - e^{2R/a} \left( \frac{a}{2} \right)^2 e^{-2r/a} \left( -\frac{2r}{a} - 1 \right) \Big|_R^\infty \right\}$$

$$= -\frac{1}{aR} \left\{ e^{-2R/a} \left[ \frac{a^2}{4} + \frac{aR}{2} + \frac{a^2}{4} + \frac{aR}{2} + \frac{a^2}{4} + \frac{a^2}{4} \right] + \left[ -\frac{aR}{2} - \frac{a^2}{4} + \frac{a^2}{4}\frac{2R}{a} - \frac{a^2}{4} + \frac{aR}{2} - \frac{a^2}{4} - \frac{a^2}{4}\frac{2R}{a} - \frac{a^2}{4} \right] \right\}$$

$$= -\frac{1}{aR} \left[ e^{-2R/a} \left( a^2 + aR \right) + \left( -a^2 \right) \right] \implies \boxed{D = \frac{a}{R} - \left( 1 + \frac{a}{R} \right) e^{-2R/a}} \quad \text{(confirms Eq. 7.47).}$$

$$X = a \langle \psi_0(r_1) \left| \frac{1}{r_1} \right| \psi_0(r_2) \rangle = a \frac{1}{\pi a^3} \int e^{-r_1/a} e^{-r_2/a} \frac{1}{r_1} d^3r$$

$$= \frac{1}{\pi a^2} \int e^{-r/a} e^{-\sqrt{r^2+R^2-2rR\cos\theta}/a} \frac{1}{r} r^2 \sin\theta \, dr \, d\theta \, d\phi = \frac{2\pi}{\pi a^2} \int_0^\infty r e^{-r/a} \left[ \int_0^\pi e^{-\sqrt{r^2+R^2-2rR\cos\theta}/a} \sin\theta \, d\theta \right] dr.$$

$$[\ldots] = -\frac{a}{rR} \left[ e^{-(r+R)/a}(r+R+a) - e^{-|r-R|/a}(|r-R|+a) \right]$$

$$X = \frac{2}{a^2} \left( -\frac{a}{R} \right) \left[ e^{-R/a} \int_0^\infty e^{-2r/a}(r+R+a) dr \right.$$

$$\left. - e^{-R/a} \int_0^R (R-r+a) dr - e^{R/a} \int_R^\infty e^{-2r/a}(r-R+a) dr \right]$$

$$= -\frac{2}{aR} \left\{ e^{-R/a} \left[ \left( \frac{a}{2} \right)^2 + (R+a)\left( \frac{a}{2} \right) \right] - e^{-R/a} \left[ (R+a)R - \frac{R^2}{2} \right] \right.$$

$$-e^{R/a}(-R+a)\left(-\frac{a}{2}e^{-2r/a}\right)\Big|_R^\infty - e^{R/a}\left(\frac{a}{2}\right)^2 e^{-2r/a}\left(-\frac{2r}{a}-1\right)\Big|_R^\infty \Bigg\}$$

$$= -\frac{2}{aR}\left[e^{-R/a}\left(\frac{a^2}{4}+\frac{aR}{2}+\frac{a^2}{2}-R^2-aR+\frac{R^2}{2}+\frac{aR}{2}-\frac{a^2}{2}-\frac{a^2}{4}\frac{2R}{a}-\frac{a^2}{4}\right)\right]$$

$$= -\frac{2}{aR}e^{-R/a}\left(-\frac{aR}{2}-\frac{R^2}{2}\right) \Longrightarrow \boxed{X = e^{-R/a}\left(1+\frac{R}{a}\right)}\qquad \text{(confirms Eq. 7.48).}$$

## Problem 7.9

There are two changes: (1) the 2 in Eq. 7.38 changes sign ... which amounts to changing the sign of $I$ in Eq. 7.43; (2) the last term in Eq. 7.44 changes sign ... which amounts to reversing the sign of $X$. Thus Eq. 7.49 becomes

$$\langle H \rangle = \left[1 + 2\frac{D-X}{1-I}\right]E_1, \quad \text{and hence Eq. 7.51 becomes}$$

$$F(x) = \frac{E_{\text{tot}}}{-E_1} = \frac{2a}{R}-1-2\frac{D-X}{1-I} = -1+\frac{2}{x}-2\frac{1/x-(1+1/x)e^{-2x}-(1+x)e^{-x}}{1-(1+x+x^2/3)e^{-x}}$$

$$= -1+\frac{2}{x}\left[\frac{1-(1+x+x^2/3)e^{-x}-1+(x+1)e^{-2x}+(x+x^2)e^{-x}}{1-(1+x+x^2/3)e^{-x}}\right]$$

$$= \boxed{-1+\frac{2}{x}\left[\frac{(1+x)e^{-2x}+\left(\frac{2}{3}x^2-1\right)e^{-x}}{1-(1+x+x^2/3)e^{-x}}\right]}.$$

The graph (with plus sign for comparison) has no minimum, and remains above $-1$, indicating that the energy is greater than for the proton and atom dissociated. Hence, no evidence of bonding here.

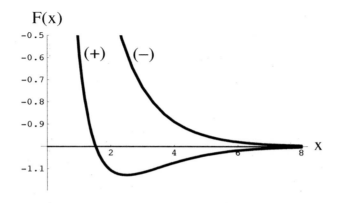

## Problem 7.10

According to *Mathematica*, the minimum occurs at $x = 2.493$, and at this point $F'' = 0.1257$.

$$m\omega^2 = V'' = -\frac{E_1}{a^2}F'', \quad \text{so} \quad \omega = \frac{1}{a}\sqrt{\frac{-(0.1257)E_1}{m}}.$$

Here $m$ is the reduced mass of the proton:   $m = \frac{m_p m_p}{m_p + m_p} = \frac{1}{2}m_p.$

$$\omega = \frac{3 \times 10^8 \text{ m/s}}{(0.529 \times 10^{-10} \text{ m})}\sqrt{\frac{(0.1257)(13.6 \text{ eV})}{(938 \times 10^6 \text{ eV})/2}} = 3.42 \times 10^{14}/\text{s}.$$

$$\frac{1}{2}\hbar\omega = \frac{1}{2}(6.58 \times 10^{-16} \text{ eV} \cdot \text{s})(3.42 \times 10^{14} /\text{s}) = \boxed{0.113 \text{ eV}} \quad \text{(ground state vibrational energy)}.$$

*Mathematica* says that at the minimum $F = -1.1297$, so the binding energy is $(0.1297)(13.6 \text{ eV}) = 1.76$ eV. Since this is substantially greater than the vibrational energy, it stays bound. The highest vibrational energy is given by $(n + \frac{1}{2})\hbar\omega = 1.76$ eV, so $n = \frac{1.76}{0.226} - \frac{1}{2} = 7.29$. I estimate $\boxed{\text{eight}}$ bound vibrational states (including $n = 0$).

## Problem 7.11

**(a)**

$$1 = \int |\psi|^2 \, dx = |A|^2 \int_{-a/2}^{a/2} \cos^2\left(\frac{\pi x}{a}\right) dx = |A|^2 \frac{a}{2} \quad \Rightarrow \quad A = \sqrt{\frac{2}{a}}.$$

$$\langle T \rangle = -\frac{\hbar^2}{2m}\int \psi \frac{d^2\psi}{dx^2} \, dx = \frac{\hbar^2}{2m}\left(\frac{\pi}{a}\right)^2 \int \psi^2 \, dx = \frac{\pi^2 \hbar^2}{2ma^2}.$$

$$\langle V \rangle = \frac{1}{2}m\omega^2 \int x^2 \psi^2 \, dx = \frac{1}{2}m\omega^2 \frac{2}{a}\int_{-a/2}^{a/2} x^2 \cos^2\left(\frac{\pi x}{a}\right) dx = \frac{m\omega^2}{a}\left(\frac{a}{\pi}\right)^3 \int_{-\pi/2}^{\pi/2} y^2 \cos^2 y \, dy$$

$$= \frac{m\omega^2 a^2}{\pi^3}\left[\frac{y^3}{6} + \left(\frac{y^2}{4} - \frac{1}{8}\right)\sin 2y + \frac{y\cos 2y}{4}\right]\Bigg|_{-\pi/2}^{\pi/2} = \frac{m\omega^2 a^2}{4\pi^2}\left(\frac{\pi^2}{6} - 1\right).$$

$$\langle H \rangle = \frac{\pi^2 \hbar^2}{2ma^2} + \frac{m\omega^2 a^2}{4\pi^2}\left(\frac{\pi^2}{6} - 1\right); \quad \frac{\partial \langle H \rangle}{\partial a} = -\frac{\pi^2 \hbar^2}{ma^3} + \frac{m\omega^2 a}{2\pi^2}\left(\frac{\pi^2}{6} - 1\right) = 0 \quad \Rightarrow$$

$$\boxed{a = \pi\sqrt{\frac{\hbar}{m\omega}}\left(\frac{2}{\pi^2/6 - 1}\right)^{1/4}.}$$

$$\langle H \rangle_{\min} = \frac{\pi^2 \hbar^2}{2m\pi^2}\frac{m\omega}{\hbar}\sqrt{\frac{\pi^2/6 - 1}{2}} + \frac{m\omega^2}{4\pi^2}\left(\frac{\pi^2}{6} - 1\right)\pi^2\frac{\hbar}{m\omega}\sqrt{\frac{2}{\pi^2/6 - 1}}$$

$$= \boxed{\frac{1}{2}\hbar\omega\sqrt{\frac{\pi^2}{3} - 2}} = \frac{1}{2}\hbar\omega(1.136) > \frac{1}{2}\hbar\omega. \quad \checkmark$$

[We do *not* need to worry about the kink at $\pm a/2$. It is true that $d^2\psi/dx^2$ has delta functions there, but since $\psi(\pm a/2) = 0$ no "extra" contribution to $T$ comes from these points.]

**(b)** Because this trial function is odd, it is orthogonal to the ground state, so by Problem 7.4 $\langle H \rangle$ will give an upper bound to the first excited state.

$$1 = \int |\psi|^2\, dx = |B|^2 \int_{-a}^{a} \sin^2\left(\frac{\pi x}{a}\right) dx = |B|^2 a \quad \Rightarrow \quad B = \frac{1}{\sqrt{a}}.$$

$$\langle T \rangle = -\frac{\hbar^2}{2m} \int \psi \frac{d^2\psi}{dx^2}\, dx = \frac{\hbar^2}{2m}\left(\frac{\pi}{a}\right)^2 \int \psi^2\, dx = \frac{\pi^2\hbar^2}{2ma^2}.$$

$$\langle V \rangle = \frac{1}{2}m\omega^2 \int x^2\psi^2\, dx = \frac{1}{2}m\omega^2 \frac{1}{a}\int_{-a}^{a} x^2 \sin^2\left(\frac{\pi x}{a}\right) dx = \frac{m\omega^2}{2a}\left(\frac{a}{\pi}\right)^3 \int_{-\pi}^{\pi} y^2 \sin^2 y\, dy$$

$$= \frac{m\omega^2 a^2}{2\pi^3}\left[\frac{y^3}{6} - \left(\frac{y^2}{4} - \frac{1}{8}\right)\sin 2y - \frac{y\cos 2y}{4}\right]\Big|_{-\pi}^{\pi} = \frac{m\omega^2 a^2}{4\pi^2}\left(\frac{2\pi^2}{3} - 1\right).$$

$$\langle H \rangle = \frac{\pi^2\hbar^2}{2ma^2} + \frac{m\omega^2 a^2}{4\pi^2}\left(\frac{2\pi^2}{3} - 1\right); \quad \frac{\partial \langle H \rangle}{\partial a} = -\frac{\pi^2\hbar^2}{ma^3} + \frac{m\omega^2 a}{2\pi^2}\left(\frac{2\pi^2}{3} - 1\right) = 0 \Rightarrow$$

$$\boxed{a = \pi\sqrt{\frac{\hbar}{m\omega}}\left(\frac{2}{2\pi^2/3 - 1}\right)^{1/4}.}$$

$$\langle H \rangle_{\min} = \frac{\pi^2\hbar^2}{2m\pi^2}\frac{m\omega}{\hbar}\sqrt{\frac{2\pi^2/3 - 1}{2}} + \frac{m\omega^2}{4\pi^2}\left(\frac{2\pi^2}{3} - 1\right)\pi^2\frac{\hbar}{m\omega}\sqrt{\frac{2}{2\pi^2/3 - 1}}$$

$$= \boxed{\frac{1}{2}\hbar\omega\sqrt{\frac{4\pi^2}{3} - 2}} = \frac{1}{2}\hbar\omega(3.341) > \frac{3}{2}\hbar\omega. \quad \checkmark$$

## Problem 7.12

We will need the following integral repeatedly:

$$\int_0^\infty \frac{x^k}{(x^2 + b^2)^l}\, dx = \frac{1}{2b^{2l-k-1}}\frac{\Gamma\left(\frac{k+1}{2}\right)\Gamma\left(\frac{2l-k-1}{2}\right)}{\Gamma(l)}.$$

**(a)**

$$1 = \int_{-\infty}^\infty |\psi|^2\, dx = 2|A|^2 \int_0^\infty \frac{1}{(x^2 + b^2)^{2n}}\, dx = \frac{|A|^2}{b^{4n-1}}\frac{\Gamma\left(\frac{1}{2}\right)\Gamma\left(\frac{4n-1}{2}\right)}{\Gamma(2n)} \Rightarrow A = \sqrt{\frac{b^{4n-1}\Gamma(2n)}{\Gamma\left(\frac{1}{2}\right)\Gamma\left(\frac{4n-1}{2}\right)}}.$$

$$\langle T \rangle = -\frac{\hbar^2}{2m}\int_{-\infty}^\infty \psi\frac{d^2\psi}{dx^2}\, dx = -\frac{\hbar^2}{2m}A^2\int_{-\infty}^\infty \frac{1}{(x^2+b^2)^n}\frac{d}{dx}\left[\frac{-2nx}{(x^2+b^2)^{n+1}}\right] dx$$

$$= \frac{n\hbar^2}{m}A^2\int_{-\infty}^\infty \frac{1}{(x^2+b^2)^n}\left[\frac{1}{(x^2+b^2)^{n+1}} - \frac{2(n+1)x^2}{(x^2+b^2)^{n+2}}\right] dx$$

$$= \frac{2n\hbar^2}{m}A^2\left[\int_0^\infty \frac{1}{(x^2+b^2)^{2n+1}}\, dx - 2(n+1)\int_0^\infty \frac{x^2}{(x^2+b^2)^{2n+2}}\, dx\right]$$

$$= \frac{2n\hbar^2}{m}\frac{b^{4n-1}\Gamma(2n)}{\Gamma\left(\frac{1}{2}\right)\Gamma\left(\frac{4n-1}{2}\right)}\left[\frac{1}{2b^{4n-1}}\frac{\Gamma\left(\frac{1}{2}\right)\Gamma\left(\frac{4n-1}{2}\right)}{\Gamma(2n+1)} - \frac{2(n+1)}{2b^{4n-1}}\frac{\Gamma\left(\frac{3}{2}\right)\Gamma\left(\frac{4n+1}{2}\right)}{\Gamma(2n+2)}\right] = \frac{\hbar^2}{4mb^2}\frac{n(4n-1)}{(2n+1)}.$$

$$\langle V \rangle = \frac{1}{2}m\omega^2 \int_{-\infty}^{\infty} \psi^2 x^2 \, dx = \frac{1}{2}m\omega^2 2A^2 \int_0^{\infty} \frac{x^2}{(x^2+b^2)^{2n}} \, dx$$

$$= m\omega^2 \frac{b^{4n-1}\Gamma(2n)}{\Gamma\left(\frac{1}{2}\right)\Gamma\left(\frac{4n-1}{2}\right)} \frac{1}{2b^{4n-3}} \frac{\Gamma\left(\frac{3}{2}\right)\Gamma\left(\frac{4n-3}{2}\right)}{\Gamma(2n)} = \frac{m\omega^2 b^2}{2(4n-3)}.$$

$$\langle H \rangle = \frac{\hbar^2}{4mb^2} \frac{n(4n-1)}{(2n+1)} + \frac{m\omega^2 b^2}{(4n-3)}; \quad \frac{\partial \langle H \rangle}{\partial b} = -\frac{\hbar^2}{2mb^3} \frac{n(4n-1)}{(2n+1)} + \frac{m\omega^2 b}{(4n-3)} = 0 \Rightarrow$$

$$b = \sqrt{\frac{\hbar}{m\omega}} \left[ \frac{n(4n-1)(4n-3)}{2(2n+1)} \right]^{1/4}.$$

$$\langle H \rangle_{\min} = \frac{\hbar^2}{4m} \frac{n(4n-1)}{(2n+1)} \frac{m\omega}{\hbar} \sqrt{\frac{2(2n+1)}{n(4n-1)(4n-3)}} + \frac{m\omega^2}{2(4n-3)} \frac{\hbar}{m\omega} \sqrt{\frac{n(4n-1)(4n-3)}{2(2n+1)}}$$

$$= \boxed{\frac{1}{2}\hbar\omega \sqrt{\frac{2n(4n-1)}{(2n+1)(4n-3)}}} = \frac{1}{2}\hbar\omega \sqrt{\frac{8n^2-2n}{8n^2-2n-3}} > \frac{1}{2}\hbar\omega. \quad \checkmark$$

**(b)**

$$1 = 2|B|^2 \int_0^{\infty} \frac{x^2}{(x^2+b^2)^{2n}} \, dx = \frac{|B|^2}{b^{4n-3}} \frac{\Gamma\left(\frac{3}{2}\right)\Gamma\left(\frac{4n-3}{2}\right)}{\Gamma(2n)} \Rightarrow B = \sqrt{\frac{b^{4n-3}\Gamma(2n)}{\Gamma\left(\frac{3}{2}\right)\Gamma\left(\frac{4n-3}{2}\right)}}.$$

$$\langle T \rangle = -\frac{\hbar^2}{2m} B^2 \int_{-\infty}^{\infty} \frac{x}{(x^2+b^2)^n} \frac{d}{dx} \left[ \frac{1}{(x^2+b^2)^n} - \frac{2nx^2}{(x^2+b^2)^{n+1}} \right] dx$$

$$= -\frac{\hbar^2 B^2}{2m} \int_{-\infty}^{\infty} \frac{x}{(x^2+b^2)^n} \left[ \frac{-2nx}{(x^2+b^2)^{n+1}} - \frac{4nx}{(x^2+b^2)^{n+1}} + \frac{4n(n+1)x^3}{(x^2+b^2)^{n+2}} \right] dx$$

$$= \frac{4n\hbar^2 B^2}{2m} \left[ 3 \int_0^{\infty} \frac{x^2}{(x^2+b^2)^{2n+1}} \, dx - 2(n+1) \int_0^{\infty} \frac{x^4}{(x^2+b^2)^{2n+2}} \, dx \right]$$

$$= \frac{2n\hbar^2}{m} \frac{b^{4n-3}\Gamma(2n)}{\Gamma\left(\frac{3}{2}\right)\Gamma\left(\frac{4n-3}{2}\right)} \left[ \frac{3}{2b^{4n-1}} \frac{\Gamma\left(\frac{3}{2}\right)\Gamma\left(\frac{4n-1}{2}\right)}{\Gamma(2n+1)} - \frac{2(n+1)}{2b^{4n-1}} \frac{\Gamma\left(\frac{5}{2}\right)\Gamma\left(\frac{4n-1}{2}\right)}{\Gamma(2n+2)} \right] = \frac{3\hbar^2}{4mb^2} \frac{n(4n-3)}{(2n+1)}.$$

$$\langle V \rangle = \frac{1}{2}m\omega^2 2B^2 \int_0^{\infty} \frac{x^4}{(x^2+b^2)^{2n}} \, dx = \frac{1}{2}m\omega^2 \frac{b^{4n-3}\Gamma(2n)}{\Gamma\left(\frac{3}{2}\right)\Gamma\left(\frac{4n-3}{2}\right)} \frac{2}{2b^{4n-5}} \frac{\Gamma\left(\frac{5}{2}\right)\Gamma\left(\frac{4n-5}{2}\right)}{\Gamma(2n)} = \frac{3}{2} \frac{m\omega^2 b^2}{(4n-5)}.$$

$$\langle H \rangle = \frac{3\hbar^2}{4mb^2} \frac{n(4n-3)}{(2n+1)} + \frac{3}{2} \frac{m\omega^2 b^2}{(4n-5)}; \quad \frac{\partial \langle H \rangle}{\partial b} = -\frac{3\hbar^2}{2mb^3} \frac{n(4n-3)}{(2n+1)} + \frac{3m\omega^2 b}{(4n-5)} = 0 \Rightarrow$$

$$b = \sqrt{\frac{\hbar}{m\omega}} \left[ \frac{n(4n-3)(4n-5)}{2(2n+1)} \right]^{1/4}.$$

$$\langle H \rangle_{\min} = \frac{3\hbar^2}{4m} \frac{n(4n-3)}{(2n+1)} \frac{m\omega}{\hbar} \sqrt{\frac{2(2n+1)}{n(4n-3)(4n-5)}} + \frac{3}{2} \frac{m\omega^2}{(4n-5)} \frac{\hbar}{m\omega} \sqrt{\frac{n(4n-3)(4n-5)}{2(2n+1)}}$$

$$= \boxed{\frac{3}{2}\hbar\omega \sqrt{\frac{2n(4n-3)}{(2n+1)(4n-5)}}} = \frac{3}{2}\hbar\omega \sqrt{\frac{8n^2-6n}{8n^2-6n-5}} > \frac{3}{2}\hbar\omega. \quad \checkmark$$

**(c)** As $n \to \infty$, $\psi$ becomes more and more "gaussian". In the figures I have plotted the trial wave functions for $n = 2$, $n = 3$, and $n = 4$, as well as the exact states (heavy line). Even for $n = 2$ the fit is pretty good, so it is hard to see the improvement, but the successive curves do move perceptibly toward the correct result.

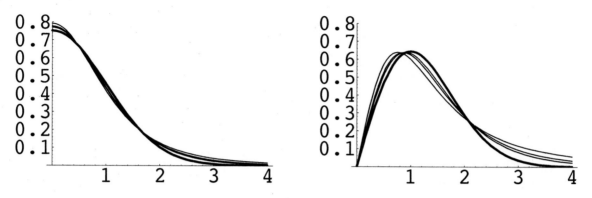

Analytically, for large $n$, $b \approx \sqrt{\dfrac{\hbar}{m\omega}} \left( \dfrac{n \cdot 4n \cdot 4n}{2 \cdot 2n} \right)^{1/4} = \sqrt{\dfrac{2n\hbar}{m\omega}}$,   so

$$(x^2 + b^2)^n = b^{2n} \left( 1 + \frac{x^2}{b^2} \right)^n \approx b^{2n} \left( 1 + \frac{m\omega x^2}{2\hbar n} \right)^n \quad \to \quad b^{2n} e^{m\omega x^2 / 2\hbar}.$$

Meanwhile, using Stirling's approximation (Eq. 5.84), in the form $\Gamma(z + 1) \approx z^z e^{-z}$:

$$A^2 = \frac{b^{4n-1}\Gamma(2n)}{\Gamma\left(\frac{1}{2}\right)\Gamma\left(2n - \frac{1}{2}\right)} \approx \frac{b^{4n-1}}{\sqrt{\pi}} \frac{(2n-1)^{2n-1} e^{-(2n-1)}}{(2n - \frac{3}{2})^{2n - 3/2} e^{-(2n - 3/2)}} \approx \frac{b^{4n-1}}{\sqrt{\pi}} \frac{1}{\sqrt{e}} \left( \frac{2n-1}{2n - \frac{3}{2}} \right)^{2n-1} \sqrt{2n - 3/2}.$$

$$\text{But} \quad \left( \frac{1 - \frac{1}{2n}}{1 - \frac{3}{4n}} \right) \approx \left( 1 - \frac{1}{2n} \right) \left( 1 + \frac{3}{4n} \right) \approx 1 + \frac{3}{4n} - \frac{1}{2n} = 1 + \frac{1}{4n};$$

$$\text{so} \quad \left( \frac{2n-1}{2n - \frac{3}{2}} \right)^{2n-1} \approx \left[ \left( 1 + \frac{1}{4n} \right)^n \right]^2 \frac{1}{1 + 1/4n} \quad \to \quad \left( e^{1/4} \right)^2 = \sqrt{e}.$$

$$= \frac{b^{4n-1}}{\sqrt{\pi e}} \sqrt{e}\sqrt{2n} = \sqrt{\frac{2n}{\pi}} b^{4n-1} \quad \Rightarrow \quad A \approx \left( \frac{2n}{\pi} \right)^{1/4} b^{2n - 1/2}. \quad \text{So}$$

$$\psi \approx \left( \frac{2n}{\pi} \right)^{1/4} b^{2n - 1/2} \frac{1}{b^{2n}} e^{-m\omega x^2 / 2\hbar} = \left( \frac{2n}{\pi} \right)^{1/4} \left( \frac{m\omega}{2n\hbar} \right)^{1/4} e^{-m\omega x^2 / 2\hbar} = \left( \frac{m\omega}{\pi\hbar} \right)^{1/4} e^{-m\omega x^2 / 2\hbar},$$

which is precisely the ground state of the harmonic oscillator (Eq. 2.59). So it's no accident that we get the exact energies, in the limit $n \to \infty$.

---

## Problem 7.13

$$1 = |A|^2 \int e^{-2br^2} r^2 \sin\theta \, dr \, d\theta \, d\phi = 4\pi |A|^2 \int_0^\infty r^2 e^{-2br^2} \, dr = |A|^2 \left( \frac{\pi}{2b} \right)^{3/2} \quad \Rightarrow \quad A = \left( \frac{2b}{\pi} \right)^{3/4}.$$

$$\langle V \rangle = -\frac{e^2}{4\pi\epsilon_0}|A|^2 4\pi \int_0^\infty e^{-2br^2}\frac{1}{r}r^2\,dr = -\frac{e^2}{4\pi\epsilon_0}\left(\frac{2b}{\pi}\right)^{3/2}4\pi\frac{1}{4b} = -\frac{e^2}{4\pi\epsilon_0}2\sqrt{\frac{2b}{\pi}}.$$

$$\langle T \rangle = -\frac{\hbar^2}{2m}|A|^2 \int e^{-br^2}(\nabla^2 e^{-br^2})\,r^2\sin\theta\,dr\,d\theta\,d\phi$$

$$\text{But}\quad (\nabla^2 e^{-br^2}) = \frac{1}{r^2}\frac{d}{dr}\left(r^2\frac{d}{dr}e^{-br^2}\right) = \frac{1}{r^2}\frac{d}{dr}\left(-2br^3 e^{-br^2}\right) = \frac{-2b}{r^2}\left(3r^2 - 2br^4\right)e^{-br^2}.$$

$$= \frac{-\hbar^2}{2m}\left(\frac{2b}{\pi}\right)^{3/2}(4\pi)(-2b)\int_0^\infty (3r^2 - 2br^4)e^{-2br^2}\,dr = \frac{\hbar^2}{m}\pi b 4\left(\frac{2b}{\pi}\right)^{3/2}\left[3\frac{1}{8b}\sqrt{\frac{\pi}{2b}} - 2b\frac{3}{32b^2}\sqrt{\frac{\pi}{2b}}\right]$$

$$= \frac{\hbar^2}{m}4\pi b\left(\frac{2b}{\pi}\right)\left(\frac{3}{8b} - \frac{3}{16b}\right) = \frac{3\hbar^2 b}{2m}.$$

$$\langle H \rangle = \frac{3\hbar^2 b}{2m} - \frac{e^2}{4\pi\epsilon_0}2\sqrt{\frac{2b}{\pi}};\quad \frac{\partial\langle H \rangle}{\partial b} = \frac{3\hbar^2}{2m} - \frac{e^2}{4\pi\epsilon_0}\sqrt{\frac{2}{\pi}}\frac{1}{\sqrt{b}} = 0 \quad\Rightarrow\quad \sqrt{b} = \frac{e^2}{4\pi\epsilon_0}\sqrt{\frac{2}{\pi}}\frac{2m}{3\hbar^2}.$$

$$\langle H \rangle_{\min} = \frac{3\hbar^2}{2m}\left(\frac{e^2}{4\pi\epsilon_0}\right)^2\frac{2}{\pi}\frac{4m^2}{9\hbar^4} - \frac{e^2}{4\pi\epsilon_0}2\sqrt{\frac{2}{\pi}}\left(\frac{e^2}{4\pi\epsilon_0}\right)\sqrt{\frac{2}{\pi}}\frac{2m}{3\hbar^2} = \left(\frac{e^2}{4\pi\epsilon_0}\right)^2\frac{m}{\hbar^2}\left(\frac{4}{3\pi} - \frac{8}{3\pi}\right)$$

$$= -\frac{m}{2\hbar^2}\left(\frac{e^2}{4\pi\epsilon_0}\right)^2\frac{8}{3\pi} = \boxed{\frac{8}{3\pi}E_1 = -11.5\text{ eV}.}$$

## Problem 7.14

Let $\psi = \frac{1}{\sqrt{\pi b^3}}e^{-r/b}$ (same as hydrogen, but with $a \to b$ adjustable). From Eq. 4.191, we have $\langle T \rangle = -E_1 = \frac{\hbar^2}{2ma^2}$ for hydrogen, so in this case $\langle T \rangle = \frac{\hbar^2}{2mb^2}$.

$$\langle V \rangle = -\frac{e^2}{4\pi\epsilon_0}\frac{4\pi}{\pi b^3}\int_0^\infty e^{-2r/b}\frac{e^{-\mu r}}{r}r^2\,dr = -\frac{e^2}{4\pi\epsilon_0}\frac{4}{b^3}\int_0^\infty e^{-(\mu+2/b)r}r\,dr = -\frac{e^2}{4\pi\epsilon_0}\frac{4}{b^3}\frac{1}{(\mu+2/b)^2} = -\frac{e^2}{4\pi\epsilon_0}\frac{1}{b(1+\frac{\mu b}{2})^2}.$$

$$\langle H \rangle = \frac{\hbar^2}{2mb^2} - \frac{e^2}{4\pi\epsilon_0}\frac{1}{b(1+\frac{\mu b}{2})^2}.$$

$$\frac{\partial\langle H \rangle}{\partial b} = -\frac{\hbar^2}{mb^3} + \frac{e^2}{4\pi\epsilon_0}\left[\frac{1}{b^2(1+\mu b/2)^2} + \frac{\mu}{b(1+\mu b/2)^3}\right] \doteq -\frac{\hbar^2}{mb^3} + \frac{e^2}{4\pi\epsilon_0}\frac{(1+3\mu b/2)}{b^2(1+\mu b/2)^3} = 0 \quad\Rightarrow$$

$$\frac{\hbar^2}{m}\left(\frac{4\pi\epsilon_0}{e^2}\right) = b\frac{(1+3\mu b/2)}{(1+\mu b/2)^3},\quad\text{or}\quad b\frac{(1+3\mu b/2)}{(1+\mu b/2)^3} = a.$$

This determines $b$, but unfortunately it's a cubic equation. So we use the fact that $\mu$ is small to obtain a suitable approximate solution. If $\mu = 0$, then $b = a$ (of course), so $\mu a \ll 1 \Longrightarrow \mu b \ll 1$ too. We'll expand in powers of $\mu b$:

$$a \approx b\left(1 + \frac{3\mu b}{2}\right)\left[1 - \frac{3\mu b}{2} + 6\left(\frac{\mu b}{2}\right)^2\right] \approx b\left[1 - \frac{9}{4}(\mu b)^2 + \frac{6}{4}(\mu b)^2\right] = b\left[1 - \frac{3}{4}(\mu b)^2\right].$$

Since the $\frac{3}{4}(\mu b)^2$ term is *already* a second-order correction, we can replace $b$ by $a$:

$$b \approx \frac{a}{\left[1 - \frac{3}{4}(\mu b)^2\right]} \approx a\left[1 + \frac{3}{4}(\mu a)^2\right].$$

$$\begin{aligned}
\langle H \rangle_{\min} &= \frac{\hbar^2}{2ma^2\left[1 + \frac{3}{4}(\mu a)^2\right]^2} - \frac{e^2}{4\pi\epsilon_0}\frac{1}{a\left[1 + \frac{3}{4}(\mu a)^2\right]\left[1 + \frac{1}{2}(\mu a)\right]^2} \\
&\approx \frac{\hbar^2}{2ma^2}\left[1 - 2\frac{3}{4}(\mu a)^2\right] - \frac{e^2}{4\pi\epsilon_0}\frac{1}{a}\left[1 - \frac{3}{4}(\mu a)^2\right]\left[1 - 2\frac{\mu a}{2} + 3\left(\frac{\mu a}{2}\right)^2\right] \\
&= -E_1\left[1 - \frac{3}{2}(\mu a)^2\right] + 2E_1\left[1 - \mu a + \frac{3}{4}(\mu a)^2 - \frac{3}{4}(\mu a)^2\right] = \boxed{E_1\left[1 - 2(\mu a) + \frac{3}{2}(\mu a)^2\right].}
\end{aligned}$$

## Problem 7.15

**(a)**

$$\mathsf{H} = \begin{pmatrix} E_a & h \\ h & E_b \end{pmatrix}; \quad \det(\mathsf{H} - \lambda) = (E_a - \lambda)(E_b - \lambda) - h^2 = 0 \implies \lambda^2 - \lambda(E_a + E_b) + E_a E_b - h^2 = 0.$$

$$\lambda = \frac{1}{2}\left(E_a + E_b \pm \sqrt{E_a^2 + 2E_a E_b + E_b^2 - 4E_a E_b + 4h^2}\right) \Rightarrow \boxed{E_\pm = \frac{1}{2}\left[E_a + E_b \pm \sqrt{(E_a - E_b)^2 + 4h^2}\right].}$$

**(b)** Zeroth order: $E_a^0 = E_a$, $E_b^0 = E_b$. First order: $E_a^1 = \langle \psi_a | H' | \psi_a \rangle = 0$, $E_b^1 = \langle \psi_b | H' | \psi_b \rangle = 0$. Second order:

$$E_a^2 = \frac{|\langle \psi_b | H' | \psi_a \rangle|^2}{E_a - E_b} = -\frac{h^2}{E_b - E_a}; \qquad E_b^2 = \frac{|\langle \psi_a | H' | \psi_b \rangle|^2}{E_b - E_a} = \frac{h^2}{E_b - E_a};$$

$$\boxed{E_- \approx E_a - \frac{h^2}{(E_b - E_a)}; \quad E_+ \approx E_b + \frac{h^2}{(E_b - E_a)}.}$$

**(c)**

$$\begin{aligned}
\langle H \rangle &= \langle \cos\phi\,\psi_a + \sin\phi\,\psi_b | (H^0 + H') | \cos\phi\,\psi_a + \sin\phi\,\psi_b \rangle \\
&= \cos^2\phi\,\langle \psi_a | H^0 | \psi_a \rangle + \sin^2\phi\,\langle \psi_b | H^0 | \psi_b \rangle + \sin\phi\cos\phi\,\langle \psi_b | H' | \psi_a \rangle + \sin\phi\cos\phi\,\langle \psi_a | H' | \psi_b \rangle \\
&= E_a\cos^2\phi + E_b\sin^2\phi + 2h\sin\phi\cos\phi.
\end{aligned}$$

$$\frac{\partial\langle H \rangle}{\partial\phi} = -E_a 2\cos\phi\sin\phi + E_b 2\sin\phi\cos\phi + 2h(\cos^2\phi - \sin^2\phi) = (E_b - E_a)\sin 2\phi + 2h\cos 2\phi = 0.$$

$$\tan 2\phi = -\frac{2h}{E_b - E_a} = -\epsilon \quad \text{where} \quad \epsilon \equiv \frac{2h}{E_b - E_a}. \quad \frac{\sin 2\phi}{\sqrt{1 - \sin^2 2\phi}} = -\epsilon; \quad \sin^2 2\phi = \epsilon^2(1 - \sin^2 2\phi);$$

$$\text{or} \quad \sin^2 2\phi(1 + \epsilon^2) = \epsilon^2; \quad \sin 2\phi = \frac{\pm\epsilon}{\sqrt{1 + \epsilon^2}}; \quad \cos^2 2\phi = 1 - \sin^2 2\phi = 1 - \frac{\epsilon^2}{1 + \epsilon^2} = \frac{1}{1 + \epsilon^2};$$

$$\cos 2\phi = \frac{\mp 1}{\sqrt{1 + \epsilon^2}} \quad \text{(sign dictated by } \tan 2\phi = \frac{\sin 2\phi}{\cos 2\phi} = -\epsilon\text{)}.$$

$$\cos^2 \phi = \frac{1}{2}(1 + \cos 2\phi) = \frac{1}{2}\left(1 \mp \frac{1}{\sqrt{1 + \epsilon^2}}\right); \quad \sin^2 \phi = \frac{1}{2}(1 - \cos 2\phi) = \frac{1}{2}\left(1 \pm \frac{1}{\sqrt{1 + \epsilon^2}}\right).$$

$$\langle H \rangle_{\min} = \frac{1}{2}E_a\left(1 \mp \frac{1}{\sqrt{1 + \epsilon^2}}\right) + \frac{1}{2}E_b\left(1 \pm \frac{1}{\sqrt{1 + \epsilon^2}}\right) \pm h\frac{\epsilon}{\sqrt{1 + \epsilon^2}} = \frac{1}{2}\left[E_a + E_b \pm \frac{(E_b - E_a + 2h\epsilon)}{\sqrt{1 + \epsilon^2}}\right]$$

But $\quad \dfrac{(E_b - E_a + 2h\epsilon)}{\sqrt{1 + \epsilon^2}} = \dfrac{(E_b - E_a) + 2h\frac{2h}{(E_b - E_a)}}{\sqrt{1 + \frac{4h^2}{(E_b - E_a)^2}}} = \dfrac{(E_b - E_a)^2 + 4h^2}{\sqrt{(E_b - E_a)^2 + 4h^2}} = \sqrt{(E_b - E_a)^2 + 4h^2}, \quad$ So

$$\langle H \rangle_{\min} = \frac{1}{2}\left[E_a + E_b \pm \sqrt{(E_b - E_a)^2 + 4h^2}\right] \quad \text{we want the minus sign (+ is maximum)}$$

$$= \boxed{\frac{1}{2}\left[E_a + E_b - \sqrt{(E_b - E_a)^2 + 4h^2}\right]}.$$

**(d)** If $h$ is small, the exact result (a) can be expanded: $E_\pm = \frac{1}{2}\left[(E_a + E_b) \pm (E_b - E_a)\sqrt{1 + \frac{4h^2}{(E_b - E_a)^2}}\right].$

$$\Longrightarrow E_\pm \approx \frac{1}{2}\left\{E_a + E_b \pm (E_b - E_a)\left[1 + \frac{2h^2}{(E_b - E_a)^2}\right]\right\} = \frac{1}{2}\left[E_a + E_b \pm (E_b - E_a) \pm \frac{2h^2}{(E_b - E_a)}\right],$$

so $\quad E_+ \approx E_b + \dfrac{h^2}{(E_b - E_a)}, \quad E_- \approx E_a - \dfrac{h^2}{(E_b - E_a)},$

confirming the perturbation theory results in (b). The variational principle (c) gets the ground state ($E_-$) *exactly* right—not too surprising since the trial wave function Eq. 7.56 is *almost* the most general state (there could be a relative phase factor $e^{i\theta}$).

---

## Problem 7.16

For the electron, $\gamma = -e/m$, so $E_\pm = \pm eB_z\hbar/2m$ (Eq. 4.161). For consistency with Problem 7.15, $E_b > E_a$, so $\chi_b = \chi_+ = \begin{pmatrix} 1 \\ 0 \end{pmatrix}, \quad \chi_a = \chi_- = \begin{pmatrix} 0 \\ 1 \end{pmatrix}, \quad E_b = E_+ = \dfrac{eB_z\hbar}{2m}, \quad E_a = E_- = -\dfrac{eB_z\hbar}{2m}.$

**(a)**

$$\langle \chi_a | H' | \chi_a \rangle = \frac{eB_x}{m}\frac{\hbar}{2}\begin{pmatrix} 0 & 1 \end{pmatrix}\begin{pmatrix} 0 & 1 \\ 1 & 0 \end{pmatrix}\begin{pmatrix} 0 \\ 1 \end{pmatrix} = \frac{eB_x\hbar}{2m}\begin{pmatrix} 0 & 1 \end{pmatrix}\begin{pmatrix} 1 \\ 0 \end{pmatrix} = 0;$$

$$\langle \chi_b | H' | \chi_b \rangle = \frac{eB_x\hbar}{2m}\begin{pmatrix} 1 & 0 \end{pmatrix}\begin{pmatrix} 0 & 1 \\ 1 & 0 \end{pmatrix}\begin{pmatrix} 1 \\ 0 \end{pmatrix} = 0; \quad \langle \chi_b | H' | \chi_a \rangle = \frac{eB_x\hbar}{2m}\begin{pmatrix} 1 & 0 \end{pmatrix}\begin{pmatrix} 0 & 1 \\ 1 & 0 \end{pmatrix}\begin{pmatrix} 0 \\ 1 \end{pmatrix} = \frac{eB_x\hbar}{2m};$$

$$\langle \chi_a | H' | \chi_b \rangle = \frac{eB_x\hbar}{2m}\begin{pmatrix} 0 & 1 \end{pmatrix}\begin{pmatrix} 0 & 1 \\ 1 & 0 \end{pmatrix}\begin{pmatrix} 1 \\ 0 \end{pmatrix} = \frac{eB_x\hbar}{2m}\begin{pmatrix} 0 & 1 \end{pmatrix}\begin{pmatrix} 0 \\ 1 \end{pmatrix} = \frac{eB_x\hbar}{2m}. \quad \text{So} \quad \boxed{h = \frac{eB_x\hbar}{2m}},$$

and the conditions of Problem 7.15 are met.

**(b)** From Problem 7.15(b),

$$E_{\text{gs}} \approx E_a - \frac{h^2}{(E_b - E_a)} = -\frac{eB_z\hbar}{2m} - \frac{(eB_x\hbar/2m)^2}{(eB_z\hbar/m)} = \boxed{-\frac{e\hbar}{2m}\left(B_z + \frac{B_x^2}{2B_z}\right).}$$

**(c)** From Problem 7.15(c), $E_{\text{gs}} = \frac{1}{2}\left[E_a + E_b - \sqrt{(E_b - E_a)^2 + 4h^2}\right]$ (it's actually the *exact* ground state).

$$E_{\text{gs}} = -\frac{1}{2}\sqrt{\left(\frac{eB_z\hbar}{m}\right)^2 + 4\left(\frac{eB_x\hbar}{2m}\right)^2} = \boxed{-\frac{e\hbar}{2m}\sqrt{B_z^2 + B_x^2}}$$

(which was obvious from the start, since the square root is simply the magnitude of the total field).

---

## Problem 7.17

**(a)**

$$\mathbf{r_1} = \frac{1}{\sqrt{2}}(\mathbf{u} + \mathbf{v}); \quad \mathbf{r_2} = \frac{1}{\sqrt{2}}(\mathbf{u} - \mathbf{v}); \quad r_1^2 + r_2^2 = \frac{1}{2}(u^2 + 2\mathbf{u}\cdot\mathbf{v} + v^2 + u^2 - 2\mathbf{u}\cdot\mathbf{v} + v^2) = u^2 + v^2.$$

$$(\nabla_1^2 + \nabla_2^2)f(\mathbf{r_1},\mathbf{r_2}) = \left(\frac{\partial^2 f}{\partial x_1^2} + \frac{\partial^2 f}{\partial y_1^2} + \frac{\partial^2 f}{\partial z_1^2} + \frac{\partial^2 f}{\partial x_2^2} + \frac{\partial^2 f}{\partial y_2^2} + \frac{\partial^2 f}{\partial z_2^2}\right).$$

$$\frac{\partial f}{\partial x_1} = \frac{\partial f}{\partial u_x}\frac{\partial u_x}{\partial x_1} + \frac{\partial f}{\partial v_x}\frac{\partial v_x}{\partial x_1} = \frac{1}{\sqrt{2}}\left(\frac{\partial f}{\partial u_x} + \frac{\partial f}{\partial v_x}\right); \quad \frac{\partial f}{\partial x_2} = \frac{\partial f}{\partial u_x}\frac{\partial u_x}{\partial x_2} + \frac{\partial f}{\partial v_x}\frac{\partial v_x}{\partial x_2} = \frac{1}{\sqrt{2}}\left(\frac{\partial f}{\partial u_x} - \frac{\partial f}{\partial v_x}\right).$$

$$\frac{\partial^2 f}{\partial x_1^2} = \frac{1}{\sqrt{2}}\frac{\partial}{\partial x_1}\left(\frac{\partial f}{\partial u_x} + \frac{\partial f}{\partial v_x}\right) = \frac{1}{\sqrt{2}}\left(\frac{\partial^2 f}{\partial u_x^2}\frac{\partial u_x}{\partial x_1} + \frac{\partial^2 f}{\partial u_x\partial v_x}\frac{\partial v_x}{\partial x_1} + \frac{\partial^2 f}{\partial v_x\partial u_x}\frac{\partial u_x}{\partial x_1} + \frac{\partial^2 f}{\partial v_x^2}\frac{\partial v_x}{\partial x_1}\right)$$

$$= \frac{1}{2}\left(\frac{\partial^2 f}{\partial u_x^2} + 2\frac{\partial^2 f}{\partial u_x\partial v_x} + \frac{\partial^2 f}{\partial v_x^2}\right);$$

$$\frac{\partial^2 f}{\partial x_2^2} = \frac{1}{\sqrt{2}}\frac{\partial}{\partial x_2}\left(\frac{\partial f}{\partial u_x} - \frac{\partial f}{\partial v_x}\right) = \frac{1}{\sqrt{2}}\left(\frac{\partial^2 f}{\partial u_x^2}\frac{\partial u_x}{\partial x_2} + \frac{\partial^2 f}{\partial u_x\partial v_x}\frac{\partial v_x}{\partial x_2} - \frac{\partial^2 f}{\partial v_x\partial u_x}\frac{\partial u_x}{\partial x_2} - \frac{\partial^2 f}{\partial v_x^2}\frac{\partial v_x}{\partial x_2}\right)$$

$$= \frac{1}{2}\left(\frac{\partial^2 f}{\partial u_x^2} - 2\frac{\partial^2 f}{\partial u_x\partial v_x} + \frac{\partial^2 f}{\partial v_x^2}\right).$$

So $\left(\dfrac{\partial^2 f}{\partial x_1^2} + \dfrac{\partial^2 f}{\partial x_2^2}\right) = \left(\dfrac{\partial^2 f}{\partial u_x^2} + \dfrac{\partial^2 f}{\partial v_x^2}\right)$, and likewise for $y$ and $z$: $\nabla_1^2 + \nabla_2^2 = \nabla_u^2 + \nabla_v^2$.

$$H = -\frac{\hbar^2}{2m}(\nabla_u^2 + \nabla_v^2) + \frac{1}{2}m\omega^2(u^2 + v^2) - \frac{\lambda}{4}m\omega^2 2v^2$$

$$= \left[-\frac{\hbar^2}{2m}\nabla_u^2 + \frac{1}{2}m\omega^2 u^2\right] + \left[-\frac{\hbar^2}{2m}\nabla_v^2 + \frac{1}{2}m\omega^2 v^2 - \frac{1}{2}\lambda m\omega^2 v^2\right]. \quad \text{QED}$$

**(b)** The energy is $\frac{3}{2}\hbar\omega$ (for the $u$ part) and $\frac{3}{2}\hbar\omega\sqrt{1-\lambda}$ (for the $v$ part): $\boxed{E_{\rm gs} = \frac{3}{2}\hbar\omega\left(1+\sqrt{1-\lambda}\right).}$

**(c)** The ground state for a *one*-dimensional oscillator is

$$\psi_0(x) = \left(\frac{m\omega}{\pi\hbar}\right)^{1/4} e^{-m\omega x^2/2\hbar} \quad \text{(Eq. 2.59)}.$$

So, for a 3-D oscillator, the ground state is $\psi_0(\mathbf{r}) = \left(\frac{m\omega}{\pi\hbar}\right)^{3/4} e^{-m\omega r^2/2\hbar}$, and for two particles

$$\psi(\mathbf{r_1},\mathbf{r_2}) = \left(\frac{m\omega}{\pi\hbar}\right)^{3/2} e^{-\frac{m\omega}{2\hbar}(r_1^2+r_2^2)}. \quad \text{(This is the analog to Eq. 7.17.)}$$

$$\langle H \rangle = \frac{3}{2}\hbar\omega + \frac{3}{2}\hbar\omega + \langle V_{ee}\rangle = 3\hbar\omega + \langle V_{ee}\rangle \quad \text{(the analog to Eq. 7.19)}.$$

$$\langle V_{ee}\rangle = -\frac{\lambda}{4}m\omega^2\left(\frac{m\omega}{\pi\hbar}\right)^3 \int e^{-\frac{m\omega}{\hbar}(r_1^2+r_2^2)} \underbrace{(\mathbf{r_1}-\mathbf{r_2})^2}_{r_1^2 - 2\mathbf{r_1}\cdot\mathbf{r_2}+r_2^2} d^3\mathbf{r_1}\, d^3\mathbf{r_2} \quad \text{(the analog to Eq. 7.20)}.$$

The $\mathbf{r_1}\cdot\mathbf{r_2}$ term integrates to zero, by symmetry, and the $r_2^2$ term is the same as the $r_1^2$ term, so

$$\begin{aligned}
\langle V_{ee}\rangle &= -\frac{\lambda}{4}m\omega^2\left(\frac{m\omega}{\pi\hbar}\right)^3 2\int e^{-\frac{m\omega}{\hbar}(r_1^2+r_2^2)} r_1^2\, d^3\mathbf{r_1}\, d^3\mathbf{r_2} \\
&= -\frac{\lambda}{2}m\omega^2\left(\frac{m\omega}{\pi\hbar}\right)^3 (4\pi)^2 \int_0^\infty e^{-m\omega r_2^2/\hbar} r_2^2\, dr_2 \int_0^\infty e^{-m\omega r_1^2/\hbar} r_1^4\, dr_1 \\
&= -\lambda\frac{8m^4\omega^5}{\pi\hbar^3}\left[\frac{1}{4}\frac{\hbar}{m\omega}\sqrt{\frac{\pi\hbar}{m\omega}}\right]\left[\frac{3}{8}\left(\frac{\hbar}{m\omega}\right)^2\sqrt{\frac{\pi\hbar}{m\omega}}\right] = -\frac{3}{4}\lambda\hbar\omega.
\end{aligned}$$

$$\langle H \rangle = 3\hbar\omega - \frac{3}{4}\lambda\hbar\omega = \boxed{3\hbar\omega\left(1 - \frac{\lambda}{4}\right).}$$

The variational principle says this must *exceed* the exact ground-state energy (b); let's check it:

$$3\hbar\omega\left(1 - \frac{\lambda}{4}\right) > \frac{3}{2}\hbar\omega\left(1+\sqrt{1-\lambda}\right) \Leftrightarrow 2 - \frac{\lambda}{2} > 1 + \sqrt{1-\lambda} \Leftrightarrow 1 - \frac{\lambda}{2} > \sqrt{1-\lambda} \Leftrightarrow 1 - \lambda + \frac{\lambda^2}{4} > 1 - \lambda.$$

It checks. In fact, expanding the exact answer in powers of $\lambda$, $E_{\rm gs} \approx \frac{3}{2}\hbar\omega(1 + 1 - \frac{1}{2}\lambda) = 3\hbar\omega\left(1 - \frac{\lambda}{4}\right)$, we recover the variational result.

---

## Problem 7.18

$$\begin{aligned}
1 = {} & = \int |\psi|^2 d^3\mathbf{r_1}\, d^3\mathbf{r_2} = |A|^2\left[\int \psi_1^2 d^3\mathbf{r_1}\int \psi_2^2 d^3\mathbf{r_2} + 2\int \psi_1\psi_2 d^3\mathbf{r_1}\int \psi_1\psi_2 d^3\mathbf{r_2} + \int \psi_2^2 d^3\mathbf{r_1}\int \psi_1^2 d^3\mathbf{r_2}\right] \\
& = |A|^2(1 + 2S^2 + 1),
\end{aligned}$$

where

$$S \equiv \int \psi_1(r)\psi_2(r)\, d^3\mathbf{r} = \frac{\sqrt{(Z_1 Z_2)^3}}{\pi a^3}\int e^{-(Z_1+Z_2)r/a}4\pi r^2 dr = \frac{4}{a^3}\left(\frac{y}{2}\right)^3\left[\frac{2a^3}{(Z_1+Z_2)^3}\right] = \left(\frac{y}{x}\right)^3.$$

$$A^2 = \frac{1}{2\left[1+(y/x)^6\right]}.$$

$$H = -\frac{\hbar^2}{2m}(\nabla_1^2 + \nabla_2^2) - \frac{e^2}{4\pi\epsilon_0}\left(\frac{1}{r_1}+\frac{1}{r_2}\right) + \frac{e^2}{4\pi\epsilon_0}\frac{1}{|\mathbf{r_1}-\mathbf{r_2}|},$$

$$H\psi = A\left\{\left[-\frac{\hbar^2}{2m}(\nabla_1^2+\nabla_2^2) - \frac{e^2}{4\pi\epsilon_0}\left(\frac{Z_1}{r_1}+\frac{Z_2}{r_2}\right)\right]\psi_1(r_1)\psi_2(r_2)\right.$$

$$\left. + \left[-\frac{\hbar^2}{2m}(\nabla_1^2+\nabla_2^2) - \frac{e^2}{4\pi\epsilon_0}\left(\frac{Z_1}{r_1}+\frac{Z_2}{r_2}\right)\right]\psi_2(r_1)\psi_1(r_2)\right\}$$

$$+ A\frac{e^2}{4\pi\epsilon_0}\left\{\left[\frac{Z_1-1}{r_1}+\frac{Z_2-1}{r_2}\right]\psi_1(r_1)\psi_2(r_2) + \left[\frac{Z_2-1}{r_1}+\frac{Z_1-1}{r_2}\right]\psi_2(r_1)\psi_1(r_2)\right\} + V_{ee}\psi,$$

where $V_{ee} \equiv \frac{e^2}{4\pi\epsilon_0}\frac{1}{|\mathbf{r_1}-\mathbf{r_2}|}$.

The term in first curly brackets is $(Z_1^2 + Z_2^2)E_1\psi_1(r_1)\psi_2(r_2) + (Z_2^2 + Z_1^2)\psi_2(r_1)\psi_1(r_2)$, so

$$H\psi = (Z_1^2 + Z_2^2)E_1\psi$$

$$+ A\frac{e^2}{4\pi\epsilon_0}\left\{\left[\frac{Z_1-1}{r_1}+\frac{Z_2-1}{r_2}\right]\psi_1(r_1)\psi_2(r_2) + \left[\frac{Z_2-1}{r_1}+\frac{Z_1-1}{r_2}\right]\psi_2(r_1)\psi_1(r_2)\right\} + V_{ee}\psi$$

$$\langle H\rangle = (Z_1^2 + Z_2^2)E_1 + \langle V_{ee}\rangle + A^2\left(\frac{e^2}{4\pi\epsilon_0}\right)$$

$$\times \left\{\langle\psi_1(r_1)\psi_2(r_2) + \psi_2(r_1)\psi_1(r_2)\left|\left(\left[\frac{Z_1-1}{r_1}+\frac{Z_2-1}{r_2}\right]\right|\psi_1(r_1)\psi_2(r_2)\rangle + \left[\frac{Z_2-1}{r_1}+\frac{Z_1-1}{r_2}\right]\right|\psi_2(r_1)\psi_1(r_2)\rangle\right)\right\}.$$

$$\{\} = (Z_1-1)\langle\psi_1(r_1)\left|\frac{1}{r_1}\right|\psi_1(r_1)\rangle + (Z_2-1)\langle\psi_2(r_2)\left|\frac{1}{r_2}\right|\psi_2(r_2)\rangle$$

$$+ (Z_2-1)\langle\psi_1(r_1)\left|\frac{1}{r_1}\right|\psi_2(r_1)\rangle\langle\psi_2(r_2)|\psi_1(r_2)\rangle$$

$$+ (Z_1-1)\langle\psi_1(r_1)|\psi_2(r_1)\rangle\langle\psi_2(r_2)\left|\frac{1}{r_2}\right|\psi_1(r_2)\rangle + (Z_1-1)\langle\psi_2(r_1)\left|\frac{1}{r_1}\right|\psi_1(r_1)\rangle\langle\psi_1(r_2)|\psi_2(r_2)\rangle$$

$$+ (Z_2-1)\langle\psi_2(r_1)|\psi_1(r_1)\rangle\langle\psi_1(r_2)\left|\frac{1}{r_2}\right|\psi_2(r_2)\rangle + (Z_2-1)\langle\psi_2(r_1)\left|\frac{1}{r_1}\right|\psi_2(r_1)\rangle$$

$$+ (Z_1-1)\langle\psi_1(r_2)\left|\frac{1}{r_2}\right|\psi_1(r_2)\rangle$$

$$= 2(Z_1-1)\left\langle\frac{1}{r}\right\rangle_1 + 2(Z_1-1)\left\langle\frac{1}{r}\right\rangle_2 + 2(Z_1-1)\langle\psi_1|\psi_2\rangle\langle\psi_1\left|\frac{1}{r}\right|\psi_2\rangle + 2(Z_2-1)\langle\psi_1|\psi_2\rangle\langle\psi_1\left|\frac{1}{r}\right|\psi_2\rangle.$$

But $\quad \left\langle \dfrac{1}{r} \right\rangle_1 = \langle \psi_1(r) \left| \dfrac{1}{r} \right| \psi_1(r) \rangle = \dfrac{Z_1}{a}; \quad \left\langle \dfrac{1}{r} \right\rangle_2 = \dfrac{Z_2}{a}, \quad$ so $\quad \langle H \rangle = (Z_1^2 + Z_2^2)E_1$

$$+ A^2 \left( \frac{e^2}{4\pi\epsilon_0} \right) 2 \left[ \frac{1}{a}(Z_1 - 1)Z_1 + \frac{1}{a}(Z_2 - 1)Z_2 + (Z_1 + Z_2 - 2)\langle \psi_1 | \psi_2 \rangle \langle \psi_1 \left| \frac{1}{r} \right| \psi_2 \rangle \right] + \langle V_{ee} \rangle.$$

And $\quad \langle \psi_1 | \psi_2 \rangle = S = (y/x)^3$, so

$$\langle \psi_1 \left| \frac{1}{r} \right| \psi_2 \rangle = \frac{\sqrt{(Z_1 Z_2)^3}}{\pi a^3} 4\pi \int e^{-(Z_1 + Z_2)r/a} \, r \, dr = \frac{y^3}{2a^3} \left[ \frac{a}{Z_1 + Z_2} \right]^2 = \frac{y^3}{2ax^2}.$$

$$\langle H \rangle = (x^2 - \tfrac{1}{2}y^2)E_1 + A^2 \left( \frac{e^2}{4\pi\epsilon_0} \right) \frac{2}{a} \left\{ \left[ Z_1^2 + Z_2^2 - (Z_1 + Z_2) \right] + (x - 2)\left( \frac{y}{x} \right)^3 \frac{y^3}{2x^2} \right\} + \langle V_{ee} \rangle$$

$$= (x^2 - \tfrac{1}{2}y^2)E_1 + 4E_1 A^2 \left[ x^2 - \tfrac{1}{2}y^2 - x + \tfrac{1}{2}(x - 2)\frac{y^6}{x^5} \right] + \langle V_{ee} \rangle.$$

$$\langle V_{ee} \rangle = \frac{e^2}{4\pi\epsilon_0} \langle \psi \left| \frac{1}{|\mathbf{r_1} - \mathbf{r_2}|} \right| \psi \rangle$$

$$= \left( \frac{e}{4\pi\epsilon_0} \right) A^2 \langle \psi_1(r_1)\psi_2(r_2) + \psi_2(r_1) + \psi_1(r_2) \left| \frac{1}{|\mathbf{r_1} - \mathbf{r_2}|} \right| \psi_1(r_1)\psi_2(r_2) + \psi_2(r_1)\psi_1(r_2) \rangle$$

$$= \left( \frac{e}{4\pi\epsilon_0} \right) A^2 \left[ 2\langle \psi_1(r_1)\psi_2(r_2) \left| \frac{1}{|\mathbf{r_1} - \mathbf{r_2}|} \right| \psi_1(r_1)\psi_2(r_2) \rangle + 2\langle \psi_1(r_1)\psi_2(r_2) \left| \frac{1}{|\mathbf{r_1} - \mathbf{r_2}|} \right| \psi_2(r_1)\psi_1(r_2) \rangle \right]$$

$$= 2\left( \frac{e}{4\pi\epsilon_0} \right) A^2 (B + C), \quad \text{where}$$

$$B \equiv \langle \psi_1(r_1)\psi_2(r_2) \left| \frac{1}{|\mathbf{r_1} - \mathbf{r_2}|} \right| \psi_1(r_1)\psi_2(r_2) \rangle; \quad C \equiv \langle \psi_1(r_1)\psi_2(r_2) \left| \frac{1}{|\mathbf{r_1} - \mathbf{r_2}|} \right| \psi_2(r_1)\psi_1(r_2) \rangle.$$

$$B = \frac{Z_1^3 Z_2^3}{(\pi a^3)^2} \int e^{-2Z_1 r_1/a} e^{-2Z_2 r_2/a} \frac{1}{|\mathbf{r_1} - \mathbf{r_2}|} \, d^3\mathbf{r_1} \, d^3\mathbf{r_2}. \quad \text{As on pp 300-301, the } \mathbf{r_2} \text{ integral is}$$

$$\int e^{-2Z_2 r_2/a} \frac{1}{\sqrt{r_1^2 + r_2^2 - 2r_1 r_2 \cos\theta_2}} \, d^3\mathbf{r_2}$$

$$= \frac{\pi a^3}{Z_2^3 r_1} \left[ 1 - \left( 1 + \frac{Z_2 r_1}{a} \right) e^{-2Z_2 r_1/a} \right] \quad \text{(Eq. 7.24, but with } a \rightarrow \frac{2}{Z_2}a\text{)}.$$

$$B = \frac{Z_1^3 Z_2^3}{(\pi a^3)^2} \frac{(\pi a^3)}{Z_2^3} 4\pi \int_0^\infty e^{-2Z_1 r_1/a} \frac{1}{r_1} \left[ 1 - \left( 1 + \frac{Z_2 r_1}{a} \right) e^{-2Z_2 r_1/a} \right] r_1^2 \, dr_1$$

$$= \frac{4Z_1^3}{a^3} \int_0^\infty \left[ r_1 e^{-2Z_1 r_1/a} - r_1 e^{-2(Z_1 + Z_2)r_1/a} - \frac{Z_2}{a} r_1^2 e^{-2(Z_1 + Z_2)r_1/a} \right] dr_1$$

$$= \frac{4Z_1^3}{a^3}\left[\left(\frac{a}{2Z_1}\right)^2 - \left(\frac{a}{2(Z_1+Z_2)}\right)^2 - \frac{Z_2}{a}2\left(\frac{a}{2(Z_1+Z_2)}\right)^3\right] = \frac{Z_1^3}{a}\left(\frac{1}{Z_1^2} - \frac{1}{(Z_1+Z_2)^2} - \frac{Z_2}{(Z_1+Z_2)^3}\right)$$

$$= \frac{Z_1 Z_2}{a(Z_1+Z_2)}\left[1 + \frac{Z_1 Z_2}{(Z_1+Z_2)^2}\right] = \frac{y^2}{4ax}\left(1 + \frac{y^2}{4x^2}\right).$$

$$C = \frac{Z_1^3 Z_2^3}{(\pi a^3)^2}\int e^{-Z_1 r_1/a}e^{-Z_2 r_2/a}e^{-Z_2 r_1/a}e^{-Z_1 r_2/a}\frac{1}{|\mathbf{r_1}-\mathbf{r_2}|}d^3\mathbf{r}_1\,d^3\mathbf{r}_2$$

$$= \frac{(Z_1 Z_2)^3}{(\pi a^3)^2}\int e^{-(Z_1+Z_2)(r_1+r_2)/a}\frac{1}{|\mathbf{r_1}-\mathbf{r_2}|}d^3\mathbf{r}_1\,d^3\mathbf{r}_2.$$

The integral is the same as in Eq. 7.20, only with $a \to \frac{4}{Z_1+Z_2}a$. Comparing Eqs. 7.20 and 7.25, we see that the integral itself was

$$\frac{5}{4a}\left(\frac{\pi a^3}{8}\right)^2 = \frac{5}{256}\pi^2 a^5. \quad \text{So} \quad C = \frac{(Z_1 Z_2)^3}{(\pi a^3)^2}\frac{5\pi^2}{256}\frac{4^5 a^5}{(Z_1+Z_2)^5} = \frac{20}{a}\frac{(Z_1 Z_2)^3}{(Z_1+Z_2)^5} = \frac{5}{16a}\frac{y^6}{x^5}.$$

$$\langle V_{ee}\rangle = 2\left(\frac{e}{4\pi\epsilon_0}\right)A^2\left[\frac{y^2}{4ax}\left(1+\frac{y^2}{4x^2}\right) + \frac{5}{16a}\frac{y^6}{x^5}\right] = 2A^2(-2E_1)\frac{y^2}{4x}\left(1+\frac{y^2}{4x^2}+\frac{5y^4}{4x^4}\right).$$

$$\langle H\rangle = E_1\left\{x^2 - \frac{1}{2}y^2 - \frac{2}{[1+(y/x)^6]}\left[x^2 - \frac{1}{2}y^2 - x + \frac{1}{2}(x-2)\frac{y^6}{x^5}\right] - \frac{2}{[1+(y/x)^6]}\frac{y^2}{4x}\left(1+\frac{y^2}{4x^2}+\frac{5y^4}{4x^4}\right)\right\}$$

$$= \frac{E_1}{(x^6+y^6)}\left\{(x^2-\frac{1}{2}y^2)(x^6+y^6) - 2x^6\left[x^2 - \frac{1}{2}y^2 - x + \frac{1}{2}\frac{y^6}{x^4} - \frac{y^6}{x^5} + \frac{y^2}{4x} + \frac{y^4}{16x^3} + \frac{5y^6}{16x^5}\right]\right\}$$

$$= \frac{E_1}{(x^6+y^6)}\left(x^8 + x^2 y^6 - \frac{1}{2}x^6 y^2 - \frac{1}{2}y^8 - 2x^8 + x^6 y^2 + 2x^7 - x^2 y^6 + 2xy^6 - \frac{1}{2}x^5 y^2 - \frac{1}{8}x^3 y^4 - \frac{5}{8}xy^6\right)$$

$$= \boxed{\frac{E_1}{(x^6+y^6)}\left(-x^8 + 2x^7 + \frac{1}{2}x^6 y^2 - \frac{1}{2}x^5 y^2 - \frac{1}{8}x^3 y^4 + \frac{11}{8}xy^6 - \frac{1}{2}y^8\right).}$$

*Mathematica* finds the minimum of $\langle H\rangle$ at $x = 1.32245$, $y = 1.08505$, corresponding to $Z_1 = 1.0392$, $Z_2 = 0.2832$. At this point, $\boxed{\langle H\rangle_{\min} = 1.0266 E_1 = -13.962 \text{ eV},}$ which *is* less than $-13.6$ eV—but not by much!

## Problem 7.19

The calculation is the same as before, but with $m_e \to m_\mu$ (reduced), where

$$m_\mu(\text{reduced}) = \frac{m_\mu m_d}{m_\mu + m_d} = \frac{m_\mu 2m_p}{m_\mu + 2m_p} = \frac{m_\mu}{1 + m_\mu/2m_p}. \quad \text{From Problem 6.28, } m_\mu = 207 m_e, \text{ so}$$

$$1 + \frac{m_\mu}{2m_p} = 1 + \left(\frac{207}{2}\right)\frac{(9.11\times 10^{-31})}{(1.67\times 10^{-27})} = 1.056; \quad m_\mu(\text{reduced}) = \frac{207\,m_e}{1.056} = 196\,m_e.$$

This shrinks the whole molecule down by a factor of almost 200, bringing the deuterons much closer together, as desired. The equilibrium separation for the electron case was $2.493\,a$ (Problem 7.10), so for muons, $R = \frac{2.493}{196}(0.529\times 10^{-10}\text{ m}) = \boxed{6.73\times 10^{-13}\text{ m}.}$

## Problem 7.20

**(a)**

$$-\frac{\hbar^2}{2m}\left(\frac{\partial^2\psi}{\partial x^2}+\frac{\partial^2\psi}{\partial y^2}\right)=E\psi. \quad \text{Let } \psi(x,y)=X(x)Y(y).$$

$$Y\frac{d^2X}{dx^2}+X\frac{d^2Y}{dy^2}=-\frac{2mE}{\hbar^2}XY; \quad \frac{1}{X}\frac{d^2X}{dx^2}+\frac{1}{Y}\frac{d^2Y}{dy^2}=-\frac{2mE}{\hbar^2}.$$

$$\frac{d^2X}{dx^2}=-k_x^2X; \quad \frac{d^2Y}{dy^2}=-k_y^2Y, \quad \text{with} \quad k_x^2+k_y^2=\frac{2mE}{\hbar^2}. \quad \text{The general solution to the } y \text{ equation is}$$

$$Y(y)=A\cos k_y y+B\sin k_y y; \quad \text{the boundary conditions } Y(\pm a)=0 \text{ yield } k_y=\frac{n\pi}{2a} \text{ with minimum } \frac{\pi}{2a}.$$

[Note that $k_y^2$ has to be positive, or you cannot meet the boundary conditions at all.] So

$$E \geq \frac{\hbar^2}{2m}\left(k_x^2+\frac{\pi^2}{4a^2}\right). \text{ For a traveling wave } k_x^2 \text{ has to be positive. } \textit{Conclusion: } \text{Any solution with } E <$$

$$\boxed{\frac{\pi^2\hbar^2}{8ma^2}} \text{ will be a bound state.}$$

**(b)**

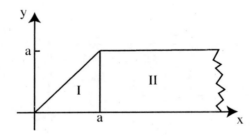

Integrate over regions I and II (in the figure), and multiply by 8.

$$I_{II}=A^2\int_{x=a}^{\infty}\int_{y=0}^{a}\left(1-\frac{y}{a}\right)^2 e^{-2\alpha x/a}dx\,dy. \quad \text{Let } u\equiv\frac{x}{a}, \ v\equiv\frac{y}{a}, \ dx=a\,du, \ dy=a\,dv.$$

$$=A^2a^2\int_1^{\infty}\int_0^1(1-v)^2e^{-2\alpha u}du\,dv=A^2a^2\left[\left.\frac{(1-v)^3}{3}\right|_0^1\times\left.\frac{e^{-2\alpha u}}{2\alpha}\right|_1^{\infty}\right]$$

$$=\frac{A^2a^2}{6\alpha}(-1)\left(-e^{-2\alpha}\right)=\boxed{\frac{A^2a^2}{6\alpha}e^{-2\alpha}}.$$

$$I_I = \frac{1}{2}A^2 \int_{x=0}^{a} \int_{y=0}^{a} \left(1 - \frac{xy}{a^2}\right)^2 e^{-2\alpha} dx\, dy$$

$$= \frac{1}{2}A^2 a^2 \int_0^1 \int_0^1 (1-uv)^2 e^{-2\alpha} du\, dv = \frac{1}{2}A^2 a^2 e^{-2\alpha} \int_0^1 \left.\frac{(1-uv)^3}{-3v}\right|_0^1 dv$$

$$= -\frac{1}{2}A^2 a^2 e^{-2\alpha} \frac{1}{3}\int_0^1 \frac{(1-v)^3-1}{v}dv = \frac{1}{6}A^2 a^2 e^{-2\alpha}\int_0^1 (v^2 - 3v + 3)dv,$$

$$= \frac{1}{6}A^2 a^2 e^{-2\alpha}\left.\left(\frac{v^3}{3} - 3\frac{v^2}{2} + 3v\right)\right|_0^1 = \boxed{\frac{11}{36}A^2 a^2 e^{-2\alpha}.}$$

Normalizing:   $8\left[\dfrac{A^2 a^2}{6\alpha}e^{-2\alpha} + \dfrac{11}{36}A^2 a^2 e^{-2\alpha}\right] = 1 \Rightarrow \boxed{A^2 = \dfrac{9\alpha}{2a^2}\dfrac{e^{2\alpha}}{(6+11\alpha)}.}$

$$\langle H\rangle = -\frac{\hbar^2}{2m}\langle\psi|\frac{\partial^2}{\partial x^2} + \frac{\partial^2}{\partial y^2}|\psi\rangle = -8\frac{\hbar^2}{2m}(J_I + J_{II}).\quad \text{[Ignore roof-lines for the moment.]}$$

$$J_{II} = A^2 \int_{x=a}^{\infty}\int_{y=0}^{a}\left(1-\frac{y}{a}\right)e^{-\alpha x/a}\left(\frac{\partial^2}{\partial x^2} + \overset{0}{\cancel{\frac{\partial^2}{\partial y^2}}}\right)\left[\left(1-\frac{y}{a}\right)e^{-\alpha x/a}\right] dx\, dy$$

$$= A^2 \int_{x=a}^{\infty}\int_{y=0}^{a}\left(1-\frac{y}{a}\right)^2\left(\frac{\alpha}{a}\right)^2 e^{-2\alpha x/a} dx\, dy = \left(\frac{\alpha}{a}\right)^2 I_{II} = \left(\frac{\alpha}{\cancel{a}}\right)^{\cancel{2}}\frac{A^2 \cancel{a^2}}{6\cancel{\alpha}}e^{-2\alpha} = \boxed{\frac{1}{6}A^2 \alpha e^{-2\alpha}.}$$

$$J_I = \frac{1}{2}A^2\int_0^a\int_0^a\left(1-\frac{xy}{a^2}\right)e^{-\alpha}\left(\frac{\partial^2}{\partial x^2} + \frac{\partial^2}{\partial y^2}\right)\left(1-\frac{xy}{a^2}\right)e^{-\alpha} dx\, dy = \boxed{0.}$$

$$\text{[Note that } \frac{\partial^2}{\partial x^2}\left(1-\frac{xy}{a^2}\right) = \frac{\partial}{\partial x}\left(-\frac{y}{a^2}\right) = 0, \text{ and likewise for } \partial^2/\partial y^2.]$$

$$\boxed{\langle H\rangle_{\text{so far}} = -\frac{2}{3}A^2\frac{\hbar^2\alpha}{m}e^{-2\alpha}.}$$

Now the roof-lines; label them as follows:

**I. Right arm:** at $y = 0 : K_I$.

**II. Central square:** at $x = 0$ and at $y = 0 : K_{II}$.

**III. Boundaries:** at $x = \pm a$ and at $y = \pm a : K_{III}$.

$$K_I = 4\left(-\frac{\hbar^2}{2m}\right)A^2\int_{x=a}^{\infty}\int_{y=-a}^{a}\left(1-\frac{|y|}{a}\right)e^{-\alpha x/a}\left(\cancel{\frac{\partial^2}{\partial x^2}} + \frac{\partial^2}{\partial y^2}\right)\left(1-\frac{|y|}{a}\right)e^{-\alpha x/a}dx\, dy.$$

$$|y| = y\Big[\theta(y) - \theta(-y)\Big],$$

$$\frac{\partial}{\partial y}\left(1-\frac{|y|}{a}\right) = -\frac{1}{a}\Big[\theta(y) - \theta(-y) + \cancel{y\delta(y)} + \cancel{y\delta(y)}\Big],$$

$$\frac{\partial^2}{\partial y^2}\left(1-\frac{|y|}{a}\right) = -\frac{1}{a}\Big[\delta(y) - \delta(-y)(-1)\Big] = -\frac{2}{a}\delta(y).$$

$$K_I = -\frac{2\hbar^2}{m}A^2 \underbrace{\int_{x=a}^{\infty} e^{-2\alpha x/a}dx}_{\clubsuit} \underbrace{\int_{y=-a}^{a} \left(1 - \frac{|y|}{a}\right)\left[-\frac{2}{a}\delta(y)\right]dy}_{\spadesuit}$$

$$\clubsuit = \left.\frac{e^{-2\alpha x/a}}{(-2\alpha/a)}\right|_{a}^{\infty} = -\frac{e^{-2\alpha}}{(-2\alpha/a)} = \frac{a}{2\alpha}e^{-2\alpha}; \quad \spadesuit = -\frac{2}{a},$$

$$= -\frac{2\hbar^2 A^2}{m}\frac{\cancel{a}}{\cancel{2}\alpha}e^{-2\alpha}\left(-\cancel{\frac{2}{a}}\right); \quad \boxed{K_I = \frac{2\hbar^2}{m\alpha}e^{-2\alpha}A^2.}$$

$$K_{II} = 4A^2\left(-\frac{\hbar^2}{2m}\right)\int_{x=0}^{a}\int_{y=-a}^{a}\left(1 - \frac{x|y|}{a^2}\right)e^{-\alpha}\left(\cancel{\frac{\partial^2}{\partial x^2}} + \frac{\partial^2}{\partial y^2}\right)\left(1 - \frac{x|y|}{a^2}\right)e^{-\alpha}dx\,dy$$

$$= -\frac{2\hbar^2}{m}A^2 e^{-2\alpha}\int_{x=0}^{a}\int_{y=-a}^{a}\left(1 - \frac{x|y|}{a^2}\right)\left[-\frac{2x}{a^2}\delta(y)\right]dx\,dy$$

$$= -\frac{2\hbar^2 A^2}{m}e^{-2\alpha}\left(-\cancel{\frac{2}{a^2}}\right)\underbrace{\int_{0}^{a}x\,dx}_{\frac{a^2}{\cancel{2}}}; \quad \boxed{K_{II} = \frac{2\hbar^2}{m}e^{-2\alpha}A^2.}$$

$$K_{III} = 8\left(-\frac{\hbar^2}{2m}\right)\int_{y=0}^{a}\int_{x=a-\epsilon}^{a+\epsilon}\psi\left(\frac{\partial^2}{\partial x^2} + \frac{\partial^2}{\partial y^2}\right)\psi\,dx\,dy.$$

In this region ($x$, $y$ both positive)    $\psi = A\left\{\begin{array}{l}\left(1 - xy/a^2\right)e^{-\alpha} \quad (x < a) \\ \left(1 - y/a\right)e^{-\alpha x/a} \quad (x > a)\end{array}\right\}$,    or

$$\psi = A\left(\left\{1 - \frac{y}{a}\left[\theta(x-a) + \frac{x}{a}\theta(a-x)\right]\right\}e^{-\alpha\left[\theta(a-x) + \frac{x}{a}\theta(x-a)\right]}\right).$$

$$\frac{\partial\psi}{\partial x} = A\left(-\frac{y}{a}\left[\cancel{\delta(x-a)} + \frac{1}{a}\theta(a-x) - \frac{x}{a}\cancel{\delta(a-x)}\right]e^{-\alpha\left[\theta(a-x) + \frac{x}{a}\theta(x-a)\right]}\right.$$

$$\left.+ \left\{1 - \frac{y}{a}\left[\theta(x-a) + \frac{x}{a}\theta(a-x)\right]\right\}e^{-\alpha\left[\theta(a-x) + \frac{x}{a}\theta(x-a)\right]}\left[\alpha\cancel{\delta(a-x)} - \frac{\alpha}{a}\theta(x-a) - \cancel{\frac{\alpha x}{a}\delta(x-a)}\right]\right)$$

[*Note:* $f(x) = x\delta(x)$ should be zero—but perhaps we should check that this is still safe when we're planning to take it's derivative:   $df/dx = \delta(x) + x\,d\delta/dx$ :

$$\int g\frac{df}{dx}dx = \int g\left[\delta(x) + x\frac{d\delta}{dx}\right]dx = g(0) + \int gx\frac{d\delta}{dx}dx$$

$$= g(0) + \cancel{gx\delta(x)|_{x=0}}^{\,0} - \int \frac{d}{dx}(gx)\delta(x)dx = g(0) - \int\left(g + x\frac{dg}{dx}\right)\delta(x)dx$$

$$= g(0) - g(0) - (xg')|_{x=0} = 0.$$

This confirms that $f(x)$ can be taken to be zero *even* when differentiated.]

So   $\delta(x-a) - \frac{x}{a}\delta(a-x) = \frac{1}{a}(a-x)\delta(a-x) = 0$.   Hence the cancellations above, leaving

$$\frac{\partial \psi}{\partial x} = A\Bigg( - \frac{y}{a^2}\theta(a - x)e^{-\alpha\left[\theta(a-x)+\frac{x}{a}\theta(x-a)\right]}$$

$$- \frac{\alpha}{a}\theta(x - a)\left\{1 - \frac{y}{a}\left[\theta(x - a) + \frac{x}{a}\theta(a - x)\right]\right\}e^{-\alpha\left[\theta(a-x)+\frac{x}{a}\theta(x-a)\right]}\Bigg)$$

$$= Ae^{-\alpha\left[\theta(a-x)+\frac{x}{a}\theta(x-a)\right]}\left( - \frac{y}{a^2}\theta(a - x) - \frac{\alpha}{a}\theta(x - a)\left\{1 - \frac{y}{a}\left[\theta(x - a) + \frac{x}{a}\theta(a - x)\right]\right\}\right)$$

$$= - \frac{A}{a}e^{-\alpha\left[\theta(a-x)+\frac{x}{a}\theta(x-a)\right]}\left[\frac{y}{a}\theta(a - x) + \alpha\theta(x - a)\left(1 - \frac{y}{a}\right)\right].$$

$$\frac{\partial^2 \psi}{\partial x^2} = - \frac{A}{a}e^{-\alpha\left[\theta(a-x)+\frac{x}{a}\theta(x-a)\right]}\Bigg\{ - \frac{y}{a}\delta(a - x) + \alpha\delta(x - a)\left(1 - \frac{y}{a}\right)$$

$$- \alpha\Bigg[ - \cancel{\delta(a - x)} + \underbrace{\frac{1}{a}\theta(x - a)}_{\text{integral } 0} + \cancel{\frac{x}{a}\delta(x - a)}\Bigg]\Bigg\}$$

$$= - \frac{A}{a}e^{-\alpha}\delta(x - a)\left[\alpha - \frac{\alpha y}{a} - \frac{y}{a}\right].$$

$$K_{III} = - \frac{4\hbar^2}{m}\int_{y=0}^{a}\int_{x=a-\epsilon}^{a+\epsilon}\psi(x,y)\left[ - \frac{A}{a}e^{-\alpha}\delta(x - a)\left(\alpha - \frac{\alpha y}{a} - \frac{y}{a}\right)\right]dx\,dy$$

$$= \frac{4\hbar^2 A}{ma}e^{-\alpha}\int_{y=0}^{a}\underbrace{\psi(a,y)}_{A(1-y/a)e^{-\alpha}}\left(\alpha - \frac{\alpha y}{a} - \frac{y}{a}\right)dy = \frac{4\hbar^2 A^2}{ma}e^{-2\alpha}\int_0^a\left(\alpha - 2\frac{\alpha y}{a} - \frac{y}{a} + \frac{\alpha y^2}{a^2} + \frac{y^2}{a^2}\right)dy$$

$$= \frac{4\hbar^2 A^2}{ma}e^{-2\alpha}\left(\alpha a - 2\frac{\alpha}{\cancel{a}}\frac{\cancel{a^2}}{2} - \frac{1}{a}\frac{a^2}{2} + \frac{\alpha}{a^2}\frac{a^3}{3} + \frac{1}{a^2}\frac{a^3}{3}\right) = \frac{4\hbar^2 A^2}{m}e^{-2\alpha}\underbrace{\left(\cancel{\alpha a} - \cancel{\alpha a} - \frac{\cancel{a}}{2} + \frac{\alpha\cancel{a}}{3} + \frac{\cancel{a}}{3}\right)}_{\frac{\alpha}{3}-\frac{1}{6}=\frac{1}{6}(2\alpha-1)}$$

$$= \frac{4\hbar^2 A^2}{6m}(2\alpha - 1)e^{-2\alpha}; \quad \boxed{K_{III} = \frac{2\hbar^2 A^2}{3m}(2\alpha - 1)e^{-2\alpha}.}$$

$$\langle H\rangle = - \frac{2}{3}A^2\frac{\hbar^2\alpha}{m}e^{-2\alpha} + \frac{2\hbar^2}{m\alpha}e^{-2\alpha}A^2 + \frac{2\hbar^2}{m}e^{-2\alpha}A^2 + \frac{2\hbar^2}{3m}A^2(2\alpha - 1)e^{-2\alpha}$$

$$= \frac{A^2 e^{-2\alpha}\hbar^2}{m}\left[ - \frac{2}{3}\alpha + \frac{2}{\alpha} + 2 + \frac{2}{3}(2\alpha - 1)\right] = \frac{2A^2 e^{-2\alpha}\hbar^2}{3m}\left( - \alpha + \frac{3}{\alpha} + 3 + 2\alpha - 1\right)$$

$$= \frac{2A^2 e^{-2\alpha}\hbar^2}{3m}\left(\alpha + 2 + \frac{3}{\alpha}\right) = \frac{2A^2 e^{-2\alpha}\hbar^2}{3m\alpha}(\alpha^2 + 2\alpha + 3) = \frac{\cancel{2}}{3}\frac{e^{-2\alpha}\hbar^2}{m\cancel{\alpha}}(\alpha^2 + 2\alpha + 3)\frac{9}{\cancel{2}}\frac{\cancel{\alpha}}{a^2}\frac{\cancel{e^{2\alpha}}}{(6 + 11\alpha)}$$

$$= \boxed{\frac{3\hbar^2}{ma^2}\frac{(\alpha^2 + 2\alpha + 3)}{(6 + 11\alpha)}.}$$

$$\frac{d\langle H\rangle}{d\alpha} = \frac{3\hbar^2}{ma^2}\frac{(6 + 11\alpha)(2\alpha + 2) - (\alpha^2 + 2\alpha + 3)(11)}{(6 + 11\alpha)^2} = 0 \quad \Rightarrow (6 + 11\alpha)(2\alpha + 2) = 11(\alpha^2 + 2\alpha + 3).$$

$$12\alpha + 12 + 22\alpha^2 + 22\alpha = 11\alpha^2 + 22\alpha + 33 \Rightarrow 11\alpha^2 + 12\alpha - 21 = 0.$$

$$\alpha = \frac{-12 \pm 2\sqrt{(12)^2 + 4 \cdot 11 \cdot 21}}{22} = \frac{-6 \pm \sqrt{36 + 231}}{11}$$

$$= \frac{-6 \pm 16.34}{11} = \frac{10.34}{11} \;[\alpha \text{ has to be } positive] = \boxed{0.940012239.}$$

$$\langle H \rangle_{\min} = \frac{3\hbar^2}{ma^2}\frac{2(\alpha+1)}{11} = \boxed{\frac{6}{11}\frac{\hbar^2}{ma^2}(\alpha+1)} = \boxed{1.058\left(\frac{\hbar^2}{ma^2}\right).} \quad \text{But} \quad E_{\text{threshold}} = \frac{\pi^2}{8}\frac{\hbar^2}{ma^2} = \boxed{1.2337\frac{\hbar^2}{ma^2},}$$

so $E_0$ is definitely *less* than $E_{\text{threshold}}$.

# Chapter 8

# The WKB Approximation

## Problem 8.1

$$\int_0^a p(x)\, dx = n\pi\hbar, \quad \text{with } n = 1, 2, 3, \dots \text{ and } \quad p(x) = \sqrt{2m[E - V(x)]} \quad \text{(Eq. 8.16)}.$$

Here $\displaystyle\int_0^a p(x)\, dx = \sqrt{2mE}\left(\frac{a}{2}\right) + \sqrt{2m(E - V_0)}\left(\frac{a}{2}\right) = \sqrt{2m}\left(\frac{a}{2}\right)\left(\sqrt{E} + \sqrt{E - V_0}\right) = n\pi\hbar$

$$\Rightarrow E + E - V_0 + 2\sqrt{E(E - V_0)} = \frac{4}{2m}\left(\frac{n\pi\hbar}{a}\right)^2 = 4E_n^0; \quad 2\sqrt{E(E - V_0)} = (4E_n^0 - 2E + V_0).$$

Square again: $\quad 4E(E - V_0) = 4E^2 - 4EV_0 = 16E_n^{0\,2} + 4E^2 + V_0^2 - 16EE_n^0 + 8E_n^0 V_0 - 4EV_0$

$$\Rightarrow 16EE_n^0 = 16E_n^{0\,2} + 8E_n^0 V_0 + V_0^2 \Rightarrow \boxed{E_n = E_n^0 + \frac{V_0}{2} + \frac{V_0^2}{16E_n^0}.}$$

Perturbation theory gave $E_n = E_n^0 + \dfrac{V_0}{2}$; the extra term goes to zero for very small $V_0$ (or, since $E_n^0 \sim n^2$), for large $n$.

---

## Problem 8.2

**(a)**

$$\frac{d\psi}{dx} = \frac{i}{\hbar} f' e^{if/\hbar}; \quad \frac{d^2\psi}{dx^2} = \frac{i}{\hbar}\left(f'' e^{if/\hbar} + \frac{i}{\hbar}(f')^2 e^{if/\hbar}\right) = \left[\frac{i}{\hbar} f'' - \frac{1}{\hbar^2}(f')^2\right] e^{if/\hbar}.$$

$$\frac{d^2\psi}{dx^2} = -\frac{p^2}{\hbar^2}\psi \implies \left[\frac{i}{\hbar} f'' - \frac{1}{\hbar^2}(f')^2\right] e^{if/\hbar} = -\frac{p^2}{\hbar^2} e^{if/\hbar} \implies i\hbar f'' - (f')^2 + p^2 = 0. \quad \text{QED}$$

**(b)** $f' = f_0' + \hbar f_1' + \hbar^2 f_2' + \cdots \Longrightarrow (f')^2 = (f_0' + \hbar f_1' + \hbar^2 f_2' + \cdots)^2 = (f_0')^2 + 2\hbar f_0' f_1' + \hbar^2[2f_0'f_2' + (f_1')^2] + \cdots$

$f'' = f_0'' + \hbar f_1'' + \hbar^2 f_2'' + \cdots$. $\quad i\hbar(f_0'' + \hbar f_1'' + \hbar^2 f_2'') - (f_0')^2 - 2\hbar f_0' f_1' - \hbar^2[2f_0'f_2' + (f_1')^2] + p^2 + \cdots = 0.$

$\hbar^0 : (f_0')^2 = p^2; \quad \hbar^1 : if_0'' = 2f_0'f_1'; \quad \hbar^2 : if_1'' = 2f_0'f_2' + (f_1')^2; \quad \cdots$

**(c)** $\dfrac{df_0}{dx} = \pm p \Longrightarrow f_0 = \pm \displaystyle\int p(x)dx + \text{constant} \; ; \; \dfrac{df_1}{dx} = \dfrac{i}{2}\dfrac{f_0''}{f_0'} = \dfrac{i}{2}\left(\dfrac{\pm p'}{\pm p}\right) = \dfrac{i}{2}\dfrac{d}{dx}\ln p \Longrightarrow f_1 = \dfrac{i}{2}\ln p + \text{ const.}$

$\psi = \exp\left(\dfrac{if}{\hbar}\right) = \exp\left[\dfrac{i}{\hbar}\left(\pm\displaystyle\int p(x)\,dx + \hbar\dfrac{i}{2}\ln p + K\right)\right] = \exp\left(\pm\dfrac{i}{\hbar}\displaystyle\int p\,dx\right)p^{-1/2}e^{iK/\hbar}$

$\quad = \dfrac{C}{\sqrt{p}}\exp\left(\pm\dfrac{i}{\hbar}\displaystyle\int p\,dx\right). \quad \text{QED}$

---

## Problem 8.3

$$\gamma = \frac{1}{\hbar}\int |p(x)|\,dx = \frac{1}{\hbar}\int_0^{2a}\sqrt{2m(V_0 - E)}\,dx = \frac{2a}{\hbar}\sqrt{2m(V_0 - E)}. \quad \boxed{T \approx e^{-4a\sqrt{2m(V_0-E)}/\hbar}.}$$

From Problem 2.33, the *exact* answer is

$$T = \frac{1}{1 + \frac{V_0^2}{4E(V_0-E)}\sinh^2\gamma}.$$

Now, the WKB approximation assumes the tunneling probability is small (p. 322)—which is to say that $\gamma$ is *large*. In this case, $\sinh\gamma = \frac{1}{2}(e^\gamma - e^{-\gamma}) \approx \frac{1}{2}e^\gamma$, and $\sinh^2\gamma \approx \frac{1}{4}e^{2\gamma}$, and the exact result reduces to

$$T \approx \frac{1}{1 + \frac{V_0^2}{16E(V_0-E)}e^{2\gamma}} \approx \left\{\frac{16E(V_0-E)}{V_0^2}\right\}e^{-2\gamma}.$$

The coefficient in { } is of order 1; the dominant dependence on $E$ is in the exponential factor. In this sense $T \approx e^{-2\gamma}$ (the WKB result).

---

## Problem 8.4

I take the masses from Thornton and Rex, *Modern Physics*, Appendix 8. They are all *atomic* masses, but the electron masses subtract out in the calculation of $E$. All masses are in atomic units (u): $1\text{ u} = 931\text{ MeV}/c^2$. The mass of He$^4$ is 4.002602 u, and that of the $\alpha$-particle is 3727 MeV$/c^2$.

$\text{U}^{238} : Z = 92, \; A = 238, \; m = 238.050784\text{ u} \rightarrow \text{Th}^{234} : m = 234.043593\text{ u}.$

$r_1 = (1.07 \times 10^{-15}\text{ m})(238)^{1/3} = 6.63 \times 10^{-15}\text{ m}.$

$E = (238.050784 - 234.043593 - 4.002602)(931)\text{ MeV} = 4.27\text{ MeV}.$

$V = \sqrt{\dfrac{2E}{m}} = \sqrt{\dfrac{(2)(4.27)}{3727}} \times 3 \times 10^8\text{ m/s} = 1.44 \times 10^7\text{ m/s}.$

$$\gamma = 1.980\frac{90}{\sqrt{4.27}} - 1.485\sqrt{90(6.63)} = 86.19 - 36.28 = 49.9.$$

$$\tau = \frac{(2)(6.63 \times 10^{-15})}{1.44 \times 10^7}e^{98.8} \text{ s} = 7.46 \times 10^{21} \text{ s} = \frac{7.46 \times 10^{21}}{3.15 \times 10^7} \text{ yr} = \boxed{2.4 \times 10^{14} \text{ yrs.}}$$

$\text{Po}^{212} : Z = 84, A = 212, m = 211.988842 \text{ u} \to \text{Pb}^{208} : m = 207.976627 \text{ u.}$

$$r_1 = (1.07 \times 10^{-15} \text{ m})(212)^{1/3} = 6.38 \times 10^{-15} \text{ m.}$$

$$E = (211.988842 - 207.976627 - 4.002602)(931) \text{ MeV} = 8.95 \text{ MeV.}$$

$$V = \sqrt{\frac{2E}{m}} = \sqrt{\frac{(2)(8.95)}{3727}} \times 3 \times 10^8 \text{ m/s} = 2.08 \times 10^7 \text{ m/s.}$$

$$\gamma = 1.980\frac{82}{\sqrt{8.95}} - 1.485\sqrt{82(6.38)} = 54.37 - 33.97 = 20.4.$$

$$\tau = \frac{(2)(6.38 \times 10^{-15})}{2.08 \times 10^7}e^{40.8} \text{ s} = \boxed{3.2 \times 10^{-4} \text{ s.}}$$

These results are *way* off—but note the extraordinary sensitivity to nuclear masses: a tiny change in $E$ produces enormous changes in $\tau$.

Much more impressive results are obtained when you plot the logarithm of lifetimes against $1/\sqrt{E}$, as in Figure 8.6. Thanks to David Rubin for pointing this out. Some experimental values are listed below (all energies in MeV):

Uranium ($Z = 92$):

| $A$ | $E$ | $\tau$ |
|---|---|---|
| 238 | 4.198 | $4.468 \times 10^9$ yr |
| 236 | 4.494 | $2.342 \times 10^7$ yr |
| 234 | 4.775 | $2.455 \times 10^5$ yr |
| 232 | 5.320 | 68.9 yr |
| 230 | 5.888 | 20.8 day |
| 228 | 6.680 | 9.1 min |
| 226 | 7.570 | 0.35 s |

Protactinium ($Z = 91$):

| $A$ | $E$ | $\tau$ |
|---|---|---|
| 224 | 7.488 | 0.79 s |
| 222 | 8.540 | 2.9 ms |
| 220 | 9.650 | 0.78 $\mu$s |
| 218 | 9.614 | 0.12 ms |

Thorium ($Z = 90$):

| $A$ | $E$ | $\tau$ |
|---|---|---|
| 232 | 4.012 | $1.405 \times 10^{10}$ yr |
| 230 | 4.687 | $7.538 \times 10^4$ yr |
| 228 | 5.423 | 1.912 yr |
| 226 | 6.337 | 30.57 min |

Radium ($Z = 88$):

| $A$ | $E$ | $\tau$ |
|---|---|---|
| 226 | 4.784 | 1600 yr |
| 224 | 5.685 | 3.66 day |
| 222 | 6.559 | 38 s |
| 220 | 7.455 | 18 ms |
| 218 | 8.389 | 25.6 $\mu$s |

## Problem 8.5

**(a)** $\boxed{V(x) = mgx.}$

**(b)**

$$-\frac{\hbar^2}{2m}\frac{d^2\psi}{dx^2} + mgx\psi = E\psi \implies \frac{d^2\psi}{dx^2} = \frac{2m^2g}{\hbar^2}\left(x - \frac{E}{mg}\right). \quad \text{Let } y \equiv x - \frac{E}{mg}, \text{ and } \alpha \equiv \left(\frac{2m^2g}{\hbar^2}\right)^{1/3}.$$

Then $\dfrac{d^2\psi}{dy^2} = \alpha^3 y\psi$. Let $z \equiv \alpha y = \alpha(x - \frac{E}{mg})$, so $\dfrac{d^2\psi}{dz^2} = z\psi$. This is the Airy equation (Eq. 8.36), and the general solution is $\psi = aAi(z) + bBi(z)$. However, $Bi(z)$ blows up for large $z$, so $b = 0$ (to make $\psi$ normalizable). Hence $\boxed{\psi(x) = aAi\left[\alpha(x - \frac{E}{mg})\right].}$

**(c)** Since $V(x) = \infty$ for $x < 0$, we require $\psi(0) = 0$; hence $Ai\left[\alpha(-E/mg)\right] = 0$. Now, the zeros of $Ai$ are $a_n$ $(n = 1, 2, 3, \dots)$. Abramowitz and Stegun list $a_1 = -2.338$, $a_2 = -4.088$, $a_3 = -5.521$, $a_4 = -6.787$, etc. Here $-\dfrac{\alpha E_n}{mg} = a_n$, or $E_n = -\dfrac{mg}{\alpha}a_n = -mg\left(\dfrac{\hbar^2}{2m^2g}\right)^{1/3}a_n$, or $\boxed{E_n = -(\frac{1}{2}mg^2\hbar^2)^{1/3}a_n.}$ In this case $\frac{1}{2}mg^2\hbar^2 = \frac{1}{2}(0.1 \text{ kg})(9.8 \text{ m/s}^2)^2(1.055 \times 10^{-34}\text{J·s})^2 = 5.34 \times 10^{-68} \text{ J}^3; \quad (\frac{1}{2}mg^2\hbar^2)^{1/3} = 3.77 \times 10^{-23} \text{ J.}$

$$\boxed{E_1 = 8.81 \times 10^{-23} \text{ J}, \quad E_2 = 1.54 \times 10^{-22} \text{ J}, \quad E_3 = 2.08 \times 10^{-22} \text{ J}, \quad E_4 = 2.56 \times 10^{-22} \text{ J.}}$$

**(d)**

$$2\langle T\rangle = \langle x\frac{dV}{dX}\rangle \text{ (Eq. 3.97)}; \quad \text{here} \quad \frac{dV}{dx} = mg, \quad \text{so} \quad \langle x\frac{dV}{dx}\rangle = \langle mgx\rangle = \langle V\rangle, \quad \text{so} \quad \langle T\rangle = \frac{1}{2}\langle V\rangle.$$

$$\text{But } \langle T\rangle + \langle V\rangle = \langle H\rangle = E_n, \quad \text{so} \quad \frac{3}{2}\langle V\rangle = E_n, \quad \text{or} \quad \langle V\rangle = \frac{2}{3}E_n. \quad \text{But } \langle V\rangle = mg\langle x\rangle, \quad \text{so} \quad \langle x\rangle = \frac{2E_n}{3mg}.$$

$$\text{For the electron, } \left(\frac{1}{2}mg^2\hbar^2\right)^{1/3} = \left[\frac{1}{2}(9.11 \times 10^{-31})(9.8)^2(1.055 \times 10^{-34})^2\right]^{1/3} = 7.87 \times 10^{-33} \text{ J.}$$

$$E_1 = 1.84 \times 10^{-32} \text{ J} = \boxed{1.15 \times 10^{-13} \text{ eV.}} \quad \langle x\rangle = \frac{2(1.84 \times 10^{-32})}{3(9.11 \times 10^{-31})(9.8)} = 1.37 \times 10^{-3} = \boxed{1.37 \text{ mm.}}$$

---

## Problem 8.6

**(a)**

$$\text{Eq. 8.47} \implies \int_0^{x_2} p(x)\,dx = (n - \frac{1}{4})\pi\hbar, \text{ where } p(x) = \sqrt{2m(E - mgx)} \text{ and } E = mgx_2 \implies x_2 = E/mg.$$

$$\int_0^{x_2} p(x)\,dx = \sqrt{2m}\int_0^{x_2}\sqrt{E - mgx}\,dx = \sqrt{2m}\left[-\frac{2}{3mg}(E - mgx)^{3/2}\right]\Big|_0^{x_2}$$

$$= -\frac{2}{3}\sqrt{\frac{2}{m}}\frac{1}{g}\left[(E - mgx_2)^{3/2} - E^{3/2}\right] = \frac{2}{3}\sqrt{\frac{2}{m}}\frac{1}{g}E^{3/2}.$$

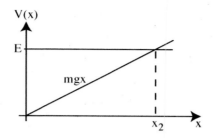

$$\frac{1}{3\sqrt{mg}}(2E)^{3/2} = (n - \frac{1}{4})\pi\hbar, \quad \text{or} \quad \boxed{E_n = \left[\frac{9}{8}\pi^2 mg^2\hbar^2(n - \frac{1}{4})^2\right]^{1/3}.}$$

**(b)**

$$\left(\frac{9}{8}\pi^2 mg^2\hbar^2\right)^{1/3} = \left[\frac{9}{8}\pi^2(0.1)(9.8)^2(1.055 \times 10^{-34})^2\right]^{1/3} = 1.0588 \times 10^{-22} \text{ J.}$$

$$E_1 = (1.0588 \times 10^{-22})\left(\frac{3}{4}\right)^{2/3} = \boxed{8.74 \times 10^{-23} \text{ J,}}$$

$$E_2 = (1.0588 \times 10^{-22})\left(\frac{7}{4}\right)^{2/3} = \boxed{1.54 \times 10^{-22} \text{ J,}}$$

$$E_3 = (1.0588 \times 10^{-22})\left(\frac{11}{4}\right)^{2/3} = \boxed{2.08 \times 10^{-22} \text{ J,}}$$

$$E_4 = (1.0588 \times 10^{-22})\left(\frac{15}{4}\right)^{2/3} = \boxed{2.56 \times 10^{-22} \text{ J.}}$$

These are in very close agreement with the exact results (Problem 8.5(c)). In fact, they agree precisely (to 3 significant digits), except for $E_1$ (for which the exact result was $8.81 \times 10^{-23}$ J).

**(c)** From Problem 8.5(d),

$$\langle x \rangle = \frac{2E_n}{3mg}, \quad \text{so} \quad 1 = \frac{2}{3}\frac{(1.0588 \times 10^{-22})}{(0.1)(9.8)}\left(n - \frac{1}{4}\right)^{2/3}, \quad \text{or} \quad \left(n - \frac{1}{4}\right)^{2/3} = 1.388 \times 10^{22}.$$

$$n = \frac{1}{4} + (1.388 \times 10^{22})^{3/2} = \boxed{1.64 \times 10^{33}.}$$

---

## Problem 8.7

$$\int_{x_1}^{x_2} p(x)\,dx = \left(n - \frac{1}{2}\right)\pi\hbar; \quad p(x) = \sqrt{2m\left(E - \frac{1}{2}m\omega^2 x^2\right)}; \quad x_2 = -x_1 = \frac{1}{\omega}\sqrt{\frac{2E}{m}}.$$

$$\left(n - \frac{1}{2}\right)\pi\hbar = m\omega\int_{-x_2}^{x_2}\sqrt{\frac{2E}{m\omega^2} - x^2}\,dx = 2m\omega\int_0^{x_2}\sqrt{x_2^2 - x^2}\,dx = m\omega\left[x\sqrt{x_2^2 - x^2} + x_2^2\sin^{-1}(x/x_2)\right]_0^{x_2}$$

$$= m\omega x_2^2 \sin^{-1}(1) = \frac{\pi}{2}m\omega x_2^2 = \frac{\pi}{2}m\omega\frac{2E}{m\omega^2} = \frac{\pi E}{\omega}. \quad \boxed{E_n = \left(n - \tfrac{1}{2}\right)\hbar\omega}\ (n = 1, 2, 3, \dots)$$

Since the WKB numbering starts with $n = 1$, whereas for oscillator states we traditionally start with $n = 0$, letting $n \to n + 1$ converts this to the usual formula $E_n = (n + \frac{1}{2})\hbar\omega$. In this case the WKB approximation yields the *exact* results.

## Problem 8.8

(a)

$$\frac{1}{2}m\omega^2 x_2^2 = E_n = \left(n + \frac{1}{2}\right)\hbar\omega \quad (\text{counting } n = 0, 1, 2, \dots); \quad \boxed{x_2 = \sqrt{\frac{(2n + 1)\hbar}{m\omega}}.}$$

(b)

$$V_{\text{lin}}(x) = \frac{1}{2}m\omega^2 x_2^2 + (m\omega^2 x_2)(x - x_2) \implies V_{\text{lin}}(x_2 + d) = \frac{1}{2}m\omega^2 x_2^2 + m\omega^2 x_2 d.$$

$$\frac{V(x_2 + d) - V_{\text{lin}}(x_2 + d)}{V(x_2)} = \frac{\frac{1}{2}m\omega^2(x_2 + d)^2 - \frac{1}{2}m\omega^2 x_2^2 - m\omega^2 x_2 d}{\frac{1}{2}m\omega^2 x_2^2}$$

$$= \frac{x_2^2 + 2x_2 d + d^2 - x_2^2 - 2x_2 d}{x_2^2} = \left(\frac{d}{x_2}\right)^2 = 0.01. \quad \boxed{d = 0.1\, x_2.}$$

(c)

$$\alpha = \left[\frac{2m}{\hbar^2}m\omega^2 x_2\right]^{1/3} \quad (\text{Eq. 8.34}), \quad \text{so} \quad 0.1\, x_2\left[\frac{2m^2\omega^2}{\hbar^2}x_2\right]^{1/3} \geq 5 \implies \left[\frac{2m^2\omega^2}{\hbar^2}x_2^4\right]^{1/3} \geq 50.$$

$$\frac{2m^2\omega^2}{\hbar^2}\frac{(2n + 1)^2\hbar^2}{m^2\omega^2} \geq (50)^3; \quad \text{or} \quad (2n + 1)^2 \geq \frac{(50)^3}{2} = 62500; \quad 2n + 1 \geq 250; \quad n \geq \frac{249}{2} = 124.5.$$

$\boxed{n_{\min} = 125.}$ However, as we saw in Problems 8.6 and 8.7, WKB may be valid at much smaller $n$.

## Problem 8.9

Shift origin to the turning point.

$$\psi_{\text{WKB}} = \begin{cases} \dfrac{1}{\sqrt{|p(x)|}}De^{-\frac{1}{\hbar}\int_x^0 |p(x')|\, dx'} & (x < 0) \\[2ex] \dfrac{1}{\sqrt{|p(x)|}}\left[Be^{\frac{i}{\hbar}\int_0^x p(x')\, dx'} + Ce^{-\frac{i}{\hbar}\int_0^x p(x')\, dx'}\right] & (x > 0) \end{cases}$$

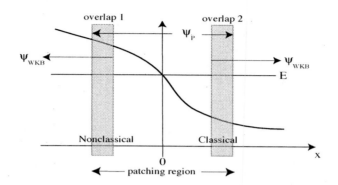

Linearized potential in the patching region:

$$V(x) \approx E + V'(0)x. \quad \text{Note}: \; V'(0) \text{ is } negative. \quad \frac{d^2\psi_p}{dx^2} = \frac{2mV'(0)}{\hbar^2}x\psi_p = -\alpha^3 x\psi_p, \quad \text{where} \, \alpha \equiv \left(\frac{2m|V'(0)|}{\hbar^2}\right)^{1/3}.$$

$$\psi_p(x) = aAi(-\alpha x) + bBi(-\alpha x). \quad \text{(Note change of sign, as compared with Eq. 8.37).}$$

$$p(x) = \sqrt{2m[E - E - V'(0)x]} = \sqrt{-2mV'(0)x} = \sqrt{2m|V'(0)|x} = \sqrt{\alpha^3 \hbar^2 x} = \hbar\alpha^{3/2}\sqrt{x}.$$

Overlap region 1 $(x < 0)$:

$$\int_x^0 |p(x')| \, dx' = \hbar\alpha^{3/2} \int_x^0 \sqrt{-x'} \, dx' = \hbar\alpha^{3/2} \left. \left(-\frac{2}{3}(-x')^{3/2}\right) \right|_x^0 = \frac{2}{3}\hbar\alpha^{3/2}(-x)^{3/2} = \frac{2}{3}\hbar(-\alpha x)^{3/2}.$$

$$\psi_{\text{WKB}} \approx \frac{1}{\hbar^{1/2}\alpha^{3/2}(-x)^{1/4}} D e^{-\frac{2}{3}(-\alpha x)^{3/2}}. \quad \text{For large positive argument } (-\alpha x \gg 1):$$

$$\psi_p \approx a\frac{1}{2\sqrt{\pi}(-\alpha x)^{1/4}} e^{-\frac{2}{3}(-\alpha x)^{3/2}} + b\frac{1}{\sqrt{\pi}(-\alpha x)^{1/4}} e^{\frac{2}{3}(-\alpha x)^{3/2}}. \quad \text{Comparing} \Rightarrow a = 2D\sqrt{\frac{\pi}{\alpha\hbar}}; \quad b = 0.$$

Overlap region 2 $(x > 0)$:

$$\int_0^x |p(x')| \, dx' = \hbar\alpha^{3/2} \int_0^x \sqrt{x'} \, dx' = \hbar\alpha^{3/2} \left. \left[\frac{2}{3}(x')^{3/2}\right] \right|_0^x = \frac{2}{3}\hbar(\alpha x)^{3/2}.$$

$$\psi_{\text{WKB}} \approx \frac{1}{\hbar^{1/2}\alpha^{3/4}x^{1/4}} \left[B e^{i\frac{2}{3}(\alpha x)^{3/2}} + C e^{-i\frac{2}{3}(\alpha x)^{3/2}}\right]. \quad \text{For large negative argument } (-\alpha x \ll -1):$$

$$\psi_p(x) \approx a\frac{1}{\sqrt{\pi}(\alpha x)^{1/4}} \sin\left[\frac{2}{3}(\alpha x)^{3/2} + \frac{\pi}{4}\right] = \frac{a}{\sqrt{\pi}(\alpha x)^{1/4}} \frac{1}{2i} \left[e^{i\pi/4}e^{i\frac{2}{3}(\alpha x)^{3/2}} - e^{-i\pi/4}e^{-i\frac{2}{3}(\alpha x)^{3/2}}\right] \quad \text{(remember}: b = 0).$$

Comparing the two: $\quad B = \frac{a}{2i}\sqrt{\frac{\alpha\hbar}{\pi}} e^{i\pi/4}, \quad C = -\frac{a}{2i}\sqrt{\frac{\alpha\hbar}{\pi}} e^{-i\pi/4}.$

Inserting the expression for $a$ from overlap region 1 : $B = -ie^{i\pi/4}D$; $C = ie^{-i\pi/4}D$.   For $x > 0$, then,

$$\psi_{\text{WKB}} = \frac{-iD}{\sqrt{p(x)}} \left[ e^{\frac{i}{\hbar}\int_0^x p(x')\,dx' + i\frac{\pi}{4}} - e^{-\frac{i}{\hbar}\int_0^x p(x')\,dx' - i\frac{\pi}{4}} \right] = \frac{2D}{\sqrt{p(x)}} \sin\left[ \frac{1}{\hbar}\int_0^x p(x')\,dx' + \frac{\pi}{4} \right].$$

Finally, switching the origin back to $x_1$:

$$\psi_{\text{WKB}}(x) = \left\{ \begin{array}{ll} \dfrac{D}{\sqrt{|p(x)|}} e^{-\frac{1}{\hbar}\int_x^{x_1} |p(x')|\,dx'}, & (x < x_1)\ ; \\[2ex] \dfrac{2D}{\sqrt{p(x)}} \sin\left[ \dfrac{1}{\hbar}\int_{x_1}^x p(x')\,dx' + \dfrac{\pi}{4} \right], & (x > x_1). \end{array} \right\} \quad \text{QED}$$

## Problem 8.10

At $x_1$, we have an upward-sloping turning point. Follow the method in the book. Shifting origin to $x_1$:

$$\psi_{\text{WKB}}(x) = \left\{ \begin{array}{ll} \dfrac{1}{\sqrt{p(x)}} \left[ Ae^{\frac{i}{\hbar}\int_x^0 p(x')\,dx'} + B^{-\frac{i}{\hbar}\int_x^0 p(x')\,dx'} \right] & (x < 0) \\[2ex] \dfrac{1}{\sqrt{p(x)}} \left[ Ce^{\frac{1}{\hbar}\int_0^x |p(x')|\,dx'} + D^{-\frac{1}{\hbar}\int_0^x |p(x')|\,dx'} \right] & (x > 0) \end{array} \right.$$

<u>In overlap region 2</u>, Eq. 8.39 becomes $\psi_{\text{WKB}} \approx \dfrac{1}{\hbar^{1/2}\alpha^{3/4}x^{1/4}} \left[ Ce^{\frac{2}{3}(\alpha x)^{3/2}} + De^{-\frac{2}{3}(\alpha x)^{3/2}} \right],$

whereas Eq. 8.40 is unchanged. Comparing them $\implies a = 2D\sqrt{\dfrac{\pi}{\alpha\hbar}}, \quad b = C\sqrt{\dfrac{\pi}{\alpha\hbar}}.$

<u>In overlap region 1</u>, Eq. 8.43 becomes $\psi_{\text{WKB}} \approx \dfrac{1}{\hbar^{1/2}\alpha^{3/4}(-x)^{1/4}} \left[ Ae^{i\frac{2}{3}(-\alpha x)^{3/2}} + Be^{-i\frac{2}{3}(-\alpha x)^{3/2}} \right],$

and Eq. 8.44 (with $b \neq 0$) generalizes to

$$\psi_p(x) \approx \frac{a}{\sqrt{\pi}(-\alpha x)^{1/4}} \sin\left[ \frac{2}{3}(-\alpha x)^{3/2} + \frac{\pi}{4} \right] + \frac{b}{\sqrt{\pi}(-\alpha x)^{1/4}} \cos\left[ \frac{2}{3}(-\alpha x)^{3/2} + \frac{\pi}{4} \right]$$

$$= \frac{1}{2\sqrt{\pi}(-\alpha x)^{1/4}} \left[ (-ia + b)e^{i\frac{2}{3}(-\alpha x)^{3/2}}e^{i\pi/4} + (ia + b)e^{-i\frac{2}{3}(-\alpha x)^{3/2}}e^{-i\pi/4} \right]. \text{ Comparing them} \implies$$

$A = \sqrt{\dfrac{\hbar\alpha}{\pi}} \left( \dfrac{-ia + b}{2} \right) e^{i\pi/4}; \quad B = \sqrt{\dfrac{\hbar\alpha}{\pi}} \left( \dfrac{ia + b}{2} \right) e^{-i\pi/4}.$   Putting in the expressions above for $a$ and $b$ :

$A = \left( \dfrac{C}{2} - iD \right) e^{i\pi/4}; \quad B = \left( \dfrac{C}{2} + iD \right) e^{-i\pi/4}.$

These are the connection formulas relating $A, B, C,$ and $D$, at $x_1$.

At $x_2$, we have a downward-sloping turning point, and follow the method of Problem 8.9. First rewrite the middle expression in Eq. 8.52:

$$\psi_{\mathrm{WKB}} = \frac{1}{\sqrt{|p(x)|}} \left[ C e^{\frac{1}{\hbar} \int_{x_1}^{x_2} |p(x')|\, dx' + \frac{1}{\hbar} \int_{x_2}^{x} |p(x')|\, dx'} + D e^{-\frac{1}{\hbar} \int_{x_1}^{x_2} |p(x')|\, dx' - \frac{1}{\hbar} \int_{x_2}^{x} |p(x')|\, dx'} \right].$$

Let $\gamma \equiv \int_{x_1}^{x_2} |p(x)|\, dx$, as before (Eq. 8.22), and let $C' \equiv D e^{-\gamma}$, $D' \equiv C e^{\gamma}$. Then (shifting the origin to $x_2$):

$$\psi_{\mathrm{WKB}} = \begin{cases} \dfrac{1}{\sqrt{|p(x)|}} \left[ C' e^{\frac{1}{\hbar} \int_{x}^{0} |p(x')|\, dx'} + D' e^{-\frac{1}{\hbar} \int_{x}^{0} |p(x')|\, dx'} \right], & (x < 0); \\[2mm] \dfrac{1}{\sqrt{p(x)}} F e^{\frac{i}{\hbar} \int_{0}^{x} p(x')\, dx'}, & (x > 0). \end{cases}$$

In the patching region $\psi_p(x) = a\,Ai(-\alpha x) + b\,Bi(-\alpha x)$, where $\alpha \equiv \left( \dfrac{2m|V'(0)|}{\hbar^2} \right)^{1/3}$; $\quad p(x) = \hbar \alpha^{3/2} \sqrt{x}$.

<u>In overlap region 1</u> $(x < 0)$: $\quad \displaystyle\int_{x}^{0} |p(x')|\, dx' = \frac{2}{3} \hbar (-\alpha x)^{3/2}$, so

$$\left. \begin{aligned} \psi_{\mathrm{WKB}} &\approx \frac{1}{\hbar^{1/2} \alpha^{3/4} (-x)^{1/4}} \left[ C' e^{\frac{2}{3}(-\alpha x)^{3/2}} + D' e^{-\frac{2}{3}(-\alpha x)^{3/2}} \right] \\ \psi_p &\approx \frac{a}{2\sqrt{\pi}(-\alpha x)^{1/4}} e^{-\frac{2}{3}(-\alpha x)^{3/2}} + \frac{b}{\sqrt{\pi}(-\alpha x)^{1/4}} e^{\frac{2}{3}(-\alpha x)^{3/2}} \end{aligned} \right\} \text{ Comparing} \implies \begin{cases} a = 2\sqrt{\dfrac{\pi}{\hbar \alpha}}\, D' \\[2mm] b = \sqrt{\dfrac{\pi}{\hbar \alpha}}\, C' \end{cases}$$

<u>In overlap region 2</u> $(x > 0)$: $\quad \displaystyle\int_{0}^{x} p(x')\, dx' = \frac{2}{3}\hbar(\alpha x)^{3/2} \implies \psi_{\mathrm{WKB}} \approx \frac{1}{\hbar^{1/2}\alpha^{3/4} x^{1/4}} F e^{i\frac{2}{3}(\alpha x)^{3/2}}.$

$$\psi_p \approx \frac{a}{\sqrt{\pi}(\alpha x)^{1/4}} \sin\left[ \frac{2}{3}(\alpha x)^{3/2} + \frac{\pi}{4} \right] + \frac{b}{\sqrt{\pi}(\alpha x)^{1/4}} \cos\left[ \frac{2}{3}(\alpha x)^{3/2} + \frac{\pi}{4} \right]$$

$$= \frac{1}{2\sqrt{\pi}(\alpha x)^{1/4}} \left[ (-ia + b) e^{i\frac{\pi}{4}} e^{i\frac{2}{3}(\alpha x)^{3/2}} + (ia + b) e^{-i\frac{\pi}{4}} e^{-i\frac{2}{3}(\alpha x)^{3/2}} \right]. \quad \text{Comparing} \implies (ia + b) = 0;$$

$$F = \sqrt{\frac{\hbar\alpha}{\pi}} \left( \frac{-ia + b}{2} \right) e^{i\pi/4} = b\sqrt{\frac{\hbar\alpha}{\pi}} e^{i\pi/4}. \quad b = \sqrt{\frac{\pi}{\hbar\alpha}} e^{-i\pi/4} F; \quad a = i\sqrt{\frac{\pi}{\hbar\alpha}} e^{-i\pi/4} F.$$

$$C' = \sqrt{\frac{\hbar\alpha}{\pi}}\, b = e^{-i\pi/4} F, \quad D' = \frac{1}{2}\sqrt{\frac{\hbar\alpha}{\pi}}\, a = \frac{i}{2} e^{-i\pi/4} F. \quad D = e^{\gamma} e^{-i\pi/4} F; \quad C = \frac{i}{2} e^{-\gamma} e^{-i\pi/4} F.$$

These are the connection formulas at $x_2$. Putting them into the equation for $A$:

$$A = \left( \frac{C}{2} - iD \right) e^{i\pi/4} = \left( \frac{i}{4} e^{-\gamma} e^{-i\pi/4} F - i e^{\gamma} e^{-i\pi/4} F \right) e^{i\pi/4} = i\left( \frac{e^{-\gamma}}{4} - e^{\gamma} \right) F.$$

$$T = \left| \frac{F}{A} \right|^2 = \frac{1}{(e^{\gamma} - \frac{e^{-\gamma}}{4})^2} = \boxed{\frac{e^{-2\gamma}}{\left[ 1 - (e^{-\gamma/2})^2 \right]^2}}.$$

If $\gamma \gg 1$, the denominator is essentially 1, and we recover $T = e^{-2\gamma}$ (Eq. 8.22).

## Problem 8.11

Equation 8.51 $\Rightarrow \left(n - \frac{1}{2}\right)\pi\hbar = 2\int_0^{x_2}\sqrt{2m(E - \alpha x^\nu)}\,dx = 2\sqrt{2mE}\int_0^{x_2}\sqrt{1 - \frac{\alpha}{E}x^\nu}\,dx;$   $E = \alpha x_2^\nu.$   Let

$z \equiv \frac{\alpha}{E}x^\nu$, so $x = \left(\frac{zE}{\alpha}\right)^{1/\nu}$;   $dx = \left(\frac{E}{\alpha}\right)^{1/\nu}\frac{1}{\nu}z^{\frac{1}{\nu}-1}\,dz.$ Then

$$\left(n - \frac{1}{2}\right)\pi\hbar = 2\sqrt{2mE}\left(\frac{E}{\alpha}\right)^{1/\nu}\frac{1}{\nu}\int_0^1 z^{\frac{1}{\nu}-1}\sqrt{1-z}\,dz = 2\sqrt{2mE}\left(\frac{E}{\alpha}\right)^{1/\nu}\frac{1}{\nu}\frac{\Gamma(1/\nu)\Gamma(3/2)}{\Gamma(\frac{1}{\nu}+\frac{3}{2})}$$

$$= 2\sqrt{2mE}\left(\frac{E}{\alpha}\right)^{1/\nu}\frac{\Gamma(\frac{1}{\nu}+1)\frac{1}{2}\sqrt{\pi}}{\Gamma(\frac{1}{\nu}+\frac{3}{2})} = \sqrt{2\pi mE}\left(\frac{E}{\alpha}\right)^{1/\nu}\frac{\Gamma(\frac{1}{\nu}+1)}{\Gamma(\frac{1}{\nu}+\frac{3}{2})}.$$

$$E^{\frac{1}{\nu}+\frac{1}{2}} = \frac{(n-\frac{1}{2})\pi\hbar}{\sqrt{2\pi m}}\alpha^{1/\nu}\frac{\Gamma(\frac{1}{\nu}+\frac{3}{2})}{\Gamma(\frac{1}{\nu}+1)};\quad \boxed{E_n = \left[\left(n - \frac{1}{2}\right)\hbar\sqrt{\frac{\pi}{2m\alpha}}\frac{\Gamma(\frac{1}{\nu}+\frac{3}{2})}{\Gamma(\frac{1}{\nu}+1)}\right]^{\left(\frac{2\nu}{\nu+2}\right)}\alpha.}$$

For $\nu = 2$:   $E_n = \left[\left(n - \frac{1}{2}\right)\hbar\sqrt{\frac{\pi}{2m\alpha}}\frac{\Gamma(2)}{\Gamma(3/2)}\right]\alpha = (n - \frac{1}{2})\hbar\sqrt{\frac{2\alpha}{m}}.$

For a harmonic oscillator, with $\alpha = \frac{1}{2}m\omega^2$,   $E_n = \left(n - \frac{1}{2}\right)\hbar\omega$ $(n = 1,2,3,\dots)$.  ✓

---

## Problem 8.12

$$V(x) = -\frac{\hbar^2 a^2}{m}\text{sech}^2(ax).\quad \text{Eq. 8.51} \Longrightarrow \left(n - \frac{1}{2}\right)\pi\hbar = 2\int_0^{x_2}\sqrt{2m\left[E + \frac{\hbar^2 a^2}{m}\text{sech}^2(ax)\right]}\,dx$$

$$= 2\sqrt{2}\hbar a\int_0^{x_2}\sqrt{\text{sech}^2(ax) + \frac{mE}{\hbar^2 a^2}}\,dx.$$

$E = -\frac{\hbar^2 a^2}{m}\text{sech}^2(ax_2)$   defines $x_2$.   Let $b \equiv -\frac{mE}{\hbar^2 a^2}$,   $z \equiv \text{sech}^2(ax)$,   so that $x = \frac{1}{a}\text{sech}^{-1}\sqrt{z}$, and hence

$$dx = \frac{1}{a}\left(\frac{-1}{\sqrt{z}\sqrt{1-z}}\right)\frac{1}{2\sqrt{z}}\,dz = -\frac{1}{2a}\frac{1}{z\sqrt{1-z}}\,dz.\quad \text{Then}\ \left(n - \frac{1}{2}\right)\pi = 2\sqrt{2}\,a\left(-\frac{1}{2a}\right)\int_{z_1}^{z_2}\frac{\sqrt{z-b}}{z\sqrt{1-z}}\,dz.$$

$$\text{Limits}: \left\{\begin{array}{l} x = 0 \implies z = \text{sech}^2(0) = 1 \\ x = x_2 \implies z = \text{sech}^2(ax_2) = -\frac{mE}{\hbar^2 a^2} = b \end{array}\right\}.\quad \left(n - \frac{1}{2}\right)\pi = \sqrt{2}\int_b^1\frac{1}{z}\sqrt{\frac{z-b}{1-z}}\,dz.$$

$$\frac{1}{z}\sqrt{\frac{z-b}{1-z}} = \frac{1}{z}\frac{(z-b)}{\sqrt{(1-z)(z-b)}} = \frac{1}{\sqrt{(1-z)(z-b)}} - \frac{b}{z\sqrt{(1-z)(z-b)}}.$$

$$\left(n - \frac{1}{2}\right)\pi = \sqrt{2}\left[\int_b^1 \frac{1}{\sqrt{(1-z)(z-b)}}\,dz - b\int_b^1 \frac{1}{z\sqrt{-b + (1+b)z - z^2}}\,dz\right]$$

$$= \sqrt{2}\left\{-2\tan^{-1}\sqrt{\frac{1-z}{z-b}} - \sqrt{b}\sin^{-1}\left[\frac{(1+b)z - 2b}{z(1-b)}\right]\right\}\Bigg|_b^1$$

$$= \sqrt{2}\left[-2\tan^{-1}(0) + 2\tan^{-1}(\infty) - \sqrt{b}\sin^{-1}(1) + \sqrt{b}\sin^{-1}(-1)\right] = \sqrt{2}\left(0 + 2\frac{\pi}{2} - \sqrt{b}\frac{\pi}{2} - \sqrt{b}\frac{\pi}{2}\right)$$

$$= \sqrt{2}\pi(1 - \sqrt{b}); \quad \frac{(n - \frac{1}{2})}{\sqrt{2}} = 1 - \sqrt{b}; \quad \sqrt{b} = 1 - \frac{1}{\sqrt{2}}\left(n - \frac{1}{2}\right).$$

Since the left side is positive, the right side must also be: $(n - \frac{1}{2}) < \sqrt{2}$, $n < \frac{1}{2} + \sqrt{2} = 0.5 + 1.414 = 1.914$. So the only possible $n$ is 1; there is only *one* bound state (which is correct—see Problem 2.51).

For $n = 1$, $\sqrt{b} = 1 - \frac{1}{2\sqrt{2}}$; $b = 1 - \frac{1}{\sqrt{2}} + \frac{1}{8} = \frac{9}{8} - \frac{1}{\sqrt{2}}$; $\boxed{E_1 = -\frac{\hbar^2 a^2}{m}\left(\frac{9}{8} - \frac{1}{\sqrt{2}}\right)} = -0.418\frac{\hbar^2 a^2}{m}$.

The *exact* answer (Problem 2.51(c)) is $-0.5\frac{\hbar^2 a^2}{m}$. Not bad.

## Problem 8.13

$$\left(n - \frac{1}{4}\right)\pi\hbar = \int_0^{r_0} \sqrt{2m\left[E - V_0\ln(r/a)\right]}\,dr; \quad E = V_0\ln(r_0/a) \text{ defines } r_0.$$

$$= \sqrt{2m}\int_0^{r_0} \sqrt{V_0\ln(r_0/a) - V_0\ln(r/a)}\,dr = \sqrt{2mV_0}\int_0^{r_0} \sqrt{\ln(r_0/r)}\,dr.$$

Let $x \equiv \ln(r_0/r)$, so $e^x = r_0/r$, or $r = r_0 e^{-x} \Longrightarrow dr = -r_0 e^{-x}dx$.

$$\left(n - \frac{1}{4}\right)\pi\hbar = \sqrt{2mV_0}(-r_0)\int_{x_1}^{x_2} \sqrt{x}e^{-e}\,dx. \quad \text{Limits}: \left\{\begin{array}{l} r = 0 \Longrightarrow x_1 = \infty \\ r = r_0 \Longrightarrow x_2 = 0 \end{array}\right\}.$$

$$\left(n - \frac{1}{4}\right)\pi\hbar = \sqrt{2mV_0}\,r_0\int_0^\infty \sqrt{x}e^{-x}\,dx = \sqrt{2mV_0}\,r_0\Gamma(3/2) = \sqrt{2mV_0}\,r_0\frac{\sqrt{\pi}}{2}.$$

$$r_0 = \sqrt{\frac{2\pi}{mV_0}}\hbar\left(n - \frac{1}{4}\right) \quad \Rightarrow \quad \boxed{E_n = V_0\ln\left[\frac{\hbar}{a}\sqrt{\frac{2\pi}{mV_0}}\left(n - \frac{1}{4}\right)\right]} = V_0\ln\left(n - \frac{1}{4}\right) + V_0\ln\left[\frac{\hbar}{a}\sqrt{\frac{2\pi}{mV_0}}\right].$$

$$E_{n+1} - E_n = V_0\ln\left(n + \frac{3}{4}\right) - V_0\ln\left(n - \frac{1}{4}\right) = V_0\ln\left(\frac{n + 3/4}{n - 1/4}\right), \text{ which is indeed independent of } m \text{ (and } a\text{).}$$

## Problem 8.14

$$\left(n - \frac{1}{2}\right)\pi\hbar = \int_{r_1}^{r_2}\sqrt{2m\left(E + \frac{e^2}{4\pi\epsilon_0}\frac{1}{r} - \frac{\hbar^2}{2m}\frac{l(l+1)}{r^2}\right)}\,dr = \sqrt{-2mE}\int_{r_1}^{r_2}\sqrt{-1 + \frac{A}{r} - \frac{B}{r^2}}\,dr,$$

where $A \equiv -\dfrac{e^2}{4\pi\epsilon_0}\dfrac{1}{E}$   and   $B \equiv -\dfrac{\hbar^2}{2m}\dfrac{l(l+1)}{E}$   are positive constants, since $E$ is negative.

$$\left(n - \frac{1}{2}\right)\pi\hbar = \sqrt{-2mE}\int_{r_1}^{r_2}\frac{\sqrt{-r^2 + Ar - B}}{r}\,dr.$$

Let $r_1$ and $r_2$ be the roots of the polynomial in the numerator:   $-r^2 + Ar - B = (r - r_1)(r_2 - r)$.

$$\left(n - \frac{1}{2}\right)\pi\hbar = \sqrt{-2mE}\int_{r_1}^{r_2}\frac{\sqrt{(r - r_1)(r_2 - r)}}{r}\,dr = \sqrt{-2mE}\,\frac{\pi}{2}\left(\sqrt{r_2} - \sqrt{r_1}\right)^2.$$

$$2\left(n - \frac{1}{2}\right)\hbar = \sqrt{-2mE}\left(r_2 + r_1 - 2\sqrt{r_1 r_2}\right).\quad \text{But } -r^2 + Ar - B = -r^2 + (r_1 + r_2)r - r_1 r_2$$

$$\implies r_1 + r_2 = A;\ r_1 r_2 = B.\quad \text{Therefore}$$

$$2\left(n - \frac{1}{2}\right)\hbar = \sqrt{-2mE}\left(A - 2\sqrt{B}\right) = \sqrt{-2mE}\left(-\frac{e^2}{4\pi\epsilon_0}\frac{1}{E} - 2\sqrt{-\frac{\hbar^2}{2m}\frac{l(l+1)}{E}}\right)$$

$$= \frac{e^2}{4\pi\epsilon_0}\sqrt{-\frac{2m}{E}} - 2\hbar\sqrt{l(l+1)}.$$

$$\frac{e^2}{4\pi\epsilon_0}\sqrt{-\frac{2m}{E}} = 2\hbar\left[n - \frac{1}{2} + \sqrt{l(l+1)}\right];\quad -\frac{E}{2m} = \frac{(e^2/4\pi\epsilon_0)^2}{4\hbar^2\left[n - \frac{1}{2} + \sqrt{l(l+1)}\right]^2}.$$

$$E = \frac{-(m/2\hbar^2)(e^2/4\pi\epsilon_0)^2}{\left[n - \frac{1}{2} + \sqrt{l(l+1)}\right]^2} = \boxed{\frac{-13.6\text{ eV}}{\left(n - \frac{1}{2} + \sqrt{l(l+1)}\right)^2}.}$$

---

## Problem 8.15

**(a)**       (i) $\boxed{\psi_{\text{WKB}}(x) = \dfrac{D}{\sqrt{|p(x)|}}e^{-\frac{1}{\hbar}\int_{x_2}^{x}|p(x')|\,dx'}}$     $(x > x_2)$;

(ii) $\psi_{\text{WKB}}(x) = \dfrac{1}{\sqrt{p(x)}}\left[Be^{\frac{i}{\hbar}\int_x^{x_2}p(x')\,dx'} + Ce^{-\frac{i}{\hbar}\int_x^{x_2}p(x')\,dx'}\right]$   $(x_1 < x < x_2)$;

(iii) $\psi_{\text{WKB}}(x) = \dfrac{1}{\sqrt{|p(x)|}}\left[Fe^{\frac{1}{\hbar}\int_x^{x_1}|p(x')|\,dx'} + Ge^{-\frac{1}{\hbar}\int_x^{x_1}|p(x')|\,dx'}\right]$   $(0 < x < x_1)$.

Equation 8.46 $\Longrightarrow$ $\boxed{\text{(ii)}\ \psi_{\text{WKB}} = \dfrac{2D}{\sqrt{p(x)}}\sin\left[\dfrac{1}{\hbar}\int_x^{x_2}p(x')\,dx' + \dfrac{\pi}{4}\right]}$   $(x_1 < x < x_2)$.

To effect the join at $x_1$, first rewrite (ii):

(ii) $\psi_{\text{WKB}} = \dfrac{2D}{\sqrt{p(x)}}\sin\left[\dfrac{1}{\hbar}\int_{x_1}^{x_2}p(x')\,dx' - \dfrac{1}{\hbar}\int_{x_1}^{x}p(x')\,dx' + \dfrac{\pi}{4}\right] = -\dfrac{2D}{\sqrt{p(x)}}\sin\left[\dfrac{1}{\hbar}\int_{x_1}^{x}p(x')\,dx' - \theta - \dfrac{\pi}{4}\right]$,

where $\theta$ is defined in Eq. 8.58. Now shift the origin to $x_1$:

$$\psi_{\text{WKB}} = \left\{ \begin{array}{ll} \dfrac{1}{\sqrt{|p(x)|}}\left[Fe^{\frac{1}{\hbar}\int_x^{0}|p(x')|\,dx'} + Ge^{-\frac{1}{\hbar}\int_x^{0}|p(x')|\,dx'}\right] & (x < 0) \\[12pt] -\dfrac{2D}{\sqrt{p(x)}}\sin\left[\dfrac{1}{\hbar}\int_0^x p(x')\,dx' - \theta - \dfrac{\pi}{4}\right] & (x > 0) \end{array} \right\}.$$

Following Problem 8.9: $\psi_p(x) = a\,Ai(-\alpha x) + b\,Bi(-\alpha x)$, with $\alpha \equiv \left(\dfrac{2m|V'(0)|}{\hbar^2}\right)^{1/3}$; $p(x) = \hbar\alpha^{3/2}\sqrt{x}$.

<u>Overlap region 1 $(x < 0)$</u>: $\displaystyle\int_x^0 |p(x')|\,dx' = \dfrac{2}{3}\hbar(-\alpha x)^{3/2}$.

$$\left. \begin{array}{l} \psi_{\text{WKB}} \approx \dfrac{1}{\hbar^{1/2}\alpha^{3/4}(-x)^{1/4}}\left[Fe^{\frac{2}{3}(-\alpha x)^{3/2}} + Ge^{-\frac{2}{3}(-\alpha x)^{3/2}}\right] \\[12pt] \psi_p \approx \dfrac{a}{2\sqrt{\pi}(-\alpha x)^{1/4}}e^{-\frac{2}{3}(-\alpha x)^{3/2}} + \dfrac{b}{\sqrt{\pi}(-\alpha x)^{1/4}}e^{\frac{2}{3}(-\alpha x)^{3/2}} \end{array} \right\} \Longrightarrow a = 2G\sqrt{\dfrac{\pi}{\hbar\alpha}};\quad b = F\sqrt{\dfrac{\pi}{\hbar\alpha}}.$$

<u>Overlap region 2 $(x > 0)$</u>: $\displaystyle\int_0^x p(x')\,dx' = \dfrac{2}{3}\hbar(\alpha x)^{3/2}$.

$$\Longrightarrow \psi_{\text{WKB}} \approx -\dfrac{2D}{\hbar^{1/2}\alpha^{3/4}x^{1/4}}\sin\left[\dfrac{2}{3}(\alpha x)^{3/2} - \theta - \dfrac{\pi}{4}\right],$$

$$\psi_p \approx \dfrac{a}{\sqrt{\pi}(\alpha x)^{1/4}}\sin\left[\dfrac{2}{3}(\alpha x)^{3/2} + \dfrac{\pi}{4}\right] + \dfrac{b}{\sqrt{\pi}(\alpha x)^{1/4}}\cos\left[\dfrac{2}{3}(\alpha x)^{3/2} + \dfrac{\pi}{4}\right].$$

Equating the two expressions: $\dfrac{-2D}{\hbar^{1/2}\alpha^{3/4}}\dfrac{1}{2i}\left[e^{i\frac{2}{3}(\alpha x)^{3/2}}e^{-i\theta}e^{-i\pi/4} - e^{-i\frac{2}{3}(\alpha x)^{3/2}}e^{i\theta}e^{i\pi/4}\right]$

$= \dfrac{1}{\sqrt{\pi}\alpha^{1/4}}\left\{\dfrac{a}{2i}\left[e^{i\frac{2}{3}(\alpha x)^{3/2}}e^{i\pi/4} - e^{-i\frac{2}{3}(\alpha x)^{3/2}}e^{-i\pi/4}\right] + \dfrac{b}{2}\left[e^{i\frac{2}{3}(\alpha x)^{3/2}}e^{i\pi/4} + e^{-i\frac{2}{3}(\alpha x)^{3/2}}e^{-i\pi/4}\right]\right\}$

$$\Longrightarrow \left\{ \begin{array}{ll} -2D\sqrt{\dfrac{\pi}{\alpha\hbar}}e^{-i\theta}e^{-i\pi/4} = (a + ib)e^{i\pi/4}, & \text{or}\quad (a + ib) = 2D\sqrt{\dfrac{\pi}{\alpha\hbar}}i e^{-i\theta} \\[12pt] 2D\sqrt{\dfrac{\pi}{\alpha\hbar}}e^{i\theta}e^{i\pi/4} = (-a + ib)e^{-i\pi/4}, & \text{or}\quad (a - ib) = -2D\sqrt{\dfrac{\pi}{\alpha\hbar}}i e^{i\theta} \end{array} \right\}$$

$$\implies \begin{cases} 2a = 2D\sqrt{\dfrac{\pi}{\alpha\hbar}} i(e^{-i\theta} - e^{i\theta}) \Rightarrow a = 2D\sqrt{\dfrac{\pi}{\alpha\hbar}}\sin\theta, \\[3mm] 2ib = 2D\sqrt{\dfrac{\pi}{\alpha\hbar}} i(e^{-i\theta} + e^{i\theta}) \Rightarrow b = 2D\sqrt{\dfrac{\pi}{\alpha\hbar}}\cos\theta. \end{cases}$$

Combining these with the results from overlap region 1 $\implies$

$$2G\sqrt{\frac{\pi}{\alpha\hbar}} = 2D\sqrt{\frac{\pi}{\alpha\hbar}}\sin\theta, \quad \text{or} \quad G = D\sin\theta; \quad F\sqrt{\frac{\pi}{\alpha\hbar}} = 2D\sqrt{\frac{\pi}{\alpha\hbar}}\cos\theta, \quad \text{or} \quad F = 2D\cos\theta.$$

Putting these into (iii) : $\boxed{\psi_{\text{WKB}}(x) = \dfrac{D}{\sqrt{|p(x)|}}\left[2\cos\theta e^{\frac{1}{\hbar}\int_x^{x_1}|p(x')|\,dx'} + \sin\theta e^{-\frac{1}{\hbar}\int_x^{x_1}|p(x')|\,dx'}\right]}$ $(0 < x < x_1).$

**(b)**

Odd($-$) case: (iii) $\implies \psi(0) = 0 \Rightarrow 2\cos\theta e^{\frac{1}{\hbar}\int_0^{x_1}|p(x')|\,dx'} + \sin\theta e^{-\frac{1}{\hbar}\int_0^{x_1}|p(x')|\,dx'} = 0.$

$\dfrac{1}{\hbar}\displaystyle\int_0^{x_1}|p(x')|\,dx' = \dfrac{1}{2}\phi$, with $\phi$ defined by Eq. 8.60. So $\sin\theta e^{-\phi/2} = -2\cos\theta e^{\phi/2}$, or $\tan\theta = -2e^{\phi}.$

Even($+$) case: (iii) $\implies \psi'(0) = 0 \Rightarrow -\dfrac{1}{2}\dfrac{D}{(|p(x)|)^{3/2}}\dfrac{d|p(x)|}{dx}\bigg|_0\left[2\cos\theta e^{\phi/2} + \sin\theta e^{-\phi/2}\right]$

$\qquad + \dfrac{D}{\sqrt{|p(x)|}}\left[2\cos\theta e^{\frac{1}{\hbar}\int_0^{x_1}|p(x')|\,dx'}\left(-\dfrac{1}{\hbar}|p(0)|\right) + \sin\theta e^{-\frac{1}{\hbar}\int_0^{x_1}|p(x')|\,dx'}\left(\dfrac{1}{\hbar}|p(0)|\right)\right] = 0.$

Now $\dfrac{d|p(x)|}{dx} = \dfrac{d}{dx}\sqrt{2m[V(x) - E]} = \sqrt{2m}\dfrac{1}{2}\dfrac{1}{\sqrt{V-E}}\dfrac{dV}{dx}$, and $\dfrac{dV}{dx}\bigg|_0 = 0$, so $\dfrac{d|p(x)|}{dx}\bigg|_0 = 0.$

$2\cos\theta e^{\phi/2} = \sin\theta e^{-\phi/2}$, or $\tan\theta = 2e^{\phi}$. Combining the two results: $\tan\theta = \pm 2e^{\phi}.$   QED

**(c)**

$$\tan\theta = \tan\left[\left(n + \frac{1}{2}\right)\pi + \epsilon\right] = \frac{\sin\left[\left(n + \frac{1}{2}\right)\pi + \epsilon\right]}{\cos\left[\left(n + \frac{1}{2}\right)\pi + \epsilon\right]} = \frac{(-1)^n\cos\epsilon}{(-1)^{n+1}\sin\epsilon} = -\frac{\cos\epsilon}{\sin\epsilon} \approx -\frac{1}{\epsilon}.$$

So $-\dfrac{1}{\epsilon} \approx \pm 2e^{\phi}$, or $\epsilon \approx \mp\dfrac{1}{2}e^{-\phi}$, or $\theta - \left(n + \dfrac{1}{2}\right)\pi \approx \mp\dfrac{1}{2}e^{-\phi}$, so $\theta \approx \left(n + \dfrac{1}{2}\right)\pi \mp \dfrac{1}{2}e^{-\phi}.$   QED

[Note: Since $\theta$ (Eq. 8.58) is positive, $n$ must be a *non-negative* integer: $n = 0, 1, 2, \ldots$. This is like harmonic oscillator (conventional) numbering, since it starts with $n = 0$.]

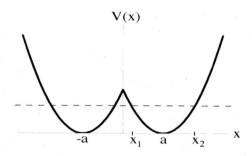

**(d)**

$$\theta = \frac{1}{\hbar} \int_{x_1}^{x_2} \sqrt{2m \left[ E - \frac{1}{2} m\omega^2 (x-a)^2 \right]} \, dx. \quad \text{Let } z = x - a \text{ (shifts the origin to a).}$$

$$= \frac{2}{\hbar} \int_0^{z_2} \sqrt{2m \left[ E - \frac{1}{2} m\omega^2 z^2 \right]} \, dz, \quad \text{where} \quad E = \frac{1}{2} m\omega^2 z_2^2.$$

$$= \frac{2}{\hbar} m\omega \int_0^{z_2} \sqrt{z_2^2 - z^2} \, dz = \frac{m\omega}{\hbar} \left[ z\sqrt{z_2^2 - z^2} + z_2^2 \sin^{-1}(z/z_2) \right] \Bigg|_0^{z_2} = \frac{m\omega}{\hbar} z_2^2 \sin^{-1}(1) = \frac{\pi}{2} \frac{m\omega}{\hbar} z_2^2,$$

$$= \frac{\pi}{2} \frac{m\omega}{\hbar} \frac{2E}{m\omega^2} = \boxed{\frac{\pi E}{\hbar\omega}}.$$

Putting this into Eq. 8.61 yields $\dfrac{\pi E}{\hbar\omega} \approx \left( n + \dfrac{1}{2} \right) \pi \mp \dfrac{1}{2} e^{-\phi},$ or $E_n^{\pm} \approx \left( n + \dfrac{1}{2} \right) \hbar\omega \mp \dfrac{\hbar\omega}{2\pi} e^{-\phi}.$ QED

**(e)**

$$\Psi(x,t) = \frac{1}{\sqrt{2}} \left( \psi_n^+ e^{-iE_n^+ t/\hbar} + \psi_n^- e^{-iE_n^- t/\hbar} \right) \implies$$

$$|\Psi(x,t)|^2 = \frac{1}{2} \left[ |\psi_n^+|^2 + |\psi_n^-|^2 + \psi_n^+ \psi_n^- \left( e^{i(E_n^- - E_n^+)t/\hbar} + e^{-i(E_n^- - E_n^+)t/\hbar} \right) \right].$$

(Note that the wave functions (i), (ii), (iii) are *real*). But $\dfrac{E_n^- - E_n^+}{\hbar} \approx \dfrac{1}{\hbar} 2 \dfrac{\hbar\omega}{2\pi} e^{-\phi} = \dfrac{\omega}{\pi} e^{-\phi},$ so

$$|\Psi(x,t)|^2 = \frac{1}{2} \left[ \psi_n^+(x)^2 + \psi_n^-(x)^2 \right] + \psi_n^+(x)\psi_n^-(x) \cos\left( \frac{\omega}{\pi} e^{-\phi} t \right).$$

It oscillates back and forth, with period $\tau = \dfrac{2\pi}{(\omega/\pi) e^{-\phi}} = \dfrac{2\pi^2}{\omega} e^{\phi}.$ QED

**(f)**

$$\phi = 2\frac{1}{\hbar} \int_0^{x_1} \sqrt{2m \left[ \frac{1}{2} m\omega^2 (x-a)^2 - E \right]} \, dx = \frac{2}{\hbar} \sqrt{2mE} \int_0^{x_1} \sqrt{\frac{m\omega^2}{2E} (x-a)^2 - 1} \, dx.$$

Let $z \equiv \sqrt{\dfrac{m}{2E}}\omega(a-x)$, so $dx = -\sqrt{\dfrac{2E}{m}}\dfrac{1}{\omega}dz$. Limits: $\left\{ \begin{array}{l} x = 0 \implies z = \sqrt{\dfrac{m}{2E}}\omega a \equiv z_0 \\ x = x_1 \implies \text{radicand } = 0 \implies z = 1 \end{array} \right\}$.

$$\phi = \frac{2}{\hbar}\sqrt{2mE}\sqrt{\frac{2E}{m}}\frac{1}{\omega}\int_1^{z_0}\sqrt{z^2-1}\,dz = \frac{4E}{\hbar\omega}\int_1^{z_0}\sqrt{z^2-1}\,dz = \frac{4E}{\hbar\omega}\frac{1}{2}\left[z\sqrt{z^2-1}-\ln(z+\sqrt{z^2-1})\right]\Big|_1^{z_0}$$

$$= \boxed{\frac{2E}{\hbar\omega}\left[z_0\sqrt{z_0^2-1}-\ln\left(z_0+\sqrt{z_0^2-1}\right)\right]},$$

where $\boxed{z_0 = a\omega\sqrt{\dfrac{m}{2E}}.}$ $V(0) = \frac{1}{2}m\omega^2 a^2$, so $V(0) \gg E \Rightarrow \dfrac{m}{2}\omega^2 a^2 \gg E \Rightarrow a\omega\sqrt{\dfrac{m}{2E}} \gg 1$, or $z_0 \gg 1$.
In that case

$$\phi \approx \frac{2E}{\hbar\omega}\left[z_0^2 - \ln(2z_0)\right] \approx \frac{2E}{\hbar\omega}z_0^2 = \frac{2E}{\hbar\omega}a^2\omega^2\frac{m}{2E} = \frac{m\omega a^2}{\hbar}.$$

This, together with Eq. 8.64, gives us the period of oscillation in a double well.

---

## Problem 8.16

**(a)** $E_n \approx \dfrac{n^2\pi^2\hbar^2}{2m(2a)^2}$. With $n = 1$, $\boxed{E_1 = \dfrac{\pi^2\hbar^2}{8ma^2}.}$

**(b)**

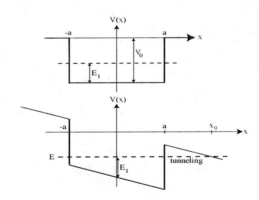

**(c)**

$$\gamma = \frac{1}{\hbar}\int_a^{x_0}|p(x)|\,dx. \quad \alpha x_0 = V_0 - E_1 \quad \Rightarrow \quad x_0 = \frac{V_0 - E_1}{\alpha}.$$

$$p(x) = \sqrt{2m\left[E - V(x)\right]}; \quad V(x) = -\alpha x, \quad E = E_1 - V_0.$$

$$= \sqrt{2m(E_1 - V_0 + \alpha x)} = \sqrt{2m\alpha}\sqrt{x - x_0}; \quad |p(x)| = \sqrt{2m\alpha}\sqrt{x_0 - x}.$$

$$\gamma = \frac{1}{\hbar}\sqrt{2m\alpha}\int_a^{x_0}\sqrt{x_0 - x}\,dx = \frac{\sqrt{2m\alpha}}{\hbar}\left[-\frac{2}{3}(x_0 - x)^{3/2}\right]\Big|_a^{x_0} = \frac{2}{3}\frac{\sqrt{2m\alpha}}{\hbar}(x_0 - a)^{3/2}.$$

Now $x_0 - a = (V_0 - E_1 - a\alpha)/\alpha$, and $a\alpha \ll \hbar^2/ma^2 \approx E_1 \ll V_0$, so we can drop $E_1$ and $a\alpha$. Then

$$\gamma \approx \frac{2}{3} \frac{\sqrt{2m\alpha}}{\hbar} \left(\frac{V_0}{\alpha}\right)^{3/2} = \boxed{\frac{\sqrt{8mV_0^3}}{3\alpha\hbar}}.$$

Equation 8.28 $\Rightarrow$ $\tau = \frac{4a}{v} e^{2\gamma}$, where $\frac{1}{2}mv^2 \approx \frac{\pi^2\hbar^2}{8ma^2} \Rightarrow v^2 = \frac{\pi^2\hbar^2}{4m^2a^2}$, or $v = \frac{\pi\hbar}{2ma}$. So

$$\tau = \frac{4a}{\pi\hbar} 2ma \, e^{2\gamma} = \boxed{\frac{8ma^2}{\pi\hbar} e^{2\gamma}}.$$

**(d)**

$$\tau = \frac{(8)\left(9.1 \times 10^{-31}\right)\left(10^{-10}\right)^2}{\pi\left(1.05 \times 10^{-34}\right)} e^{2\gamma} = \left(2 \times 10^{-19}\right) e^{2\gamma};$$

$$\gamma = \frac{\sqrt{(8)\left(9.1 \times 10^{-31}\right)\left(20 \times 1.6 \times 10^{-19}\right)^3}}{(3)\left(1.6 \times 10^{-19}\right)\left(7 \times 10^6\right)\left(1.05 \times 10^{-34}\right)} = 4.4 \times 10^4; \quad e^{2\gamma} = e^{8.8 \times 10^4} = \left(10^{\log e}\right)^{8.8 \times 10^4} = 10^{38,000}.$$

$$\tau = \left(2 \times 10^{-19}\right) \times 10^{38,000} \text{ s} = \boxed{10^{38,000} \text{ yr.}}$$

Seconds, years ... it hardly matters; nor is the factor out front significant. This is a huge number—the age of the universe is about $10^{10}$ years. In any event, this is clearly *not* something to worry about.

---

## Problem 8.17

Equation 8.22 $\Rightarrow$ the tunneling probability: $T = e^{-2\gamma}$, where

$$\gamma = \frac{1}{\hbar} \int_0^{x_0} \sqrt{2m(V-E)} \, dx. \quad \text{Here} \quad V(x) = mgx, \quad E = 0, \quad x_0 = \sqrt{R^2 + (h/2)^2} - h/2 \text{ (half the diagonal).}$$

$$= \frac{\sqrt{2m}}{\hbar} \sqrt{mg} \int_0^{x_0} x^{1/2} \, dx = \frac{m}{\hbar} \sqrt{2g} \frac{2}{3} x^{3/2} \Big|_0^{x_0} = \frac{2m}{3\hbar} \sqrt{2g} \, x_0^{3/2}.$$

I estimate: $h = 10$ cm, $R = 3$ cm, $m = 300$ gm; let $g = 9.8$ m/s$^2$. Then $x_0 = \sqrt{9 + 25} - 5 = 0.83$ cm, and

$$\gamma = \frac{(2)(0.3)}{(3)(1.05 \times 10^{-34})} \sqrt{(2)(9.8)} \, (0.0083)^{3/2} = 6.4 \times 10^{30}.$$

Frequency of "attempts": say $f = v/2R$. We want the product of the number of attempts ($ft$) and the probability of toppling at each attempt ($T$), to be 1:

$$t \frac{v}{2R} e^{-2\gamma} = 1 \quad \Rightarrow \quad t = \frac{2R}{v} e^{2\gamma}.$$

Estimating the thermal velocity: $\frac{1}{2}mv^2 = \frac{1}{2}k_B T$ (I'm done with the tunneling probability; from now on $T$ is the temperature, 300 K) $\Rightarrow v = \sqrt{k_B T/m}$.

$$t = 2R\sqrt{\frac{m}{k_B T}} e^{2\gamma} = 2(0.03)\sqrt{\frac{0.3}{(1.4 \times 10^{-23})(300)}} e^{12.8 \times 10^{30}} = 5 \times 10^8 \left(10^{\log e}\right)^{13 \times 10^{30}} = \left(5 \times 10^8\right) \times 10^{5.6 \times 10^{30}} \text{ s}$$

$$= \boxed{16 \times 10^{5.6 \times 10^{30}} \text{ yr.}}$$

Don't hold your breath.

---

# Chapter 9

# Time-Dependent Perturbation Theory

**Problem 9.1**

$\psi_{nlm} = R_{nl}Y_l^m$.   From Tables 4.3 and 4.7:

$$\psi_{100} = \frac{1}{\sqrt{\pi a^3}} e^{-r/a}; \quad \psi_{200} = \frac{1}{\sqrt{8\pi a^3}} \left(1 - \frac{r}{2a}\right) e^{-r/2a};$$

$$\psi_{210} = \frac{1}{\sqrt{32\pi a^3}} \frac{r}{a} e^{-r/2a} \cos\theta; \quad \psi_{21\pm1} = \mp \frac{1}{\sqrt{64\pi a^3}} \frac{r}{a} e^{r/2a} \sin\theta\, e^{\pm i\phi}.$$

But $r\cos\theta = z$ and $r\sin\theta e^{\pm i\phi} = r\sin\theta(\cos\phi \pm i\sin\phi) = r\sin\theta\cos\phi \pm ir\sin\theta\sin\phi = x \pm iy$.   So $|\psi|^2$ is an *even* function of $z$ in all cases, and hence $\int z|\psi|^2 dx\,dy\,dz = 0$, so $\boxed{H'_{ii} = 0.}$   Moreover, $\psi_{100}$ is even in $z$, and so are $\psi_{200}$, $\psi_{211}$, and $\psi_{21-1}$, so $\boxed{H'_{ij} = 0}$ for all *except*

$$H'_{100,210} = -eE\frac{1}{\sqrt{\pi a^3}}\frac{1}{\sqrt{32\pi a^3}}\frac{1}{a}\int e^{-r/a}e^{-r/2a}z^2\,d^3\mathbf{r} = -\frac{eE}{4\sqrt{2}\pi a^4}\int e^{-3r/2a}r^2\cos^2\theta\, r^2\sin\theta\,dr\,d\theta\,d\phi$$

$$= -\frac{eE}{4\sqrt{2}\pi a^4}\int_0^\infty r^4 e^{-3r/2a}dr\int_0^\pi \cos^2\theta\sin\theta\,d\theta\int_0^{2\pi}d\phi = -\frac{eE}{4\sqrt{2}\pi a^4}4!\left(\frac{2a}{3}\right)^5\frac{2}{3}2\pi = \boxed{-\left(\frac{2^8}{3^5\sqrt{2}}\right)eEa,}$$

or $\boxed{-0.7449\,eEa.}$

---

**Problem 9.2**

$\dot{c}_a = -\frac{i}{\hbar}H'_{ab}e^{-i\omega_0 t}c_b; \quad \dot{c}_b = -\frac{i}{\hbar}H'_{ba}e^{i\omega_0 t}c_a$.   Differentiating with respect to $t$:

$$\ddot{c}_b = -\frac{i}{\hbar}H'_{ba}\left[i\omega_0 e^{i\omega_0 t}c_a + e^{i\omega_0 t}\dot{c}_a\right] = i\omega_0\left[-\frac{i}{\hbar}H'_{ba}e^{i\omega_0 t}c_a\right] - \frac{i}{\hbar}H'_{ba}e^{i\omega_o t}\left[-\frac{i}{\hbar}H'_{ab}e^{-i\omega_0 t}c_b\right], \text{ or}$$

$$\ddot{c}_b = i\omega_0 \dot{c}_b - \frac{1}{\hbar^2}|H'_{ab}|^2 c_b. \quad \text{Let} \quad \alpha^2 \equiv \frac{1}{\hbar^2}|H'_{ab}|^2. \quad \text{Then} \quad \ddot{c}_b - i\omega_0 \dot{c}_b + \alpha^2 c_b = 0.$$

This is a linear differential equation with constant coefficients, so it can be solved by a function of the form $c_b = e^{\lambda t}$:

$$\lambda^2 - i\omega_0 \lambda + \alpha^2 = 0 \implies \lambda = \frac{1}{2}\left[i\omega_0 \pm \sqrt{-\omega_0^2 - 4\alpha^2}\right] = \frac{i}{2}(\omega_0 \pm \omega), \quad \text{where} \quad \omega \equiv \sqrt{\omega_0^2 + 4\alpha^2}.$$

The general solution is therefore

$$c_b(t) = Ae^{i(\omega_0+\omega)/2} + Be^{i(\omega_0-\omega)/2} = e^{i\omega_0 t/2}\left(Ae^{i\omega t/2} + Be^{-i\omega t/2}\right), \quad \text{or}$$

$$c_b(t) = e^{i\omega_0 t/2}\left[C\cos(\omega t/2) + D\sin(\omega t/2)\right]. \quad \text{But} \quad c_b(0) = 0, \quad \text{so} \quad C = 0, \quad \text{and hence}$$

$$c_b(t) = De^{i\omega_0 t/2}\sin(\omega t/2). \quad \text{Then}$$

$$\dot{c}_b = D\left[\frac{i\omega_0}{2}e^{i\omega_0 t/2}\sin(\omega t/2) + \frac{\omega}{2}e^{i\omega_0 t/2}\cos(\omega t/2)\right] = \frac{\omega}{2}De^{i\omega_0 t/2}\left[\cos(\omega t/2) + i\frac{\omega_0}{\omega}\sin(\omega t/2)\right] = -\frac{i}{\hbar}H'_{ba}e^{i\omega_0 t}c_a.$$

$$c_a = \frac{i\hbar}{H'_{ba}}\frac{\omega}{2}e^{-i\omega_0 t/2}D\left[\cos(\omega t/2) + i\frac{\omega_0}{\omega}\sin(\omega t/2)\right]. \quad \text{But} \quad c_a(0) = 1, \quad \text{so} \quad \frac{i\hbar}{H'_{ba}}\frac{\omega}{2}D = 1. \quad \text{Conclusion:}$$

$$\boxed{\begin{aligned} c_a(t) &= e^{-i\omega_0 t/2}\left[\cos(\omega t/2) + i\frac{\omega_0}{\omega}\sin(\omega t/2)\right], \\ c_b(t) &= \frac{2H'_{ba}}{i\hbar\omega}e^{i\omega_0 t/2}\sin(\omega t/2), \end{aligned}} \quad \text{where} \quad \boxed{\omega \equiv \sqrt{\omega_0^2 + 4\frac{|H'_{ab}|^2}{\hbar^2}}.}$$

$$|c_a|^2 + |c_b|^2 = \cos^2(\omega t/2) + \frac{\omega_0^2}{\omega^2}\sin^2(\omega t/2) + \frac{4|H'_{ab}|^2}{\hbar^2\omega^2}\sin^2(\omega t/2)$$

$$= \cos^2(\omega t/2) + \frac{1}{\omega^2}\left(\omega_0^2 + 4\frac{|H'_{ab}|^2}{\hbar^2}\right)\sin^2(\omega t/2) = \cos^2(\omega t/2) + \sin^2(\omega t/2) = 1. \quad \checkmark$$

---

## Problem 9.3

This is a tricky problem, and I thank Prof. Onuttom Narayan for showing me the correct solution. The safest approach is to represent the delta function as a sequence of rectangles:

$$\delta_\epsilon(t) = \begin{cases} (1/2\epsilon), & -\epsilon < t < \epsilon, \\ 0, & \text{otherwise.} \end{cases}$$

Then Eq. 9.13 $\Rightarrow$

$$\begin{cases} t < -\epsilon: & c_a(t) = 1, \ c_b(t) = 0, \\ t > \epsilon: & c_a(t) = a, \ c_b(t) = b, \\ -\epsilon < t < \epsilon: & \begin{cases} \dot{c}_a = -\frac{i\alpha}{2\epsilon\hbar}e^{-i\omega_0 t}c_b, \\ \dot{c}_b = -\frac{i\alpha^*}{2\epsilon\hbar}e^{i\omega_0 t}c_a. \end{cases} \end{cases}$$

In the interval $-\epsilon < t < \epsilon$,

$$\frac{d^2c_b}{dt^2} = -\frac{i\alpha^*}{2\epsilon\hbar}\left[i\omega_0 e^{i\omega_0 t}c_a + e^{i\omega_0 t}\left(\frac{-i\alpha}{2\epsilon\hbar}e^{-i\omega_0 t}c_b\right)\right] = -\frac{i\alpha^*}{2\epsilon\hbar}\left[i\omega_0\frac{i2\epsilon\hbar}{\alpha^*}\frac{dc_b}{dt} - \frac{i\alpha}{2\epsilon\hbar}c_b\right] = i\omega_0\frac{dc_b}{dt} - \frac{|\alpha|^2}{(2\epsilon\hbar)^2}c_b.$$

Thus $c_b$ satisfies a homogeneous linear differential equation with constant coefficients:

$$\frac{d^2c_b}{dt^2} - i\omega_0\frac{dc_b}{dt} + \frac{|\alpha|^2}{(2\epsilon\hbar)^2}c_b = 0.$$

Try a solution of the form $c_b(t) = e^{\lambda t}$:

$$\lambda^2 - i\omega_0\lambda + \frac{|\alpha|^2}{(2\epsilon\hbar)^2} = 0 \Rightarrow \lambda = \frac{i\omega_0 \pm \sqrt{-\omega_0^2 - |\alpha|^2/(\epsilon\hbar)^2}}{2},$$

or

$$\lambda = \frac{i\omega_0}{2} \pm \frac{i\omega}{2}, \quad \text{where } \omega \equiv \sqrt{\omega_0^2 + |\alpha|^2/(\epsilon\hbar)^2}.$$

The general solution is

$$c_b(t) = e^{i\omega_0 t/2}\left(Ae^{i\omega t/2} + Be^{-i\omega t/2}\right).$$

But

$$c_b(-\epsilon) = 0 \Rightarrow Ae^{-i\omega\epsilon/2} + Be^{i\omega\epsilon/2} = 0 \Rightarrow B = -Ae^{-i\omega\epsilon},$$

so

$$c_b(t) = Ae^{i\omega_0 t/2}\left(e^{i\omega t/2} - e^{-i\omega(\epsilon+t/2)}\right).$$

Meanwhile

$$c_a(t) = \frac{2i\epsilon\hbar}{\alpha^*}e^{-i\omega_0 t}\dot{c}_b = \frac{2i\epsilon\hbar}{\alpha^*}e^{-i\omega_0 t/2}A\left[\frac{i\omega_0}{2}\left(e^{i\omega t/2} - e^{-i\omega(\epsilon+t/2)}\right) + \frac{i\omega}{2}\left(e^{i\omega t/2} + e^{-i\omega(\epsilon+t/2)}\right)\right]$$

$$= -\frac{\epsilon\hbar}{\alpha^*}e^{-i\omega_0 t/2}A\left[(\omega+\omega_0)e^{i\omega t/2} + (\omega-\omega_0)e^{-i\omega(\epsilon+t/2)}\right].$$

But $\quad c_a(-\epsilon) = 1 = -\frac{\epsilon\hbar}{\alpha^*}e^{i(\omega_0-\omega)\epsilon/2}A\left[(\omega+\omega_0) + (\omega-\omega_0)\right] = -\frac{2\epsilon\hbar\omega}{\alpha^*}e^{i(\omega_0-\omega)\epsilon/2}A, \quad$ so $\quad A = -\frac{\alpha^*}{2\epsilon\hbar\omega}e^{i(\omega-\omega_0)\epsilon/2}.$

$$c_a(t) = \frac{1}{2\omega}e^{-i\omega_0(t+\epsilon)/2}\left[(\omega+\omega_0)e^{i\omega(t+\epsilon)/2} + (\omega-\omega_0)e^{-i\omega(t+\epsilon)/2}\right]$$

$$= e^{-i\omega_0(t+\epsilon)/2}\left\{\cos\left[\frac{\omega(t+\epsilon)}{2}\right] + i\frac{\omega_0}{\omega}\sin\left[\frac{\omega(t+\epsilon)}{2}\right]\right\};$$

$$c_b(t) = -\frac{i\alpha^*}{2\epsilon\hbar\omega}e^{i\omega_0(t-\epsilon)/2}\left[e^{i\omega(t+\epsilon)/2} - e^{-i\omega(t+\epsilon)/2}\right] = -\frac{i\alpha^*}{\epsilon\hbar\omega}e^{i\omega_0(t-\epsilon)/2}\sin\left[\frac{\omega(t+\epsilon)}{2}\right].$$

Thus

$$a = c_a(\epsilon) = e^{-i\omega_0\epsilon}\left[\cos(\omega\epsilon) + i\frac{\omega_0}{\omega}\sin(\omega\epsilon)\right], \quad b = c_b(\epsilon) = -\frac{i\alpha^*}{\epsilon\hbar\omega}\sin(\omega\epsilon).$$

This is for the rectangular pulse; it remains to take the limit $\epsilon \to 0$: $\omega \to |\alpha|/\epsilon\hbar$, so

$$a \to \cos\left(\frac{|\alpha|}{\hbar}\right) + i\frac{\omega_0\epsilon\hbar}{|\alpha|}\sin\left(\frac{|\alpha|}{\hbar}\right) \to \cos\left(\frac{|\alpha|}{\hbar}\right), \quad b \to -\frac{i\alpha^*}{|\alpha|}\sin\left(\frac{|\alpha|}{\hbar}\right),$$

and we conclude that for the delta function

$$
\boxed{
\begin{aligned}
c_a(t) &= \begin{cases} 1, & t < 0, \\ \cos(|\alpha|/\hbar), & t > 0; \end{cases} \\[2mm]
c_b(t) &= \begin{cases} 0, & t < 0, \\ -i\sqrt{\dfrac{\alpha^*}{\alpha}}\,\sin(|\alpha|/\hbar), & t > 0. \end{cases}
\end{aligned}
}
$$

Obviously, $|c_a(t)|^2 + |c_b(t)|^2 = 1$ in both time periods. Finally,

$$\boxed{P_{a\to b} = |b|^2 = \sin^2(|\alpha|/\hbar).}$$

---

## Problem 9.4

**(a)**

$$
\left.
\begin{aligned}
\text{Eq. 9.10} &\implies \dot{c}_a = -\frac{i}{\hbar}\left[c_a H'_{aa} + c_b H'_{ab} e^{-i\omega_0 t}\right] \\
\text{Eq. 9.11} &\implies \dot{c}_b = -\frac{i}{\hbar}\left[c_b H'_{bb} + c_a H'_{ba} e^{i\omega_0 t}\right]
\end{aligned}
\right\}
\quad \text{(these are \emph{exact}, and replace Eq. 9.13).}
$$

<u>Initial conditions:</u> $\quad c_a(0) = 1, \quad c_b(0) = 0.$

<u>Zeroth order:</u> $\quad c_a(t) = 1, \quad c_b(t) = 0.$

$$
\underline{\text{First order:}}\quad
\begin{cases}
\dot{c}_a = -\dfrac{i}{\hbar} H'_{aa} \\[2mm]
\dot{c}_b = -\dfrac{i}{\hbar} H'_{ba} e^{i\omega_0 t}
\end{cases}
\implies
\boxed{
\begin{aligned}
c_a(t) &= 1 - \frac{i}{\hbar}\int_0^t H'_{aa}(t')\,dt' \\[2mm]
c_b(t) &= -\frac{i}{\hbar}\int_0^t H'_{ba}(t')e^{i\omega_0 t'}\,dt'
\end{aligned}
}
$$

$$|c_a|^2 = \left[1 - \frac{i}{\hbar}\int_0^t H'_{aa}(t')\,dt'\right]\left[1 + \frac{i}{\hbar}\int_0^t H'_{aa}(t')\,dt'\right] = 1 + \left[\frac{1}{\hbar}\int_0^t H'_{aa}(t')\,dt'\right]^2 = 1 \text{ (to first order in } H').$$

$$|c_b|^2 = \left[-\frac{i}{\hbar}\int_0^t H'_{ba}(t')e^{i\omega_0 t'}\,dt'\right]\left[\frac{i}{\hbar}\int_0^t H'_{ab}(t')e^{-i\omega_0 t'}\,dt'\right] = 0 \text{ (to first order in } H').$$

So $|c_a|^2 + |c_b|^2 = 1$ (to first order).

**(b)**

$$\dot{d}_a = e^{\frac{i}{\hbar}\int_0^t H'_{aa}(t')\,dt'}\left(\frac{i}{\hbar}H'_{aa}\right)c_a + e^{\frac{i}{\hbar}\int_0^t H'_{aa}(t')\,dt'}\dot{c}_a. \quad \text{But } \dot{c}_a = -\frac{i}{\hbar}\left[c_a H'_{aa} + c_b H'_{ab} e^{-i\omega_0 t}\right]$$

Two terms cancel, leaving

$$\dot{d}_a = -\frac{i}{\hbar} e^{\frac{i}{\hbar}\int_0^t H'_{aa}(t')\,dt'} c_b H'_{ab} e^{-i\omega_0 t}. \quad \text{But } c_b = e^{-\frac{i}{\hbar}\int_0^t H'_{bb}(t')\,dt'} d_b.$$

$$= -\frac{i}{\hbar} e^{\frac{i}{\hbar}\int_0^t \left[H'_{aa}(t') - H'_{bb}(t')\right]dt'} H'_{ab} e^{-i\omega_0 t} d_b, \quad \text{or} \quad \dot{d}_a = -\frac{i}{\hbar} e^{i\phi} H'_{ab} e^{-i\omega_0 t} d_b.$$

Similarly,

$$\dot{d}_b = e^{\frac{i}{\hbar}\int_0^t H'_{bb}(t')\,dt'}\left(\frac{i}{\hbar}H'_{bb}\right)c_b + e^{\frac{i}{\hbar}\int_0^t H'_{bb}(t')\,dt'}\dot{c}_b. \quad \text{But } \dot{c}_b = -\frac{i}{\hbar}\left[c_b H'_{bb} + c_a H'_{ba}e^{i\omega_0 t}\right].$$

$$= -\frac{i}{\hbar}e^{\frac{i}{\hbar}\int_0^t H'_{bb}(t')\,dt'}c_a H'_{ba}e^{i\omega_0 t}. \quad \text{But } c_a = e^{-\frac{i}{\hbar}\int_0^t H'_{aa}(t')\,dt'}d_a.$$

$$= -\frac{i}{\hbar}e^{\frac{i}{\hbar}\int_0^t\left[H'_{bb}(t')-H'_{aa}(t')\right]dt'}H'_{ba}e^{i\omega_0 t}d_a = -\frac{i}{\hbar}e^{-i\phi}H'_{ba}e^{i\omega_0 t}d_a. \quad \text{QED}$$

**(c)**

Initial conditions: $\quad c_a(0) = 1 \Longrightarrow d_a(0) = 1; \quad c_b(0) = 0 \Longrightarrow d_b(0) = 0.$

Zeroth order: $\quad d_a(t) = 1, \quad d_b(t) = 0.$

First order: $\quad \dot{d}_a = 0 \Longrightarrow d_a(t) = 1 \Longrightarrow \boxed{c_a(t) = e^{-\frac{i}{\hbar}\int_0^t H'_{aa}(t')\,dt'}.}$

$$\dot{d}_b = -\frac{i}{\hbar}e^{-i\phi}H'_{ba}e^{i\omega_0 t} \Longrightarrow d_b = -\frac{i}{\hbar}\int_0^t e^{-i\phi(t')}H'_{ba}(t')e^{i\omega_0 t'}\,dt' \Longrightarrow$$

$$\boxed{c_b(t) = -\frac{i}{\hbar}e^{-\frac{i}{\hbar}\int_0^t H'_{bb}(t')dt'}\int_0^t e^{-i\phi(t')}H'_{ba}(t')e^{i\omega_0 t'}\,dt'.}$$

These don't *look* much like the results in (a), but remember, we're only working to *first order* in $H'$, so $c_a(t) \approx 1 - \frac{i}{\hbar}\int_0^t H'_{aa}(t')\,dt'$ (to this order), while for $c_b$, the factor $H_{ba}$ in the integral means it is *already* first order and hence both the exponential factor in front and $e^{-i\phi}$ should be replaced by 1. Then $c_b(t) \approx -\frac{i}{\hbar}\int_0^t H'_{ba}(t')e^{i\omega_0 t'}\,dt'$, and we recover the results in (a).

---

## Problem 9.5

Zeroth order: $\quad c_a^{(0)}(t) = a, \quad c_b^{(0)}(t) = b.$

First order: $\quad \begin{cases} \dot{c}_a = -\frac{i}{\hbar}H'_{ab}e^{-i\omega_0 t}b \Longrightarrow c_a^{(1)}(t) = a - \frac{ib}{\hbar}\int_0^t H'_{ab}(t')e^{-i\omega_0 t'}\,dt'. \\[2mm] \dot{c}_b = -\frac{i}{\hbar}H'_{ba}e^{i\omega_0 t}a \Longrightarrow c_b^{(1)}(t) = b - \frac{ia}{\hbar}\int_0^t H'_{ba}(t')e^{i\omega_0 t'}\,dt'. \end{cases}$

Second order: $\quad \dot{c}_a = -\frac{i}{\hbar}H'_{ab}e^{-i\omega_0 t}\left[b - \frac{ia}{\hbar}\int_0^t H'_{ba}(t')e^{i\omega_0 t'}\,dt'\right] \Longrightarrow$

$$\boxed{c_a^{(2)}(t) = a - \frac{ib}{\hbar}\int_0^t H'_{ab}(t')e^{-i\omega_0 t'}\,dt' - \frac{a}{\hbar^2}\int_0^t H'_{ab}(t')e^{-i\omega_0 t'}\left[\int_0^{t'}H'_{ba}(t'')e^{i\omega_0 t''}\,dt''\right]dt'.}$$

To get $c_b$, just switch $a \leftrightarrow b$ (which entails also changing the sign of $\omega_0$):

$$\boxed{c_b^{(2)}(t) = b - \frac{ia}{\hbar}\int_0^t H'_{ba}(t')e^{i\omega_0 t'}\,dt' - \frac{b}{\hbar^2}\int_0^t H'_{ba}(t')e^{i\omega_0 t'}\left[\int_0^{t'}H'_{ab}(t'')e^{-i\omega_0 t''}\,dt''\right]dt'.}$$

---

## Problem 9.6

For $H'$ independent of $t$, Eq. 9.17 $\implies c_b^{(2)}(t) = c_b^{(1)}(t) = -\frac{i}{\hbar} H'_{ba} \int_0^t e^{i\omega_0 t'} dt' \implies$

$$c_b^{(2)}(t) = -\frac{i}{\hbar} H'_{ba} \left. \frac{e^{i\omega_0 t'}}{i\omega_0} \right|_0^t = \boxed{-\frac{H'_{ba}}{\hbar\omega_0} \left( e^{i\omega_0 t} - 1 \right).} \quad \text{Meanwhile Eq. 9.18} \implies$$

$$c_a^{(2)}(t) = 1 - \frac{1}{\hbar^2} |H'_{ab}|^2 \int_0^t e^{-i\omega_0 t'} \left[ \int_0^{t'} e^{i\omega_0 t''} dt'' \right] dt' = 1 - \frac{1}{\hbar^2} |H'_{ab}|^2 \frac{1}{i\omega_0} \int_0^t \left( 1 - e^{-i\omega_0 t'} \right) dt'$$

$$= 1 + \frac{i}{\omega_0 \hbar^2} |H'_{ab}|^2 \left. \left( t' + \frac{e^{-i\omega_0 t'}}{i\omega_0} \right) \right|_0^t = \boxed{1 + \frac{i}{\omega_0 \hbar^2} |H'_{ab}|^2 \left[ t + \frac{1}{i\omega_0} \left( e^{-i\omega_0 t} - 1 \right) \right].}$$

For comparison with the exact answers (Problem 9.2), note first that $c_b(t)$ is already first order (because of the $H'_{ba}$ in front), whereas $\omega$ differs from $\omega_0$ only in second order, so it suffices to replace $\omega \to \omega_0$ in the exact formula to get the second-order result:

$$c_b(t) \approx \frac{2H'_{ba}}{i\hbar\omega_0} e^{i\omega_0 t/2} \sin\left(\omega_0 t/2\right) = \frac{2H'_{ba}}{i\hbar\omega_0} e^{i\omega_0 t/2} \frac{1}{2i} \left( e^{i\omega_0 t/2} - e^{-i\omega_0 t/2} \right) = -\frac{H'_{ba}}{\hbar\omega_0} \left( e^{i\omega_0 t} - 1 \right),$$

in agreement with the result above. Checking $c_a$ is more difficult. Note that

$$\omega = \omega_0 \sqrt{1 + \frac{4|H'_{ab}|^2}{\omega_0^2 \hbar^2}} \approx \omega_0 \left( 1 + 2\frac{|H'_{ab}|^2}{\omega_0^2 \hbar^2} \right) = \omega_0 + 2\frac{|H'_{ab}|^2}{\omega_0 \hbar^2}; \quad \frac{\omega_0}{\omega} \approx 1 - 2\frac{|H'_{ab}|^2}{\omega_0^2 \hbar^2}.$$

Taylor expansion:

$$\begin{cases} \cos(x + \epsilon) = \cos x - \epsilon \sin x \implies \cos\left(\omega t/2\right) = \cos\left( \frac{\omega_0 t}{2} + \frac{|H'_{ab}|^2 t}{\omega_0 \hbar^2} \right) \approx \cos\left(\omega_0 t/2\right) - \frac{|H'_{ab}|^2 t}{\omega_0 \hbar^2} \sin\left(\omega_0 t/2\right) \\[4mm] \sin(x + \epsilon) = \sin x + \epsilon \cos x \implies \sin\left(\omega t/2\right) = \sin\left( \frac{\omega_0 t}{2} + \frac{|H'_{ab}|^2 t}{\omega_0 \hbar^2} \right) \approx \sin\left(\omega_0 t/2\right) + \frac{|H'_{ab}|^2 t}{\omega_0 \hbar^2} \cos\left(\omega_0 t/2\right) \end{cases}$$

$$c_a(t) \approx e^{-i\omega_0 t/2} \left\{ \cos\left( \frac{\omega_0 t}{2} \right) - \frac{|H'_{ab}|^2 t}{\omega_0 \hbar^2} \sin\left( \frac{\omega_0 t}{2} \right) + i\left( 1 - 2\frac{|H'_{ab}|^2}{\omega_0^2 \hbar^2} \right) \left[ \sin\left( \frac{\omega_0 t}{2} \right) + \frac{|H'_{ab}|^2 t}{\omega_0 \hbar^2} \cos\left( \frac{\omega_0 t}{2} \right) \right] \right\}$$

$$= e^{-i\omega_0 t/2} \left\{ \left[ \cos\left( \frac{\omega_0 t}{2} \right) + i\sin\left( \frac{\omega_0 t}{2} \right) \right] - \frac{|H'_{ab}|^2}{\omega_0 \hbar^2} \left[ t\left( \sin\left( \frac{\omega_0 t}{2} \right) - i\cos\left( \frac{\omega_0 t}{2} \right) \right) + \frac{2i}{\omega_0} \sin\left( \frac{\omega_0 t}{2} \right) \right] \right\}$$

$$= e^{-i\omega_0 t/2} \left\{ e^{i\omega_0 t/2} - \frac{|H'_{ab}|^2}{\omega_0 \hbar^2} \left[ -it e^{i\omega_0 t/2} + \frac{2i}{\omega} \frac{1}{2i} \left( e^{i\omega_0 t/2} - e^{-i\omega_0 t/2} \right) \right] \right\}$$

$$= 1 - \frac{|H'_{ab}|^2}{\omega_0 \hbar^2} \left[ -it + \frac{1}{\omega_0} \left( 1 - e^{-i\omega_0 t} \right) \right] = 1 + \frac{i}{\omega_0 \hbar^2} |H'_{ab}|^2 \left[ t + \frac{1}{i\omega_0} \left( e^{-i\omega_0 t} - 1 \right) \right], \quad \text{as above.} \quad \checkmark$$

## Problem 9.7

(a)

$$\dot{c}_a = -\frac{i}{2\hbar} V_{ab} e^{i\omega t} e^{-i\omega_0 t} c_b; \quad \dot{c}_b = -\frac{i}{2\hbar} V_{ba} e^{-i\omega t} e^{i\omega_0 t} c_a.$$

Differentiate the latter, and substitute in the former:

$$\ddot{c}_b = -i\frac{V_{ba}}{2\hbar}\left[i(\omega_0-\omega)e^{i(\omega_0-\omega)t}c_a + e^{i(\omega_0-\omega)t}\dot{c}_a\right]$$

$$= i(\omega_0-\omega)\left[-i\frac{V_{ba}}{2\hbar}e^{i(\omega_0-\omega)t}c_a\right] - i\frac{V_{ba}}{2\hbar}e^{i(\omega_0-\omega)t}\left[-i\frac{V_{ab}}{2\hbar}e^{-i(\omega_0-\omega)t}c_b\right] = i(\omega_0-\omega)\dot{c}_b - \frac{|V_{ab}|^2}{(2\hbar)^2}c_b.$$

$\dfrac{d^2c_b}{dt^2} + i(\omega-\omega_0)\dfrac{dc_b}{dt} + \dfrac{|V_{ab}|^2}{4\hbar^2}c_b = 0.$   Solution is of the form $c_b = e^{\lambda t}:$   $\lambda^2 + i(\omega-\omega_0)\lambda + \dfrac{|V_{ab}|^2}{4\hbar^2} = 0.$

$$\lambda = \frac{1}{2}\left[-i(\omega-\omega_0) \pm \sqrt{-(\omega-\omega_0)^2 - \frac{|V_{ab}|^2}{\hbar^2}}\right] = i\left[-\frac{(\omega-\omega_0)}{2} \pm \omega_r\right], \text{ with } \omega_r \text{ defined in Eq. 9.30.}$$

General solution: $c_b(t) = Ae^{i\left[-\frac{(\omega-\omega_0)}{2}+\omega_r\right]t} + Be^{i\left[-\frac{(\omega-\omega_0)}{2}+\omega_r\right]t} = e^{-i(\omega-\omega_0)t/2}\left[Ae^{i\omega_r t} + Be^{-i\omega_r t}\right],$

or, more conveniently: $c_b(t) = e^{-i(\omega-\omega_0)t/2}\left[C\cos(\omega_r t) + D\sin(\omega_r t)\right].$   But $c_b(0) = 0$, so $C = 0:$

$$c_b(t) = De^{i(\omega_0-\omega)t/2}\sin(\omega_r t). \quad \dot{c}_b = D\left[i\left(\frac{\omega_0-\omega}{2}\right)e^{i(\omega_0-\omega)t/2}\sin(\omega_r t) + \omega_r e^{i(\omega_0-\omega)t/2}\cos(\omega_r t)\right];$$

$$c_a(t) = i\frac{2\hbar}{V_{ba}}e^{i(\omega-\omega_0)t}\dot{c}_b = i\frac{2\hbar}{V_{ba}}e^{i(\omega-\omega_0)t/2}D\left[i\left(\frac{\omega_0-\omega}{2}\right)\sin(\omega_r t) + \omega_r\cos(\omega_r t)\right]. \quad \text{But } c_a(0) = 1:$$

$$1 = i\frac{2\hbar}{V_{ba}}D\omega_r, \quad \text{or} \quad D = \frac{-iV_{ba}}{2\hbar\omega_r}.$$

$$\boxed{c_b(t) = -\frac{i}{2\hbar\omega_r}V_{ba}e^{i(\omega_0-\omega)t/2}\sin(\omega_r t), \quad c_a(t) = e^{i(\omega-\omega_0)t/2}\left[\cos(\omega_r t) + i\left(\frac{\omega_0-\omega}{2\omega_r}\right)\sin(\omega_r t)\right].}$$

**(b)**

$$P_{a\to b}(t) = |c_b(t)|^2 = \boxed{\left(\frac{|V_{ab}|}{2\hbar\omega_r}\right)^2\sin^2(\omega_r t).} \quad \text{The largest this gets (when } \sin^2 = 1\text{) is} \quad \frac{|V_{ab}|^2/\hbar^2}{4\omega_r^2},$$

and the denominator,   $4\omega_r^2 = (\omega-\omega_0)^2 + |V_{ab}|^2/\hbar^2$, exceeds the numerator, so $P \leq 1$ (and 1 only if $\omega = \omega$

$$|c_a|^2 + |c_b|^2 = \cos^2(\omega_r t) + \left(\frac{\omega_0-\omega}{2\omega_r}\right)^2\sin^2(\omega_r t) + \left(\frac{|V_{ab}|}{2\hbar\omega_r}\right)^2\sin^2(\omega_r t)$$

$$= \cos^2(\omega_r t) + \frac{(\omega-\omega_0)^2 + (|V_{ab}|/\hbar)^2}{4\omega_r^2}\sin^2(\omega_r t) = \cos^2(\omega_r t) + \sin^2(\omega_r t) = 1. \quad \checkmark$$

**(c)** If   $\boxed{|V_{ab}|^2 \ll \hbar^2(\omega-\omega_0)^2,}$   then $\omega_r \approx \dfrac{1}{2}|\omega-\omega_0|$,   and $P_{a\to b} \approx \dfrac{|V_{ab}|^2}{\hbar^2}\dfrac{\sin^2\left(\frac{\omega-\omega_0}{2}t\right)}{(\omega-\omega_0)^2}$,   confirming Eq. 9.28.

**(d)** $\omega_r t = \pi \Longrightarrow \boxed{t = \pi/\omega_r.}$

## Problem 9.8

Spontaneous emission rate (Eq. 9.56): $A = \dfrac{\omega^3 |\wp|^2}{3\pi\epsilon_0 \hbar c^3}$. Thermally stimulated emission rate (Eq. 9.47):

$$R = \frac{\pi}{3\epsilon_0 \hbar^2}|\wp|^2 \rho(\omega), \quad \text{with} \quad \rho(\omega) = \frac{\hbar}{\pi^2 c^3}\frac{\omega^3}{\left(e^{\hbar\omega/k_B T}-1\right)} \quad \text{(Eq. 9.52)}.$$

So the ratio is

$$\frac{A}{R} = \frac{\omega^3 |\wp|^2}{3\pi\epsilon_0 \hbar c^3} \cdot \frac{3\epsilon_0 \hbar^2}{\pi |\wp|^2} \cdot \frac{\pi^2 c^3 \left(e^{\hbar\omega/k_B T}-1\right)}{\hbar\omega^3} = e^{\hbar\omega/k_B T} - 1.$$

The ratio is a monotonically increasing function of $\omega$, and is 1 when

$$e^{\hbar\omega/k_b t} = 2, \quad \text{or} \quad \frac{\hbar\omega}{k_B T} = \ln 2, \quad \omega = \frac{k_B T}{\hbar}\ln 2, \quad \text{or} \quad \nu = \frac{\omega}{2\pi} = \frac{k_B T}{h}\ln 2. \quad \text{For } T = 300 \text{ K,}$$

$$\nu = \frac{(1.38 \times 10^{-23} \text{ J/K})(300 \text{ K})}{(6.63 \times 10^{-34} \text{ J}\cdot\text{s})}\ln 2 = 4.35 \times 10^{12} \text{ Hz.}$$

For higher frequencies, (including light, at $10^{14}$ Hz), spontaneous emission dominates.

## Problem 9.9

(a) Simply remove the factor $\left(e^{\hbar\omega/k_B T}-1\right)$ in the denominator of Eq. 5.113: $\boxed{\rho_0(\omega) = \dfrac{\hbar\omega^3}{\pi^2 c^3}.}$

(b) Plug this into Eq. 9.47:

$$R_{b\to a} = \frac{\pi}{3\epsilon_0 \hbar^2}|\wp|^2 \frac{\hbar\omega^3}{\pi^2 c^3} = \boxed{\frac{\omega^3 |\wp|^2}{3\pi\epsilon_0 \hbar c^3},}$$

reproducing Eq. 9.56.

## Problem 9.10

$N(t) = e^{-t/\tau}N(0)$  (Eqs. 9.58 and 9.59). After one half-life, $N(t) = \frac{1}{2}N(0)$, so $\frac{1}{2} = e^{-t/\tau}$, or $2 = e^{t/\tau}$, so $t/\tau = \ln 2$, or $\boxed{t_{1/2} = \tau\ln 2.}$

## Problem 9.11

In Problem 9.1 we calculated the matrix elements of $z$; all of them are zero except $\langle 1\,0\,0|z|2\,1\,0\rangle = \dfrac{2^8}{3^5\sqrt{2}}a$. As for $x$ and $y$, we noted that $|1\,0\,0\rangle$, $|2\,0\,0\rangle$, and $|2\,1\,0\rangle$ are *even* (in $x$, $y$), whereas $|2\,1\pm1\rangle$ is odd. So the only non-zero matrix elements are $\langle 1\,0\,0|x|2\,1\pm 1\rangle$ and $\langle 1\,0\,0|y|2\,1\pm 1\rangle$. Using the wave functions in Problem 9.1:

$$\langle 1\,0\,0|x|2\,1\pm 1\rangle = \frac{1}{\sqrt{\pi a^3}}\left(\frac{\mp 1}{8\sqrt{\pi a^3}}\right)\frac{1}{a}\int e^{-r/a}r e^{-r/2a}\sin\theta\, e^{\pm i\phi}(r\sin\theta\cos\phi)r^2\sin\theta\, dr\, d\theta\, d\phi$$

$$= \mp\frac{1}{8\pi a^4}\int_0^\infty r^4 e^{-3r/2a}dr\int_0^\pi \sin^3\theta\, d\theta\int_0^{2\pi}(\cos\phi\pm i\sin\phi)\cos\phi\, d\phi$$

$$= \frac{\mp 1}{8\pi a^4}\left[4!\left(\frac{2a}{3}\right)^5\right]\left(\frac{4}{3}\right)(\pi) = \mp\frac{2^7}{3^5}a.$$

$$\langle 1\,0\,0|y|2\,1\pm 1\rangle = \frac{\mp 1}{8\pi a^4}\left[4!\left[\frac{2a}{3}\right]^5\right]\left(\frac{4}{3}\right)\int_0^{2\pi}(\cos\phi\pm i\sin\phi)\sin\phi\, d\phi$$

$$= \frac{\mp 1}{8\pi a^4}\left[4!\left(\frac{2a}{3}\right)^5\right]\left(\frac{4}{3}\right)(\pm i\pi) = -i\frac{2^7}{3^5}a.$$

$$\langle 1\,0\,0|\mathbf{r}|2\,0\,0\rangle = 0;\quad \langle 1\,0\,0|\mathbf{r}|2\,1\,0\rangle = \frac{2^7\sqrt{2}}{3^5}a\,\hat{k};\quad \langle 1\,0\,0|\mathbf{r}|2\,1\pm 1\rangle = \frac{2^7}{3^5}a\left(\mp\hat{i}-i\,\hat{j}\right),\quad\text{and hence}$$

$$\wp^2 = 0\ (\text{for }|2\,0\,0\rangle\to|1\,0\,0\rangle),\quad\text{and }|\wp|^2 = (qa)^2\frac{2^{15}}{3^{10}}\ (\text{for }|2\,1\,0\rangle\to 1\,0\,0\rangle\text{ and }|2\,1\pm 1\rangle\to|1\,0\,0\rangle).$$

Meanwhile, $\quad\omega = \dfrac{E_2 - E_1}{\hbar} = \dfrac{1}{\hbar}\left(\dfrac{E_1}{4} - E_1\right) = -\dfrac{3E_1}{4\hbar},\quad$ so for the three $l = 1$ states:

$$A = -\frac{3^3 E_1^3}{2^6\hbar^3}\frac{(ea)^2 2^{15}}{3^{10}}\frac{1}{3\pi\epsilon_0\hbar c^3} = -\frac{2^9}{3^8\pi}\frac{E_1^3 e^2 a^2}{\epsilon_0\hbar^4 c^3} = \frac{2^{10}}{3^8}\left(\frac{E_1}{mc^2}\right)^2\frac{c}{a}$$

$$= \frac{2^{10}}{3^8}\left(\frac{13.6}{0.511\times 10^6}\right)^2\frac{(3.00\times 10^8\text{ m/s})}{(0.529\times 10^{-10}\text{ m})} = 6.27\times 10^8/\text{s};\quad \tau = \frac{1}{A} = \boxed{1.60\times 10^{-9}\text{ s}}$$

for the three $l = 1$ states (all have the *same* lifetime); $\boxed{\tau = \infty}$ for the $l = 0$ state.

---

## Problem 9.12

$$[L^2, z] = [L_x^2, z] + [L_y^2, z] + [L_z^2, z] = L_x[L_x, z] + [L_x, z]L_x + L_y[L_y, z] + [L_y, z]L_y + L_z[L_z, z] + [L_z, z]L_z$$

But $\begin{cases}[L_x, z] = [yp_z - zp_y, z] = [yp_z, z] - [zp_y, z] = y[p_z, z] = -i\hbar y,\\[L_y, z] = [zp_x - xp_z, z] = [zp_x, z] - [xp_z, z] = -x[p_z, z] = i\hbar x,\\[L_z, z] = [xp_y - yp_x, z] = [xp_y, z] - [yp_x, z] = 0.\end{cases}$

So: $\quad [L^2, z] = L_x(-i\hbar y) + (-i\hbar y)L_x + L_y(i\hbar x) + (i\hbar x)L_y = i\hbar(-L_x y - yL_x + L_y x + xL_y).$

But $\begin{cases}L_x y = L_x y - yL_x + yL_x = [L_x, y] + yL_x = i\hbar z + yL_x,\\L_y x = L_y x - xL_y + xL_y = [L_y, x] + xL_y = -i\hbar z + xL_y.\end{cases}$

So: $[L^2, z] = i\hbar(2xL_y - i\hbar z - 2yL_x - i\hbar z) \implies \boxed{[L^2, z] = 2i\hbar(xL_y - yL_x - i\hbar z)}$.

$$[L^2, [L^2, z]] = 2i\hbar \left\{ [L^2, xL_y] - [L^2, yL_x] - i\hbar[L^2, z] \right\}$$
$$= 2i\hbar \left\{ [L^2, x]L_y + x[L^2, L_y] - [L^2, y]L_x - y[L^2, L_x] - i\hbar(L^2 z - zL^2) \right\}.$$

But $[L^2, L_y] = [L^2, L_x] = 0$  (Eq. 4.102),  so

$$[L^2, [L^2, z]] = 2i\hbar \left\{ (yL_z - zL_y - i\hbar x) L_y - 2i\hbar (zL_x - xL_z - i\hbar y) L_x - i\hbar \left( L^2 z - zL^2 \right) \right\},  \text{ or}$$

$$[L^2, [L^2, z]] = -2\hbar^2 \left( 2yL_zL_y \underbrace{-2zL_y^2 - 2zL_x^2}_{-2z(L_x^2 + L_y^2 + L_z^2) + 2zL_z^2} -2i\hbar xL_y + 2xL_zL_x + 2i\hbar yL_x - L^2 z + zL^2 \right)$$

$$= -2\hbar^2 \left( 2yL_zL_y - 2i\hbar xL_y + 2xL_zL_x + 2i\hbar yL_x + 2zL_z^2 - 2zL^2 - L^2 z + zL^2 \right)$$

$$= -2\hbar^2 \left( zL^2 + L^2 z \right) - 4\hbar^2 \left[ \underbrace{(yL_z - i\hbar x)}_{L_z y} L_y + \underbrace{(xL_z + i\hbar y)}_{L_z x} L_x + zL_zL_z \right]$$

$$= 2\hbar^2 \left( zL^2 + L^2 z \right) - 4\hbar^2 \underbrace{(L_z yL_y + L_z xL_x + L_z zL_z)}_{L_z(\mathbf{r} \cdot \mathbf{L}) = 0} = 2\hbar^2(zL^2 + L^2 z).  \text{ QED}$$

## Problem 9.13

$$|n\,0\,0\rangle = R_{n0}(r)Y_0^0(\theta, \phi) = \frac{1}{\sqrt{4\pi}} R_{n0}(r),  \text{ so }  \langle n'\,0\,0|\mathbf{r}|n\,0\,0\rangle = \frac{1}{4\pi} \int R_{n'0}(r)R_{n0}(r)(x\,\hat{i} + y\,\hat{j} + z\,\hat{k})\,dx\,dy\,dz.$$

But the integrand is odd in $x, y$, or $z$, so the integral is zero.

## Problem 9.14

(a)

$$\boxed{|3\,0\,0\rangle \rightarrow \left\{ \begin{array}{c} |2\,1\,0\rangle \\ |2\,1\,1\rangle \\ |2\,1\,{-1}\rangle \end{array} \right\} \rightarrow |1\,0\,0\rangle.}  (|3\,0\,0\rangle \rightarrow |2\,0\,0\rangle \text{ and } |3\,0\,0\rangle \rightarrow |1\,0\,0\rangle \text{ violate } \Delta l = \pm 1 \text{ rule.})$$

(b)

From Eq. 9.72:    $\langle 2\,1\,0|\mathbf{r}|3\,0\,0\rangle = \langle 2\,1\,0|z|3\,0\,0\rangle\,\hat{k}.$

From Eq. 9.69:    $\langle 2\,1\pm 1|\mathbf{r}|3\,0\,0\rangle = \langle 2\,1\pm 1|x|3\,0\,0\rangle\,\hat{i} + \langle 2\,1\pm 1|y|3\,0\,0\rangle\,\hat{j}.$

From Eq. 9.70:    $\pm\langle 2\,1\pm 1|x|3\,0\,0\rangle = i\langle 2\,1\pm 1|y|3\,0\,0\rangle.$

Thus    $|\langle 2\,1\,0|\mathbf{r}|3\,0\,0\rangle|^2 = |\langle 2\,1\,0|z|3\,0\,0\rangle|^2$    and    $|\langle 2\,1\pm 1|\mathbf{r}|3\,0\,0\rangle|^2 = 2|\langle 2\,1\pm 1|x|3\,0\,0\rangle|^2,$

so there are really just two matrix elements to calculate.

$$\psi_{21m} = R_{21}Y_1^m, \quad \psi_{300} = R_{30}Y_0^0. \quad \text{From Table 4.3:}$$

$$\int Y_1^0 Y_0^0 \cos\theta \sin\theta\, d\theta\, d\phi = \sqrt{\frac{3}{4\pi}}\sqrt{\frac{1}{4\pi}}\int_0^\pi \cos^2\theta\sin\theta\, d\theta \int_0^{2\pi} d\phi = \frac{\sqrt{3}}{4\pi}\left(-\frac{\cos^3\theta}{3}\right)\Bigg|_0^\pi (2\pi) = \frac{\sqrt{3}}{2}\left(\frac{2}{3}\right) = \frac{1}{\sqrt{3}}.$$

$$\int \left(Y_1^{\pm 1}\right)^* Y_0^0 \sin^2\theta\cos\phi\, d\theta\, d\phi = \mp\sqrt{\frac{3}{8\pi}}\sqrt{\frac{1}{4\pi}}\int_0^\pi \sin^3\theta\, d\theta \int_0^{2\pi} \cos\phi\, e^{\mp i\phi}\, d\phi$$

$$= \mp\frac{1}{4\pi}\sqrt{\frac{3}{2}}\left(\frac{4}{3}\right)\left[\int_0^{2\pi} \cos^2\phi\, d\phi \mp i\int_0^{2\pi} \cos\phi\sin\phi\, d\phi\right] = \mp\frac{1}{\pi\sqrt{6}}(\pi\mp 0) = \mp\frac{1}{\sqrt{6}}.$$

From Table 4.7:

$$K \equiv \int_0^\infty R_{21}R_{30}\, r^3\, dr = \frac{1}{\sqrt{24}a^{3/2}}\frac{2}{\sqrt{27}a^{3/2}}\int_0^\infty \frac{r}{a}e^{-r/2a}\left[1 - \frac{2}{3}\frac{r}{a} + \frac{2}{27}\left(\frac{r}{a}\right)^2\right]e^{-r/3a}r^3\, dr$$

$$= \frac{1}{9\sqrt{2}a^3}a^4\int_0^\infty \left(1 - \frac{2}{3}u + \frac{2}{27}u^2\right)u^4 e^{-5u/6}\, du = \frac{a}{9\sqrt{2}}\left[4!\left(\frac{6}{5}\right)^5 - \frac{2}{3}5!\left(\frac{6}{5}\right)^6 + \frac{2}{27}6!\left(\frac{6}{5}\right)^7\right]$$

$$= \frac{a}{9\sqrt{2}}\frac{4!\,6^5}{5^6}\left(5 - \frac{2}{3}6\cdot 5 + \frac{2}{27}6^3\right) = \frac{a}{9\sqrt{2}}\frac{4!\,6^5}{5^6} = \frac{2^7 3^4}{5^6}\sqrt{2}\,a.$$

So:

$$\langle 2\,1\pm 1|x|3\,0\,0\rangle = \int R_{21}(Y_1^{\pm 1})^*(r\sin\theta\cos\phi)R_{30}Y_0^0\, r^2\sin\theta\, dr\, d\theta\, d\phi = K\left(\mp\frac{1}{\sqrt{6}}\right).$$

$$\langle 2\,1\,0|z|3\,0\,0\rangle = \int R_{21}Y_1^0(r\cos\theta)R_{30}Y_0^0\, r^2\sin\theta\, dr\, d\theta\, d\phi = K\left(\frac{1}{\sqrt{3}}\right).$$

$$|\langle 2\,1\,0|\mathbf{r}|3\,0\,0\rangle|^2 = |\langle 2\,1\,0|z|3\,0\,0\rangle|^2 = K^2/3;$$

$$|\langle 2\,1\pm 1|\mathbf{r}|3\,0\,0\rangle|^2 = 2|\langle 2\,1\pm 1|x|3\,0\,0\rangle|^2 = K^2/3.$$

Evidently the three transition rates are *equal*, and hence $\boxed{1/3}$ go by each route.

**(c)** For each mode, $\quad A = \dfrac{\omega^3 e^2|\langle\mathbf{r}\rangle|^2}{3\pi\epsilon_0\hbar c^3}; \quad$ here $\quad \omega = \dfrac{E_3 - E_2}{\hbar} = \dfrac{1}{\hbar}\left(\dfrac{E_1}{9} - \dfrac{E_1}{4}\right) = -\dfrac{5}{36}\dfrac{E_1}{\hbar}, \quad$ so the *total* decay rate is

$$R = 3\left(-\frac{5}{36}\frac{E_1}{\hbar}\right)^3 \frac{e^2}{3\pi\epsilon_0\hbar c^3}\frac{1}{3}\left(\frac{2^7 3^4}{5^6}\sqrt{2}a\right)^2 = 6\left(\frac{2}{5}\right)^9\left(\frac{E_1}{mc^2}\right)^2\left(\frac{c}{a}\right)$$

$$= 6\left(\frac{2}{5}\right)^9\left(\frac{13.6}{0.511\times 10^6}\right)^2\left(\frac{3\times 10^8}{0.529\times 10^{-10}}\right)/\text{s} = 6.32\times 10^6/\text{s}. \quad \tau = \frac{1}{R} = \boxed{1.58\times 10^{-7}\ \text{s.}}$$

## Problem 9.15

**(a)**

$$\Psi(t) = \sum c_n(t) e^{-iE_n t/\hbar} \psi_n. \quad H\Psi = i\hbar \frac{\partial \Psi}{\partial t}; \quad H = H_0 + H'(t); \quad H_0 \psi_n = E_n \psi_n. \quad \text{So}$$

$$\sum c_n e^{-iE_n t/\hbar} E_n \psi_n + \sum c_n e^{-iE_n t/\hbar} H' \psi_n = i\hbar \sum \dot{c}_n e^{-iE_n t/\hbar} \psi_n + i\hbar \left(-\frac{i}{\hbar}\right) \sum c_n E_n e^{-iE_n t/\hbar} \psi_n.$$

The first and last terms cancel, so

$$\sum c_n e^{-iE_n t/\hbar} H' \psi_n = i\hbar \sum \dot{c}_n e^{-iE_n t/\hbar} \psi_n. \quad \text{Take the inner product with } \psi_m:$$

$$\sum c_n e^{-iE_n t/\hbar} \langle \psi_m | H' | \psi_n \rangle = i\hbar \sum \dot{c}_n e^{-iE_n t/\hbar} \langle \psi_m | \psi_n \rangle.$$

Assume orthonormality of the unperturbed states, $\langle \psi_m | \psi_n \rangle = \delta_{mn}$, and define $H'_{mn} \equiv \langle \psi_m | H' | \psi_n \rangle$.

$$\sum c_n e^{-iE_n t/\hbar} H'_{mn} = i\hbar \dot{c}_m e^{-iE_m t/\hbar}, \quad \text{or} \quad \boxed{\dot{c}_m = -\frac{i}{\hbar} \sum_n c_n H'_{mn} e^{i(E_m - E_n)t/\hbar}.}$$

**(b)** Zeroth order: $c_N(t) = 1$, $c_m(t) = 0$ for $m \neq N$. Then in first order:

$$\dot{c}_N = -\frac{i}{\hbar} H'_{NN}, \quad \text{or} \quad \boxed{c_N(t) = 1 - \frac{i}{\hbar} \int_0^t H'_{NN}(t')\, dt',} \quad \text{whereas for } m \neq N:$$

$$\dot{c}_m = -\frac{i}{\hbar} H'_{mN} e^{i(E_m - E_N)t/\hbar}, \quad \text{or} \quad \boxed{c_m(t) = -\frac{i}{\hbar} \int_0^t H'_{mN}(t') e^{i(E_m - E_N)t'/\hbar}\, dt'.}$$

**(c)**

$$c_M(t) = -\frac{i}{\hbar} H'_{MN} \int_0^t e^{i(E_M - E_N)t'/\hbar}\, dt' = -\frac{i}{\hbar} H'_{MN} \left[ \frac{e^{i(E_M - E_N)t'/\hbar}}{i(E_M - E_N)/\hbar} \right]\Bigg|_0^t = -H'_{MN} \left[ \frac{e^{i(E_M - E_N)t/\hbar} - 1}{E_M - E_N} \right]$$

$$= -\frac{H'_{MN}}{(E_M - E_N)} e^{i(E_M - E_N)t/2\hbar} 2i \sin\left( \frac{E_M - E_N}{2\hbar} t \right).$$

$$P_{N \to M} = |c_M|^2 = \boxed{\frac{4|H'_{MN}|^2}{(E_M - E_N)^2} \sin^2\left( \frac{E_M - E_N}{2\hbar} t \right).}$$

**(d)**

$$c_M(t) = -\frac{i}{\hbar} V_{MN} \frac{1}{2} \int_0^t \left( e^{i\omega t'} + e^{-i\omega t'} \right) e^{i(E_M - E_N)t'/\hbar}\, dt'$$

$$= -\frac{iV_{MN}}{2\hbar} \left[ \frac{e^{i(\hbar\omega + E_M - E_N)t'/\hbar}}{i(\hbar\omega + E_M - E_N)/\hbar} + \frac{e^{i(-\hbar\omega + E_M - E_N)t'/\hbar}}{i(-\hbar\omega + E_M - E_N)/\hbar} \right]\Bigg|_0^t.$$

If $E_M > E_N$, the second term dominates, and transitions occur only for $\omega \approx (E_M - E_N)/\hbar$:

$$c_M(t) \approx -\frac{iV_{MN}}{2\hbar} \frac{1}{(i/\hbar)(E_M - E_N - \hbar\omega)} e^{i(E_M - E_N - \hbar\omega)t/2\hbar} 2i \sin\left(\frac{E_M - E_N - \hbar\omega}{2\hbar}t\right), \text{ so}$$

$$P_{N \to M} = |c_M|^2 = \frac{|V_{MN}|^2}{(E_M - E_N - \hbar\omega)^2} \sin^2\left(\frac{E_M - E_N - \hbar\omega}{2\hbar}t\right).$$

If $E_M < E_N$ the first term dominates, and transitions occur only for $\omega \approx (E_N - E_M)/\hbar$:

$$c_M(t) \approx -\frac{iV_{MN}}{2\hbar} \frac{1}{(i/\hbar)(E_M - E_N + \hbar\omega)} e^{i(E_M - E_N + \hbar\omega)t/2\hbar} 2i \sin\left(\frac{E_M - E_N + \hbar\omega}{2\hbar}t\right), \text{ and hence}$$

$$P_{N \to M} = \frac{|V_{MN}|^2}{(E_M - E_N + \hbar\omega)^2} \sin^2\left(\frac{E_M - E_N + \hbar\omega}{2\hbar}t\right).$$

Combining the two results, we conclude that transitions occur to states with energy $E_M \approx E_N \pm \hbar\omega$, and

$$\boxed{P_{N \to M} = \frac{|V_{MN}|^2}{(E_M - E_N \pm \hbar\omega)^2} \sin^2\left(\frac{E_M - E_N \pm \hbar\omega}{2\hbar}t\right).}$$

(e) For light,   $V_{ba} = -\wp E_0$ (Eq. 9.34).   The rest is as before (Section 9.2.3), leading to Eq. 9.47:

$$\boxed{R_{N \to M} = \frac{\pi}{3\epsilon_0 \hbar^2} |\wp|^2 \rho(\omega), \text{ with } \omega = \pm(E_M - E_N)/\hbar}$$   (+ sign $\Rightarrow$ absorption, $-$ sign $\Rightarrow$ stimulated emission).

---

## Problem 9.16

For example (c):

$$\boxed{c_N(t) = 1 - \frac{i}{\hbar} H'_{NN} t; \quad c_m(t) = -2i \frac{H'_{mN}}{(E_m - E_N)} e^{i(E_m - E_N)t/2\hbar} \sin\left(\frac{E_m - E_N}{2\hbar}t\right) \ (m \neq N).}$$

$$|c_N|^2 = 1 + \frac{1}{\hbar^2}|H'_{NN}|^2 t^2, \quad |c_m|^2 = 4\frac{|H'_{mN}|^2}{(E_m - E_N)^2} \sin^2\left(\frac{E_m - E_N}{2\hbar}t\right), \text{ so}$$

$$\sum_m |c_m|^2 = 1 + \frac{t^2}{\hbar^2}|H'_{NN}|^2 + 4\sum_{m \neq N} \frac{|H'_{mN}|^2}{(E_m - E_N)^2} \sin^2\left(\frac{E_m - E_N}{2\hbar}t\right).$$

This is plainly *greater* than 1! But remember: The $c$'s are accurate only to *first* order in $H'$; to this order the $|H'|^2$ terms do not belong. Only if terms of *first* order appeared in the sum would there be a genuine problem with normalization.

For example (d):

$$c_N = 1 - \frac{i}{\hbar} V_{NN} \int_0^t \cos(\omega t')\, dt' = 1 - \frac{i}{\hbar} V_{NN} \left.\frac{\sin(\omega t')}{\omega}\right|_0^t \implies \boxed{c_N(t) = 1 - \frac{i}{\hbar\omega} V_{NN} \sin(\omega t).}$$

$$c_m(t) = -\frac{V_{mN}}{2} \left[ \frac{e^{i(E_m - E_N + \hbar\omega)t/\hbar} - 1}{(E_m - E_N + \hbar\omega)} + \frac{e^{i(E_m - E_N - \hbar\omega)t/\hbar} - 1}{(E_m - E_N - \hbar\omega)} \right] \quad (m \neq N).$$ So

$$|c_N|^2 = 1 + \frac{|V_{NN}|^2}{(\hbar\omega)^2} \sin^2(\omega t); \quad \text{and in the rotating wave approximation}$$

$$|c_m|^2 = \frac{|V_{mN}|^2}{(E_m - E_N \pm \hbar\omega)^2} \sin^2\left( \frac{E_m - E_N \pm \hbar\omega}{2\hbar} t \right) \quad (m \neq N).$$

Again, ostensibly $\sum |c_m|^2 > 1$, but the "extra" terms are of *second* order in $H'$, and hence do not belong (to first order).

You would do $\boxed{\text{better to use } 1 - \sum_{m \neq N} |c_m|^2.}$ Schematically: $c_m = a_1 H + a_2 H^2 + \cdots$, so $|c_m|^2 = a_1^2 H^2 + 2a_1 a_2 H^3 + \cdots$, whereas $c_N = 1 + b_1 H + b_2 H^2 + \cdots$, so $|c_N|^2 = 1 + 2b_1 H + (2b_2 + b_1^2)H^2 + \cdots$. Thus knowing $c_m$ to *first* order (i.e., knowing $a_1$) gets you $|c_m|^2$ to *second* order, but knowing $c_N$ to first order (i.e., $b_1$) does *not* get you $|c_N|^2$ to second order (you'd also need $b_2$). It is precisely this $b_2$ term that would cancel the "extra" (second-order) terms in the calculations of $\sum |c_m|^2$ above.

## Problem 9.17

(a)

Equation 9.82 $\Rightarrow \dot{c}_m = -\frac{i}{\hbar} \sum_n c_n H'_{mn} e^{i(E_m - E_n)t/\hbar}$. Here $H'_{mn} = \langle \psi_m | V_0(t) | \psi_n \rangle = \delta_{mn} V_0(t)$.

$$\dot{c}_m = -\frac{i}{\hbar} c_m V_0(t); \quad \frac{dc_m}{c_m} = -\frac{i}{\hbar} V_0(t)\,dt \Rightarrow \ln c_m = -\frac{i}{\hbar} \int V_0(t')\,dt' + constant.$$

$$c_m(t) = c_m(0) e^{-\frac{i}{\hbar} \int_0^t V_0(t')\,dt'}. \quad \text{Let } \Phi(t) \equiv -\frac{1}{\hbar} \int_0^t V_0(t')\,dt'; \quad c_m(t) = e^{i\Phi} c_m(0). \quad \text{Hence}$$

$|c_m(t)|^2 = |c_m(0)|^2$, and there are *no* transitions. $\boxed{\Phi(T) = -\frac{1}{\hbar} \int_0^T V_0(t)\,dt.}$

(b)

Eq. 9.84 $\Rightarrow c_N(t) \approx 1 - \frac{i}{\hbar} \int_0^t V_0(t')\,dt = 1 + i\Phi.$

Eq. 9.85 $\Rightarrow c_m(t) = -\frac{i}{\hbar} \int_0^t \delta_{mN} V_0(t') e^{i(E_m - E_N)t'/\hbar}\,dt' = 0 \ (m \neq N).$

$\boxed{\begin{array}{l} c_N(t) = 1 + i\Phi(t), \\ c_m(t) = 0 \ (m \neq N). \end{array}}$

The *exact* answer is $c_N(t) = e^{i\Phi(t)}$, $c_m(t) = 0$, and they *are* consistent, since $e^{i\Phi} \approx 1 + i\Phi$, to first order.

## Problem 9.18

Use result of Problem 9.15(c).   Here   $E_n = \dfrac{n^2\pi^2\hbar^2}{2ma^2}$,   so   $E_2 - E_1 = \dfrac{3\pi^2\hbar^2}{2ma^2}$.

$$H'_{12} = \frac{2}{a}\int_0^{a/2}\sin\left(\frac{\pi}{a}x\right)V_0\sin\left(\frac{2\pi}{a}x\right)\,dx$$

$$= \frac{2V_0}{a}\left[\frac{\sin\left(\frac{\pi}{a}x\right)}{2(\pi/a)} - \frac{\sin\left(\frac{3\pi}{a}x\right)}{2(3\pi/a)}\right]\Bigg|_0^{a/2} = \frac{V_0}{\pi}\left[\sin\left(\frac{\pi}{2}\right) - \frac{1}{3}\sin\left(\frac{3\pi}{2}\right)\right] = \frac{4V_0}{3\pi}.$$

Eq. 9.86 $\implies P_{1\to2} = 4\left(\frac{4V_0}{3\pi}\right)\left(\frac{2ma^2}{3\pi^2\hbar^2}\right)^2\sin^2\left(\frac{3\pi^2\hbar}{4ma^2}t\right) = \boxed{\left[\frac{16ma^2V_0}{9\pi^3\hbar^2}\sin\left(\frac{3\pi^2\hbar T}{4ma^2}\right)\right]^2}.$

[Actually, in this case $H'_{11}$ and $H'_{22}$ are nonzero:

$$H'_{11} = \langle\psi_1|H'|\psi_1\rangle = \frac{2}{a}V_0\int_0^{a/2}\sin^2\left(\frac{\pi}{a}x\right)\,dx = \frac{V_0}{2}, \quad H'_{22} = \langle\psi_2|H'|\psi_2\rangle = \frac{2}{a}V_0\int_0^{a/2}\sin^2\left(\frac{2\pi}{a}x\right)\,dx = \frac{V_0}{2}.$$

However, this does not affect the answer, for according to Problem 9.4, $c_1(t)$ picks up an innocuous phase factor, while $c_2(t)$ is not affected at all, in first order (formally, this is because $H'_{bb}$ is multiplied by $c_b$, in Eq. 9.11, and in zeroth order $c_b(t) = 0$).]

## Problem 9.19

Spontaneous absorption would involve taking energy (a photon) from the ground state of the electromagnetic field. But you can't *do* that, because the gound state already has the lowest allowed energy.

## Problem 9.20

(a)

$$H = -\gamma\mathbf{B}\cdot\mathbf{S} = -\gamma\left(B_xS_x + B_yS_y + B_zS_z\right);$$

$$\mathsf{H} = -\gamma\frac{\hbar}{2}\left(B_x\sigma_x + B_y\sigma_y + B_z\sigma_z\right) = -\frac{\gamma\hbar}{2}\left[B_x\begin{pmatrix}0 & 1\\1 & 0\end{pmatrix} + B_y\begin{pmatrix}0 & -i\\i & 0\end{pmatrix} + B_z\begin{pmatrix}1 & 0\\0 & -1\end{pmatrix}\right]$$

$$= -\frac{\gamma\hbar}{2}\begin{pmatrix}B_z & B_x - iB_y\\B_x + iB_y & -B_z\end{pmatrix} = -\frac{\gamma\hbar}{2}\begin{pmatrix}B_0 & B_{\mathrm{rf}}(\cos\omega t + i\sin\omega t)\\B_{\mathrm{rf}}(\cos\omega t - i\sin\omega t) & -B_0\end{pmatrix}$$

$$= \boxed{-\frac{\gamma\hbar}{2}\begin{pmatrix}B_0 & B_{\mathrm{rf}}e^{i\omega t}\\B_{\mathrm{rf}}e^{-i\omega t} & -B_0\end{pmatrix}}.$$

(b) $i\hbar\dot{\chi} = \mathsf{H}\chi \Rightarrow$

$$i\hbar\begin{pmatrix}\dot{a}\\\dot{b}\end{pmatrix} = -\frac{\gamma\hbar}{2}\begin{pmatrix}B_0 & B_{\mathrm{rf}}e^{i\omega t}\\B_{\mathrm{rf}}e^{-i\omega t} & -B_0\end{pmatrix}\begin{pmatrix}a\\b\end{pmatrix} = -\frac{\gamma\hbar}{2}\begin{pmatrix}B_0a & B_{\mathrm{rf}}e^{i\omega t}b\\B_{\mathrm{rf}}e^{-i\omega t}a & -B_0b\end{pmatrix} \quad\Rightarrow$$

$$\begin{cases}\dot{a} = i\dfrac{\gamma}{2}\left(B_0a + B_{\mathrm{rf}}e^{i\omega t}b\right) = \dfrac{i}{2}\left(\Omega e^{i\omega t}b + \omega_0 a\right),\\[2mm]\dot{b} = -i\dfrac{\gamma}{2}\left(B_0b - B_{\mathrm{rf}}e^{-i\omega t}a\right) = \dfrac{i}{2}\left(\Omega e^{-i\omega t}a - \omega_0 b\right).\end{cases}$$

**(c)** You can decouple the equations by differentiating with respect to $t$, but it is simpler just to *check* the quoted results. First of all, they clearly satisfy the initial conditions: $a(0) = a_0$ and $b(0) = b_0$. Differentiating $a$:

$$\dot{a} = \frac{i\omega}{2}a + \left\{ -a_0\frac{\omega'}{2}\sin(\omega't/2) + \frac{i}{\omega'}[a_0(\omega_0 - \omega) + b_0\Omega]\frac{\omega'}{2}\cos(\omega't/2) \right\} e^{i\omega t/2}$$

$$= \frac{i}{2}e^{i\omega t/2}\left\{ \omega a_0\cos(\omega't/2) + i\frac{\omega}{\omega'}[a_0(\omega_0 - \omega) + b_0\Omega]\sin(\omega't/2) \right.$$

$$\left. + i\omega'a_0\sin(\omega't/2) + [a_0(\omega_0 - \omega) + b_0\Omega]\cos(\omega't/2) \right\}$$

Equation 9.90 says this should be equal to

$$\frac{i}{2}\left(\Omega e^{i\omega t}b + \omega_0 a\right) = \frac{i}{2}e^{i\omega t/2}\left\{ \Omega b_0\cos(\omega't/2) + i\frac{\Omega}{\omega'}[b_0(\omega - \omega_0) + a_0\Omega]\sin(\omega't/2) \right.$$

$$\left. + \omega_0 a_0\cos(\omega't/2) + i\frac{\omega_0}{\omega'}[a_0(\omega_0 - \omega) + b_0\Omega]\sin(\omega't/2) \right\}.$$

By inspection the $\cos(\omega't/2)$ terms in the two expressions are equal; it remains to check that

$$i\frac{\omega}{\omega'}[a_0(\omega_0 - \omega) + b_0\Omega] + i\omega'a_0 = i\frac{\Omega}{\omega'}[b_0(\omega - \omega_0) + a_0\Omega] + i\frac{\omega_0}{\omega'}[a_0(\omega_0 - \omega) + b_0\Omega],$$

which is to say

$$a_0\omega(\omega_0 - \omega) + b_0\omega\Omega + a_0(\omega')^2 = b_0\Omega(\omega - \omega_0) + a_0\Omega^2 + a_0\omega_0(\omega_0 - \omega) + b_0\omega_0\Omega,$$

or

$$a_0\left[\omega\omega_0 - \omega^2 + (\omega')^2 - \Omega^2 - \omega_0^2 + \omega_0\omega\right] = b_0\left[\Omega\omega - \omega_0\Omega + \omega_0\Omega - \omega\Omega\right] = 0.$$

Substituting Eq. 9.91 for $\omega'$, the coefficient of $a_0$ on the left becomes

$$2\omega\omega_0 - \omega^2 + (\omega - \omega_0)^2 + \Omega^2 - \Omega^2 - \omega_0^2 = 0. \quad \checkmark$$

The check of $b(t)$ is identical, with $a \leftrightarrow b$, $\omega_0 \to -\omega_0$, and $\omega \to -\omega$.

**(d)**

$$b(t) = i\frac{\Omega}{\omega'}\sin(\omega't/2)e^{-i\omega t/2}; \quad P(t) = |b(t)|^2 = \boxed{\left(\frac{\Omega}{\omega'}\right)^2\sin^2(\omega't/2).}$$

**(e)**

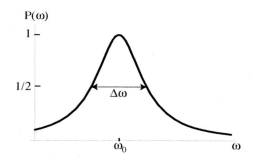

The maximum ($P_{\max} = 1$) occurs (obviously) at $\omega = \omega_0$.

$P = \frac{1}{2} \Rightarrow (\omega - \omega_0)^2 = \Omega^2 \Rightarrow \omega = \omega_0 \pm \Omega$, so $\Delta\omega = \omega_+ - \omega_- = \boxed{2\Omega.}$

**(f)** $B_0 = 10,000$ gauss $= 1$ T; $\quad B_{rf} = 0.01$ gauss $= 1 \times 10^{-6}$ T. $\quad \omega_0 = \gamma B_0$. Comparing Eqs. 4.156 and 6.85, $\quad \gamma = \dfrac{g_p e}{2 m_p}$, where $\quad g_p = 5.59$. So

$$\nu_{res} = \frac{\omega_0}{2\pi} = \frac{g_p e}{4\pi m_p} B_0 = \frac{(5.59)(1.6 \times 10^{-19})}{4\pi(1.67 \times 10^{-27})}(1) = \boxed{4.26 \times 10^7 \text{ Hz.}}$$

$$\Delta\nu = \frac{\Delta\omega}{2\pi} = \frac{\Omega}{\pi} = \frac{\gamma}{2\pi} 2 B_{rf} = \nu_{res} \frac{2 B_{rf}}{B_0} = (4.26 \times 10^7)(2 \times 10^{-6}) = \boxed{85.2 \text{ Hz.}}$$

## Problem 9.21

**(a)**

$$H' = -q\mathbf{E} \cdot \mathbf{r} = -q(\mathbf{E}_0 \cdot \mathbf{r})(\mathbf{k} \cdot \mathbf{r})\sin(\omega t). \quad \text{Write } \mathbf{E}_0 = E_0 \hat{n}, \ \mathbf{k} = \frac{\omega}{c}\hat{k}. \quad \text{Then}$$

$$H' = -q\frac{E_0 \omega}{c}(\hat{n} \cdot \mathbf{r})(\hat{k} \cdot \mathbf{r})\sin(\omega t). \quad H'_{ba} = -\frac{qE_0 \omega}{c}\langle b|(\hat{n} \cdot \mathbf{r})(\hat{k} \cdot \mathbf{r})|a\rangle \sin(\omega t).$$

This is the analog to Eq. 9.33: $H'_{ba} = -qE_0\langle b|\hat{n} \cdot \mathbf{r}|a\rangle \cos\omega t$. The rest of the analysis is identical to the dipole case (except that it is $\sin(\omega t)$ instead of $\cos(\omega t)$, but this amounts to resetting the clock, and clearly has no effect on the transition rate). We can skip therefore to Eq. 9.56, except for the factor of $1/3$, which came from the averaging in Eq. 9.46:

$$A = \frac{\omega^3}{\pi\epsilon_0 \hbar c^3}\frac{q^2 \omega^2}{c^2}|\langle b|(\hat{n} \cdot \mathbf{r})(\hat{k} \cdot \mathbf{r})|a\rangle|^2 = \boxed{\frac{q^2 \omega^5}{\pi\epsilon_0 \hbar c^5}|\langle b|(\hat{n} \cdot \mathbf{r})(\hat{k} \cdot \mathbf{r})|a\rangle|^2.}$$

**(b)** Let the oscillator lie along the $x$ direction, so $(\hat{n} \cdot \mathbf{r}) = \hat{n}_x x$ and $\hat{k} \cdot \mathbf{r} = \hat{k}_x x$. For a transition from $n$ to $n'$, we have

$$A = \frac{q^2 \omega^5}{\pi\epsilon_0 \hbar c^5}\left(\hat{k}_x \hat{n}_x\right)^2|\langle n'|x^2|n\rangle|^2. \quad \text{From Example 2.5,} \quad \langle n'|x^2|n\rangle = \frac{\hbar}{2m\bar{\omega}}\langle n'|(a_+^2 + a_+ a_- + a_- a_+ + a_-^2)|n\rangle,$$

where $\bar{\omega}$ is the frequency of the *oscillator*, not to be confused with $\omega$, the frequency of the electromagnetic *wave*. Now, for spontaneous emission the final state must be *lower* in energy, so $n' < n$, and hence the only surviving term is $a_-^2$. Using Eq. 2.66:

$$\langle n'|x^2|n\rangle = \frac{\hbar}{2m\bar{\omega}}\langle n'|\sqrt{n(n-1)}|n-2\rangle = \frac{\hbar}{2m\bar{\omega}}\sqrt{n(n-1)}\,\delta_{n',n-2}.$$

Evidently transitions only go from $|n\rangle$ to $|n-2\rangle$, and hence

$$\omega = \frac{E_n - E_{n-2}}{\hbar} = \frac{1}{\hbar}\left[(n+\tfrac{1}{2})\hbar\bar{\omega} - (n-2+\tfrac{1}{2})\hbar\bar{\omega}\right] = 2\bar{\omega}.$$

$$\langle n'|x^2|n\rangle = \frac{\hbar}{m\omega}\sqrt{n(n-1)}\,\delta_{n',n-2}; \quad R_{n\to n-2} = \frac{q^2 \omega^5}{\pi\epsilon_0 \hbar c^5}(\hat{k}_x \hat{n}_x)^2 \frac{\hbar^2}{m^2 \omega^2} n(n-1).$$

It remains to calculate the average of $(\hat{k}_x \hat{n}_x)^2$. It's easiest to reorient the oscillator along a direction $\hat{r}$, making angle $\theta$ with the $z$ axis, and let the radiation be incident from the $z$ direction (so $\hat{k}_x \to \hat{k}_r = \cos\theta$).

Averaging over the two polarizations ($\hat{i}$ and $\hat{j}$): $\langle \hat{n}_r^2 \rangle = \frac{1}{2}\left(\hat{i}_r^2 + \hat{j}_r^2\right) = \frac{1}{2}\left(\sin^2\theta\cos^2\phi + \sin^2\theta\sin^2\phi\right) = \frac{1}{2}\sin^2\theta$. Now average overall directions:

$$\langle \hat{k}_r^2 \hat{n}_r^2 \rangle = \frac{1}{4\pi}\int \frac{1}{2}\sin^2\theta\cos^2\theta\sin\theta\,d\theta\,d\phi = \frac{1}{8\pi}2\pi\int_0^\pi (1-\cos^2\theta)\cos^2\theta\sin\theta\,d\theta$$

$$= \frac{1}{4}\left[-\frac{\cos^3\theta}{3} + \frac{\cos^5\theta}{5}\right]\Bigg|_0^\pi = \frac{1}{4}\left(\frac{2}{3} - \frac{2}{5}\right) = \frac{1}{15}.$$

$$\boxed{R = \frac{1}{15}\frac{q^2\hbar\omega^3}{\pi\epsilon_0 m^2 c^5}n(n-1).}$$ Comparing Eq. 9.63: $\quad \dfrac{R(\text{forbidden})}{R(\text{allowed})} = \boxed{\dfrac{2}{5}(n-1)\dfrac{\hbar\omega}{mc^2}.}$

For a nonrelativistic system, $\hbar\omega \ll mc^2$; hence the term "forbidden".

**(c)** If both the initial state and the final state have $l = 0$, the wave function is independent of angle ($Y_0^0 = 1/\sqrt{4\pi}$), and the angular part of the integral is:

$$\langle a|(\hat{n}\cdot\mathbf{r})(\hat{k}\cdot\mathbf{r})|b\rangle = \cdots \int (\hat{n}\cdot\mathbf{r})(\hat{k}\cdot\mathbf{r})\sin\theta\,d\theta\,d\phi = \cdots \frac{4\pi}{3}(\hat{n}\cdot\hat{k}) \quad \text{(Eq. 6.95)}.$$

But $\hat{n}\cdot\hat{k} = 0$, since electromagnetic waves are transverse. So $R = 0$ in this case, both for allowed and for forbidden transitions.

---

## Problem 9.22

[This is done in Fermi's *Notes on Quantum Mechanics* (Chicago, 1995), Section 24, but I am looking for a more accessible treatment.]

---

# Chapter 10

# The Adiabatic Approximation

**Problem 10.1**

(a)

Let $\quad (mvx^2 - 2E_n^i at)/2\hbar w = \phi(x,t).\quad \Phi_n = \sqrt{\dfrac{2}{w}}\sin\left(\dfrac{n\pi}{w}x\right)e^{i\phi},\quad$ so

$$\frac{\partial \Phi_n}{\partial t} = \sqrt{2}\left(-\frac{1}{2}\frac{1}{w^{3/2}}v\right)\sin\left(\frac{n\pi}{w}x\right)e^{i\phi} + \sqrt{\frac{2}{w}}\left[-\frac{n\pi x}{w^2}v\cos\left(\frac{n\pi}{w}x\right)\right]e^{i\phi} + \sqrt{\frac{2}{w}}\sin\left(\frac{n\pi}{w}x\right)\left(i\frac{\partial \phi}{\partial t}\right)e^{i\phi}$$

$$= \left[-\frac{v}{2w} - \frac{n\pi xv}{w^2}\cot\left(\frac{n\pi}{w}x\right) + i\frac{\partial \phi}{\partial t}\right]\Phi_n.\quad \frac{\partial \phi}{\partial t} = \frac{1}{2\hbar}\left[-\frac{2E_n^i a}{w} - \frac{v}{w^2}\left(mvx^2 - 2E_n^i at\right)\right] = -\frac{E_n^i a}{\hbar w} - \frac{v}{w}\phi.$$

$$i\hbar\frac{\partial \Phi_n}{\partial t} = -i\hbar\left[\frac{v}{2w} + \frac{n\pi xv}{w^2}\cot\left(\frac{n\pi}{w}x\right) + i\frac{E_n^i a}{\hbar w} + i\frac{v}{w}\phi\right]\Phi_n.$$

$$H\Phi_n = -\frac{\hbar^2}{2m}\frac{\partial^2 \Phi_n}{\partial x^2}.\quad \frac{\partial \Phi_n}{\partial x} = \sqrt{\frac{2}{w}}\left[\frac{n\pi}{w}\cos\left(\frac{n\pi}{w}x\right)\right]e^{i\phi} + \sqrt{\frac{2}{w}}\sin\left(\frac{n\pi}{w}x\right)e^{i\phi}\left(i\frac{\partial \phi}{\partial x}\right).$$

$$\frac{\partial \phi}{\partial x} = \frac{mvx}{\hbar w}.\quad \frac{\partial \Phi_n}{\partial x} = \left[\frac{n\pi}{w}\cot\left(\frac{n\pi}{w}x\right) + i\frac{mvx}{\hbar w}\right]\Phi_n.$$

$$\frac{\partial^2 \Phi_n}{\partial x^2} = \left[-\left(\frac{n\pi}{w}\right)^2\csc^2\left(\frac{n\pi}{w}x\right) + \frac{imb}{\hbar w}\right]\Phi_n + \left[\frac{n\pi}{w}\cot\left(\frac{n\pi}{w}x\right) + i\frac{mvx}{\hbar w}\right]^2\Phi_n.$$

So the Schrödinger equation $(i\hbar\partial\Phi_n/\partial t = H\Phi_n)$ is satisfied $\Leftrightarrow$

$$-i\hbar\left[\frac{v}{2w} + \frac{n\pi xv}{w^2}\cot\left(\frac{n\pi}{w}x\right) + i\frac{E_n^i a}{\hbar w} + i\frac{v}{w}\phi\right]$$

$$= -\frac{\hbar^2}{2m}\left\{-\left(\frac{n\pi}{w}\right)^2\csc^2\left(\frac{n\pi}{w}x\right) + \frac{imv}{\hbar w} + \left[\frac{n\pi}{w}\cot\left(\frac{n\pi}{w}x\right) + i\frac{mvx}{\hbar w}\right]^2\right\}$$

<u>Cotangent terms:</u> $\quad -i\hbar\left(\dfrac{n\pi xv}{w^2}\right) \overset{?}{=} -\dfrac{\hbar^2}{2m}\left(2\dfrac{n\pi}{w}i\dfrac{mvx}{\hbar w}\right) = -i\hbar\dfrac{n\pi vx}{w^2}.\quad\checkmark$

<u>Remaining trig terms on right:</u>

$$-\left(\frac{n\pi}{w}\right)^2\csc^2\left(\frac{n\pi}{w}x\right) + \left(\frac{n\pi}{w}\right)^2\cot^2\left(\frac{n\pi}{w}x\right) = -\left(\frac{n\pi}{w}\right)^2\left[\frac{1-\cos^2\left(n\pi x/w\right)}{\sin^2\left(n\pi x/w\right)}\right] = -\left(\frac{n\pi}{w}\right)^2.$$

This leaves:

$$i\left[\frac{v}{2w} + i\frac{E_n^i a}{\hbar w} + i\frac{v}{w}\left(\frac{mvx^2 - 2E_n^i at}{2\hbar w}\right)\right] \overset{?}{=} \frac{\hbar}{2m}\left[-\left(\frac{n\pi}{w}\right)^2 + \frac{imv}{\hbar w} - \frac{m^2v^2x^2}{\hbar^2 w^2}\right]$$

$$\frac{i\!\!\!/v}{2} - \frac{E_n^i a}{\hbar} - \frac{mv^2\!\!\!\!/x^2}{2\hbar w} + \frac{vE_n^i at}{\hbar w} \overset{?}{=} -\frac{\hbar n^2\pi^2}{2mw} + \frac{i\!\!\!/v}{2} - \frac{mv^2\!\!\!\!/x^2}{2\hbar w}$$

$$-\frac{E_n^i a}{\hbar w}(w - vt) \overset{?}{=} -\frac{E_n^i a^2}{\hbar w} \overset{?}{=} -\frac{\hbar n^2\pi^2}{2mw} \Leftrightarrow -\frac{n^2\pi^2\hbar^2}{2ma^2}\frac{a^2}{\hbar w} = -\frac{\hbar n^2\pi^2}{2mw} = \text{r.h.s.}\quad\checkmark$$

So $\Phi_n$ *does* satisfy the Schrödinger equation, and since $\Phi_n(x,t) = (\cdots)\sin\left(n\pi x/w\right)$, it fits the boundary conditions: $\quad \Phi_n(0,t) = \Phi_n(w,t) = 0$.

**(b)**

Equation 10.4 $\implies \Psi(x,0) = \sum c_n\Phi_n(x,0) = \sum c_n\sqrt{\dfrac{2}{a}}\sin\left(\dfrac{n\pi}{a}x\right)e^{imvx^2/2\hbar a}$.

Multiply by $\sqrt{\dfrac{2}{a}}\sin\left(\dfrac{n'\pi}{a}x\right)e^{-imvx^2/2\hbar a}\quad$ and integrate:

$$\sqrt{\frac{2}{a}}\int_0^a \Psi(x,0)\sin\left(\frac{n'\pi}{a}x\right)e^{-imvx^2/2\hbar a}\,dx = \sum c_n\underbrace{\left[\frac{2}{a}\int_0^\pi \sin\left(\frac{n\pi}{a}x\right)\sin\left(\frac{n'\pi}{a}x\right)\,dx\right]}_{\delta_{nn'}} = c'_n.$$

So, in general: $\quad c_n = \sqrt{\dfrac{2}{a}}\displaystyle\int_0^a e^{-imvx^2/2\hbar a}\sin\left(\dfrac{n\pi}{a}x\right)\Psi(x,0)\,dx$. In this particular case,

$$c_n = \frac{2}{a}\int_0^a e^{-imvx^2/2\hbar a}\sin\left(\frac{n\pi}{a}\right)\sin\left(\frac{\pi}{a}x\right)\,dx. \quad \text{Let} \quad \frac{\pi}{a}x \equiv z; \quad dx = \frac{a}{\pi}dz; \quad \frac{mvx^2}{2\hbar a} = \frac{mvz^2}{2\hbar a}\frac{a^2}{\pi^2} = \frac{mva}{2\pi^2\hbar}z^2.$$

$$c_n = \frac{2}{\pi}\int_0^\pi e^{-i\alpha z^2}\sin(nz)\sin(z)\,dz. \quad \text{QED}$$

**(c)**

$$w(T_e) = 2a \Rightarrow a + vT_e = 2a \Rightarrow vT_e = a \Rightarrow \boxed{T_e a/v;} \quad e^{-iE_1 t/\hbar} \Rightarrow \omega = \frac{E_1}{\hbar} \Rightarrow T_i = \frac{2\pi}{\omega} = 2\pi \frac{\hbar}{E_1}, \text{ or}$$

$$T_i = \frac{2\pi\hbar}{\pi^2\hbar^2} 2ma^2 = \frac{4}{\pi} \frac{ma^2}{\hbar}. \quad \boxed{T_i = \frac{4ma^2}{\pi\hbar}.} \quad \text{Adiabatic} \Rightarrow T_e \gg T_i \Rightarrow \frac{a}{v} \gg \frac{4ma^2}{\pi\hbar} \Rightarrow \frac{4}{\pi} \frac{mav}{\hbar} \ll 1, \text{ or}$$

$$8\pi \left( \frac{mav}{2\pi^2\hbar} \right) = 8\pi\alpha \ll 1, \quad \text{so} \quad \alpha \ll 1. \quad \text{Then } c_n = \frac{2}{\pi} \int_0^\pi \sin(nz) \sin(z) dz = \boxed{\delta_{n1}.} \quad \text{Therefore}$$

$$\boxed{\Psi(x,t) = \sqrt{\frac{2}{w}} \sin\left(\frac{\pi x}{w}\right) e^{i(mvx^2 - 2E_1^i at)/2\hbar w},}$$

which (apart from a phase factor) is the ground state of the instantaneous well, of width $w$, as required by the adiabatic theorem. (Actually, the first term in the exponent, which is at most $\frac{mva^2}{2\hbar a} = \frac{mva}{2\hbar} \ll 1$ and could be dropped, in the adiabatic regime.)

**(d)**

$$\theta(t) = -\frac{1}{\hbar} \left( \frac{\pi^2\hbar^2}{2m} \right) \int_0^t \frac{1}{(a+vt')^2} dt' = -\frac{\pi^2\hbar}{2m} \left[ -\frac{1}{v} \left( \frac{1}{a+vt'} \right) \right] \Big|_0^t$$

$$= -\frac{\pi^2\hbar}{2mv} \left( \frac{1}{a} - \frac{1}{w} \right) = -\frac{\pi^2\hbar}{2mv} \left( \frac{vt}{aw} \right) = -\frac{\pi^2\hbar t}{2maw}.$$

So (dropping the $\frac{mvx^2}{2\hbar w}$ term, as explained in (c)) $\quad \Psi(x,t) = \sqrt{\frac{2}{w}} \sin\left(\frac{\pi x}{w}\right) e^{-iE_1^i at/\hbar w} \quad$ can be written

$\left( \text{since } -\frac{E_1^i at}{\hbar w} = -\frac{\pi^2\hbar^2}{2ma^2} \frac{at}{\hbar w} = -\frac{\pi^2\hbar t}{2maw} = \theta \right)$: $\quad \boxed{\Psi(x,t) = \sqrt{\frac{2}{w}} \sin\left(\frac{\pi x}{w}\right) e^{i\theta}.}$

This is exactly what one would naively expect: For a *fixed* well (of width $a$) we'd have $\Psi(x,t) = \Psi_1(x)e^{-iE_1 t/\hbar}$; for the (adiabatically) *expanding* well, simply replace $a$ by the (time-dependent) width $w$, and *integrate* to get the accumulated phase factor, noting that $E_1$ is now a function of $t$.

---

## Problem 10.2

To show: $\quad i\hbar \frac{\partial \chi}{\partial t} = H\chi, \quad$ where $\chi$ is given by Eq. 10.31 and $H$ is given by Eq. 10.25.

$$\frac{\partial \chi}{\partial t} =$$

$$\begin{pmatrix} \frac{\lambda}{2} \left[ -\sin\left(\frac{\lambda t}{2}\right) - i\frac{(\omega_1 - \omega)}{\lambda} \cos\left(\frac{\lambda t}{2}\right) \right] \cos\left(\frac{\alpha}{2}\right) e^{-i\omega t/2} - \frac{i\omega}{2} \left[ \cos\left(\frac{\lambda t}{2}\right) - \frac{i(\omega_1 - \omega)}{\lambda} \sin\left(\frac{\lambda t}{2}\right) \right] \cos\left(\frac{\alpha}{2}\right) e^{-i\omega t/2} \\ \frac{\lambda}{2} \left[ -\sin\left(\frac{\lambda t}{2}\right) - i\frac{(\omega_1 + \omega)}{\lambda} \cos\left(\frac{\lambda t}{2}\right) \right] \sin\left(\frac{\alpha}{2}\right) e^{i\omega t/2} + \frac{i\omega}{2} \left[ \cos\left(\frac{\lambda t}{2}\right) - \frac{i(\omega_1 + \omega)}{\lambda} \sin\left(\frac{\lambda t}{2}\right) \right] \sin\left(\frac{\alpha}{2}\right) e^{i\omega t/2} \end{pmatrix}$$

$$H\chi =$$

$$\frac{\hbar\omega_1}{2}\begin{pmatrix} \cos\alpha\left[\cos(\frac{\lambda t}{2}) - i\frac{(\omega_1-\omega)}{\lambda}\sin(\frac{\lambda t}{2})\right]\cos\frac{\alpha}{2}e^{-i\omega t/2} + e^{-i\omega t}\sin\alpha\left[\cos(\frac{\lambda t}{2}) - \frac{i(\omega_1+\omega)}{\lambda}\sin(\frac{\lambda t}{2})\right]\sin\frac{\alpha}{2}e^{i\omega t/2} \\ e^{i\omega t}\cos\alpha\left[\cos(\frac{\lambda t}{2}) - i\frac{(\omega_1-\omega)}{\lambda}\sin(\frac{\lambda t}{2})\right]\cos\frac{\alpha}{2}e^{-i\omega t/2} - \cos\alpha\left[\cos(\frac{\lambda t}{2}) - \frac{i(\omega_1+\omega)}{\lambda}\sin(\frac{\lambda t}{2})\right]\sin\frac{\alpha}{2}e^{i\omega t/2} \end{pmatrix}$$

(1) Upper elements:

$$i\hbar\left\{\frac{\lambda}{2}\left[-\sin\left(\frac{\lambda t}{2}\right) - i\frac{(\omega_1-\omega)}{\lambda}\cos\left(\frac{\lambda t}{2}\right)\right]\cos\frac{\alpha}{2} - \frac{i\omega}{2}\left[\cos\left(\frac{\lambda t}{2}\right) - \frac{i(\omega_1-\omega)}{\lambda}\sin\left(\frac{\lambda t}{2}\right)\right]\cos\frac{\alpha}{2}\right\}$$

$$\overset{?}{=} \frac{\hbar\omega_1}{2}\left\{\left[\cos\left(\frac{\lambda t}{2}\right) - i\frac{(\omega_1-\omega)}{\lambda}\sin\left(\frac{\lambda t}{2}\right)\right]\cos\alpha\cos\frac{\alpha}{2} + \left[\cos\left(\frac{\lambda t}{2}\right) - i\frac{(\omega_1+\omega)}{\lambda}\sin\left(\frac{\lambda t}{2}\right)\right]\underbrace{\sin\alpha}_{\star}\sin\frac{\alpha}{2}\right\},$$

where $\star = 2\sin\frac{\alpha}{2}\cos\frac{\alpha}{2}$

The sine terms:

$$\sin\left(\frac{\lambda t}{2}\right)\left[-i\lambda - \frac{i\omega(\omega_1-\omega)}{\lambda} + \frac{\omega_1(\omega_1-\omega)}{\lambda}\cos\alpha + \frac{i\omega_1(\omega_1+\omega)}{\lambda}2\sin^2\frac{\alpha}{2}\right] \overset{?}{=} 0.$$

$$\frac{i}{\lambda}\sin\left(\frac{\lambda t}{2}\right)\left[-\omega^2 - \omega_1^2 + 2\omega\omega_1\cos\alpha - \omega\omega_1 + \omega^2 + (\omega_1^2 - \omega\omega_1)\cos\alpha + (\omega_1^2 + \omega\omega_1)(1 - \cos\alpha)\right]$$

$$= -\frac{i}{\lambda}\sin\left(\frac{\lambda t}{2}\right)\left[-\omega_1^2 + 2\omega\omega_1\cos\alpha - \omega\omega_1 + \omega_1^2\cos\alpha - \omega\omega_1\cos\alpha + \omega_1^2 + \omega\omega_1 - \omega_1^2\cos\alpha - \omega\omega_1\cos\alpha\right] = 0. \checkmark$$

The cosine terms:

$$\cos\left(\frac{\lambda t}{2}\right)\left[(\omega_1 - \omega) + \omega - \omega_1\cos\alpha - \omega_1 2\sin^2\frac{\alpha}{2}\right] = -\omega_1\cos\left(\frac{\lambda t}{2}\right)[-1 + \cos\alpha + (1 - \cos\alpha)] = 0. \checkmark$$

(2) Lower elements:

$$i\hbar\left\{\frac{\lambda}{2}\left[-\sin\left(\frac{\lambda t}{2}\right) - i\frac{(\omega_1+\omega)}{\lambda}\cos\left(\frac{\lambda t}{2}\right)\right]\sin\frac{\alpha}{2} + \frac{i\omega}{2}\left[\cos\left(\frac{\lambda t}{2}\right) - \frac{i(\omega_1+\omega)}{\lambda}\sin\left(\frac{\lambda t}{2}\right)\right]\sin\frac{\alpha}{2}\right\}$$

$$\overset{?}{=} \frac{\hbar\omega_1}{2}\left\{\left[\cos\left(\frac{\lambda t}{2}\right) - i\frac{(\omega_1-\omega)}{\lambda}\sin\left(\frac{\lambda t}{2}\right)\right]2\sin\frac{\alpha}{2}\cos^2\frac{\alpha}{2} - \left[\cos\left(\frac{\lambda t}{2}\right) - \frac{i(\omega_1+\omega)}{\lambda}\sin\left(\frac{\lambda t}{2}\right)\right]\cos\alpha\sin\frac{\alpha}{2}\right\}.$$

The sine terms:

$$\sin\left(\frac{\lambda t}{2}\right)\left[-i\lambda + \frac{i\omega(\omega_1+\omega)}{\lambda} + \frac{i\omega_1(\omega_1-\omega)}{\lambda}2\cos^2\left(\frac{\alpha}{2}\right) - \frac{i\omega_1(\omega_1+\omega)}{\lambda}\cos\alpha\right] \overset{?}{=} 0.$$

$$\frac{i}{\lambda}\sin\left(\frac{\lambda t}{2}\right)\left[-\omega^2 - \omega_1^2 + 2\omega\omega_1\cos\alpha + \omega\omega_1 + \omega^2 + (\omega_1^2 - \omega\omega_1)(1 + \cos\alpha) - (\omega_1^2 + \omega\omega_1)\cos\alpha\right]$$

$$= \frac{i}{\lambda}\sin\left(\frac{\lambda t}{2}\right)\left[-\omega_1^2 + 2\omega\omega_1\cos\alpha + \omega\omega_1 + \omega_1^2 - \omega\omega_1 + \omega_1^2\cos\alpha - \omega\omega_1\cos\alpha - \omega_1^2\cos\alpha - \omega\omega_1\cos\alpha\right] = 0. \checkmark$$

The cosine terms:

$$\cos\left(\frac{\lambda t}{2}\right)\left[(\omega_1 + \omega) - \omega - \omega_1 2\cos^2\frac{\alpha}{2} + \omega_1\cos\alpha\right] = \cos\left(\frac{\lambda t}{2}\right)[\omega_1 - \omega_1(1 + \cos\alpha) + \omega_1\cos\alpha] = 0. \checkmark$$

As for Eq. 10.33:

$$\left[\cos\left(\frac{\lambda t}{2}\right) - i\frac{(\omega_1 - \omega\cos\alpha)}{\lambda}\sin\left(\frac{\lambda t}{2}\right)\right]e^{-i\omega t/2}\begin{pmatrix}\cos\frac{\alpha}{2}\\e^{i\omega t}\sin\frac{\alpha}{2}\end{pmatrix} + i\left[\frac{\omega}{\lambda}\sin\alpha\sin\left(\frac{\lambda t}{2}\right)\right]e^{-i\omega t/2}\begin{pmatrix}\sin\frac{\alpha}{2}\\-e^{i\omega t}\cos\frac{\alpha}{2}\end{pmatrix}$$

$$= \begin{pmatrix}\alpha\\\beta\end{pmatrix}, \quad \text{with}$$

$$\alpha = \left\{\left[\cos\left(\frac{\lambda t}{2}\right) - \frac{i\omega_1}{\lambda}\sin\left(\frac{\lambda t}{2}\right)\right]\cos\frac{\alpha}{2} + \frac{i\omega}{\lambda}\underbrace{\left[\cos\alpha\cos\frac{\alpha}{2} + \sin\alpha\sin\frac{\alpha}{2}\right]}_{\cos(\alpha-\frac{\alpha}{2})=\cos\frac{\alpha}{2}}\sin\left(\frac{\lambda t}{2}\right)\right\}e^{-i\omega t/2}$$

$$= \left[\cos\left(\frac{\lambda t}{2}\right) - \frac{i(\omega_1 - \omega)}{\lambda}\sin\left(\frac{\lambda t}{2}\right)\right]\cos\frac{\alpha}{2}e^{-i\omega t/2} \quad \text{(confirming the top entry).}$$

$$\beta = \left\{\left[\cos\left(\frac{\lambda t}{2}\right) - \frac{i\omega_1}{\lambda}\sin\left(\frac{\lambda t}{2}\right)\right]\sin\frac{\alpha}{2} + \frac{i\omega}{\lambda}\underbrace{\left[\cos\alpha\sin\frac{\alpha}{2} - \sin\alpha\cos\frac{\alpha}{2}\right]}_{\sin(\frac{\alpha}{2}-\alpha)=-\sin\frac{\alpha}{2}}\sin\left(\frac{\lambda t}{2}\right)\right\}e^{i\omega t/2}$$

$$= \left[\cos\left(\frac{\lambda t}{2}\right) - \frac{i(\omega_1 + \omega)}{\lambda}\sin\left(\frac{\lambda t}{2}\right)\right]\sin\frac{\alpha}{2}e^{i\omega t/2} \quad \text{(confirming the bottom entry).}$$

$$|c_+|^2 + |c_-|^2 = \cos^2\left(\frac{\lambda t}{2}\right) + \frac{(\omega_1 - \omega\cos\alpha)^2}{\lambda^2}\sin^2\left(\frac{\lambda t}{2}\right) + \frac{\omega^2}{\lambda^2}\sin^2\alpha\sin^2\left(\frac{\lambda t}{2}\right)$$

$$= \cos^2\left(\frac{\lambda t}{2}\right) + \frac{1}{\lambda^2}\underbrace{\left(\omega_1^2 - 2\omega\omega_1\cos\alpha + \omega^2\cos^2\alpha + \omega^2\sin^2\alpha\right)}_{\omega^2+\omega_1^2-2\omega\omega_1\cos\alpha=\lambda^2}\sin^2\left(\frac{\lambda t}{2}\right)$$

$$= \cos^2\left(\frac{\lambda t}{2}\right) + \sin^2\left(\frac{\lambda t}{2}\right) = 1. \quad \checkmark$$

---

## Problem 10.3

(a)

$$\psi_n(x) = \sqrt{\frac{2}{w}}\sin\left(\frac{n\pi}{w}x\right). \quad \text{In this case } R = w.$$

$$\frac{\partial\psi_n}{\partial R} = \sqrt{2}\left(-\frac{1}{2}\frac{1}{w^{3/2}}\right)\sin\left(\frac{n\pi}{w}x\right) + \sqrt{\frac{2}{w}}\left(-\frac{n\pi}{w^2}x\right)\cos\left(\frac{n\pi}{w}x\right);$$

$$\left\langle \psi_n \left| \frac{\partial \psi_n}{\partial R} \right. \right\rangle = \int_0^w \psi_n \frac{\partial \psi_n}{\partial R} dx$$

$$= -\frac{1}{w^2} \int_0^w \sin^2 \left( \frac{n\pi}{w} x \right) dx - \frac{2n\pi}{w^3} \int_0^w x \underbrace{\sin \left( \frac{n\pi}{w} x \right) \cos \left( \frac{n\pi}{w} x \right)}_{\frac{1}{2} \sin \left( \frac{2n\pi}{w} x \right)} dx$$

$$= -\frac{1}{w^2} \left( \frac{w}{2} \right) - \frac{n\pi}{w^3} \int_0^w x \sin \left( \frac{2n\pi}{w} x \right) dx$$

$$= -\frac{1}{2w} - \frac{n\pi}{w^3} \left[ \left( \frac{w}{2n\pi} \right)^2 \sin \left( \frac{2n\pi}{w} x \right) - \frac{wx}{2n\pi} \cos \left( \frac{2n\pi}{w} x \right) \right] \Big|_0^w$$

$$= -\frac{1}{2w} - \frac{n\pi}{w^3} \left[ -\frac{w^2}{2n\pi} \cos(2n\pi) \right] = -\frac{1}{2w} + \frac{1}{2w} = 0.$$

So Eq. 10.42 $\implies$ $\boxed{\gamma_n(t) = 0.}$ (If the eigenfunctions are *real*, the geometric phase vanishes.)

**(b)**

Equation 10.39 $\implies \theta_n(t) = \frac{1}{\hbar} \int_0^t \frac{n^2 \pi^2 \hbar^2}{2mw^2} dt' = -\frac{n^2 \pi^2 \hbar}{2m} \int \frac{1}{w^2} \frac{dt'}{dw} dw;$

$$\theta_n = -\frac{n^2 \pi^2 \hbar}{2mv} \int_{w_1}^{w_2} \frac{1}{w^2} dw = \frac{n^2 \pi^2 \hbar}{2mv} \left( \frac{1}{w} \right) \Big|_{w_1}^{w_2} = \boxed{\frac{n^2 \pi^2 \hbar}{2mv} \left( \frac{1}{w_2} - \frac{1}{w_1} \right).}$$

**(c)** $\boxed{\text{Zero.}}$

---

## Problem 10.4

$\psi = \frac{\sqrt{m\alpha}}{\hbar} e^{-m\alpha|x|/\hbar^2}.$ Here $R = \alpha,$ so

$$\frac{\partial \psi}{\partial R} = \frac{\sqrt{m}}{\hbar} \left( \frac{1}{2} \frac{1}{\sqrt{\alpha}} \right) e^{-m\alpha|x|/\hbar^2} + \frac{\sqrt{m\alpha}}{\hbar} \left( -\frac{m|x|}{\hbar^2} \right) e^{-m\alpha|x|/\hbar^2}.$$

$$\psi \frac{\partial \psi}{\partial R} = \frac{\sqrt{m\alpha}}{\hbar} \left[ \frac{1}{2\hbar} \sqrt{\frac{m}{\alpha}} - \frac{m\sqrt{m\alpha}}{\hbar^3} |x| \right] e^{-2m\alpha|x|/\hbar^2} = \left( \frac{m}{2\hbar^2} - \frac{m^2 \alpha}{\hbar^4} |x| \right) e^{-2m\alpha|x|/\hbar^2}.$$

$$\left\langle \psi \left| \frac{\partial \psi}{\partial R} \right. \right\rangle = 2 \left[ \frac{m}{2\hbar^2} \int_0^\infty e^{-2m\alpha x/\hbar^2} dx - \frac{m^2 \alpha}{\hbar^4} \int_0^\infty x e^{-2m\alpha x/\hbar^2} dx \right] = \frac{m}{\hbar^2} \left( \frac{\hbar^2}{2m\alpha} \right) - \frac{2m^2 \alpha}{\hbar^4} \left( \frac{\hbar^2}{2m\alpha} \right)^2$$

$$= \frac{1}{2\alpha} - \frac{1}{2\alpha} = 0. \quad \text{So Eq. 10.42} \implies \boxed{\gamma(t) = 0.}$$

$$E = -\frac{m\alpha^2}{2\hbar^2}, \quad \text{so } \theta(t) = -\frac{1}{\hbar} \int_0^T \left( -\frac{m\alpha^2}{2\hbar^2} \right) dt' = \frac{m}{2\hbar^3} \int_{\alpha_1}^{\alpha_2} \alpha^2 \frac{dt'}{d\alpha} d\alpha = \frac{m}{2\hbar^3 c} \int_{\alpha_1}^{\alpha_2} \alpha^2 d\alpha = \boxed{\frac{m}{6\hbar^2 c} \left( \alpha_2^3 - \alpha_1^3 \right).}$$

## Problem 10.5

According to Eq. 10.44 the geometric phase is

$$\gamma_n(t) = i \int_{\mathbf{R}_i}^{\mathbf{R}_f} \langle \psi_n | \nabla_R \psi_n \rangle \cdot d\mathbf{R}.$$

Now $\langle \psi_n | \psi_n \rangle = 1$, so

$$\nabla_R \langle \psi_n | \psi_n \rangle = \langle \nabla_R \psi_n | \psi_n \rangle + \langle \psi_n | \nabla_R \psi_n \rangle = \langle \psi_n | \nabla_R \psi_n \rangle^* + \langle \psi_n | \nabla_R \psi_n \rangle = 0,$$

and hence $\langle \psi_n | \nabla_R \psi_n \rangle$ is *pure imaginary*. If $\psi_n$ is real, then, $\langle \psi_n | \nabla_R \psi_n \rangle$ must in fact be *zero*.
Suppose we introduce a phase factor to *make* the (originally real) wave function complex:

$$\psi_n' = e^{i\phi_n(\mathbf{R})} \psi_n, \quad \text{where } \psi_n \text{ is real.} \quad \text{Then} \quad \nabla_R \psi_n' = e^{i\phi_n} \nabla_R \psi_n + i(\nabla_R \phi_n) e^{i\phi_n} \psi_n. \quad \text{So}$$

$$\langle \psi_n' | \nabla_R \psi_n' \rangle = e^{-i\phi_n} e^{i\phi_n} \langle \psi_n | \nabla_R \psi_n \rangle + i e^{-i\phi_n} (\nabla_R \phi_n) e^{i\phi_n} \langle \psi_n | \psi_n \rangle. \quad \text{But} \quad \langle \psi_n | \psi_n \rangle = 1, \quad \text{and}$$

$$\langle \psi_n | \nabla_R \psi_n \rangle = 0 \quad \text{(as we just found), so} \quad \langle \psi_n' | \nabla_R \psi_n' \rangle = i \nabla_R \phi_n, \quad \text{and Eq. 10.44} \implies$$

$$\gamma_n'(t) = i \int_{R_i}^{R_f} i \nabla_R(\phi_n) \cdot d\mathbf{R} = -[\phi_n(\mathbf{R}_f) - \phi_n(\mathbf{R}_i)], \quad \text{so Eq. 10.38 gives:}$$

$$\Psi_n'(x,t) = \psi_n'(x,t) e^{-\frac{i}{\hbar} \int_0^t E_n(t')dt'} e^{-i[\phi_n(\mathbf{R}_f) - \phi_n(\mathbf{R}_i)]}.$$

The wave function picks up a (trivial) phase factor, whose only function is precisely to kill the phase factor we put in "by hand":

$$\Psi_n'(x,t) = \left[ \psi_n(x,t) e^{-\frac{i}{\hbar} \int_0^t E_n(t')dt'} \right] e^{i\phi_n(\mathbf{R}_i)} = \Psi_n(x,t) e^{i\phi_n(\mathbf{R}_i)}.$$

In particular, for a *closed* loop $\phi_n(\mathbf{R}_f) = \phi_n(\mathbf{R}_i)$, so $\gamma_n'(T) = 0$.

---

## Problem 10.6

$$H = \frac{e}{m} \mathbf{B} \cdot \mathbf{S}. \quad \text{Here} \quad \mathbf{B} = B_0 \left[ \sin\theta \cos\phi\, \hat{i} + \sin\theta \sin\phi\, \hat{j} + \cos\theta\, \hat{k} \right]; \quad \text{take spin matrices from Problem 4.31.}$$

$$H = \frac{eB_0}{m} \frac{\hbar}{\sqrt{2}} \left[ \sin\theta\cos\phi \begin{pmatrix} 0 & 1 & 0 \\ 1 & 0 & 1 \\ 0 & 1 & 0 \end{pmatrix} + \sin\theta\sin\phi \begin{pmatrix} 0 & -i & 0 \\ i & 0 & -i \\ 0 & i & 0 \end{pmatrix} + \cos\theta \begin{pmatrix} \sqrt{2} & 0 & 0 \\ 0 & 0 & 0 \\ 0 & 0 & -\sqrt{2} \end{pmatrix} \right]$$

$$= \frac{eB_0\hbar}{\sqrt{2}\,m} \begin{pmatrix} \sqrt{2}\cos\theta & e^{-i\phi}\sin\theta & 0 \\ e^{i\phi}\sin\theta & 0 & e^{-i\phi}\sin\theta \\ 0 & e^{i\phi}\sin\theta & -\sqrt{2}\cos\theta \end{pmatrix}.$$

We need the "spin up" eigenvector: $\quad H\chi_+ = \dfrac{eB_0}{m}\hbar\chi_+.$

$$\begin{pmatrix} \sqrt{2}\cos\theta & e^{-i\phi}\sin\theta & 0 \\ e^{i\phi}\sin\theta & 0 & e^{-i\phi}\sin\theta \\ 0 & e^{i\phi}\sin\theta & -\sqrt{2}\cos\theta \end{pmatrix} \begin{pmatrix} a \\ b \\ c \end{pmatrix} = \sqrt{2} \begin{pmatrix} a \\ b \\ c \end{pmatrix} \implies \begin{cases} \text{(i)} & \sqrt{2}\cos\theta a + e^{-i\phi}\sin\theta b = \sqrt{2}a. \\ \text{(ii)} & e^{i\phi}\sin\theta a + e^{-i\phi}\sin\theta c = \sqrt{2}b. \\ \text{(iii)} & e^{i\phi}\sin\theta b - \sqrt{2}\cos\theta c = \sqrt{2}c. \end{cases}$$

(i) $\Rightarrow b = \sqrt{2}e^{i\phi}\left(\dfrac{1-\cos\theta}{\sin\theta}\right)a = \sqrt{2}e^{i\phi}\tan(\theta/2)\,a;$ (iii) $\Rightarrow b = \sqrt{2}e^{-i\phi}\left(\dfrac{1+\cos\theta}{\sin\theta}\right)c = \sqrt{2}e^{-i\phi}\cot(\theta/2)\,c.$

Thus $c = e^{2i\phi}\tan^2(\theta/2)\,a;$ (ii) is redundant. Normalize: $|a|^2 + 2\tan^2(\theta/2)|a|^2 + \tan^4(\theta/2)|a|^2 = 1 \Rightarrow$

$$|a|^2\left[1+\tan^2(\theta/2)\right]^2 = |a|^2\left[\dfrac{1}{\cos(\theta/2)}\right]^4 = 1 \Rightarrow |a|^2 = \cos^4(\theta/2).$$

Pick $a = e^{-i\phi}\cos^2(\theta/2);$ then $b = \sqrt{2}\sin(\theta/2)\cos(\theta/2)$ and $c = e^{i\phi}\sin^2(\theta/2),$ and

$$\boxed{\chi_+ = \begin{pmatrix} e^{-i\phi}\cos^2(\theta/2) \\ \sqrt{2}\sin(\theta/2)\cos(\theta/2) \\ e^{i\phi}\sin^2(\theta/2) \end{pmatrix}.}$$ This is the spin-1 analog to Eq. 10.57.

$$\nabla\chi_+ = \frac{\partial\chi_+}{\partial r}\,\hat{r} + \frac{1}{r}\frac{\partial\chi_+}{\partial\theta}\,\hat{\theta} + \frac{1}{r\sin\theta}\frac{\partial\chi_+}{\partial\phi}\,\hat{\phi}$$

$$= \frac{1}{r}\begin{pmatrix} -e^{-i\phi}\cos(\theta/2)\sin(\theta/2) \\ \sqrt{2}\left[\cos^2(\theta/2)-\sin^2(\theta/2)\right]/2 \\ e^{i\phi}\sin(\theta/2)\cos(\theta/2) \end{pmatrix}\hat{\theta} + \frac{1}{r\sin\theta}\begin{pmatrix} -ie^{-i\phi}\cos^2(\theta/2) \\ 0 \\ ie^{i\phi}\sin^2(\theta/2) \end{pmatrix}\hat{\phi}.$$

$$\langle\chi_+|\nabla\chi_+\rangle = \frac{1}{r}\left\{-\cos^2(\theta/2)\left[\cos(\theta/2)\sin(\theta/2)\right] + \sin(\theta/2)\cos(\theta/2)\left[\cos^2(\theta/2)-\sin^2(\theta/2)\right]\right.$$
$$\left. + \sin^2(\theta/2)\left[\sin(\theta/2)\cos(\theta/2)\right]\right\}\hat{\theta}$$
$$+ \frac{1}{r\sin\theta}\left\{\cos^2(\theta/2)\left[-i\cos^2(\theta/2)\right] + \sin^2(\theta/2)\left[i\sin^2(\theta/2)\right]\right\}\hat{\phi}$$
$$= \frac{i}{r\sin\theta}\left[\sin^4(\theta/2) - \cos^4(\theta/2)\right]\hat{\phi}$$
$$= \frac{i}{r\sin\theta}\left[\sin^2(\theta/2) + \cos^2(\theta/2)\right]\left[\sin^2(\theta/2) - \cos^2(\theta/2)\right]\hat{\phi}$$
$$= \frac{i}{r\sin\theta}(1)(-\cos\theta)\,\hat{\phi} = -\frac{i}{r}\cot\theta\,\hat{\phi}.$$

$$\nabla\times\langle\chi_+|\nabla\chi_+\rangle = \frac{1}{r\sin\theta}\frac{\partial}{\partial\theta}\left[\sin\theta\left(-\frac{i}{r}\cot\theta\right)\right]\hat{r} = \frac{-i}{r^2\sin\theta}\frac{\partial}{\partial\theta}(\cos\theta)\,\hat{r} = \frac{i\sin\theta}{r^2\sin\theta}\,\hat{r} = \frac{i}{r^2}\,\hat{r}.$$

Equation 10.51 $\Longrightarrow \gamma_+(T) = i\displaystyle\int \frac{i}{r^2}r^2 d\Omega = \boxed{-\Omega.}$

---

## Problem 10.7

**(a)** Giving $H$ a test function $f$ to act upon:

$$Hf = \frac{1}{2m}\left(\frac{\hbar}{i}\nabla - q\mathbf{A}\right)\cdot\left(\frac{\hbar}{i}\nabla f - q\mathbf{A}f\right) + q\varphi f$$

$$= \frac{1}{2m}\left[-\hbar^2\nabla\cdot(\nabla f) - \frac{q\hbar}{i}\underbrace{\nabla\cdot(\mathbf{A}f)}_{(\nabla\cdot A)f + \mathbf{A}\cdot(\nabla f)} - \frac{q\hbar}{i}\mathbf{A}\cdot(\nabla f) + q^2\mathbf{A}\cdot\mathbf{A}f\right] + q\varphi f.$$

But $\nabla \cdot \mathbf{A} = 0$ and $\varphi = 0$ (see comments after Eq. 10.66), so

$$Hf = \frac{1}{2m} \left[ -\hbar^2 \nabla^2 f + 2iq\hbar \mathbf{A} \cdot \nabla f + q^2 A^2 f \right], \quad \text{or} \quad H = \frac{1}{2m} \left[ -\hbar^2 \nabla^2 + q^2 A^2 + 2iq\hbar \mathbf{A} \cdot \nabla \right]. \quad \text{QED}$$

**(b)** Apply $\left( \frac{\hbar}{i} \nabla - q\mathbf{A} \right) \cdot$ to both sides of Eq. 10.78:

$$\left( \frac{\hbar}{i} \nabla - q\mathbf{A} \right)^2 \Psi = \left( \frac{\hbar}{i} \nabla - q\mathbf{A} \right) \cdot \left( \frac{\hbar}{i} e^{ig} \nabla \Psi' \right) = -\hbar^2 \nabla \cdot (e^{ig} \nabla \Psi') - \frac{q\hbar}{i} e^{ig} \mathbf{A} \cdot \nabla \Psi'.$$

But $\nabla \cdot (e^{ig} \nabla \Psi') = ie^{ig} (\nabla g) \cdot (\nabla \Psi') + e^{ig} \nabla \cdot (\nabla \Psi')$ and $\nabla g = \frac{q}{\hbar} \mathbf{A}$, so the right side is

$$-i\hbar^2 \frac{q}{\hbar} e^{ig} \mathbf{A} \cdot \nabla \Psi' - \hbar^2 e^{ig} \nabla^2 \Psi' + iq\hbar e^{ig} \mathbf{A} \cdot \nabla \Psi' = -\hbar^2 e^{ig} \nabla^2 \Psi'. \quad \text{QED}$$

---

## Problem 10.8

**(a)** Schrödinger equation:

$$-\frac{\hbar^2}{2m} \frac{d^2\psi}{dx^2} = E\psi, \quad \text{or} \quad \frac{d^2\psi}{dx^2} = -k^2\psi \quad (k \equiv \sqrt{2mE}/\hbar) \quad \begin{cases} 0 < x < \frac{1}{2}a + \epsilon, \\ \frac{1}{2}a + \epsilon < x < a. \end{cases}$$

Boundary conditions: $\psi(0) = \psi(\frac{1}{2}a + \epsilon) = \psi(a) = 0.$

Solution:

(1) $0 < x < \frac{1}{2}a + \epsilon$: $\quad \psi(x) = A \sin kx + B \cos kx.$ But $\quad \psi(0) = 0 \Rightarrow B = 0,$ and

$$\psi(\tfrac{1}{2}a + \epsilon) = 0 \Rightarrow \begin{cases} k(\frac{1}{2}a + \epsilon) = n\pi \quad (n = 1, 2, 3, \dots) \Rightarrow E_n = n^2\pi^2\hbar^2/2m(a/2 + \epsilon)^2, \\ \text{or else} \quad A = 0. \end{cases}$$

(2) $\frac{1}{2}a + \epsilon < x < a$: $\quad \psi(x) = F \sin k(a - x) + G \cos k(a - x).$ But $\quad \psi(a) = 0 \Rightarrow G = 0,$ and

$$\psi(\tfrac{1}{2}a + \epsilon) = 0 \Rightarrow \begin{cases} k(\frac{1}{2}a - \epsilon) = n'\pi \quad (n' = 1, 2, 3, \dots) \Rightarrow E_{n'} = (n')^2\pi^2\hbar^2/2m(a/2 - \epsilon)^2, \\ \text{or else} \quad F = 0. \end{cases}$$

The ground state energy is $\begin{cases} \text{either} \quad E_1 = \dfrac{\pi^2\hbar^2}{2m(\frac{1}{2}a + \epsilon)^2} \quad (n = 1), \quad \text{with} \quad F = 0, \\[3mm] \text{or else} \quad E_{1'} = \dfrac{\pi^2\hbar^2}{2m(\frac{1}{2}a - \epsilon)^2} \quad (n' = 1), \quad \text{with} \quad A = 0. \end{cases}$

Both are allowed energies, but $E_1$ is (slightly) lower (assuming $\epsilon$ is positive), so the ground state is

$$\boxed{\psi(x) = \begin{cases} \sqrt{\dfrac{2}{\frac{1}{2}a + \epsilon}} \sin\left( \dfrac{\pi x}{\frac{1}{2}a + \epsilon} \right), & 0 \le x \le \frac{1}{2}a + \epsilon; \\ 0, & \frac{1}{2}a + \epsilon \le x \le a. \end{cases}}$$

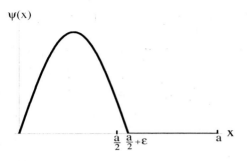

**(b)**

$$-\frac{\hbar^2}{2m}\frac{d^2\psi}{dx^2}+f(t)\delta(x-\tfrac{1}{2}a-\epsilon)\psi = E\psi \quad\Rightarrow\quad \psi(x) = \begin{cases} A\sin kx, & 0 \le x < \tfrac{1}{2}a+\epsilon, \\ F\sin k(a-x), & \tfrac{1}{2}a+\epsilon < x \le a, \end{cases} \quad \text{where} \quad k \equiv \frac{\sqrt{2mE}}{\hbar}.$$

Continuity in $\psi$ at $x = \tfrac{1}{2}a + \epsilon$ :

$$A\sin k\left(\tfrac{1}{2}a+\epsilon\right) = F\sin k\left(a-\tfrac{1}{2}a-\epsilon\right) = F\sin k\left(\tfrac{1}{2}a-\epsilon\right) \quad\Rightarrow\quad F = A\frac{\sin k\left(\tfrac{1}{2}a+\epsilon\right)}{\sin k\left(\tfrac{1}{2}a-\epsilon\right)}.$$

Discontinuity in $\psi'$ at $x = \tfrac{1}{2}a + \epsilon$ (Eq. 2.125):

$$-Fk\cos k(a-x)-Ak\cos kx = \frac{2mf}{\hbar^2}A\sin kx \;\Rightarrow\; F\cos k\left(\tfrac{1}{2}a-\epsilon\right)+A\cos k\left(\tfrac{1}{2}a+\epsilon\right) = -\left(\frac{2mf}{\hbar^2 k}\right)A\sin k\left(\tfrac{1}{2}a+\epsilon\right).$$

$$A\frac{\sin k\left(\tfrac{1}{2}a+\epsilon\right)}{\sin k\left(\tfrac{1}{2}a-\epsilon\right)}\cos k\left(\tfrac{1}{2}a-\epsilon\right) + A\cos k\left(\tfrac{1}{2}a+\epsilon\right) = -\left(\frac{2T}{z}\right)A\sin k\left(\tfrac{1}{2}a+\epsilon\right).$$

$$\sin k\left(\tfrac{1}{2}a+\epsilon\right)\cos k\left(\tfrac{1}{2}a-\epsilon\right) + \cos k\left(\tfrac{1}{2}a+\epsilon\right)\sin k\left(\tfrac{1}{2}a-\epsilon\right) = -\left(\frac{2T}{z}\right)\sin k\left(\tfrac{1}{2}a+\epsilon\right)\sin k\left(\tfrac{1}{2}a-\epsilon\right).$$

$$\sin k\left(\tfrac{1}{2}a+\epsilon+\tfrac{1}{2}a-\epsilon\right) = -\left(\frac{2T}{z}\right)\frac{1}{2}\left[\cos k\left(\tfrac{1}{2}a+\epsilon-\tfrac{1}{2}a+\epsilon\right) - \cos k\left(\tfrac{1}{2}a+\epsilon+\tfrac{1}{2}a-\epsilon\right)\right].$$

$$\sin ka = -\frac{T}{z}\left(\cos 2k\epsilon - \cos ka\right) \quad\Rightarrow\quad \boxed{z\sin z = T[\cos z - \cos(z\delta)].}$$

**(c)**

$$\sin z = \frac{T}{z}(\cos z - 1) \quad\Rightarrow\quad \frac{z}{T} = \frac{\cos z - 1}{\sin z} = -\tan(z/2) \quad\Rightarrow\quad \boxed{\tan(z/2) = -\frac{z}{T}.}$$

Plot $\tan(z/2)$ and $-z/T$ on the same graph, and look for intersections:

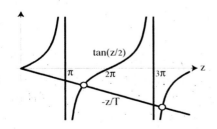

As $t : 0 \to \infty$, $T : 0 \to \infty$, and the straight line rotates counterclockwise from 6 o'clock to 3 o'clock, so the smallest $z$ goes from $\pi$ to $2\pi$, and the ground state energy goes from $ka = \pi \Rightarrow E(0) = \dfrac{\hbar^2 \pi^2}{2ma^2}$ (appropriate to a well of width $a$) to $ka = 2\pi \Rightarrow E(\infty) = \dfrac{\hbar^2 \pi^2}{2m(a/2)^2}$ (appropriate for a well of width $a/2$.

**(d)** Mathematica yields the following table:

| $T$ | 0 | 1 | 5 | 20 | 100 | 1000 |
|---|---|---|---|---|---|---|
| $z$ | 3.14159 | 3.67303 | 4.76031 | 5.72036 | 6.13523 | 6.21452 |

**(e)** $P_r = \dfrac{I_r}{I_r + I_l} = \dfrac{1}{1 + (I_l/I_r)}$,   where

$$I_l = \int_0^{a/2+\epsilon} A^2 \sin^2 kx\, dx = A^2 \left[ \frac{1}{2}x - \frac{1}{4k}\sin(2kx) \right] \Big|_0^{a/2+\epsilon}$$

$$= A^2 \left\{ \frac{1}{2}\left(\frac{a}{2} + \epsilon\right) - \frac{1}{4k}\sin\left[2k\left(\frac{a}{2}+\epsilon\right)\right] \right\} = \frac{a}{4}A^2 \left[ 1 + \frac{2\epsilon}{a} - \frac{1}{ka}\sin\left(ka + \frac{2\epsilon}{a}ka\right) \right]$$

$$= \frac{a}{4}A^2 \left[ 1 + \delta - \frac{1}{z}\sin(z + z\delta) \right].$$

$$I_r = \int_{a/2+\epsilon}^a F^2 \sin^2 k(a-x)\, dx. \quad \text{Let} \quad u \equiv a - x,\ du = -dx.$$

$$= -F^2 \int_{a/2-\epsilon}^0 \sin^2 ku\, du = F^2 \int_0^{a/2-\epsilon} \sin^2 ku\, du = \frac{a}{4}F^2 \left[ 1 - \delta - \frac{1}{z}\sin(z - z\delta) \right].$$

$$\frac{I_l}{I_r} = \frac{A^2 \left[ 1 + \delta - (1/z)\sin(z+z\delta) \right]}{F^2 \left[ 1 - \delta - (1/z)\sin(z-z\delta) \right]}. \quad \text{But (from (b))} \quad \frac{A^2}{F^2} = \frac{\sin^2 k(a/2 - \epsilon)}{\sin^2 k(a/2 + \epsilon)} = \frac{\sin^2[z(1-\delta)/2]}{\sin^2[z(1+\delta)/2]}.$$

$$= \frac{I_+}{I_-}, \quad \text{where} \quad \boxed{I_\pm \equiv \left[ 1 \pm \delta - \frac{1}{z}\sin z(1\pm\delta) \right] \sin^2[z(1 \mp \delta)/2].} \quad \boxed{P_r = \frac{1}{1 + (I_+/I_-)}.}$$

Using $\delta = 0.01$ and the $z$'s from (d), Mathematica gives

| $T$ | 0 | 1 | 5 | 20 | 100 | 1000 |
|---|---|---|---|---|---|---|
| $P_r$ | 0.490001 | 0.486822 | 0.471116 | 0.401313 | 0.146529 | 0.00248443 |

As $t : 0 \to \infty$ (so $T : 0 \to \infty$), the probability of being in the right half drops from almost $1/2$ to zero—the particle gets sucked out of the slightly smaller side, as it heads for the ground state in (a).

**(f)**

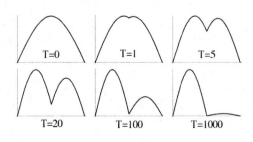

## Problem 10.9

**(a)** Check the answer given: $\quad x_c = \omega \int_0^t f(t') \sin\left[\omega(t - t')\right] dt' \implies x_c(0) = 0. \quad \checkmark$

$$\dot{x}_c = \omega f(t) \sin\left[\omega(t - t)\right] + \omega^2 \int_0^t f(t') \cos\left[\omega(t - t')\right] dt' = \omega^2 \int_0^t f(t') \cos\left[\omega(t - t')\right] dt' \Rightarrow \dot{x}_c(0) = 0. \quad \checkmark$$

$$\ddot{x}_c = \omega^2 f(t) \cos\left[\omega(t - t)\right] - \omega^3 \int_0^t f(t') \sin\left[\omega(t - t')\right] dt' = \omega^2 f(t) - \omega^2 x_c.$$

Now the classical equation of motion is $m(d^2x/dt^2) = -m\omega^2 x + m\omega^2 f$. For the proposed solution, $m(d^2x_c/dt^2) = m\omega^2 f - m\omega^2 x_c$, so it *does* satisfy the equation of motion, with the appropriate boundary conditions.

**(b)** Let $\quad z \equiv x - x_c \quad$ (so $\psi_n(x - x_c) = \psi_n(z)$, and $z$ depends on $t$ as well as $x$).

$$\frac{\partial \Psi}{\partial t} = \frac{d\psi_n}{dz}(-\dot{x}_c)e^{i\{\}} + \psi_n e^{i\{\}}\frac{i}{\hbar}\left[-\left(n + \frac{1}{2}\right)\hbar\omega + m\ddot{x}_c\left(x - \frac{x_c}{2}\right) - \frac{m}{2}\dot{x}_c^2 + \frac{m\omega^2}{2}fx_c\right]$$

$$[\ ] = -\left(n + \frac{1}{2}\right)\hbar\omega + \frac{m\omega^2}{2}\left[2x(f - x_c) + x_c^2 - \frac{\dot{x}_c^2}{\omega^2}\right].$$

$$\frac{\partial \Psi}{\partial t} = -\dot{x}_c \frac{d\psi_n}{dz}e^{i\{\}} + i\Psi\left\{-\left(n + \frac{1}{2}\right)\hbar\omega + \frac{m\omega^2}{2\hbar}\left[2x(f - x_c) + x_c^2 - \frac{\dot{x}_c^2}{\omega^2}\right]\right\}.$$

$$\frac{\partial \Psi}{\partial x} = \frac{d\psi_n}{dz}e^{i\{\}} + \psi_n e^{i\{\}}\frac{i}{\hbar}(m\dot{x}_c); \quad \frac{\partial^2 \Psi}{\partial x^2} = \frac{d^2\psi_n}{dz^2}e^{i\{\}} + 2\frac{d\psi_n}{dz}e^{i\{\}}\frac{i}{\hbar}(m\dot{x}_c) - \left(\frac{m\dot{x}_c}{\hbar}\right)^2\psi_n e^{i\{\}}.$$

$$H\Psi = -\frac{\hbar^2}{2m}\frac{\partial^2 \Psi}{\partial x^2} + \frac{1}{2}m\omega^2 x^2\Psi - m\omega^2 fx\Psi$$

$$= -\frac{\hbar^2}{2m}\frac{d^2\psi_n}{dz^2}e^{i\{\}} - \frac{\hbar^2}{2m}2\frac{d\psi_n}{dz}e^{i\{\}}\frac{im\dot{x}_c}{\hbar} + \frac{\hbar^2}{2m}\left(\frac{m\dot{x}_c}{\hbar}\right)^2\Psi + \frac{1}{2}m\omega^2 x^2\Psi - m\omega^2 fx\Psi.$$

But $\quad -\dfrac{\hbar^2}{2m}\dfrac{d^2\psi_n}{dz^2} + \dfrac{1}{2}m\omega^2 z^2\psi_n = \left(n + \dfrac{1}{2}\right)\hbar\omega\psi_n, \quad$ so

$$H\Psi = \left(n + \frac{1}{2}\right)\hbar\omega\Psi - \frac{1}{2}m\omega^2 z^2\Psi - i\hbar\dot{x}_c\frac{d\psi_n}{dz}e^{i\{\}} + \frac{m}{2}\dot{x}_c^2\Psi + \frac{1}{2}m\omega^2 x^2\Psi - m\omega^2 fx\Psi$$

$$\stackrel{?}{=} i\hbar\frac{\partial \Psi}{\partial t} = -i\hbar\dot{x}_c\frac{d\psi_n}{dz}e^{i\{\}} - \hbar\Psi\left[-\left(n + \frac{1}{2}\right)\omega + \frac{m\omega^2}{2\hbar}\left(2xf - 2xx_c + x_c^2 - \frac{1}{\omega^2}\dot{x}_c^2\right)\right]$$

$$-\frac{1}{2}m\omega^2 z^2 + \frac{m}{2}\dot{x}_c^2 + \frac{1}{2}m\omega^2 x^2 - m\omega^2 fx \stackrel{?}{=} -\frac{m\omega^2}{2}\left(2xf - 2xx_c + x_c^2 - \frac{1}{\omega^2}\dot{x}_c^2\right)$$

$$z^2 - x^2 \stackrel{?}{=} -2xx_c + x_c^2; \quad z^2 \stackrel{?}{=} (x^2 - 2xx_c + x_c^2) = (x - x_c)^2. \quad \checkmark$$

**(c)**

$$\text{Eq. 10.90} \Rightarrow H = -\frac{\hbar^2}{2m}\frac{\partial^2}{\partial x^2} + \frac{1}{2}m\omega^2\left(x^2 - 2xf + f^2\right) - \frac{1}{2}m\omega^2 f^2. \quad \text{Shift origin:} \quad u \equiv x - f.$$

$$H = \left[-\frac{\hbar^2}{2m}\frac{\partial^2}{\partial u^2} + \frac{1}{2}m\omega^2 u^2\right] - \left[\frac{1}{2}m\omega^2 f^2\right].$$

The first term is a simple harmonic oscillator in the variable $u$; the second is a *constant* (with respect to position). So the eigenfunctions are $\psi_n(u)$, and the eigenvalues are harmonic oscillator ones, $(n + \frac{1}{2})\hbar\omega$, less the constant: $E_n = (n + \frac{1}{2})\hbar\omega - \frac{1}{2}m\omega^2 f^2$.

**(d)** Note that $\sin\left[\omega(t - t')\right] = \frac{1}{\omega}\frac{d}{dt'}\cos\left[\omega(t - t')\right]$, so $x_c(t) = \int_0^t f(t')\frac{d}{dt'}\cos\left[\omega(t - t')\right]dt'$, or

$$x_c(t) = f(t')\cos\left[\omega(t - t')\right]\Big|_0^t - \int_0^t\left(\frac{df}{dt'}\right)\cos\left[\omega(t - t')\right]dt' = f(t) - \int_0^t\left(\frac{df}{dt'}\right)\cos\left[\omega(t - t')\right]dt'$$

(since $f(0) = 0$). Now, for an *adiabatic* process we want $df/dt$ very small; specifically: $\boxed{\dfrac{df}{dt'} \ll \omega f(t)}$

$(0 < t' \le t)$. Then the integral is negligible compared to $f(t)$, and we have $\boxed{x_c(t) \approx f(t).}$ (Physically, this says that if you pull on the spring very gently, no fancy oscillations will occur; the mass just moves along as though attached to a *string* of fixed length.)

**(e)** Put $x_c \approx f$ into Eq. 10.92, using Eq. 10.93:

$$\Psi(x, t) = \psi_n(x, t)e^{\frac{i}{\hbar}\left[-(n+\frac{1}{2})\hbar\omega t + m\dot{f}(x - f/2) + \frac{m\omega^2}{2}\int_0^t f^2(t')dt'\right]}.$$

The dynamic phase (Eq. 10.39) is

$$\theta_n(t) = -\frac{1}{\hbar}\int_0^t E_n(t')dt' = -(n + \frac{1}{2})\hbar\omega t + \frac{m\omega^2}{2\hbar}\int_0^t f^2(t')dt', \quad \text{so} \quad \Psi(x, t) = \psi_n(x, t)e^{i\theta_n(t)}e^{i\gamma_n(t)},$$

confirming Eq. 10.94, with the geometric phase given (ostensibly) by $\gamma_n(t) = \frac{m}{\hbar}\dot{f}(x - f/2)$. But the eigenfunctions here are *real*, and hence(Problem 10.5) the geometric phase should be *zero*. The point is that (in the adiabatic approximation) $\dot{f}$ is extremely small (see above), and hence in this limit $\frac{m}{\hbar}\dot{f}(x - f/2) \approx 0$ (at least, in the only region of $x$ where $\psi_n(x, t)$ is nonzero).

---

## Problem 10.10

**(a)**

$$\dot{c}_m = -\sum_j \delta_{jn}e^{i\gamma_n}\langle\psi_m|\dot{\psi}_j\rangle e^{i(\theta_j - \theta_m)} = -\langle\psi_m|\frac{\partial\psi_n}{\partial t}\rangle e^{i\gamma_n}e^{i(\theta_n - \theta_m)} \quad \Rightarrow$$

$$\boxed{c_m(t) = c_m(0) - \int_0^t\langle\psi_m|\frac{\partial\psi_n}{\partial t'}\rangle e^{i\gamma_n}e^{i(\theta_n - \theta_m)}dt'.}$$

**(b)** From Problem 10.9:

$$\psi_n(x,t) = \psi_n(x-f) = \psi_n(u), \quad \text{where} \quad u \equiv x - f,$$

and $\psi_n(u)$ is the $n$th state of the ordinary harmonic oscillator; $\quad \dfrac{\partial \psi_n}{\partial t} = \dfrac{\partial \psi_n}{\partial u}\dfrac{\partial u}{\partial t} = -\dot{f}\dfrac{\partial \psi_n}{\partial u}.$

But $\quad \hat{p} = \dfrac{\hbar}{i}\dfrac{\partial}{\partial u}, \quad$ so $\quad \langle \psi_m | \dfrac{\partial \psi_n}{\partial t} \rangle = -\dfrac{i}{\hbar}\dot{f}\langle m|p|n \rangle, \quad$ where (from Problem 3.33):

$$\langle m|p|n \rangle = i\sqrt{\frac{m\hbar\omega}{2}}\left(\sqrt{m}\delta_{n,m-1} - \sqrt{n}\delta_{m,n-1}\right). \quad \text{Thus:}$$

$$\langle \psi_m | \frac{\partial \psi_n}{\partial t} \rangle = \dot{f}\sqrt{\frac{m\omega}{2\hbar}}\left(\sqrt{m}\delta_{n,m-1} - \sqrt{n}\delta_{m,n-1}\right).$$

Evidently transitions occur only to the immediately adjacent states, $\quad n \pm 1, \quad$ and

**(1)** $m = n+1$ :

$$c_{n+1} = -\int_0^t \left(\dot{f}\sqrt{\frac{m\omega}{2\hbar}}\sqrt{n+1}\right)e^{i\gamma_n}e^{i(\theta_n - \theta_{n+1})}dt'.$$

But $\gamma_n = 0$, because the eigenfunctions are real (Problem 10.5), and (Eq. 10.39)

$$\theta_n = -\frac{1}{\hbar}(n+\frac{1}{2})\hbar\omega t \implies \theta_n - \theta_{n+1} = \left[-(n+\frac{1}{2}) + (n+1+\frac{1}{2})\right]\omega t = \omega t.$$

So $\quad \boxed{c_{n+1} = -\sqrt{\dfrac{m\omega}{2\hbar}}\sqrt{n+1}\int_0^t \dot{f}e^{i\omega t'}dt'.}$

**(2)** $m = n-1$ **:**

$$c_{n-1} = -\int_0^t \left(-\dot{f}\sqrt{\frac{m\omega}{2\hbar}}\sqrt{n}\right)e^{i\gamma_n}e^{i(\theta_n - \theta_{n-1})}dt';$$

$$\theta_n - \theta_{n-1} = \left[-(n+\frac{1}{2}) + (n-1+\frac{1}{2})\right]\omega t = -\omega t. \quad \boxed{c_{n-1} = \sqrt{\frac{m\omega}{2\hbar}}\sqrt{n}\int_0^t \dot{f}e^{-i\omega t'}dt'.}$$

# Chapter 11

# Scattering

## Problem 11.1

(a)

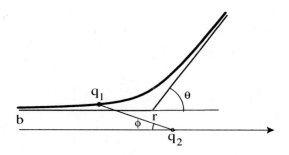

Conservation of energy:   $E = \dfrac{1}{2}m(\dot{r} + r^2\dot{\phi}^2) + V(r),$   where   $V(r) = \dfrac{q_1 q_2}{4\pi\epsilon}\dfrac{1}{r}.$

Conservation of angular momentum:   $J = mr^2\dot{\phi}.$   So   $\dot{\phi} = \dfrac{J}{mr^2}.$

$\dot{r}^2 + \dfrac{J^2}{m^2 r^2} = \dfrac{2}{m}(E - V).$   We want $r$ as a function of $\phi$ (not $t$).   Also, let $u \equiv 1/r.$   Then

$\dot{r} = \dfrac{dr}{dt} = \dfrac{dr}{du}\dfrac{du}{d\phi}\dfrac{d\phi}{dt} = \left(-\dfrac{1}{u^2}\right)\dfrac{du}{d\phi}\dfrac{J}{m}u^2 = -\dfrac{J}{m}\dfrac{du}{d\phi}.$   Then:   $\left(-\dfrac{J}{m}\dfrac{du}{d\phi}\right)^2 + \dfrac{J^2}{m^2}u^2 = \dfrac{2}{m}(E - V),$   or

$\left(\dfrac{du}{d\phi}\right)^2 = \dfrac{2m}{J^2}(E - V) - u^2;$   $\dfrac{du}{d\phi} = \sqrt{\dfrac{2m}{J^2}(E - V) - u^2};$   $d\phi = \dfrac{du}{\sqrt{\dfrac{2m}{J^2}(E - V) - u^2}} = \dfrac{du}{\sqrt{I(u)}},$   where

$I(u) \equiv \dfrac{2m}{J^2}(E - V) - u^2$.   Now, the particle $q_1$ starts out at $r = \infty$ ($u = 0$), $\phi = 0$, and the point

of closest approach is $r_{\min}$ ($u_{\max}$), $\Phi$ :    $\Phi = \displaystyle\int_0^{u_{\max}} \dfrac{du}{\sqrt{I}}$.   It now swings through an equal angle $\Phi$

on the way *out*, so    $\Phi + \Phi + \theta = \pi$,   or   $\theta = \pi - 2\Phi$.   $\theta = \pi - 2\displaystyle\int_0^{u_{\max}} \dfrac{du}{\sqrt{I(u)}}$.

So far this is *general*; now we put in the specific potential:

$$I(u) = \dfrac{2mE}{J^2} - \dfrac{2m}{J^2}\dfrac{q_1 q_2}{4\pi\epsilon_0}u - u^2 = (u_2 - u)(u - u_1), \quad \text{where } u_1 \text{ and } u_2 \text{ are the two roots.}$$

(Since   $du/d\phi = \sqrt{I(u)}$,   $u_{\max}$ is one of the roots; setting   $u_2 > u_1$, $u_{\max} = u_2$.)

$$\theta = \pi - 2\int_0^{u_2} \dfrac{du}{\sqrt{(u_2 - u)(u - u_1)}} = \pi + 2\sin^{-1}\left(\dfrac{-2u + u_1 + u_2}{u_2 - u_1}\right)\Bigg|_0^{u_2}$$

$$= \pi + 2\left[\sin^{-1}(-1) - \sin^{-1}\left(\dfrac{u_1 + u_2}{u_2 - u_1}\right)\right]$$

$$= \pi + 2\left[-\dfrac{\pi}{2} - \sin^{-1}\left(\dfrac{u_1 + u_2}{u_2 - u_1}\right)\right] = -2\sin^{-1}\left(\dfrac{u_1 + u_2}{u_2 - u_1}\right).$$

Now $J = mvb$, $E = \frac{1}{2}mv^2$, where $v$ is the incoming velocity, so $J^2 = m^2 b^2 (2E/m) = 2mb^2 E$, and hence $2m/J^2 = 1/b^2 E$. So

$$I(u) = \dfrac{1}{b^2} - \dfrac{1}{b^2}\left(\dfrac{1}{E}\dfrac{q_1 q_2}{4\pi\epsilon_0}\right)u - u^2. \quad \text{Let } A \equiv \dfrac{q_1 q_2}{4\pi\epsilon_0 E}, \quad \text{so} \quad -I(u) = u^2 + \dfrac{A}{b^2}u - \dfrac{1}{b^2}.$$

To get the roots:    $u^2 + \dfrac{A}{b^2}u - \dfrac{1}{b^2} = 0 \implies u = \dfrac{1}{2}\left[-\dfrac{A}{b^2} \pm \sqrt{\dfrac{A^2}{b^4} + \dfrac{4}{b^2}}\right] = \dfrac{A}{2b^2}\left[-1 \pm \sqrt{1 + \left(\dfrac{2b}{A}\right)^2}\right].$

Thus   $u_2 = \dfrac{A}{2b^2}\left[-1 + \sqrt{1 + \left(\dfrac{2b}{A}\right)^2}\right]$,   $u_1 = \dfrac{A}{2b^2}\left[-1 - \sqrt{1 + \left(\dfrac{2b}{A}\right)^2}\right]$;   $\dfrac{u_1 + u_2}{u_2 - u_1} = \dfrac{-1}{\sqrt{1 + (2b/A)^2}}$.

$\theta = 2\sin^{-1}\left(\dfrac{1}{\sqrt{1 + (2b/A)^2}}\right)$,   or   $\dfrac{1}{\sqrt{1 + (2b/A)^2}} = \sin\left(\dfrac{\theta}{2}\right)$;   $1 + \left(\dfrac{2b}{A}\right)^2 = \dfrac{1}{\sin^2(\theta/2)}$;

$\left(\dfrac{2b}{A}\right)^2 = \dfrac{1 - \sin^2(\theta/2)}{\sin^2(\theta/2)} = \dfrac{\cos^2(\theta/2)}{\sin^2(\theta/2)}$;   $\dfrac{2b}{A} = \cot(\theta/2)$,   or   $\boxed{b = \dfrac{q_1 q_2}{8\pi\epsilon_0 E}\cot(\theta/2).}$

**(b)**

$$D(\theta) = \frac{b}{\sin\theta}\left|\frac{db}{d\theta}\right|. \quad \text{Here } \frac{db}{d\theta} = \frac{q_1 q_2}{8\pi\epsilon_0 E}\left(-\frac{1}{2\sin^2(\theta/2)}\right).$$

$$= \frac{1}{2\sin(\theta/2)\cos(\theta/2)}\frac{q_1 q_2}{8\pi\epsilon_0 E}\frac{\cos(\theta/2)}{\sin(\theta/2)}\frac{q_1 q_2}{8\pi\epsilon_0 E}\frac{1}{2\sin^2(\theta/2)} = \boxed{\left[\frac{q_1 q_2}{16\pi\epsilon_0 E\sin^2(\theta/2)}\right]^2}.$$

**(c)**

$$\sigma = \int D(\theta)\sin\theta\,d\theta\,d\phi = 2\pi\left(\frac{q_1 q_2}{8\pi\epsilon_0 E}\right)^2\int_0^\pi \frac{\sin\theta}{\sin^4(\theta/2)}\,d\theta.$$

This integral does not converge, for near $\theta = 0$ (and again near $\pi$) we have $\sin\theta \approx \theta$, $\sin(\theta/2) \approx \theta/2$, so the integral goes like $16\int_0^\epsilon \theta^{-3}\,d\theta = -8\theta^{-2}\big|_0^\epsilon \to \infty$.

---

## Problem 11.2

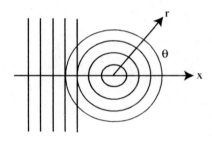

**Two dimensions:** $\boxed{\psi(r,\theta) \approx A\left[e^{ikx} + f(\theta)\frac{e^{ikr}}{\sqrt{r}}\right].}$

**One dimension:** $\boxed{\psi(x) \approx A\left[e^{ikx} + f(x/|x|)e^{-ikx}\right].}$

---

## Problem 11.3

Multiply Eq. 11.32 by $P_{l'}(\cos\theta)\sin\theta\,d\theta$ and integrate from 0 to $\pi$, exploiting the orthogonality of the Legendre polynomials (Eq. 4.34)—which, with the change of variables $x \equiv \cos\theta$, says

$$\int_0^\pi P_l(\cos\theta)P_{l'}(\cos\theta)\sin\theta\,d\theta = \left(\frac{2}{2l+1}\right)\delta_{ll'}.$$

The delta function collapses the sum, and we get

$$2i^{l'}\left[j_{l'}(ka) + ika_{l'}h_{l'}^{(1)}(ka)\right] = 0,$$

and hence (dropping the primes)

$$a_l = -\frac{j_l(ka)}{ikh_l^{(1)}(ka)}. \quad \text{QED}$$

---

## Problem 11.4

Keeping only the $l = 0$ terms, Eq. 11.29 says that in the exterior region:

$$\psi \approx A\left[j_0(kr) + ika_0 h_0^{(1)}(kr)\right] P_0(\cos\theta) = A\left[\frac{\sin(kr)}{kr} + ika_0\left(-i\frac{e^{ikr}}{kr}\right)\right] = A\left[\frac{\sin(kr)}{kr} + a_0\frac{e^{ikr}}{r}\right] \quad (r > a).$$

In the internal region Eq. 11.18 (with $n_l$ eliminated because it blows up at the origin) yields

$$\psi(r) \approx bj_0(kr) = b\frac{\sin(kr)}{kr} \quad (r < a).$$

The boundary conditions hold independently for each $l$, as you can check by keeping the summation over $l$ and exploiting the orthogonality of the Legendre polynomials:

**(1)** $\psi$ continuous at $r = a$: $\quad A\left[\frac{\sin ka}{ka} + a_0\frac{e^{ika}}{a}\right] = b\frac{\sin ka}{ka}$.

**(2)** $\psi'$ discontinuous at $r = a$: Integrating the radial equation across the delta function gives

$$-\frac{\hbar^2}{2m}\int \frac{d^2u}{dr^2}\,dr + \int\left[\alpha\delta(r-a) + \frac{\hbar^2}{2m}\frac{l(l+1)}{r^2}\right]u\,dr \Rightarrow -\frac{\hbar^2}{2m}\Delta u' + \alpha u(a) = 0, \quad\text{or}\quad \Delta u' = \frac{2m\alpha}{\hbar^2}u(a).$$

Now $\quad u = rR, \quad$ so $u' = R + rR'$; $\quad \Delta u' = \Delta R + a\Delta R' = a\Delta R' = \frac{2m\alpha}{\hbar^2}aR(a)$, or $\Delta\psi' = \frac{2m\alpha}{\hbar^2}\psi(a) = \frac{\beta}{a}\psi(a)$.

$$\frac{A}{ka}\left[k\cos(ka) + a_0 ik^2 e^{ika}\right] - \frac{A}{ka^2}[\cancel{\sin(ka) + a_0 ke^{ika}}] - \frac{b}{ka}k\cos(ka) + \frac{b}{ka^2}\cancel{\sin ka} = \frac{\beta}{a}b\frac{\sin(ka)}{ka}.$$

The indicated terms cancel (by **(1)**), leaving $\quad A\left[\cos(ka) + ia_0 ke^{ika}\right] = b\left[\cos(ka) + \frac{\beta}{ka}\sin(ka)\right]$.

Using **(1)** to eliminate $b$: $\quad A\left[\cos(ka) + ia_0 ke^{ika}\right] = \left[\cot(ka) + \frac{\beta}{ka}\right]\left[\sin(ka) + a_0 ke^{ika}\right]A$.

$$\cancel{\cos(ka)} + ia_0 ke^{ika} = \cancel{\cos(ka)} + \frac{\beta}{ka}\sin(ka) + a_0 k\cot(ka)e^{ika} + \beta\frac{a_0}{a}e^{ika}.$$

$$ia_0 ke^{ika}\left[1 + i\cot(ka) + i\frac{\beta}{ka}\right] = \frac{\beta}{ka}\sin(ka). \quad \text{But } ka \ll 1, \text{ so } \sin(ka) \approx ka, \text{ and } \cot(ka) = \frac{\cos(ka)}{\sin(ka)} \approx \frac{1}{ka}.$$

$$ia_0 k(1 + ika)\left[1 + \frac{i}{ka}(1 + \beta)\right] = \beta; \quad ia_0 k\left[1 + \frac{i}{ka}(1 + \beta) + ika - 1 - \beta\right] \approx ia_0 k\left[\frac{i}{ka}(1 + \beta)\right] = \beta.$$

$$\boxed{a_0 = -\frac{a\beta}{1 + \beta}.}$$ Equation 11.25 $\Rightarrow f(\theta) \approx a_0 = \boxed{-\frac{a\beta}{1 + \beta}.}$ Equation 11.14 $\Rightarrow D = |f|^2 = \boxed{\left(\frac{a\beta}{1 + \beta}\right)^2.}$

Equation 11.27 $\Rightarrow \sigma = 4\pi D = \boxed{4\pi\left(\frac{a\beta}{1 + \beta}\right)^2.}$

---

## Problem 11.5

**(a)** In the region to the left

$$\psi(x) = Ae^{ikx} + B^{-ikx} \quad (x \leq -a).$$

In the region $-a < x < 0$, the Schrödinger equation gives

$$-\frac{h^2}{2m}\frac{d^2\psi}{dx^2} - V_0\psi = E\psi \quad \Rightarrow \quad \frac{d^2\psi}{dx^2} = -k'\psi$$

where $k' = \sqrt{2m(E + V_0)}/\hbar$.    The general solution is

$$\psi = C\sin(k'x) + D\cos(k'x)$$

But $\psi(0) = 0$ implies $D = 0$, so

$$\psi(x) = C\sin(k'x) \quad (-a \leq x \leq 0).$$

The continuity of $\psi(x)$ and $\psi'(x)$ at $x = -a$ says

$$Ae^{-ika} + Be^{ika} = -C\sin(k'a), \quad ikAe^{-ika} - ikBe^{ika} = k'C\cos(k'a).$$

Divide and solve for $B$:

$$\frac{ikAe^{-ika} - ikBe^{ika}}{Ae^{-ika} + Be^{ika}} = -k'\cot(k'a),$$

$$ikAe^{-ika} - ikBe^{ika} = -Ae^{-ika}k'\cot(k'a) - Be^{ika}k'\cot(k'a),$$

$$Be^{ika}\left[-ik + k'\cot(k'a)\right] = Ae^{-ika}\left[-ik - k'\cot(k'a)\right].$$

$$\boxed{B = Ae^{-2ika}\left[\frac{k - ik'\cot(k'a)}{k + ik'\cot(k'a)}\right].}$$

**(b)**

$$|B|^2 = |A|^2\left[\frac{k - ik'\cot(k'a)}{k + ik'\cot(k'a)}\right] \cdot \left[\frac{k + ik'\cot(k'a)}{k - ik'\cot(k'a)}\right] = |A|^2. \quad \checkmark$$

**(c)** From part (a) the wave function for $x < -a$ is

$$\psi(x) = Ae^{ikx} + Ae^{-2ika}\left[\frac{k - ik'\cot(k'a)}{k + ik'\cot(k'a)}\right]e^{-ikx}.$$

But by definition of the phase shift (Eq. 11.40)

$$\psi(x) = A\left[e^{ikx} - e^{i(2\delta - kx)}\right].$$

so

$$e^{-2ika}\left[\frac{k - ik'\cot(k'a)}{k + ik'\cot(k'a)}\right] = -e^{2i\delta}.$$

This is *exact*. For a very deep well, $E \ll V_0$, $k = \sqrt{2mE}/\hbar \ll \sqrt{2m(E + V_0)}/\hbar = k'$, so

$$e^{-2ika}\left[\frac{-ik'\cot(k'a)}{ik'\cot(k'a)}\right] = -e^{2i\delta}; \quad e^{-2ika} = e^{2i\delta}; \quad \boxed{\delta = -ka.}$$

## Problem 11.6

From Eq. 11.46, $a_l = \dfrac{1}{k} e^{i\delta_l} \sin \delta_l$, and Eq. 11.33, $a_l = i \dfrac{j_l(ka)}{k h_l^{(1)}(ka)}$, it follows that $e^{i\delta_l} \sin \delta_l = i \dfrac{j_l(ka)}{h_l^{(1)}(ka)}$.

But (Eq. 11.19) $h_l^{(1)}(x) = j_l(x) + i n_l(x)$, so

$$e^{i\delta_l} \sin \delta_l = i \frac{j_l(ka)}{j_l(x) + i n_l(x)} = i \frac{1}{1 + i(n/j)} = i \frac{1 - i(n/j)}{1 + (n/j)^2} = \frac{(n/j) + i}{1 + (n/j)^2},$$

(writing $(n/j)$ as shorthand for $n_l(ka)/j_l(ka)$). Equating the real and imaginary parts:

$$\cos \delta_l \sin \delta_l = \frac{(n/j)}{1 + (n/j)^2}; \quad \sin^2 \delta_l = \frac{1}{1 + (n/j)^2}.$$

Dividing the second by the first, I conclude that

$$\tan \delta_l = \frac{1}{(n/j)}, \quad \text{or} \quad \boxed{\delta_l = \tan^{-1} \left[ \frac{j_l(ka)}{n_l(ka)} \right].}$$

## Problem 11.7

$$r > a : \; u(r) = A \sin(kr + \delta);$$

$$r < a : \; u(r) = B \sin kr + D \cos kr = B \sin kr, \quad \text{because } u(0) = 0 \Longrightarrow D = 0.$$

Continuity at $r = a \Longrightarrow B \sin(ka) = A \sin(ka + \delta) \Longrightarrow B = A \dfrac{\sin(ka + \delta)}{\sin(ka)}$. So $u(r) = A \dfrac{\sin(ka + \delta)}{\sin(ka)} \sin kr$.

From Problem 11.4,

$$\Delta \left( \frac{du}{dr} \right) \bigg|_{r=a} = \frac{\beta}{a} u(a) \Rightarrow Ak \cos(ka + \delta) - A \frac{\sin(ka + \delta)}{\sin(ka)} k \cos(ka) = \frac{\beta}{a} A \sin(ka + \delta).$$

$$\cos(ka + \delta) - \frac{\sin(ka + \delta)}{\sin(ka)} \cos(ka) = \frac{\beta}{ka} \sin(ka + \delta),$$

$$\sin(ka) \cos(ka + \delta) - \sin(ka + \delta) \cos(ka) = \frac{\beta}{ka} \sin(ka + \delta) \sin(ka),$$

$$\sin(ka - ka - \delta) = \frac{\beta}{ka} \sin(ka) \left[ \sin(ka) \cos \delta + \cos(ka) \sin \delta \right],$$

$$-\sin \delta = \beta \frac{\sin^2(ka)}{ka} \left[ \cos \delta + \cot(ka) \sin \delta \right]; \quad -1 = \beta \frac{\sin^2(ka)}{ka} \left[ \cot \delta + \cot(ka) \right].$$

$$\cot \delta = -\cot(ka) - \frac{ka}{\beta \sin^2(ka)}; \quad \boxed{\cot \delta = - \left[ \cot(ka) + \frac{ka}{\beta \sin^2(ka)} \right].}$$

## Problem 11.8

$$G = -\frac{e^{ikr}}{4\pi r} \implies \nabla G = -\frac{1}{4\pi}\left(\frac{1}{r}\nabla e^{ikr} + e^{ikr}\nabla\frac{1}{r}\right) \implies$$

$$\nabla^2 G = \nabla \cdot (\nabla G) = -\frac{1}{4\pi}\left[2\left(\nabla\frac{1}{r}\right)\cdot(\nabla e^{ikr}) + \frac{1}{r}\nabla^2(e^{ikr}) + e^{ikr}\nabla^2\left(\frac{1}{r}\right)\right].$$

But $\nabla\frac{1}{r} = -\frac{1}{r^2}\hat{r}$; $\quad \nabla(e^{ikr}) = ike^{ikr}\hat{r}$; $\quad \nabla^2 e^{ikr} = ik\nabla\cdot(e^{ikr}\hat{r}) = ik\frac{1}{r^2}\frac{d}{dr}(r^2 e^{ikr})$

(see reference in footnote 12) $\implies \nabla^2 e^{ikr} = \frac{ik}{r^2}(2re^{ikr} + ikr^2 e^{ikr}) = ike^{ikr}\left(\frac{2}{r} + ik\right)$;

$$\nabla^2\left(\frac{1}{r}\right) = -4\pi\delta^3(\mathbf{r}). \quad \text{So} \quad \nabla^2 G = -\frac{1}{4\pi}\left[2\left(-\frac{1}{r^2}\hat{r}\right)\cdot(ike^{ikr}\hat{r}) + \frac{1}{r}ike^{ikr}\left(\frac{2}{r} + ik\right) - 4\pi e^{ikr}\delta^3(\mathbf{r})\right].$$

But $\quad e^{ikr}\delta^3(\mathbf{r}) = \delta^3(\mathbf{r})$, so

$$\nabla^2 G = \delta^3(\mathbf{r}) - \frac{1}{4\pi}e^{ikr}\left[-\frac{2ik}{r^2} + \frac{2ik}{r^2} - \frac{k^2}{r}\right] = \delta^3(\mathbf{r}) + k^2\frac{e^{ikr}}{4\pi r} = \delta^3(\mathbf{r}) - k^2 G.$$

Therefore $\quad (\nabla^2 + k^2)G = \delta^3(\mathbf{r}). \quad$ QED

---

## Problem 11.9

$$\psi = \frac{1}{\sqrt{\pi a^3}}e^{-r/a}; \quad V = -\frac{e^2}{4\pi\epsilon_0 r} = -\frac{\hbar^2}{ma}\frac{1}{r} \quad \text{(Eq. 4.72)}; \quad k = i\frac{\sqrt{-2mE}}{\hbar} = \frac{i}{a}.$$

In this case there is no "incoming" wave, and $\psi_0(\mathbf{r}) = 0$. Our problem is to show that

$$-\frac{m}{2\pi\hbar^2}\int \frac{e^{ik|\mathbf{r}-\mathbf{r}_0|}}{|\mathbf{r}-\mathbf{r}_0|}V(\mathbf{r}_0)\psi(\mathbf{r}_0)\,d^3\mathbf{r}_0 = \psi(\mathbf{r}).$$

We proceed to evaluate the left side (call it $I$):

$$I = \left(-\frac{m}{2\pi\hbar^2}\right)\left(-\frac{\hbar^2}{ma}\right)\frac{1}{\sqrt{\pi a^3}}\int \frac{e^{-|\mathbf{r}-\mathbf{r}_0|/a}}{|\mathbf{r}-\mathbf{r}_0|}\frac{1}{r_0}e^{-r_0/a}\,d^3\mathbf{r}_0$$

$$= \frac{1}{2\pi a}\frac{1}{\sqrt{\pi a^3}}\int \frac{e^{-\sqrt{r^2+r_0^2-2rr_0\cos\theta}/a}e^{-r_0/a}}{\sqrt{r^2+r_0^2-2rr_0\cos\theta}\,r_0}r_0^2\sin\theta\,dr_0\,d\theta\,d\phi.$$

(I have set the $z_0$ axis along the—fixed—direction $\mathbf{r}$, for convenience.) Doing the $\phi$ integral ($2\pi$):

$$I = \frac{1}{a\sqrt{\pi a^3}}\int_0^\infty r_0 e^{-r_0/a}\left[\int_0^\pi \frac{e^{-\sqrt{r^2+r_0^2-2rr_0\cos\theta}/a}}{\sqrt{r^2+r_0^2-2rr_0\cos\theta}}\sin\theta\,d\theta\right]dr_0. \quad \text{The } \theta \text{ integral is}$$

$$\int_0^\pi \frac{e^{-\sqrt{r^2+r_0^2-2rr_0\cos\theta}/a}}{\sqrt{r^2+r_0^2-2rr_0\cos\theta}}\sin\theta\, d\theta = -\frac{a}{rr_0}\, e^{-\sqrt{r^2+r_0^2-2rr_0\cos\theta}/a}\Big|_0^\pi = -\frac{a}{rr_0}\left[e^{-(r+r_0)/a}-e^{-|r-r_0|/a}\right].$$

$$\begin{aligned}
I &= -\frac{1}{r\sqrt{\pi a^3}}\int_0^\infty e^{-r_0/a}\left[e^{-(r_0+r)/a}-e^{-|r_0-r|/a}\right]dr_0 \\
&= -\frac{1}{r\sqrt{\pi a^3}}\left[e^{-r/a}\int_0^\infty e^{-2r_0/a}\,dr_0 - e^{-r/a}\int_0^r dr - e^{r/a}\int_r^\infty e^{-2r_0/a}\,dr_0\right] \\
&= -\frac{1}{r\sqrt{\pi a^3}}\left[e^{-r/a}\left(\frac{a}{2}\right) - e^{-r/a}(r) - e^{r/a}\left(-\frac{a}{2}e^{-2r_0/a}\right)\Big|_r^\infty\right] \\
&= -\frac{1}{r\sqrt{\pi a^3}}\left[\frac{a}{2}e^{-r/a} - re^{-r/a} - \frac{a}{2}e^{r/a}e^{-2r/a}\right] = \frac{1}{\sqrt{\pi a^3}}e^{-r/a} = \psi(r). \quad \text{QED}
\end{aligned}$$

## Problem 11.10

For the potential in Eq. 11.81, Eq. 11.88 $\implies$

$$f(\theta) = -\frac{2m}{\hbar^2\kappa}V_0\int_0^a r\sin(\kappa r)\,dr = -\frac{2mV_0}{\hbar^2\kappa}\left[\frac{1}{\kappa^2}\sin(\kappa r)-\frac{r}{\kappa}\cos(\kappa r)\right]\Big|_0^a = \boxed{-\frac{2mV_0}{\hbar^2\kappa^3}\left[\sin(\kappa a)-\kappa a\cos(\kappa a)\right],}$$

where (Eq. 11.89) $\kappa = 2k\sin(\theta/2)$. For low-energy scattering ($ka \ll 1$):

$$\sin(\kappa a) \approx \kappa a - \frac{1}{3!}(\kappa a)^3; \quad \cos(\kappa a) = 1 - \frac{1}{2}(\kappa a)^2; \quad \text{so}$$

$$f(\theta) \approx -\frac{2mV_0}{\hbar^2\kappa^3}\left[\kappa a - \frac{1}{6}(\kappa a)^3 - \kappa a + \frac{1}{2}(\kappa a)^3\right] = \boxed{-\frac{2}{3}\frac{mV_0 a^3}{\hbar^2},} \quad \text{in agreement with Eq. 11.82.}$$

## Problem 11.11

$$\sin(\kappa r) = \frac{1}{2i}\left(e^{i\kappa r}-e^{-i\kappa r}\right), \quad \text{so} \quad \int_0^\infty e^{-\mu r}\sin(\kappa r)\,dr = \frac{1}{2i}\int_0^\infty\left[e^{-(\mu-i\kappa)r}-e^{-(\mu+i\kappa)r}\right]dr$$

$$= \frac{1}{2i}\left[\frac{e^{-(\mu-i\kappa)r}}{-(\mu-i\kappa)}-\frac{e^{-(\mu+i\kappa)r}}{-(\mu+i\kappa)}\right]\Big|_0^\infty = \frac{1}{2i}\left[\frac{1}{\mu-i\kappa}-\frac{1}{\mu+i\kappa}\right] = \frac{1}{2i}\left(\frac{\mu+i\kappa-\mu+i\kappa}{\mu^2+\kappa^2}\right) = \frac{\kappa}{\mu^2+\kappa^2}.$$

$$\text{So} \quad f(\theta) = -\frac{2m\beta}{\hbar^2\kappa}\frac{\kappa}{\mu^2+\kappa^2} = -\frac{2m\beta}{\hbar^2(\mu^2+\kappa^2)}. \quad \text{QED}$$

## Problem 11.12

Equation 11.91 $\Longrightarrow D(\theta) = |f(\theta)|^2 = \left(\dfrac{2m\beta}{\hbar^2}\right)^2 \dfrac{1}{(\mu^2 + \kappa^2)^2}$,    where Eq. 11.89 $\Rightarrow \kappa = 2k\sin(\theta/2)$.

$$\sigma = \int D(\theta) \sin\theta \, d\theta \, d\phi = 2\pi \left(\frac{2m\beta}{\hbar^2}\right)^2 \frac{1}{\mu^4} \int_0^\pi \frac{1}{\left[1 + (2k/\mu)^2 \sin^2(\theta/2)\right]^2} 2\sin(\theta/2)\cos(\theta/2) \, d\theta.$$

Let   $\dfrac{2k}{\mu}\sin(\theta/2) \equiv x$,   so   $2\sin(\theta/2) = \dfrac{\mu}{k}x$,   and   $\cos(\theta/2)\,d\theta = \dfrac{\mu}{k}\,dx$.   Then

$$\sigma = 2\pi \left(\frac{2m\beta}{\hbar^2}\right)^2 \frac{1}{\mu^4}\left(\frac{\mu}{k}\right)^2 \int_{x_0}^{x_1} \frac{x}{(1+x^2)^2}\, dx. \quad \text{The limits are} \left\{ \begin{array}{l} \theta = 0 \Longrightarrow x = x_0 = 0, \\ \theta = \pi \Longrightarrow x = x_1 = 2k/\mu. \end{array} \right\} \quad \text{So}$$

$$\sigma = 2\pi \left(\frac{2m\beta}{\hbar^2}\right)^2 \frac{1}{(\mu k)^2}\left[-\frac{1}{2}\frac{1}{(1+x^2)}\right]\Big|_0^{2k/\mu} = \pi \left(\frac{2m\beta}{\hbar^2}\right)^2 \frac{1}{(\mu k)^2}\left[1 - \frac{1}{1 + (2k/\mu)^2}\right]$$

$$= \pi \left(\frac{2m\beta}{\hbar^2}\right)^2 \frac{1}{(\mu k)^2}\left[\frac{4(k/\mu)^2}{1 + 4k^2/\mu^2}\right] = \pi \left(\frac{4m\beta}{\hbar^2}\right)^2 \frac{1}{\mu^2}\frac{1}{\mu^2 + 4k^2}. \quad \text{But} \quad k^2 = \frac{2mE}{\hbar^2}, \text{ so}$$

$$\boxed{\sigma = \pi \left(\frac{4m\beta}{\mu\hbar}\right)^2 \frac{1}{(\mu k)^2 + 8mE}.}$$

## Problem 11.13

(a)

$$V(\mathbf{r}) = \alpha\delta(r - a). \quad \text{Eq. 11.80} \Longrightarrow f = -\frac{m}{2\pi\hbar^2}\int V(\mathbf{r})\, d^3\mathbf{r} = -\frac{m}{2\pi\hbar^2}\alpha 4\pi \int_0^\infty \delta(r-a)r^2 dr.$$

$$\boxed{f = -\frac{2m\alpha}{\hbar^2}a^2;} \quad D = |f|^2 = \boxed{\left(\frac{2m\alpha}{\hbar^2}a^2\right)^2;} \quad \sigma = 4\pi D = \boxed{\pi\left(\frac{4m\alpha}{\hbar^2}a^2\right)^2.}$$

(b)

$$\text{Eq. 11.88} \Longrightarrow f = -\frac{2m}{\hbar^2\kappa}\alpha\int_0^\infty r\delta(r-a)\sin(\kappa r)\, dr = \boxed{-\frac{2m\alpha}{\hbar^2\kappa}a\sin(\kappa a)} \quad (\kappa = 2k\sin(\theta/2)).$$

(c) Note first that (b) reduces to (a) in the low-energy regime ($ka \ll 1 \Longrightarrow \kappa a \ll 1$). Since Problem 11.4 was also for low energy, what we must confirm is that Problem 11.4 reproduces (a) in the regime for which the Born approximation holds. Inspection shows that the answer to Problem 11.4 does reduce to $f = -2m\alpha a^2/\hbar^2$ when $\beta \ll 1$, which is to say when $f/a \ll 1$. This is the appropriate condition, since (Eq. 11.12) $f/a$ is a measure of the relative size of the scattered wave, in the interaction region.

## Problem 11.14

$$\mathbf{F} = \frac{1}{4\pi\epsilon_0}\frac{q_1 q_2}{r^2}\hat{r}; \quad F_\perp = \frac{1}{4\pi\epsilon_0}\frac{q_1 q_2}{r^2}\cos\phi; \quad \cos\phi = \frac{b}{r}, \quad \text{so} \quad F_\perp = \frac{1}{4\pi\epsilon_0}\frac{q_1 q_2 b}{r^3}; \quad dt = \frac{dx}{v}.$$

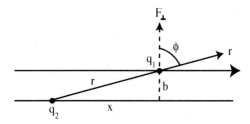

$$I_\perp = \int F_\perp \, dt = \frac{1}{4\pi\epsilon_0}\frac{q_1 q_2 b}{v}\int_{-\infty}^{\infty}\frac{dx}{(x^2 + b^2)^{3/2}}. \quad \text{But}$$

$$\int_{-\infty}^{\infty}\frac{dx}{(x^2+b^2)^{3/2}} = 2\int_{0}^{\infty}\frac{dx}{(x^2+b^2)^{3/2}} = \left.\frac{2x}{b^2\sqrt{x^2+b^2}}\right|_0^{\infty} = \frac{2}{b^2}, \quad \text{so} \quad I_\perp = \frac{1}{4\pi\epsilon_0}\frac{2q_1 q_2}{bv}.$$

$$\tan\theta = \frac{I_\perp}{mv} = \frac{q_1 q_2}{4\pi\epsilon_0}\frac{1}{b(\frac{1}{2}mv^2)} = \frac{q_1 q_2}{4\pi\epsilon_0}\frac{1}{bE}. \quad \boxed{\theta = \tan^{-1}\left[\frac{q_1 q_2}{4\pi\epsilon_0 bE}\right].}$$

$$b = \frac{q_1 q_2}{4\pi\epsilon_0}\frac{1}{E\tan\theta} = \left(\frac{q_1 q_2}{8\pi\epsilon_0 E}\right)(2\cot\theta).$$

The exact answer is the same, only with $\cot(\theta/2)$ in place of $2\cot\theta$. So I must show that $\cot(\theta/2) \approx 2\cot\theta$, for small $\theta$ (that's the regime in which the impulse approximation should work). Well:

$$\cot(\theta/2) = \frac{\cos(\theta/2)}{\sin(\theta/2)} \approx \frac{1}{\theta/2} = \frac{2}{\theta}, \quad \text{for small } \theta, \quad \text{while} \quad 2\cot\theta = 2\frac{\cos\theta}{\sin\theta} \approx 2\frac{1}{\theta}. \quad \text{So it works.}$$

## Problem 11.15

First let's set up the general formalism. From Eq. 11.101:

$$\psi(\mathbf{r}) = \psi_0(\mathbf{r}) + \int g(\mathbf{r}-\mathbf{r}_0)V(\mathbf{r}_0)\psi_0(\mathbf{r}_0)\, d^3\mathbf{r}_0 + \int g(\mathbf{r}-\mathbf{r}_0)V(\mathbf{r}_0)\left[\int g(\mathbf{r}_0-\mathbf{r}_1)V(\mathbf{r}_1)\psi_0(\mathbf{r}_1)\, d^3\mathbf{r}_1\right]d^3\mathbf{r}_0 + \cdots$$

Put in $\psi_0(\mathbf{r}) = Ae^{ikz}$, $g(\mathbf{r}) = -\frac{m}{2\pi\hbar^2}\frac{e^{ikr}}{r}$:

$$\psi(\mathbf{r}) = Ae^{ikz} - \frac{mA}{2\pi\hbar^2}\int\frac{e^{ik|\mathbf{r}-\mathbf{r}_0|}}{|\mathbf{r}-\mathbf{r}_0|}V(\mathbf{r}_0)e^{ikz_0}\, d^3\mathbf{r}_0$$

$$+ \left(\frac{m}{2\pi\hbar^2}\right)^2 A\int\frac{e^{ik|\mathbf{r}-\mathbf{r}_0|}}{|\mathbf{r}-\mathbf{r}_0|}V(\mathbf{r}_0)\left[\int\frac{e^{ik|\mathbf{r}_0-\mathbf{r}_1|}}{|\mathbf{r}_0-\mathbf{r}_1|}V(\mathbf{r}_1)e^{ikz_1}\, d^3\mathbf{r}_1\right]d^3\mathbf{r}_0.$$

In the scattering region $r \gg r_0$, Eq. 11.73 $\implies \dfrac{e^{ik|\mathbf{r}-\mathbf{r}_0|}}{|\mathbf{r}-\mathbf{r}_0|} \approx \dfrac{e^{ikr}}{r} e^{-i\mathbf{k}\cdot\mathbf{r}_0}$,   with   $\mathbf{k} \equiv k\hat{r}$,   so

$$\psi(\mathbf{r}) = A\left\{ e^{ikz} - \frac{m}{2\pi\hbar^2}\frac{e^{ikr}}{r}\int e^{-i\mathbf{k}\cdot\mathbf{r}_0}V(\mathbf{r}_0)e^{ikz_0}d^3\mathbf{r}_0 \right.$$

$$\left. \left(\frac{m}{2\pi\hbar^2}\right)^2 \frac{e^{ikr}}{r}\int e^{-i\mathbf{k}\cdot\mathbf{r}_0}V(\mathbf{r}_0)\left[\int \frac{e^{ik|\mathbf{r}_0-\mathbf{r}_1|}}{|\mathbf{r}_0-\mathbf{r}_1|}V(\mathbf{r}_1)e^{ikz_1}d^3\mathbf{r}_1\right]d^3\mathbf{r}_0 \right\}$$

$$\boxed{f(\theta,\phi) = -\frac{m}{2\pi\hbar^2}\int e^{i(\mathbf{k}'-\mathbf{k})\cdot\mathbf{r}}V(\mathbf{r})\,d^3\mathbf{r} + \left(\frac{m}{2\pi\hbar^2}\right)^2\int e^{-i\mathbf{k}\cdot\mathbf{r}}V(\mathbf{r})\left[\int \frac{e^{ik|\mathbf{r}-\mathbf{r}_0|}}{|\mathbf{r}-\mathbf{r}_0|}V(\mathbf{r}_0)e^{ikz_0}d^3\mathbf{r}_0\right]d^3\mathbf{r}.}$$

I simplified the subscripts, since there is no longer any possible ambiguity. For *low-energy* scattering we drop the exponentials (see p. 414):

$$\boxed{f(\theta,\phi) \approx -\frac{m}{2\pi\hbar^2}\int V(\mathbf{r})\,d^3\mathbf{r} + \left(\frac{m}{2\pi\hbar^2}\right)^2\int V(\mathbf{r})\left[\int \frac{1}{|\mathbf{r}-\mathbf{r}_0|}V(\mathbf{r}_0)\,d^3\mathbf{r}_0\right]d^3\mathbf{r}.}$$

Now apply this to the potential in Eq. 11.81:

$$\int \frac{1}{|\mathbf{r}-\mathbf{r}_0|}V(\mathbf{r}_0)\,d^3\mathbf{r}_0 = V_0\int_0^a \frac{1}{|\mathbf{r}-\mathbf{r}_0|}r_0^2\sin\theta_0\,dr_0\,d\theta_0\,d\phi_0.$$

Orient the $z_0$ axis along $\mathbf{r}$, so $|\mathbf{r}-\mathbf{r}_0| = r^2 + r_0^2 - 2rr_0\cos\theta_0$.

$$\int \frac{1}{|\mathbf{r}-\mathbf{r}_0|}V(\mathbf{r}_0)\,d^3\mathbf{r}_0 = V_0 2\pi\int_0^a r_0^2\left[\int_0^\pi \frac{1}{\sqrt{r^2+r_0^2-2rr_0\cos\theta_0}}\sin\theta_0\,d\theta_0\right]dr_0.$$   But

$$\int_0^\pi \frac{1}{\sqrt{r^2+r_0^2-2rr_0\cos\theta_0}}\sin\theta_0\,d\theta_0 = \frac{1}{rr_0}\sqrt{r^2+r_0^2-2rr_0\cos\theta_0}\,\Big|_0^\pi = \frac{1}{rr_0}\left[(r_0+r)-|r_0-r|\right] = \begin{cases} 2/r, & r_0 < r; \\ 2/r_0, & r_0 > r. \end{cases}$$

Here $r < a$ (from the "outer" integral), so

$$\int \frac{1}{|\mathbf{r}-\mathbf{r}_0|}V(\mathbf{r}_0)\,d^3\mathbf{r}_0 = 4\pi V_0\left[\frac{1}{r}\int_0^r r_0^2\,dr_0 + \int_r^a r_0\,dr_0\right] = 4\pi V_0\left[\frac{1}{r}\frac{r^3}{3} + \frac{1}{2}(a^2-r^2)\right] = 2\pi V_0\left(a^2 - \frac{1}{3}r^2\right).$$

$$\int V(\mathbf{r})\left[\int \frac{1}{|\mathbf{r}-\mathbf{r}_0|}V(\mathbf{r}_0)\,d^3\mathbf{r}_0\right]d^3\mathbf{r} = V_0(2\pi V_0)4\pi\int_0^a\left(a^2-\frac{1}{3}r^2\right)r^2\,dr = 8\pi^2 V_0^2\left[a^2\frac{a^3}{3} - \frac{1}{3}\frac{a^5}{5}\right] = \frac{32}{15}\pi^2 V_0^2 a^5.$$

$$f(\theta) = -\frac{m}{2\pi\hbar^2}V_0\frac{4}{3}\pi a^3 + \left(\frac{m}{2\pi\hbar^2}\right)^2\frac{32}{15}\pi^2 V_0^2 a^5 = \boxed{-\left(\frac{2mV_0 a^3}{3\hbar^2}\right)\left[1 - \frac{4}{5}\left(\frac{mV_0 a^2}{\hbar^2}\right)\right].}$$

---

## Problem 11.16

$$\left(\frac{d^2}{dx^2} + k^2\right)G(x) = \delta(x) \quad \text{(analog to Eq. 11.52)}. \quad G(x) = \frac{1}{\sqrt{2\pi}}\int e^{isx}g(s)\,ds \quad \text{(analog to Eq. 11.54)}.$$

$$\left(\frac{d^2}{dx^2} + k^2\right) G = \frac{1}{\sqrt{2\pi}} \int (-s^2 + k^2) g(s) e^{isx} ds = \delta(x) = \frac{1}{2\pi} \int e^{isx} ds \implies g(s) = \frac{1}{\sqrt{2\pi}(k^2 - s^2)}.$$

$$G(x) = \frac{1}{2\pi} \int_{-\infty}^{\infty} \frac{e^{isx}}{k^2 - s^2} ds. \quad \text{Skirt the poles as in Fig. 11.10.} \quad \text{For } x > 0, \text{ close above:}$$

$$G(x) = -\frac{1}{2\pi} \oint \left(\frac{e^{isx}}{s+k}\right) \frac{1}{s-k} ds = -\frac{1}{2\pi} 2\pi i \left(\frac{e^{isx}}{s+k}\right)\Bigg|_{s=k} = -i \frac{e^{ikx}}{2k}. \quad \text{For} \quad x < 0, \text{ close below:}$$

$$G(x) = +\frac{1}{2\pi} \oint \left(\frac{e^{isx}}{s-k}\right) \frac{1}{s+k} ds = \frac{1}{2\pi} 2\pi i \left(\frac{e^{isx}}{s-k}\right)\Bigg|_{s=-k} = -i \frac{e^{-ikx}}{2k}.$$

In either case, then, $\boxed{G(x) = -\dfrac{i}{2k} e^{ik|x|}.}$ (Analog to Eq. 11.65.)

$$\psi(x) = G(x - x_0) \frac{2m}{\hbar^2} V(x_0) \psi(x_0) \, dx_0 = -\frac{i}{2k} \frac{2m}{\hbar^2} \int e^{ik|x - x_0|} V(x_0) \psi(x_0) \, dx_0,$$

plus any solution $\psi_0(x)$ to the homogeneous Schrödinger equation:

$$\left(\frac{d^2}{dx^2} + k^2\right) \psi_0(x) = 0. \quad \text{So:}$$

$$\boxed{\psi(x) = \psi_0(x) - \frac{im}{\hbar^2 k} \int_{-\infty}^{\infty} e^{ik|x - x_0|} V(x_0) \psi(x_0) \, dx_0.}$$

## Problem 11.17

For the Born approximation let $\psi_0(x) = A e^{ikx}$, and $\psi(x) \approx A e^{ikx}$.

$$\psi(x) \approx A \left[ e^{ikx} - \frac{im}{\hbar^2 k} \int_{-\infty}^{\infty} e^{ik|x - x_0|} V(x_0) e^{ikx_0} dx_0 \right]$$

$$= A \left[ e^{ikx} - \frac{im}{\hbar^2 k} \int_{-\infty}^{x} e^{ik(x - x_0)} V(x_0) e^{ikx_0} dx_0 - \frac{im}{\hbar^2 k} \int_{x}^{\infty} e^{ik(x_0 - x)} V(x_0) e^{ikx_0} dx_0 \right].$$

$$\boxed{\psi(x) = A \left[ e^{ikx} - \frac{im}{\hbar^2 k} e^{ikx} \int_{-\infty}^{x} V(x_0) \, dx_0 - \frac{im}{\hbar^2 k} e^{-ikx} \int_{x}^{\infty} e^{2ikx_0} V(x_0) \, dx_0 \right].}$$

Now assume $V(x)$ is localized; for large positive $x$, the third term is zero, and

$$\psi(x) = A e^{ikx} \left[ 1 - \frac{im}{\hbar^2 k} \int_{-\infty}^{\infty} V(x_0) \, dx_0 \right]. \quad \text{This is the transmitted wave.}$$

For large negative $x$ the middle term is zero:

$$\psi(x) = A \left[ e^{ikx} - \frac{im}{\hbar^2 k} e^{-ikx} \int_{-\infty}^{\infty} e^{2ikx_0} V(x_0) dx_0 \right].$$

Evidently the first term is the incident wave and the second the reflected wave:

$$\boxed{R = \left(\frac{m}{\hbar^2 k}\right)^2 \left|\int_{-\infty}^{\infty} e^{2ikx} V(x)\, dx\right|^2.}$$

If you try in the same spirit to calculate the transmission coefficient, you get

$$T = \left|1 - \frac{im}{\hbar^2 k}\int_{-\infty}^{\infty} V(x)dx\right|^2 = 1 + \left(\frac{m}{\hbar^2 k}\right)^2 \left[\int_{-\infty}^{\infty} V(x)dx\right]^2,$$

which is nonsense (greater than 1). The first Born approximation gets $R$ right, but all you can say to this order is $T \approx 1$ (you would do better using $T = 1 - R$).

---

## Problem 11.18

<u>Delta function:</u>    $V(x) = -\alpha\delta(x)$.    $\int_{-\infty}^{\infty} e^{2ikx} V(x)\, dx = -\alpha$,    so    $R = \left(\dfrac{m\alpha}{\hbar^2 k}\right)^2$,

or, in terms of energy ($k^2 = 2mE/\hbar^2$):

$$R = \frac{m^2\alpha^2}{2mE\hbar^2} = \frac{m\alpha^2}{2\hbar^2 E}; \quad T = 1 - R = \boxed{1 - \frac{m\alpha^2}{2\hbar^2 E}.}$$

The exact answer (Eq. 2.141) is $\dfrac{1}{1 + \frac{m\alpha^2}{2\hbar^2 E}} \approx 1 - \dfrac{m\alpha^2}{2\hbar^2 E}$,    so they agree provided $E \gg \dfrac{m\alpha}{2\hbar^2}$.

<u>Finite square well:</u>    $V(x) = \begin{cases} -V_0 & (-a < x < a) \\ 0 & (\text{otherwise}) \end{cases}$.

$$\int_{-\infty}^{\infty} e^{2ikx} V(x)\, dx = -V_0 \int_{-a}^{a} e^{2ikx} dx = -V_0 \left.\frac{e^{2ikx}}{2ik}\right|_{-a}^{a} = -\frac{V_0}{k}\left(\frac{e^{2ika} - e^{-2ika}}{2i}\right) = -\frac{V_0}{k}\sin(2ka).$$

So    $R = \left[\dfrac{m}{\hbar^2 k}\right]^2 \left(\dfrac{V_0}{k}\sin(2ka)\right)^2$.    $\boxed{T = 1 - \left[\dfrac{V_0}{2E}\sin\left(\dfrac{2a}{\hbar}\sqrt{2mE}\right)\right]^2.}$

If $E \gg V_0$, the exact answer (Eq. 2.169) becomes

$$T^{-1} \approx 1 + \left[\frac{V_0}{2E}\sin\left(\frac{2a}{\hbar}\sqrt{2mE}\right)\right]^2 \implies T \approx 1 - \left(\frac{V_0}{2E}\sin\left[\frac{2a}{\hbar}\sqrt{2mE}\right]\right)^2,$$

so they agree provided $E \gg V_0$.

---

## Problem 11.19

The Legendre polynomials satisfy $P_l(1) = 1$ (see footnote 30, p. 124), so Eq. 11.47 $\Rightarrow$

$$f(0) = \frac{1}{k}\sum_{l=0}^{\infty}(2l + 1)e^{i\delta_l}\sin\delta_l. \quad \text{Therefore} \quad \text{Im}[f(0)] = \frac{1}{k}\sum_{l=0}^{\infty}(2l + 1)\sin^2\delta_l,$$

and hence (Eq. 11.48):

$$\sigma = \frac{4\pi}{k}\text{Im}[f(0)]. \quad \text{QED}$$

---

## Problem 11.20

Using Eq. 11.88 and integration by parts:

$$f(\theta) = -\frac{2m}{\hbar^2 \kappa} \int_0^\infty r A e^{-\mu r^2} \sin(\kappa r)\, dr = -\frac{2mA}{\hbar^2 \kappa} \int_0^\infty \frac{d}{dr}\left(-\frac{1}{2\mu} e^{-\mu r^2}\right) \sin(\kappa r)\, dr$$

$$= \frac{2mA}{2\mu\hbar^2 \kappa}\left\{ e^{-\mu r^2} \sin(\kappa r)\Big|_0^\infty - \int_0^\infty e^{-\mu r^2} \frac{d}{dr}\left[\sin(\kappa r)\right]\, dr \right\}$$

$$= \frac{mA}{\mu\hbar^2 \kappa}\left\{ 0 - \kappa \int_0^\infty e^{-\mu r^2}\cos(\kappa r)\, dr \right\} = -\frac{mA}{\mu\hbar^2}\left(\frac{\sqrt{\pi}}{2\sqrt{\mu}} e^{-\kappa^2/4\mu}\right)$$

$$= -\frac{mA\sqrt{\pi}}{2\hbar^2 \mu^{3/2}} e^{-\kappa^2/4\mu}, \quad \text{where} \quad \kappa = 2k\sin(\theta/2) \quad \text{(Eq. 11.89)}.$$

From Eq. 11.14, then,

$$\frac{d\sigma}{d\Omega} = \frac{\pi m^2 A^2}{4\hbar^4 \mu^3} e^{-\kappa^2/2\mu},$$

and hence

$$\sigma = \int \frac{d\sigma}{d\Omega}\, d\Omega = \frac{\pi m^2 A^2}{4\hbar^4 \mu^3} \int e^{-4k^2 \sin^2(\theta/2)/2\mu} \sin\theta\, d\theta\, d\phi$$

$$= \frac{\pi^2 m^2 A^2}{2\hbar^4 \mu^3} \int_0^\pi e^{-2k^2 \sin^2(\theta/2)/\mu} \sin\theta\, d\theta; \quad \text{write } \sin\theta = 2\sin(\theta/2)\cos(\theta/2) \quad \text{and let } x \equiv \sin(\theta/2)$$

$$= \frac{\pi^2 m^2 A^2}{2\hbar^4 \mu^3} \int_0^1 e^{-2k^2 x^2/\mu} 2x\, 2\, dx = \frac{2\pi^2 m^2 A^2}{\hbar^4 \mu^3} \int_0^1 x e^{-2k^2 x^2/\mu}\, dx$$

$$= \frac{2\pi^2 m^2 A^2}{\hbar^4 \mu^3}\left[-\frac{\mu}{4k^2} e^{-2k^2 x^2/\mu}\right]\Big|_0^1 = -\frac{\pi^2 m^2 A^2}{2\hbar^4 \mu^2 k^2}\left(e^{-2k^2/\mu} - 1\right)$$

$$= \boxed{\frac{\pi^2 m^2 A^2}{2\hbar^4 \mu^2 k^2}\left(1 - e^{-2k^2/\mu}\right).}$$

# Chapter 12

# Afterword

## Problem 12.1

Suppose, on the contrary, that

$$\alpha|\phi_a(1)\rangle|\phi_b(2)\rangle + \beta|\phi_b(1)\rangle|\phi_a(2)\rangle = |\psi_r(1)\rangle|\psi_s(2)\rangle,$$

for some one-particle states $|\psi_r\rangle$ and $|\psi_s\rangle$. Because $|\phi_a\rangle$ and $|\phi_b\rangle$ constitute a complete set of one-particle states (this is a two-level system), any other one-particle state can be expressed as a linear combination of them. In particular,

$$|\psi_r\rangle = A|\phi_a\rangle + B|\phi_b\rangle, \quad \text{and} \quad |\psi_s\rangle = C|\phi_a\rangle + D|\phi_b\rangle,$$

for some complex numbers $A$, $B$, $C$, and $D$. Thus

$$\alpha|\phi_a(1)\rangle|\phi_b(2)\rangle + \beta|\phi_b(1)\rangle|\phi_a(2)\rangle = \big[A|\phi_a(1)\rangle + B|\phi_b(1)\rangle\big]\big[C|\phi_a(2)\rangle + D|\phi_b(2)\rangle\big]$$

$$= AC|\phi_a(1)\rangle|\phi_a(2)\rangle + AD|\phi_a(1)\rangle|\phi_b(2)\rangle + BC|\phi_b(1)\rangle|\phi_a(2)\rangle + BD|\phi_b(1)\rangle|\phi_b(2)\rangle.$$

(i)   Take the inner product with $\langle\phi_a(1)|\langle\phi_b(2)|$:   $\alpha = AD$.
(ii)   Take the inner product with $\langle\phi_a(1)|\langle\phi_a(2)|$:   $0 = AC$.
(iii)   Take the inner product with $\langle\phi_b(1)|\langle\phi_a(2)|$:   $\beta = BC$.
(iv)   Take the inner product with $\langle\phi_b(1)|\langle\phi_b(2)|$:   $0 = BD$.

(ii) $\Rightarrow$ either $A = 0$ or $C = 0$. But if $A = 0$, then (i) $\Rightarrow \alpha = 0$, which is excluded by assumption, whereas if $C = 0$, then (iii) $\Rightarrow \beta = 0$, which is likewise excluded. *Conclusion:* It is impossible to express this state as a product of one-particle states.   QED

---

# Appendix A

# Linear Algebra

## Problem A.1

(a) Yes; two-dimensional.

(b) No; the sum of two such vectors has $a_z = 2$, and is not in the subset. Also, the null vector (0,0,0) is not in the subset.

(c) Yes; one-dimensional.

---

## Problem A.2

(a) Yes; $1, x, x^2, \ldots, x^{N-1}$ is a convenient basis. Dimension: N.

(b) Yes; $1, x^2, x^4, \ldots.$ Dimension $N/2$ (if $N$ is even) or $(N+1)/2$ (if $N$ is odd).

(c) No. The sum of two such "vectors" is not in the space.

(d) Yes; $(x-1), (x-1)^2, (x-1)^3, \ldots, (x-1)^{N-1}.$ Dimension: $N-1.$

(e) No. The sum of two such "vectors" would have value 2 at $x = 0$.

---

## Problem A.3

Suppose $|\alpha\rangle = a_1|e_1\rangle + a_2|e_2\rangle + \cdots a_n|e_n\rangle$ and $|\alpha\rangle = b_1|e_1\rangle + b_2|e_2\rangle + \cdots + b_n|e_n\rangle$. Subtract: $0 = (a_1 - b_1)|e_1\rangle + (a_2 - b_2)|e_2\rangle + \cdots + (a_n - b_n)|e_n\rangle$. Suppose $a_j \neq b_j$ for some $j$; then we can divide by $(a_j - b_j)$ to get:

$$|e_j\rangle = -\frac{(a_1 - b_1)}{(a_j - b_j)}|e_1\rangle - \frac{(a_2 - b_2)}{(a_j - b_j)}|e_2\rangle - \cdots - 0|e_j\rangle - \cdots - \frac{(a_n - b_n)}{(a_j - b_j)}|e_n\rangle,$$

so $|e_j\rangle$ is linearly dependent on the others, and hence $\{|e_j\rangle\}$ is not a basis. If $\{|e_j\rangle\}$ *is* a basis, therefore, the components *must* all be equal $(a_1 = b_1, a_2 = b_2, \ldots, a_n = b_n)$.     QED

---

## Problem A.4

(i)

$$\langle e_1|e_1\rangle = |1+i|^2 + 1 + |i|^2 = (1+i)(1-i) + 1 + (i)(-i) = 1 + 1 + 1 + 1 = 4. \quad \|e_1\| = 2.$$

$$\boxed{|e_1'\rangle = \frac{1}{2}(1+i)\,\hat{i} + \frac{1}{2}\,\hat{j} + \frac{i}{2}\,\hat{k}.}$$

(ii)

$$\langle e_1'|e_2\rangle = \frac{1}{2}(1-i)(i) + \frac{1}{2}(3) + \left(\frac{-i}{2}\right)1 = \frac{1}{2}(i+1+3-i) = 2.$$

$$|e_2''\rangle \equiv |e_2\rangle - \langle e_1'|e_2\rangle|e_1'\rangle = (i-1-i)\hat{i} + (3-1)\hat{j} + (1-i)\hat{k} = (-1)\hat{i} + (2)\hat{j} + (1-i)\hat{k}.$$

$$\langle e_2''|e_2''\rangle = 1 + 4 + 2 = 7. \quad \boxed{|e_2'\rangle = \frac{1}{\sqrt{7}}[-\hat{i} + 2\hat{j} + (1-i)\hat{k}].}$$

(iii)

$$\langle e_1'|e_3\rangle = \frac{1}{2}28 = 14; \quad \langle e_2'|e_3\rangle = \frac{2}{\sqrt{7}}28 = 8\sqrt{7}.$$

$$|e_3''\rangle = |e_3\rangle - \langle e_1'|e_3\rangle|e_1'\rangle - \langle e_2'|e_3\rangle|e_2'\rangle = |e_3\rangle - 7|e_1\rangle - 8|e_2''\rangle$$
$$= (0 - 7 - 7i + 8)\hat{i} + (28 - 7 - 16)\hat{j} + (0 - 7i - 8 + 8i)\hat{k} = (1 - 7i)\hat{i} + 5\hat{j} + (-8+i)\hat{k}.$$

$$\|e_3''\|^2 = 1 + 49 + 25 + 64 + 1 = 140. \quad \boxed{|e_3'\rangle = \frac{1}{2\sqrt{35}}[(1-7i)\hat{i} + 5\hat{j} + (-8+i)\hat{k}].}$$

## Problem A.5

From Eq. A.21:    $\langle\gamma|\gamma\rangle = \langle\gamma|\left(|\beta\rangle - \frac{\langle\alpha|\beta\rangle}{\langle\alpha|\alpha\rangle}|\alpha\rangle\right) = \langle\gamma|\beta\rangle - \frac{\langle\alpha|\beta\rangle}{\langle\alpha|\alpha\rangle}\langle\gamma|\alpha\rangle.$    From Eq. A.19:

$$\langle\gamma|\beta\rangle^* = \langle\beta|\gamma\rangle = \langle\beta|\left(|\beta\rangle - \frac{\langle\alpha|\beta\rangle}{\langle\alpha|\alpha\rangle}|\alpha\rangle\right) = \langle\beta|\beta\rangle - \frac{\langle\alpha|\beta\rangle}{\langle\alpha|\alpha\rangle}\langle\beta|\alpha\rangle = \langle\beta|\beta\rangle - \frac{|\langle\alpha|\beta\rangle|^2}{\langle\alpha|\alpha\rangle}, \text{ which is } \textit{real.}$$

$$\langle\gamma|\alpha\rangle^* = \langle\alpha|\gamma\rangle = \langle\alpha|\left(|\beta\rangle - \frac{\langle\alpha|\beta\rangle}{\langle\alpha|\alpha\rangle}|\alpha\rangle\right) = \langle\alpha|\beta\rangle - \frac{\langle\alpha|\beta\rangle}{\langle\alpha|\alpha\rangle}\langle\alpha|\alpha\rangle = 0. \quad \langle\gamma|\alpha\rangle = 0. \quad \text{So (Eq. A.20):}$$

$$\langle\gamma|\gamma\rangle = \langle\beta|\beta\rangle - \frac{|\langle\alpha|\beta\rangle|^2}{\langle\alpha|\alpha\rangle} \geq 0, \text{ and hence } |\langle\alpha|\beta\rangle|^2 \leq \langle\alpha|\alpha\rangle\langle\beta|\beta\rangle. \quad \text{QED}$$

## Problem A.6

$$\langle\alpha|\beta\rangle = (1-i)(4-i) + (1)(0) + (-i)(2-2i) = 4 - 5i - 1 - 2i - 2 = 1 - 7i; \quad \langle\beta|\alpha\rangle = 1 + 7i;$$

$$\langle\alpha|\alpha\rangle = 1 + 1 + 1 + 1 = 4; \quad \langle\beta|\beta\rangle = 16 + 1 + 4 + 4 = 25; \quad \cos\theta = \sqrt{\frac{1+49}{4\cdot 25}} = \frac{1}{\sqrt{2}}; \quad \boxed{\theta = 45°.}$$

## Problem A.7

Let $\quad |\gamma\rangle \equiv |\alpha\rangle + |\beta\rangle; \quad \langle\gamma|\gamma\rangle = \langle\gamma|\alpha\rangle + \langle\gamma|\beta\rangle.$

$\langle\gamma|\alpha\rangle^* = \langle\alpha|\gamma\rangle = \langle\alpha|\alpha\rangle + \langle\alpha|\beta\rangle \Longrightarrow \langle\gamma|\alpha\rangle = \langle\alpha|\alpha\rangle + \langle\beta|\alpha\rangle.$

$\langle\gamma|\beta\rangle^* = \langle\beta|\gamma\rangle = \langle\beta|\alpha\rangle + \langle\beta|\beta\rangle \Longrightarrow \langle\gamma|\beta\rangle = \langle\alpha|\beta\rangle + \langle\beta|\beta\rangle.$

$\|(|\alpha\rangle + |\beta\rangle)\|^2 = \langle\gamma|\gamma\rangle = \langle\alpha|\alpha\rangle + \langle\beta|\beta\rangle + \langle\alpha|\beta\rangle + \langle\beta|\alpha\rangle.$

But $\quad \langle\alpha|\beta\rangle + \langle\beta|\alpha\rangle = 2\mathrm{Re}(\langle\alpha|\beta\rangle) \leq 2|\langle\alpha|\beta\rangle| \leq 2\sqrt{\langle\alpha|\alpha\rangle\langle\beta|\beta\rangle}$ (by Schwarz inequality), so $\|(|\alpha\rangle + |\beta\rangle)\|^2 \leq \|\alpha\|^2 + \|\beta\|^2 + 2\|\alpha\|\|\beta\| = (\|\alpha\| + \|\beta\|)^2$, and hence $\|(|\alpha\rangle + |\beta\rangle)\| \leq \|\alpha\| + \|\beta\|.$   QED

## Problem A.8

(a) $\boxed{\begin{pmatrix} 1 & 1 & 0 \\ 2 & 1 & 3 \\ 3i & (3-2i) & 4 \end{pmatrix}.}$

(b) $\begin{pmatrix} (-2+0-1) & (0+1+3i) & (i+0+2i) \\ (4+0+3i) & (0+0+9) & (-2i+0+6) \\ (4i+0+2i) & (0-2i+6) & (2+0+4) \end{pmatrix} = \boxed{\begin{pmatrix} -3 & (1+3i) & 3i \\ (4+3i) & 9 & (6-2i) \\ 6i & (6-2i) & 6 \end{pmatrix}.}$

(c) $\mathsf{BA} = \begin{pmatrix} (-2+0+2) & (2+0-2) & (2i+0-2i) \\ (0+2+0) & (0+0+0) & (0+3+0) \\ (-i+6+4i) & (i+0-4i) & (-1+9+4) \end{pmatrix} = \begin{pmatrix} 0 & 0 & 0 \\ 2 & 0 & 3 \\ (6+3i) & -3i & 12 \end{pmatrix}.$

$[\mathsf{A},\mathsf{B}] = \mathsf{AB} - \mathsf{BA} = \boxed{\begin{pmatrix} -3 & (1+3i) & 3i \\ (2+3i) & 9 & (3-2i) \\ (-6+3i) & (6+i) & -6 \end{pmatrix}.}$

(d) $\boxed{\begin{pmatrix} -1 & 2 & 2i \\ 1 & 0 & -2i \\ i & 3 & 2 \end{pmatrix}.}$

(e) $\boxed{\begin{pmatrix} -1 & 1 & -i \\ 2 & 0 & 3 \\ -2i & 2i & 2 \end{pmatrix}.}$

**(f)** $\boxed{\begin{pmatrix} -1 & 2 & -2i \\ 1 & 0 & 2i \\ -i & 3 & 2 \end{pmatrix}}.$

**(g)** $4 + 0 + 0 - 1 - 0 - 0 = \boxed{3.}$

**(h)**

$$\mathsf{B}^{-1} = \frac{1}{3}\tilde{\mathsf{C}}; \quad \mathsf{C} = \begin{pmatrix} \left|\begin{smallmatrix}1&0\\3&2\end{smallmatrix}\right| & -\left|\begin{smallmatrix}0&0\\i&2\end{smallmatrix}\right| & \left|\begin{smallmatrix}0&1\\i&3\end{smallmatrix}\right| \\ -\left|\begin{smallmatrix}0&-i\\3&2\end{smallmatrix}\right| & \left|\begin{smallmatrix}2&-i\\i&2\end{smallmatrix}\right| & -\left|\begin{smallmatrix}2&0\\i&3\end{smallmatrix}\right| \\ \left|\begin{smallmatrix}0&-i\\1&0\end{smallmatrix}\right| & -\left|\begin{smallmatrix}2&-i\\0&0\end{smallmatrix}\right| & \left|\begin{smallmatrix}2&0\\0&1\end{smallmatrix}\right| \end{pmatrix} = \begin{pmatrix} 2 & 0 & -i \\ -3i & 3 & -6 \\ i & 0 & 2 \end{pmatrix}. \quad \boxed{\mathsf{B}^{-1} = \frac{1}{3}\begin{pmatrix} 2 & -3i & i \\ 0 & 3 & 0 \\ -i & -6 & 2 \end{pmatrix}.}$$

$$\mathsf{B}\mathsf{B}^{-1} = \frac{1}{3}\begin{pmatrix} (4+0-1) & (-6i+0+6i) & (2i+0-2i) \\ (0+0+0) & (0+3+0) & (0+0+0) \\ (2i+0-2i) & (3+9-12) & (-1+0+4) \end{pmatrix} = \frac{1}{3}\begin{pmatrix} 3 & 0 & 0 \\ 0 & 3 & 0 \\ 0 & 0 & 3 \end{pmatrix} = \begin{pmatrix} 1 & 0 & 0 \\ 0 & 1 & 0 \\ 0 & 0 & 1 \end{pmatrix}. \quad \checkmark$$

$\det\mathsf{A} = 0 + 6i + 4 - 0 - 6i - 4 = 0.$  $\boxed{\text{No;}}$  A does *not* have an inverse.

---

## Problem A.9

**(a)**

$$\begin{pmatrix} -i+2i+2i \\ 2i+0+6 \\ -2+4+4 \end{pmatrix} = \boxed{\begin{pmatrix} 3i \\ 6+2i \\ 6 \end{pmatrix}.}$$

**(b)**

$$\begin{pmatrix} -i & -2i & 2 \end{pmatrix} \begin{pmatrix} 2 \\ 1-i \\ 0 \end{pmatrix} = -2i - 2i(1-i) + 0 = \boxed{-2-4i.}$$

**(c)**

$$\begin{pmatrix} i & 2i & 2 \end{pmatrix} \begin{pmatrix} 2 & 0 & -i \\ 0 & 1 & 0 \\ i & 3 & 2 \end{pmatrix} \begin{pmatrix} 2 \\ 1-i \\ 0 \end{pmatrix} = \begin{pmatrix} i & 2i & 2 \end{pmatrix} \begin{pmatrix} 4 \\ 1-i \\ 3-i \end{pmatrix} = 4i + 2i(1-i) + 2(3-i) = \boxed{8+4i.}$$

**(d)**

$$\begin{pmatrix} i \\ 2i \\ 2 \end{pmatrix} \begin{pmatrix} 2 & (1+i) & 0 \end{pmatrix} = \boxed{\begin{pmatrix} 2i & (-1+i) & 0 \\ 4i & (-2+2i) & 0 \\ 4 & (2+2i) & 0 \end{pmatrix}.}$$

---

## Problem A.10

(a) $\boxed{\mathsf{S} = \dfrac{1}{2}(\mathsf{T} + \tilde{\mathsf{T}});}$ $\boxed{\mathsf{A} = \dfrac{1}{2}(\mathsf{T} - \tilde{\mathsf{T}}).}$

(b) $\boxed{\mathsf{R} = \dfrac{1}{2}(\mathsf{T} + \mathsf{T}^*);}$ $\boxed{\mathsf{M} = \dfrac{1}{2}(\mathsf{T} - \mathsf{T}^*).}$

(c) $\boxed{\mathsf{H} = \dfrac{1}{2}(\mathsf{T} + \mathsf{T}^\dagger);}$ $\boxed{\mathsf{K} = \dfrac{1}{2}(\mathsf{T} - \mathsf{T}^\dagger).}$

## Problem A.11

$$(\widetilde{\mathsf{ST}})_{ki} = (\mathsf{ST})_{ik} = \sum_{j=1}^n S_{ij}T_{jk} = \sum_{j=1}^n \tilde{T}_{kj}\tilde{S}_{ji} = (\tilde{\mathsf{T}}\tilde{\mathsf{S}})_{ki} \Rightarrow \widetilde{\mathsf{ST}} = \tilde{\mathsf{T}}\tilde{\mathsf{S}}. \quad \text{QED}$$

$$(\mathsf{ST})^\dagger = (\widetilde{\mathsf{ST}})^* = (\tilde{\mathsf{T}}\tilde{\mathsf{S}})^* = \tilde{\mathsf{T}}^*\tilde{\mathsf{S}}^* = \mathsf{T}^\dagger\mathsf{S}^\dagger. \quad \text{QED}$$

$$(\mathsf{T}^{-1}\mathsf{S}^{-1})(\mathsf{ST}) = \mathsf{T}^{-1}(\mathsf{S}^{-1}\mathsf{S})\mathsf{T} = \mathsf{T}^{-1}\mathsf{T} = \mathsf{I} \Rightarrow (\mathsf{ST})^{-1} = \mathsf{T}^{-1}\mathsf{S}^{-1}. \quad \text{QED}$$

$$\mathsf{U}^\dagger = \mathsf{U}^{-1}, \; \mathsf{W}^\dagger = \mathsf{W}^{-1} \Rightarrow (\mathsf{WU})^\dagger = \mathsf{U}^\dagger\mathsf{W}^\dagger = \mathsf{U}^{-1}\mathsf{W}^{-1} = (\mathsf{WU})^{-1} \Rightarrow \mathsf{WU} \text{ is unitary.}$$

$$\mathsf{H} = \mathsf{H}^\dagger, \; \mathsf{J} = \mathsf{J}^\dagger \Rightarrow (\mathsf{HJ})^\dagger = \mathsf{J}^\dagger\mathsf{H}^\dagger = \mathsf{JH};$$

the product is hermitian $\Leftrightarrow$ this is HJ, i.e. $\Leftrightarrow$ $\boxed{[\mathsf{H}, \mathsf{J}] = 0}$ (they *commute*).

$$(\mathsf{U} + \mathsf{W})^\dagger = \mathsf{U}^\dagger + \mathsf{W}^\dagger = \mathsf{U}^{-1} + \mathsf{W}^{-1} \overset{?}{=} (\mathsf{U} + \mathsf{W})^{-1}. \quad \boxed{\text{No;}} \text{ the sum of two unitary matrices is } not \text{ unitary.}$$

$$(\mathsf{H} + \mathsf{J})^\dagger = \mathsf{H}^\dagger + \mathsf{J}^\dagger = \mathsf{H} + \mathsf{J}. \quad \boxed{\text{Yes;}} \text{ the sum of two hermitian matrices } is \text{ hermitian.}$$

## Problem A.12

$$\mathsf{U}^\dagger\mathsf{U} = \mathsf{I} \implies (\mathsf{U}^\dagger\mathsf{U})_{ik} = \delta_{ik} \implies \sum_{j=1}^n U_{ij}^\dagger U_{jk} = \sum_{j=1}^n U_{ji}^* U_{jk} = \delta_{ik}.$$

Construct the set of $n$ vectors $a^{(j)}{}_i \equiv U_{ij}$ ($a^{(j)}$ is the $j$-th column of U; its $i$-th component is $U_{ij}$). Then

$$\mathsf{a}^{(i)\dagger}\mathsf{a}^{(k)} = \sum_{j=1}^n a^{(i)}{}_j^* a^{(k)}{}_j = \sum_{j=1}^n U_{ji}^* U_{jk} = \delta_{ik},$$

so these vectors are orthonormal. Similarly,

$$\mathsf{UU}^\dagger = \mathsf{I} \implies (\mathsf{UU}^\dagger)_{ik} = \delta_{ik} \implies \sum_{j=1}^n U_{ij}U_{jk}^\dagger = \sum_{j=1}^n U_{kj}^* U_{ij} = \delta_{ki}.$$

This time let the vectors $\mathsf{b}^{(j)}$ be the *rows* of U: $b^{(j)}{}_i \equiv U_{ji}$. Then

$$\mathsf{b}^{(k)\dagger}\mathsf{b}^{(i)} = \sum_{j=1}^n b^{(k)}{}_j^* b^{(i)}{}_j = \sum_{j=1}^n U_{kj}^* U_{ij} = \delta_{ki},$$

so the rows are also orthonormal.

## Problem A.13

$H^\dagger = H$ (hermitian) $\Rightarrow \det H = \det(H^\dagger) = \det(\tilde{H}^*) = (\det \tilde{H})^* = (\det H)^* \Rightarrow \det H$ is real. ✓

$U^\dagger = U^{-1}$ (unitary) $\Rightarrow \det(UU^\dagger) = (\det U)(\det U^\dagger) = (\det U)(\det \tilde{U})^* = |\det U|^2 = \det I = 1$, so $\det U = 1$. ✓

$\tilde{S} = S^{-1}$ (orthogonal) $\Rightarrow \det(S\tilde{S}) = (\det S)(\det \tilde{S}) = (\det S)^2 = 1$, so $\det S = \pm 1$. ✓

---

## Problem A.14

(a)

$$\hat{i}' = \cos\theta\,\hat{i} + \sin\theta\,\hat{j}; \quad \hat{j}' = -\sin\theta\,\hat{i} + \cos\theta\,\hat{j}; \quad \hat{k}' = \hat{k}. \quad T_a = \begin{pmatrix} \cos\theta & -\sin\theta & 0 \\ \sin\theta & \cos\theta & 0 \\ 0 & 0 & 1 \end{pmatrix}.$$

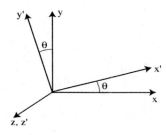

(b)

$$\hat{i}' = \hat{j}; \quad \hat{j}' = \hat{k}; \quad \hat{k}' = \hat{i}. \quad T_b = \begin{pmatrix} 0 & 0 & 1 \\ 1 & 0 & 0 \\ 0 & 1 & 0 \end{pmatrix}.$$

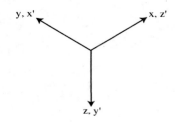

(c)

$$\hat{i}' = \hat{i}; \quad \hat{j}' = \hat{j}; \quad \hat{k}' = -\hat{k}. \quad T_c = \begin{pmatrix} 1 & 0 & 0 \\ 0 & 1 & 0 \\ 0 & 0 & -1 \end{pmatrix}.$$

**(d)**

$$\tilde{\mathsf{T}}_a\mathsf{T}_a = \begin{pmatrix} \cos\theta & \sin\theta & 0 \\ -\sin\theta & \cos\theta & 0 \\ 0 & 0 & 1 \end{pmatrix}\begin{pmatrix} \cos\theta & -\sin\theta & 0 \\ \sin\theta & \cos\theta & 0 \\ 0 & 0 & 1 \end{pmatrix} = \begin{pmatrix} 1 & 0 & 0 \\ 0 & 1 & 0 \\ 0 & 0 & 1 \end{pmatrix}. \quad \checkmark$$

$$\tilde{\mathsf{T}}_b\mathsf{T}_b = \begin{pmatrix} 0 & 1 & 0 \\ 0 & 0 & 1 \\ 1 & 0 & 0 \end{pmatrix}\begin{pmatrix} 0 & 0 & 1 \\ 1 & 0 & 0 \\ 0 & 1 & 0 \end{pmatrix} = \begin{pmatrix} 1 & 0 & 0 \\ 0 & 1 & 0 \\ 0 & 0 & 1 \end{pmatrix}. \quad \checkmark \qquad \tilde{\mathsf{T}}_c\mathsf{T}_c = \begin{pmatrix} 1 & 0 & 0 \\ 0 & 1 & 0 \\ 0 & 0 & -1 \end{pmatrix}\begin{pmatrix} 1 & 0 & 0 \\ 0 & 1 & 0 \\ 0 & 0 & -1 \end{pmatrix} = \begin{pmatrix} 1 & 0 & 0 \\ 0 & 1 & 0 \\ 0 & 0 & 1 \end{pmatrix}. \quad \checkmark$$

$$\det\mathsf{T}_a = \cos^2\theta + \sin^2\theta = \boxed{1.} \quad \det\mathsf{T}_b = \boxed{1.} \quad \det\mathsf{T}_c = \boxed{-1.}$$

---

## Problem A.15

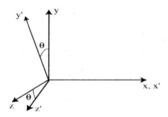

$$\hat{i}' = \hat{i}; \quad \hat{j}' = \cos\theta\,\hat{j} + \sin\theta\,\hat{k}; \quad \hat{k}' = \cos\theta\,\hat{k} - \sin\theta\,\hat{j}. \quad \boxed{\mathsf{T}_x(\theta) = \begin{pmatrix} 1 & 0 & 0 \\ 0 & \cos\theta & -\sin\theta \\ 0 & \sin\theta & \cos\theta \end{pmatrix}.}$$

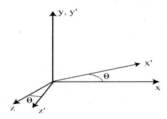

$$\hat{i}' = \cos\theta\,\hat{i} - \sin\theta\,\hat{k}; \quad \hat{j}' = \hat{j}; \quad \hat{k}' = \cos\theta\,\hat{k} + \sin\theta\,\hat{i}. \quad \boxed{\mathsf{T}_y(\theta) = \begin{pmatrix} \cos\theta & 0 & \sin\theta \\ 0 & 1 & 0 \\ -\sin\theta & 0 & \cos\theta \end{pmatrix}.}$$

$$\hat{i}' = \hat{j}; \quad \hat{j}' = -\hat{i}; \quad \hat{k}' = \hat{k}. \quad \boxed{\mathsf{S} = \begin{pmatrix} 0 & -1 & 0 \\ 1 & 0 & 0 \\ 0 & 0 & 1 \end{pmatrix}.} \quad \mathsf{S}^{-1} = \begin{pmatrix} 0 & 1 & 0 \\ -1 & 0 & 0 \\ 0 & 0 & 1 \end{pmatrix}.$$

$$ST_xS^{-1} = \begin{pmatrix} 0 & -1 & 0 \\ 1 & 0 & 0 \\ 0 & 0 & 1 \end{pmatrix} \begin{pmatrix} 1 & 0 & 0 \\ 0 & \cos\theta & -\sin\theta \\ 0 & \sin\theta & \cos\theta \end{pmatrix} \begin{pmatrix} 0 & 1 & 0 \\ -1 & 0 & 0 \\ 0 & 0 & 1 \end{pmatrix}$$

$$= \begin{pmatrix} 0 & -1 & 0 \\ 1 & 0 & 0 \\ 0 & 0 & 1 \end{pmatrix} \begin{pmatrix} 0 & 1 & 0 \\ -\cos\theta & 0 & -\sin\theta \\ -\sin\theta & 0 & \cos\theta \end{pmatrix} = \begin{pmatrix} \cos\theta & 0 & \sin\theta \\ 0 & 1 & 0 \\ -\sin\theta & 0 & \cos\theta \end{pmatrix} = T_y(\theta).$$

$$ST_yS^{-1} = \begin{pmatrix} 0 & -1 & 0 \\ 1 & 0 & 0 \\ 0 & 0 & 1 \end{pmatrix} \begin{pmatrix} \cos\theta & 0 & \sin\theta \\ 0 & 1 & 0 \\ -\sin\theta & 0 & \cos\theta \end{pmatrix} \begin{pmatrix} 0 & 1 & 0 \\ -1 & 0 & 0 \\ 0 & 0 & 1 \end{pmatrix}$$

$$= \begin{pmatrix} 0 & -1 & 0 \\ 1 & 0 & 0 \\ 0 & 0 & 1 \end{pmatrix} \begin{pmatrix} 0 & \cos\theta & \sin\theta \\ -1 & 0 & 0 \\ 0 & -\sin\theta & \cos\theta \end{pmatrix} = \begin{pmatrix} 1 & 0 & 0 \\ 0 & \cos\theta & \sin\theta \\ 0 & -\sin\theta & \cos\theta \end{pmatrix} = T_x(-\theta).$$

Is this what we would expect? Yes, for rotation about the $x$ axis now means rotation about the $y$ axis, and rotation about the $y$ axis has become rotation about the $-x$ axis—which is to say, rotation in the opposite direction about the $+x$ axis.

---

## Problem A.16

From Eq. A.64 we have

$$A^fB^f = SA^eS^{-1}SB^eS^{-1} = S(A^eB^e)S^{-1} = SC^eS^{-1} = C^f. \quad \checkmark$$

Suppose $S^\dagger = S^{-1}$ and $H^e = H^{e\dagger}$ (S unitary, $H^e$ hermitian). Then

$$H^{f\dagger} = (SH^eS^{-1})^\dagger = (S^{-1})^\dagger H^{e\dagger}S^\dagger = SH^eS^{-1} = H^f, \text{ so } H^f \text{ is hermitian.} \quad \checkmark$$

In an orthonormal basis, $\langle\alpha|\beta\rangle = a^\dagger b$ (Eq. A.50). So if $\{|f_i\rangle\}$ is orthonormal, $\langle\alpha|\beta\rangle = a^{f\dagger}b^f$. But $b^f = Sb^e$ (Eq. A.63), and also $a^{f\dagger} = a^{e\dagger}S^\dagger$. So $\langle\alpha|\beta\rangle = a^{e\dagger}S^\dagger Sb^e$. This is equal to $a^{e\dagger}b^e$ (and hence $\{|e_i\rangle\}$ is also orthonormal), for all vectors $|\alpha\rangle$ and $|\beta\rangle \Leftrightarrow S^\dagger S = I$, i.e. S is unitary.

---

## Problem A.17

$$\text{Tr}(T_1T_2) = \sum_{i=1}^{n}(T_1T_2)_{ii} = \sum_{i=1}^{n}\sum_{j=1}^{n}(T_1)_{ij}(T_2)_{ji} = \sum_{j=1}^{n}\sum_{i=1}^{n}(T_2)_{ji}(T_1)_{ij} = \sum_{j=1}^{n}(T_2T_1)_{jj} = \text{Tr}(T_2T_1).$$

Is $\text{Tr}(T_1T_2T_3) = \text{Tr}(T_2T_1T_3)$? $\boxed{\text{No.}}$ Counterexample:

$$T_1 = \begin{pmatrix} 0 & 1 \\ 0 & 0 \end{pmatrix}, \quad T_2 = \begin{pmatrix} 0 & 0 \\ 1 & 0 \end{pmatrix}, \quad T_3 = \begin{pmatrix} 1 & 0 \\ 0 & 0 \end{pmatrix}.$$

$$T_1T_2T_3 = \begin{pmatrix} 0 & 1 \\ 0 & 0 \end{pmatrix}\begin{pmatrix} 0 & 0 \\ 1 & 0 \end{pmatrix}\begin{pmatrix} 1 & 0 \\ 0 & 0 \end{pmatrix} = \begin{pmatrix} 0 & 1 \\ 0 & 0 \end{pmatrix}\begin{pmatrix} 0 & 0 \\ 1 & 0 \end{pmatrix} = \begin{pmatrix} 1 & 0 \\ 0 & 0 \end{pmatrix} \implies \text{Tr}(T_1T_2T_3) = 1.$$

$$T_2T_1T_3 = \begin{pmatrix} 0 & 0 \\ 1 & 0 \end{pmatrix}\begin{pmatrix} 0 & 1 \\ 0 & 0 \end{pmatrix}\begin{pmatrix} 1 & 0 \\ 0 & 0 \end{pmatrix} = \begin{pmatrix} 0 & 0 \\ 1 & 0 \end{pmatrix}\begin{pmatrix} 0 & 0 \\ 1 & 0 \end{pmatrix} = \begin{pmatrix} 0 & 0 \\ 0 & 0 \end{pmatrix} \implies \text{Tr}(T_2T_1T_3) = 0.$$

---

# Problem A.18

*Eigenvalues:*

$$\begin{vmatrix} (\cos\theta - \lambda) & -\sin\theta \\ \sin\theta & (\cos\theta - \lambda) \end{vmatrix} = (\cos\theta - \lambda)^2 + \sin^2\theta = \cos^2\theta - 2\lambda\cos\theta + \lambda^2 + \sin^2\theta = 0, \text{ or } \lambda^2 - 2\lambda\cos\theta + 1 = 0.$$

$$\lambda = \frac{2\cos\theta \pm \sqrt{4\cos^2\theta - 4}}{2} = \cos\theta \pm \sqrt{-\sin^2\theta} = \cos\theta \pm i\sin\theta = \boxed{e^{\pm i\theta}.}$$

So there are two eigenvalues, both of them complex. Only if $\sin\theta = 0$ does this matrix possess *real* eigenvalues, i.e., only if $\boxed{\theta = 0 \text{ or } \pi.}$

*Eigenvectors:*

$$\begin{pmatrix} \cos\theta & -\sin\theta \\ \sin\theta & \cos\theta \end{pmatrix} \begin{pmatrix} \alpha \\ \beta \end{pmatrix} = e^{\pm i\theta} \begin{pmatrix} \alpha \\ \beta \end{pmatrix} \implies \cos\theta\,\alpha - \sin\theta\,\beta = (\cos\theta \pm i\sin\theta)\alpha \Rightarrow \beta = \mp i\alpha. \quad \text{Normalizing:}$$

$$\boxed{\mathsf{a}^{(1)} = \frac{1}{\sqrt{2}}\begin{pmatrix} 1 \\ -i \end{pmatrix}; \quad \mathsf{a}^{(2)} = \frac{1}{\sqrt{2}}\begin{pmatrix} 1 \\ i \end{pmatrix}.}$$

*Diagonalization:*

$$(\mathsf{S}^{-1})_{11} = a_1^{(1)} = \frac{1}{\sqrt{2}}; \quad (\mathsf{S}^{-1})_{12} = a_1^{(2)} = \frac{1}{\sqrt{2}}; \quad (\mathsf{S}^{-1})_{21} = a_2^{(1)} = \frac{-i}{\sqrt{2}}; \quad (\mathsf{S}^{-1})_{22} = a_2^{(2)} = \frac{i}{\sqrt{2}}.$$

$$\mathsf{S}^{-1} = \frac{1}{\sqrt{2}}\begin{pmatrix} 1 & 1 \\ -i & i \end{pmatrix}; \quad \text{inverting:} \quad \mathsf{S} = \frac{1}{\sqrt{2}}\begin{pmatrix} 1 & i \\ 1 & -i \end{pmatrix}.$$

$$\mathsf{STS}^{-1} = \frac{1}{2}\begin{pmatrix} 1 & i \\ 1 & -i \end{pmatrix}\begin{pmatrix} \cos\theta & -\sin\theta \\ \sin\theta & \cos\theta \end{pmatrix}\begin{pmatrix} 1 & 1 \\ -i & i \end{pmatrix} = \frac{1}{2}\begin{pmatrix} 1 & i \\ 1 & -i \end{pmatrix}\begin{pmatrix} (\cos\theta + i\sin\theta) & (\cos\theta - i\sin\theta) \\ (\sin\theta - i\cos\theta) & (\sin\theta + i\cos\theta) \end{pmatrix}$$

$$= \frac{1}{2}\begin{pmatrix} 1 & i \\ 1 & -i \end{pmatrix}\begin{pmatrix} e^{i\theta} & e^{-i\theta} \\ -ie^{i\theta} & ie^{-i\theta} \end{pmatrix} = \frac{1}{2}\begin{pmatrix} 2e^{i\theta} & 0 \\ 0 & 2e^{-i\theta} \end{pmatrix} = \begin{pmatrix} e^{i\theta} & 0 \\ 0 & e^{-i\theta} \end{pmatrix}. \quad \checkmark$$

---

# Problem A.19

$$\begin{vmatrix} (1 - \lambda) & 1 \\ 0 & (1 - \lambda) \end{vmatrix} = (1 - \lambda)^2 = 0 \implies \boxed{\lambda = 1} \quad \text{(only one eigenvalue)}.$$

$$\begin{pmatrix} 1 & 1 \\ 0 & 1 \end{pmatrix}\begin{pmatrix} \alpha \\ \beta \end{pmatrix} = \begin{pmatrix} \alpha \\ \beta \end{pmatrix} \implies \alpha + \beta = \alpha \implies \beta = 0; \quad \boxed{\mathsf{a} = \begin{pmatrix} 1 \\ 0 \end{pmatrix}}$$

(only one eigenvector—up to an arbitrary constant factor). Since the eigenvectors do not span the space, this matrix $\boxed{\text{cannot be diagonalized.}}$ [If it *could* be diagonalized, the diagonal form would have to be $\begin{pmatrix} 1 & 0 \\ 0 & 1 \end{pmatrix}$, since the only eigenvalue is 1. But in that case $\mathsf{I} = \mathsf{SMS}^{-1}$. Multiplying from the left by $\mathsf{S}^{-1}$ and on the right by $\mathsf{S}$ : $\mathsf{S}^{-1}\mathsf{IS} = \mathsf{S}^{-1}\mathsf{SMS}^{-1}\mathsf{S} = \mathsf{M}$. But $\mathsf{S}^{-1}\mathsf{IS} = \mathsf{S}^{-1}\mathsf{S} = \mathsf{I}$. So $\mathsf{M} = \mathsf{I}$, which is false.]

---

## Problem A.20

Expand the determinant (Eq. A.72) by minors, using the first column:

$$\det(\mathsf{T} - \lambda 1) = (T_{11} - \lambda) \begin{vmatrix} (T_{22} - \lambda) & \cdots & & \cdots \\ \vdots & \ddots & \\ \vdots & & (T_{nn} - \lambda) \end{vmatrix} + \sum_{j=2}^{n} T_{j1} \text{ cofactor}(T_{j1}).$$

But the cofactor of $T_{j1}$ (for $j > 1$) is missing *two* of the original diagonal elements: $(T_{11} - \lambda)$ (from the first column), and $(T_{jj} - \lambda)$ (from the $j$-th row). So its highest power of $\lambda$ will be $(n - 2)$. Thus terms in $\lambda^n$ and $\lambda^{n-1}$ come exclusively from the first term above. Indeed, the same argument applied now to the cofactor of $(T_{11} - \lambda)$ – and repeated as we expand *that* determinant – shows that *only the product of the diagonal elements* contributes to $\lambda^n$ and $\lambda^{n-1}$:

$$(T_{11} - \lambda)(T_{22} - \lambda) \cdots (T_{nn} - \lambda) = (-\lambda)^n + (-\lambda)^{n-1}(T_{11} + T_{22} + \cdots + T_{nn}) + \cdots$$

Evidently then, $C_n = (-1)^n$, and $C_{n-1} = (-1)^{n-1} \text{Tr}(\mathsf{T})$. To get $C_0$ – the term with *no* factors of $\lambda$ – we simply set $\lambda = 0$. Thus $C_0 = \det(\mathsf{T})$. For a $3 \times 3$ matrix:

$$\begin{vmatrix} (T_{11} - \lambda) & T_{12} & T_{13} \\ T_{21} & (T_{22} - \lambda) & T_{23} \\ T_{31} & T_{32} & (T_{33} - \lambda) \end{vmatrix}$$

$$= (T_{11} - \lambda)(T_{22} - \lambda)(T_{33} - \lambda) + T_{12}T_{23}T_{31} + T_{13}T_{21}T_{32}$$
$$\quad - T_{31}T_{13}(T_{22} - \lambda) - T_{32}T_{23}(T_{11} - \lambda) - T_{12}T_{21}(T_{33} - \lambda)$$
$$= -\lambda^3 + \lambda^2(T_{11} + T_{22} + T_{33}) - \lambda(T_{11}T_{22} + T_{11}T_{33} + T_{22}T_{33}) + \lambda(T_{13}T_{31} + T_{23}T_{32} + T_{12}T_{21})$$
$$\quad + T_{11}T_{22}T_{33} + T_{12}T_{23}T_{31} + T_{13}T_{21}T_{32} - T_{31}T_{13}T_{22} - T_{32}T_{23}T_{11} - T_{12}T_{21}T_{33}$$
$$= -\lambda^3 + \lambda^2 \text{Tr}(\mathsf{T}) + \lambda C_1 + \det(\mathsf{T}), \quad \text{with}$$

$$\boxed{C_1 = (T_{13}T_{31} + T_{23}T_{32} + T_{12}T_{21}) - (T_{11}T_{22} + T_{11}T_{33} + T_{22}T_{33}).}$$

---

## Problem A.21

The characteristic equation is an $n$-th order polynomial, which can be factored in terms of its $n$ (complex) roots:

$$(\lambda_1 - \lambda)(\lambda_2 - \lambda) \cdots (\lambda_n - \lambda) = (-\lambda)^n + (-\lambda)^{n-1}(\lambda_1 + \lambda_2 + \cdots + \lambda_n) + \cdots + (\lambda_1 \lambda_2 \cdots \lambda_n) = 0.$$

Comparing Eq. A.84, it follows that $\text{Tr}(\mathsf{T}) = \lambda_1 + \lambda_2 + \cdots \lambda_n$ and $\det(\mathsf{T}) = \lambda_1 \lambda_2 \cdots \lambda_n$.   QED

---

## Problem A.22

(a)

$$[\mathsf{T}_1^f, \mathsf{T}_2^f] = \mathsf{T}_1^f \mathsf{T}_2^f - \mathsf{T}_2^f \mathsf{T}_1^f = \mathsf{S}\mathsf{T}_1^e \mathsf{S}^{-1} \mathsf{S}\mathsf{T}_2^e \mathsf{S}^{-1} - \mathsf{S}\mathsf{T}_2^e \mathsf{S}^{-1} \mathsf{S}\mathsf{T}_1^e \mathsf{S}^{-1} = \mathsf{S}\mathsf{T}_1^e \mathsf{T}_2^e \mathsf{S}^{-1} - \mathsf{S}\mathsf{T}_2^e \mathsf{T}_1^e \mathsf{S}^{-1} = \mathsf{S}[\mathsf{T}_1^e, \mathsf{T}_2^e]\mathsf{S}^{-1} = 0. \quad \checkmark$$

**(b)** Suppose $SAS^{-1} = D$ and $SBS^{-1} = E$, where D and E are *diagonal*:

$$D = \begin{pmatrix} d_1 & 0 & \cdots & 0 \\ 0 & d_2 & \cdots & 0 \\ \vdots & & \ddots & \vdots \\ 0 & 0 & \cdots & d_n \end{pmatrix}, \quad E = \begin{pmatrix} e_1 & 0 & \cdots & 0 \\ 0 & e_2 & \cdots & 0 \\ \vdots & & \ddots & \vdots \\ 0 & 0 & \cdots & e_n \end{pmatrix}.$$

Then

$$[A, B] = AB - BA = (S^{-1}DS)(S^{-1}ES) - (S^{-1}ES)(S^{-1}DS) = S^{-1}DES - S^{-1}EDS = S^{-1}[D, E]S.$$

But *diagonal* matrices *always* commute:

$$DE = \begin{pmatrix} d_1 e_1 & 0 & \cdots & 0 \\ 0 & d_2 e_2 & \cdots & 0 \\ \vdots & & \ddots & \vdots \\ 0 & 0 & \cdots & d_n e_n \end{pmatrix} = ED,$$

so   $[A, B] = 0$.   QED

---

## Problem A.23

**(a)**

$$M^\dagger = \begin{pmatrix} 1 & 1 \\ 1 & -i \end{pmatrix}; \quad MM^\dagger = \begin{pmatrix} 2 & (1-i) \\ (1+i) & 2 \end{pmatrix}, \quad M^\dagger M = \begin{pmatrix} 2 & (1+i) \\ (1-i) & 2 \end{pmatrix}; \quad [M, M^\dagger] = \begin{pmatrix} 0 & -2i \\ 2i & 0 \end{pmatrix} \neq 0. \quad \boxed{\text{No.}}$$

**(b)** Find the eigenvalues:

$$\begin{vmatrix} (1-\lambda) & 1 \\ 1 & (i-\lambda) \end{vmatrix} = (1-\lambda)(i-\lambda) - 1 = i - \lambda(1+i) + \lambda^2 - 1 = 0;$$

$$\lambda = \frac{(1+i) \pm \sqrt{(1+i)^2 - 4(i-1)}}{2} = \frac{(1+i) \pm \sqrt{4-2i}}{2}.$$

Since there are two distinct eigenvalues, there must be two linearly independent eigenvectors, and that's enough to span the space. So $\boxed{\text{this matrix } is \text{ diagonalizable,}}$ even though it is not normal.

---

## Problem A.24

Let $|\gamma\rangle = |\alpha\rangle + c|\beta\rangle$, for some complex number $c$. Then

$$\langle\gamma|\hat{T}\gamma\rangle = \langle\alpha|\hat{T}\alpha\rangle + c\langle\alpha|\hat{T}\beta\rangle + c^*\langle\beta|\hat{T}\alpha\rangle + |c|^2\langle\beta|\hat{T}\beta\rangle, \text{ and}$$

$$\langle\hat{T}\gamma|\gamma\rangle = \langle\hat{T}\alpha|\alpha\rangle + c^*\langle\hat{T}\beta|\alpha\rangle + c\langle\hat{T}\alpha|\beta\rangle + |c|^2\langle\hat{T}\beta|\beta\rangle.$$

Suppose $\langle\hat{T}\gamma|\gamma\rangle = \langle\gamma|\hat{T}\gamma\rangle$ for *all* vectors. For instance, $\langle\hat{T}\alpha|\alpha\rangle = \langle\alpha|\hat{T}\alpha\rangle$ and $\langle\hat{T}\beta|\beta\rangle = \langle\beta|\hat{T}\beta\rangle$), so

$$c\langle\alpha|\hat{T}\beta\rangle + c^*\langle\beta|\hat{T}\alpha\rangle = c\langle\hat{T}\alpha|\beta\rangle + c^*\langle\hat{T}\beta|\alpha\rangle, \text{ and this holds for } any \text{ complex number} \quad c.$$

In particular, for $c = 1$: $\langle\alpha|\hat{T}\beta\rangle + \langle\beta|\hat{T}\alpha\rangle = \langle\hat{T}\alpha|\beta\rangle + \langle\hat{T}\beta|\alpha\rangle$, while for $c = i$: $\langle\alpha|\hat{T}\beta\rangle - \langle\beta|\hat{T}\alpha\rangle = \langle\hat{T}\alpha|\beta\rangle - \langle\hat{T}\beta|\alpha\rangle$. (I canceled the $i$'s). Adding: $\langle\alpha|\hat{T}\beta\rangle = \langle\hat{T}\alpha|\beta\rangle$.   QED

---

## Problem A.25

**(a)**

$$\mathsf{T}^\dagger = \tilde{\mathsf{T}}^* = \begin{pmatrix} 1 & 1-i \\ 1+i & 0 \end{pmatrix} = \mathsf{T}. \quad \checkmark$$

**(b)**

$$\begin{vmatrix} (1-\lambda) & (1-i) \\ (1+i) & (0-\lambda) \end{vmatrix} = -(1-\lambda)\lambda - 1 - 1 = 0; \quad \lambda^2 - \lambda - 2 = 0; \quad \lambda = \frac{1 \pm \sqrt{1+8}}{2} = \frac{1 \pm 3}{2}. \quad \boxed{\lambda_1 = 2, \ \lambda_2 = -1.}$$

**(c)**

$$\begin{pmatrix} 1 & (1-i) \\ (1+i) & 0 \end{pmatrix} \begin{pmatrix} \alpha \\ \beta \end{pmatrix} = 2 \begin{pmatrix} \alpha \\ \beta \end{pmatrix} \Longrightarrow \alpha + (1-i)\beta = 2\alpha \Longrightarrow \alpha = (1-i)\beta.$$

$$|\alpha|^2 + |\beta|^2 = 1 \Longrightarrow 2|\beta|^2 + |\beta|^2 = 1 \Longrightarrow \beta = \frac{1}{\sqrt{3}}. \quad \boxed{\mathsf{a}^{(1)} = \frac{1}{\sqrt{3}} \begin{pmatrix} 1-i \\ 1 \end{pmatrix}.}$$

$$\begin{pmatrix} 1 & (1-i) \\ (1+i) & 0 \end{pmatrix} \begin{pmatrix} \alpha \\ \beta \end{pmatrix} = - \begin{pmatrix} \alpha \\ \beta \end{pmatrix} \Longrightarrow \alpha + (1-i)\beta = -\alpha; \quad \alpha = -\frac{1}{2}(1-i)\beta.$$

$$\frac{1}{4} 2|\beta|^2 + |\beta|^2 = 1 \Longrightarrow \frac{3}{2}|\beta|^2 = 1; \quad \beta = \sqrt{\frac{2}{3}}. \quad \boxed{\mathsf{a}^{(2)} = \frac{1}{\sqrt{6}} \begin{pmatrix} i-1 \\ 2 \end{pmatrix}.}$$

$$\mathsf{a}^{(1)\dagger}\mathsf{a}^{(2)} = \frac{1}{3\sqrt{2}} \left( (1+i) \ 1 \right) \begin{pmatrix} (i-1) \\ 2 \end{pmatrix} = \frac{1}{3\sqrt{2}}(i - 1 - 1 - i + 2) = 0. \quad \checkmark$$

**(d)**

$$\text{Eq. A.81} \Longrightarrow (\mathsf{S}^{-1})_{11} = a_1^{(1)} = \frac{1}{\sqrt{3}}(1-i); \quad (\mathsf{S}^{-1})_{12} = a_1^{(2)} = \frac{1}{\sqrt{6}}(i-1);$$

$$(\mathsf{S}^{-1})_{21} = a_2^{(1)} = \frac{1}{\sqrt{3}}; \quad (\mathsf{S}^{-1})_{22} = a_2^{(2)} = \frac{2}{\sqrt{6}}.$$

$$\mathsf{S}^{-1} = \frac{1}{\sqrt{3}} \begin{pmatrix} (1-i) & (i-1)/\sqrt{2} \\ 1 & \sqrt{2} \end{pmatrix}; \quad \mathsf{S} = (\mathsf{S}^{-1})^\dagger = \frac{1}{\sqrt{3}} \begin{pmatrix} (1+i) & 1 \\ (-i-1)/\sqrt{2} & \sqrt{2} \end{pmatrix}.$$

$$\mathsf{STS}^{-1} = \frac{1}{3} \begin{pmatrix} (1+i) & 1 \\ -(1+i)/\sqrt{2} & \sqrt{2} \end{pmatrix} \begin{pmatrix} 1 & (1-i) \\ (1+i) & 0 \end{pmatrix} \begin{pmatrix} (1-i) & (i-1)/\sqrt{2} \\ 1 & \sqrt{2} \end{pmatrix}$$

$$= \frac{1}{3} \begin{pmatrix} (1+i) & 1 \\ -(1+i)/\sqrt{2} & \sqrt{2} \end{pmatrix} \begin{pmatrix} 2(1-i) & (1-i)/\sqrt{2} \\ 2 & -\sqrt{2} \end{pmatrix} = \frac{1}{3} \begin{pmatrix} 6 & 0 \\ 0 & -3 \end{pmatrix} = \begin{pmatrix} 2 & 0 \\ 0 & -1 \end{pmatrix}. \quad \checkmark$$

**(e)**

$$\boxed{\text{Tr}(\mathsf{T}) = 1;} \quad \det(\mathsf{T}) = 0 - (1+i)(1-i) = \boxed{-2.} \quad \text{Tr}(\mathsf{STS}^{-1}) = 2 - 1 = 1. \quad \checkmark \quad \det(\mathsf{STS}^{-1}) = -2. \quad \checkmark$$

## Problem A.26

**(a)**

$$\det(\mathsf{T}) = 8 - 1 - 1 - 2 - 2 - 2 = \boxed{0.} \quad \text{Tr}(\mathsf{T}) = 2 + 2 + 2 = \boxed{6.}$$

**(b)**

$$\begin{vmatrix} (2-\lambda) & i & 1 \\ -i & (2-\lambda) & i \\ 1 & -i & (2-\lambda) \end{vmatrix} = (2-\lambda)^3 - 1 - 1 - (2-\lambda) - (2-\lambda) - (2-\lambda) = 8 - 12\lambda + 6\lambda^2 - \lambda^3 - 8 + 3\lambda = 0.$$

$$-\lambda^3 + 6\lambda^2 - 9\lambda = -\lambda(\lambda^2 - 6\lambda + 9) = -\lambda(\lambda - 3)^2 = 0. \quad \boxed{\lambda_1 = 0, \ \lambda_2 = \lambda_3 = 3.}$$

$$\lambda_1 + \lambda_2 + \lambda_3 = 6 = \text{Tr}(\mathsf{T}). \quad \checkmark \quad \lambda_1\lambda_2\lambda_3 = 0 = \det(\mathsf{T}). \quad \checkmark \quad \text{Diagonal form:} \quad \boxed{\begin{pmatrix} 0 & 0 & 0 \\ 0 & 3 & 0 \\ 0 & 0 & 3 \end{pmatrix}.}$$

**(c)**

$$\begin{pmatrix} 2 & i & 1 \\ -i & 2 & i \\ 1 & -i & 2 \end{pmatrix} \begin{pmatrix} \alpha \\ \beta \\ \gamma \end{pmatrix} = 0 \implies \begin{cases} 2\alpha + i\beta + \gamma = 0 \\ -i\alpha + 2\beta + i\gamma = 0 \implies \alpha + 2i\beta - \gamma = 0 \end{cases}.$$

Add the two equations: $3\alpha + 3i\beta = 0 \implies \beta = i\alpha; \quad 2\alpha - \alpha + \gamma = 0 \implies \gamma = -\alpha.$

$$\mathsf{a}^{(1)} = \begin{pmatrix} \alpha \\ i\alpha \\ -\alpha \end{pmatrix}. \quad \text{Normalizing:} \ |\alpha|^2 + |\alpha|^2 + |\alpha|^2 = 1 \implies \alpha = \frac{1}{\sqrt{3}}. \quad \boxed{\mathsf{a}^{(1)} = \frac{1}{\sqrt{3}} \begin{pmatrix} 1 \\ i \\ -1 \end{pmatrix}.}$$

$$\begin{pmatrix} 2 & i & 1 \\ -i & 2 & i \\ 1 & -i & 2 \end{pmatrix} \begin{pmatrix} \alpha \\ \beta \\ \gamma \end{pmatrix} = 3 \begin{pmatrix} \alpha \\ \beta \\ \gamma \end{pmatrix} \implies \begin{cases} 2\alpha + i\beta + \gamma = 3\alpha & \implies -\alpha + i\beta + \gamma = 0, \\ -i\alpha + 2\beta + i\gamma = 3\beta & \implies \alpha - i\beta - \gamma = 0, \\ \alpha - i\beta + 2\gamma = 3\gamma & \implies \alpha - i\beta - \gamma = 0. \end{cases}$$

The three equations are redundant – there is only *one* condition here: $\alpha - i\beta - \gamma = 0$. We could pick $\gamma = 0, \ \beta = -i\alpha$, or $\beta = 0, \ \gamma = \alpha$. Then

$$\mathsf{a}_0^{(2)} = \begin{pmatrix} \alpha \\ -i\alpha \\ 0 \end{pmatrix}; \quad \mathsf{a}_0^{(3)} = \begin{pmatrix} \alpha \\ 0 \\ \alpha \end{pmatrix}.$$

But these are not orthogonal, so we use the Gram-Schmidt procedure (Problem A.4); first normalize $\mathsf{a}_0^{(2)}$:

$$\boxed{\mathsf{a}^{(2)} = \frac{1}{\sqrt{2}} \begin{pmatrix} 1 \\ -i \\ 0 \end{pmatrix}.}$$

$$\mathsf{a}^{(2)\dagger}\mathsf{a}_0^{(3)} = \frac{\alpha}{\sqrt{2}} \begin{pmatrix} 1 & i & 0 \end{pmatrix} \begin{pmatrix} 1 \\ 0 \\ 1 \end{pmatrix} = \frac{\alpha}{\sqrt{2}}. \quad \text{So} \quad \mathsf{a}_0^{(3)} - (\mathsf{a}^{(2)\dagger}\mathsf{a}_0^{(3)})\mathsf{a}^{(2)} = \alpha \begin{pmatrix} 1 \\ 0 \\ 1 \end{pmatrix} - \frac{\alpha}{2} \begin{pmatrix} 1 \\ -i \\ 0 \end{pmatrix} = \alpha \begin{pmatrix} 1/2 \\ i/2 \\ 1 \end{pmatrix}.$$

Normalize:     $|\alpha|^2 \left( \dfrac{1}{4} + \dfrac{1}{4} + 1 \right) = \dfrac{3}{2}|\alpha|^2 = 1 \implies \alpha = \sqrt{\dfrac{2}{3}}.$ $\boxed{a^{(3)} = \dfrac{1}{\sqrt{6}} \begin{pmatrix} 1 \\ i \\ 2 \end{pmatrix}.}$

Check orthogonality:

$$a^{(1)\dagger} a^{(2)} = \frac{1}{\sqrt{6}}\,(1 \ -i \ -1) \begin{pmatrix} 1 \\ -i \\ 0 \end{pmatrix} = \frac{1}{\sqrt{6}}(1 - 1 + 0) = 0. \ \checkmark$$

$$a^{(1)\dagger} a^{(3)} = \frac{1}{3\sqrt{2}}\,(1 \ -i \ -1) \begin{pmatrix} 1 \\ i \\ 2 \end{pmatrix} = \frac{1}{3\sqrt{2}}(1 + 1 - 2) = 0. \ \checkmark$$

**(d)** $S^{-1}$ is the matrix whose columns are the eigenvectors of $T$ (Eq. A.81):

$$S^{-1} = \frac{1}{\sqrt{6}} \begin{pmatrix} \sqrt{2} & \sqrt{3} & 1 \\ \sqrt{2}\,i & -\sqrt{3}\,i & i \\ -\sqrt{2} & 0 & 2 \end{pmatrix}; \quad S = (S^{-1})^{\dagger} = \boxed{\frac{1}{\sqrt{6}} \begin{pmatrix} \sqrt{2} & -\sqrt{2}\,i & -\sqrt{2} \\ \sqrt{3} & \sqrt{3}\,i & 0 \\ 1 & -i & 2 \end{pmatrix}.}$$

$$STS^{-1} = \frac{1}{6} \begin{pmatrix} \sqrt{2} & -\sqrt{2}\,i & -\sqrt{2} \\ \sqrt{3} & \sqrt{3}\,i & 0 \\ 1 & -i & 2 \end{pmatrix} \underbrace{\begin{pmatrix} 2 & i & 1 \\ -i & 2 & i \\ 1 & -i & 2 \end{pmatrix} \begin{pmatrix} \sqrt{2} & \sqrt{3} & 1 \\ \sqrt{2}\,i & -\sqrt{3}\,i & i \\ -\sqrt{2} & 0 & 2 \end{pmatrix}}_{\begin{pmatrix} 0 & 3\sqrt{3} & 3 \\ 0 & -3\sqrt{3}\,i & 3i \\ 0 & 0 & 6 \end{pmatrix}} = \frac{1}{6}\begin{pmatrix} 0 & 0 & 0 \\ 0 & 18 & 0 \\ 0 & 0 & 18 \end{pmatrix} = \begin{pmatrix} 0 & 0 & 0 \\ 0 & 3 & 0 \\ 0 & 0 & 3 \end{pmatrix}. \ \checkmark$$

---

## Problem A.27

**(a)** $\langle \hat{U}\alpha | \hat{U}\beta \rangle = \langle \hat{U}^{\dagger}\hat{U}\alpha | \beta \rangle = \langle \alpha | \beta \rangle. \ \checkmark$

**(b)** $\hat{U}|\alpha\rangle = \lambda|\alpha\rangle \implies \langle \hat{U}\alpha | \hat{U}\alpha \rangle = |\lambda|^2 \langle \alpha | \alpha \rangle.$   But from (a) this is also $\langle \alpha | \alpha \rangle.$   So $|\lambda| = 1. \ \checkmark$

**(c)** $\hat{U}|\alpha\rangle = \lambda|\alpha\rangle, \ \hat{U}|\beta\rangle = \mu|\beta\rangle \implies |\beta\rangle = \mu\hat{U}^{-1}|\beta\rangle,$ so $\hat{U}^{\dagger}|\beta\rangle = \dfrac{1}{\mu}|\beta\rangle = \mu^*|\beta\rangle$   (from (b)).

$\langle \beta | \hat{U}\alpha \rangle = \lambda\langle \beta | \alpha \rangle = \langle \hat{U}^{\dagger}\beta | \alpha \rangle = \mu\langle \beta | \alpha \rangle,$ or $(\lambda - \mu)\langle \beta | \alpha \rangle = 0.$   So if $\lambda \neq \mu,$ then $\langle \beta | \alpha \rangle = 0.$   QED

---

## Problem A.28

**(a) (i)**

$$M^2 = \begin{pmatrix} 0 & 0 & 4 \\ 0 & 0 & 0 \\ 0 & 0 & 0 \end{pmatrix}; \quad M^3 = \begin{pmatrix} 0 & 0 & 0 \\ 0 & 0 & 0 \\ 0 & 0 & 0 \end{pmatrix}, \quad \text{so}$$

$$e^{\mathsf{M}} = \begin{pmatrix} 1 & 0 & 0 \\ 0 & 1 & 0 \\ 0 & 0 & 1 \end{pmatrix} + \begin{pmatrix} 0 & 1 & 3 \\ 0 & 0 & 4 \\ 0 & 0 & 0 \end{pmatrix} + \frac{1}{2}\begin{pmatrix} 0 & 0 & 4 \\ 0 & 0 & 0 \\ 0 & 0 & 0 \end{pmatrix} = \boxed{\begin{pmatrix} 1 & 1 & 5 \\ 0 & 1 & 4 \\ 0 & 0 & 1 \end{pmatrix}}.$$

**(ii)**

$$\mathsf{M}^2 = \begin{pmatrix} -\theta^2 & 0 \\ 0 & -\theta^2 \end{pmatrix} = -\theta^2\mathsf{I}; \quad \mathsf{M}^3 = -\theta^3\mathsf{M}; \quad \mathsf{M}^4 = \theta^4\mathsf{I}; \quad \text{etc.}$$

$$\begin{aligned} e^{\mathsf{M}} &= \mathsf{I} + \theta\begin{pmatrix} 0 & 1 \\ -1 & 0 \end{pmatrix} - \frac{1}{2}\theta^2\mathsf{I} - \frac{\theta^3}{3!}\begin{pmatrix} 0 & 1 \\ -1 & 0 \end{pmatrix} + \frac{\theta^4}{4!}\mathsf{I} + \cdots \\ &= \left(1 - \frac{\theta^2}{2} + \frac{\theta^4}{4!} - \cdots\right)\mathsf{I} + \left(\theta - \frac{\theta^3}{3!} + \frac{\theta^5}{5!} - \cdots\right)\begin{pmatrix} 0 & 1 \\ -1 & 0 \end{pmatrix} \\ &= \cos\theta\begin{pmatrix} 1 & 0 \\ 0 & 1 \end{pmatrix} + \sin\theta\begin{pmatrix} 0 & 1 \\ -1 & 0 \end{pmatrix} = \boxed{\begin{pmatrix} \cos\theta & \sin\theta \\ -\sin\theta & \cos\theta \end{pmatrix}}. \end{aligned}$$

**(b)**

$$\mathsf{S}\mathsf{M}\mathsf{S}^{-1} = \mathsf{D} = \begin{pmatrix} d_1 & & 0 \\ & \ddots & \\ 0 & & d_n \end{pmatrix} \quad \text{for some } \mathsf{S}.$$

$$\mathsf{S}e^{\mathsf{M}}\mathsf{S}^{-1} = \mathsf{S}\left(\mathsf{I} + \mathsf{M} + \frac{1}{2}\mathsf{M}^2 + \frac{1}{3!}\mathsf{M}^3 + \cdots\right)\mathsf{S}^{-1}. \quad \text{Insert } \mathsf{S}\mathsf{S}^{-1} = \mathsf{I}:$$

$$\begin{aligned} \mathsf{S}e^{\mathsf{M}}\mathsf{S}^{-1} &= \mathsf{I} + \mathsf{S}\mathsf{M}\mathsf{S}^{-1} + \frac{1}{2}\mathsf{S}\mathsf{M}\mathsf{S}^{-1}\mathsf{S}\mathsf{M}\mathsf{S}^{-1} + \frac{1}{3!}\mathsf{S}\mathsf{M}\mathsf{S}^{-1}\mathsf{S}\mathsf{M}\mathsf{S}^{-1}\mathsf{S}\mathsf{M}\mathsf{S}^{-1} + \cdots \\ &= \mathsf{I} + \mathsf{D} + \frac{1}{2}\mathsf{D}^2 + \frac{1}{3!}\mathsf{D}^3 + \cdots = e^{\mathsf{D}}. \quad \text{Evidently} \end{aligned}$$

$$\det(e^{\mathsf{D}}) = \det(\mathsf{S}e^{\mathsf{M}}\mathsf{S}^{-1}) = \det(\mathsf{S})\det(e^{\mathsf{M}})\det(\mathsf{S}^{-1}) = \det(e^{\mathsf{M}}). \quad \text{But}$$

$$\mathsf{D}^2 = \begin{pmatrix} d_1^2 & & 0 \\ & \ddots & \\ 0 & & d_n^2 \end{pmatrix}, \quad \mathsf{D}^3 = \begin{pmatrix} d_1^3 & & 0 \\ & \ddots & \\ 0 & & d_n^3 \end{pmatrix}, \quad \mathsf{D}^k = \begin{pmatrix} d_1^k & & 0 \\ & \ddots & \\ 0 & & d_n^k \end{pmatrix}, \quad \text{so}$$

$$e^{\mathsf{D}} = \mathsf{I} + \begin{pmatrix} d_1 & & 0 \\ & \ddots & \\ 0 & & d_n \end{pmatrix} + \frac{1}{2}\begin{pmatrix} d_1^2 & & 0 \\ & \ddots & \\ 0 & & d_n^2 \end{pmatrix} + \frac{1}{3!}\begin{pmatrix} d_1^3 & & 0 \\ & \ddots & \\ 0 & & d_n^3 \end{pmatrix} + \cdots = \begin{pmatrix} e^{d_1} & & 0 \\ & \ddots & \\ 0 & & e^{d_n} \end{pmatrix}.$$

$$\det(e^{\mathsf{D}}) = e^{d_1}e^{d_2}\cdots e^{d_n} = e^{(d_1 + d_2 + \cdots d_n)} = e^{\operatorname{Tr}\mathsf{D}} = e^{\operatorname{Tr}\mathsf{M}} \text{ (Eq. A.68), so } \det(e^{\mathsf{M}}) = e^{\operatorname{Tr}\mathsf{M}}. \quad \text{QED}$$

**(c)** Matrices that *commute* obey the same algebraic rules as ordinary *numbers*, so the standard proofs of $e^{x+y} = e^x e^y$ will do the job. Here are two:

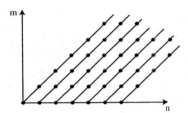

**(i)** <u>Combinatorial Method:</u> Use the binomial theorem (valid if multiplication is commutative):

$$e^{M+N} = \sum_{n=0}^{\infty} \frac{1}{n!}(M+N)^n = \sum_{n=0}^{\infty} \frac{1}{n!} \sum_{m=0}^{n} \binom{n}{m} M^m N^{n-m} = \sum_{n=0}^{\infty} \sum_{m=0}^{n} \frac{1}{m!(n-m)!} M^m N^{n-m}.$$

Instead of summing *vertically* first, for fixed $n$ $(m : 0 \to n)$, sum *horizontally* first, for fixed $m$ $(n : m \to \infty,$ or $k \equiv n - m : 0 \to \infty)$—see diagram (each dot represents a term in the double sum).

$$e^{M+N} = \sum_{m=0}^{\infty} \frac{1}{m!} M^m \sum_{k=0}^{\infty} \frac{1}{k!} N^k = e^M e^N. \quad \text{QED}$$

**(ii)** <u>Analytic Method:</u> Let

$$S(\lambda) \equiv e^{\lambda M} e^{\lambda N}; \quad \frac{dS}{d\lambda} = M e^{\lambda M} e^{\lambda N} + e^{\lambda M} N e^{\lambda N} = (M+N) e^{\lambda M} e^{\lambda N} = (M+N)S.$$

(The second equality, in which we pull $N$ through $e^{\lambda M}$, would not hold if $M$ and $N$ did not commute.) Solving the differential equation: $S(\lambda) = A e^{(M+N)\lambda}$, for some constant $A$. But $S(0) = I$, so $A = 1$, and hence $e^{\lambda M} e^{\lambda N} = e^{\lambda(M+N)}$, and (setting $\lambda = 1$) we conclude that $e^M e^N = e^{(M+N)}$. [This method generalizes most easily when $M$ and $N$ do *not* commute—leading to the famous Baker-Campbell-Hausdorf lemma.]

As a counterexample when $[M, N] \neq 0$, let $M = \begin{pmatrix} 0 & 1 \\ 0 & 0 \end{pmatrix}$, $N = \begin{pmatrix} 0 & 0 \\ -1 & 0 \end{pmatrix}$. Then $M^2 = N^2 = 0$, so

$$e^M = I + M = \begin{pmatrix} 1 & 1 \\ 0 & 1 \end{pmatrix}, \quad e^N = I + N = \begin{pmatrix} 1 & 0 \\ -1 & 1 \end{pmatrix}; \quad e^M e^N = \begin{pmatrix} 1 & 1 \\ 0 & 1 \end{pmatrix} \begin{pmatrix} 1 & 0 \\ -1 & 1 \end{pmatrix} = \begin{pmatrix} 0 & 1 \\ -1 & 1 \end{pmatrix}.$$

But $(M+N) = \begin{pmatrix} 0 & 1 \\ -1 & 0 \end{pmatrix}$, so (from a(ii)): $e^{M+N} = \begin{pmatrix} \cos(1) & \sin(1) \\ -\sin(1) & \cos(1) \end{pmatrix}$.

The two are clearly not equal.

**(d)**

$$e^{iH} = \sum_{n=0}^{\infty} \frac{1}{n!} i^n H^n \implies (e^{iH})^\dagger = \sum_{n=0}^{\infty} \frac{1}{n!} (-i)^n (H^\dagger)^n = \sum_{n=0}^{\infty} \frac{1}{n!} (-i)^n H^n = e^{-iH} \quad \text{(for H hermitian).}$$

$$(e^{iH})^\dagger (e^{iH}) = e^{-iH} e^{iH} = e^{i(H-H)} = I, \text{ using (c). So } e^{iH} \text{ is unitary.} \quad \checkmark$$

## 2ⁿᵈ Edition – 1ˢᵗ Edition Problem Correlation Grid

**N = New**
**M = 1/e problem number (modified for 2/e)**
**X = 2/e problem number (unchanged from 1/e)**

| Chapter 1 | | | Chapter 2 | | | Chapter 2 (cont.) | |
|:---:|:---:|---|:---:|:---:|---|:---:|:---:|
| **2/e** | **1/e** | | **2/e** | **1/e** | | **2/e** | **1/e** |
| 1 | 1 | | 1 | 1 | | 45 | 42 |
| 2N | | | 2 | 2 | | 46 | 43 |
| 3 | 6 | | 3 | 3 | | 47 | 44 |
| 4 | 7 | | 4 | 5 | | 48N | |
| 5 | 8 | | 5 | 6M | | 49 | 45 |
| 6 | 11 | | 6 | 7 | | 50 | 47 |
| 7 | 12 | | 7N | | | 51 | 48M |
| 8 | 13 | | 8N | | | 52 | 34M, 35M |
| 9 | 14 | | 9N | | | 53 | 49 |
| 10 | 2 | | 10 | 13M | | 54N | |
| 11 | 3 | | 11 | 14 | | 55N | |
| 12 | 4 | | 12 | 37 | | 56N | |
| 13 | 5 | | 13 | 17M | | | |
| 14 | 9M | | 14N | | | | |
| 15 | 10 | | 15 | 15 | | | |
| 16N | | | 16 | 16 | | | |
| 17N | | | 17 | 18 | | | |
| 18N | | | 18 | 19M | | | |
| | | | 19N | | | | |
| | | | 20 | 20 | | | |
| | | | 21N | | | | |
| | | | 22 | 22 | | | |
| | | | 23 | 23 | | | |
| | | | 24 | 24 | | | |
| | | | 25N | | | | |
| | | | 26 | 25 | | | |
| | | | 27 | 26 | | | |
| | | | 28 | 27 | | | |
| | | | 29 | 28 | | | |
| | | | 30 | 29 | | | |
| | | | 31 | 30 | | | |
| | | | 32 | 31 | | | |
| | | | 33 | 32 | | | |
| | | | 34 | 33 | | | |
| | | | 35 | 41M | | | |
| | | | 36 | 4M | | | |
| | | | 37 | 36 | | | |
| | | | 38 | 3.48 | | | |
| | | | 39N | | | | |
| | | | 40N | | | | |
| | | | 41N | | | | |
| | | | 42 | 38 | | | |
| | | | 43 | 40 | | | |
| | | | 44 | 39 | | | |

**2nd Edition – 1st Edition Problem Correlation Grid**

N = New
M = 1/e problem number (modified for 2/e)
(M) = 1/e problem number (distant model for 2/e)
X = 2/e problem number (unchanged from 1/e)

| Chapter 3 | | | Chapter 4 | | | Chapter 4 (cont.) | |
|---|---|---|---|---|---|---|---|
| 2/e | 1/e | | 2/e | 1/e | | 2/e | 1/e |
| 1N | | | 1 | 1 | | 43 | 43 |
| 2N | (33M) | | 2 | 2 | | 44N | |
| 3N | (21M) | | 3 | 3 | | 45 | 14 |
| 4N | (12M) | | 4 | 4 | | 46 | 15 |
| 5N | | | 5 | 5 | | 47N | |
| 6N | | | 6 | 6 | | 48N | |
| 7N | | | 7 | 7M | | 49N | |
| 8N | | | 8 | 8 | | 50 | 44 |
| 9N | | | 9 | 9M | | 51 | 45M |
| 10N | | | 10 | 10 | | 52 | 46 |
| 11 | 38 | | 11 | 11 | | 53N | |
| 12 | 51 | | 12 | 12 | | 54 | 47 |
| 13 | 41M | | 13 | 13 | | 55 | 48 |
| 14 | 39 | | 14N | | | 56 | 49 |
| 15N | | | 15N | | | 57 | 50 |
| 16 | 42 | | 16 | 17 | | 58N | |
| 17 | 43 | | 17 | 16 | | 59 | 51 |
| 18 | 44 | | 18 | 19 | | 60 | 52M |
| 19 | 45 | | 19 | 20 | | 61 | 53 |
| 20 | 46 | | 20 | 21 | | | |
| 21 | 57M | | 21N | | | | |
| 22N | | | 22 | 22 | | | |
| 23N | | | 23 | 23 | | | |
| 24 | 57M | | 24 | 25 | | | |
| 25 | 25M | | 25 | 26 | | | |
| 26N | | | 26 | 27 | | | |
| 27N | | | 27 | 28 | | | |
| 28 | 52M | | 28 | 29 | | | |
| 29N | | | 29 | 30 | | | |
| 30N | | | 30 | 31M | | | |
| 31 | 53 | | 31 | 32 | | | |
| 32 | 56 | | 32 | 33 | | | |
| 33 | 50 | | 33 | 34 | | | |
| 34 | 49M | | 34 | 35 | | | |
| 35N | | | 35 | 36 | | | |
| 36N | | | 36 | 37 | | | |
| 37N | | | 37 | 38 | | | |
| 38N | | | 38 | 39 | | | |
| 39 | 55 | | 39 | 40 | | | |
| 40N | | | 40 | 41 | | | |
| | | | 41N | | | | |
| | | | 42 | 42 | | | |

## 2nd Edition – 1st Edition Problem Correlation Grid

N = New
M = 1/e problem number (modified for 2/e)
X = 2/e problem number (unchanged from 1/e)

| Chapter 5 | | | Chapter 6 | | | Chapter 7 | |
|---|---|---|---|---|---|---|---|
| 2/e | 1/e | | 2/e | 1/e | | 2/e | 1/e |
| 1 | 1 | | 1 | 1M | | 1 | 1 |
| 2 | 2 | | 2 | 2 | | 2 | 2M |
| 3N | | | 3 | 3 | | 3 | 3M |
| 4 | 3 | | 4 | 4 | | 4 | 4 |
| 5 | 4 | | 5 | 5 | | 5 | 5 |
| 6 | 5 | | 6 | 6 | | 6 | 6 |
| 7 | 6 | | 7 | 7 | | 7 | 7 |
| 8 | 7 | | 8 | 8 | | 8 | 8 |
| 9 | 8 | | 9 | 9 | | 9 | 9 |
| 10 | 9 | | 10N | | | 10 | 10 |
| 11 | 10 | | 11 | 10 | | 11N | |
| 12 | 11M | | 12 | 11 | | 12N | |
| 13 | 11M | | 13 | 12 | | 13 | 11 |
| 14 | 12 | | 14 | 13 | | 14 | 12 |
| 15N | | | 15N | | | 15 | 13 |
| 16 | 13 | | 16 | 14 | | 16 | 14 |
| 17 | 14 | | 17 | 15 | | 17 | 15 |
| 18 | 15M | | 18 | 16 | | 18 | 16 |
| 19 | 16M | | 19 | 17 | | 19 | 17 |
| 20 | 17M | | 20 | 18 | | 20N | |
| 21 | 18 | | 21 | 19 | | | |
| 22 | 19M | | 22 | 20 | | | |
| 23 | 20 | | 23 | 21 | | | |
| 24 | 21M | | 24 | 22 | | | |
| 25 | 22 | | 25 | 23 | | | |
| 26 | 23 | | 26 | 24 | | | |
| 27 | 24 | | 27 | 25 | | | |
| 28 | 25 | | 28 | 26 | | | |
| 29 | 26 | | 29N | | | | |
| 30 | 27M | | 30N | | | | |
| 31 | 28 | | 31N | | | | |
| 32N | | | 32 | 27 | | | |
| 33 | 29 | | 33 | 28 | | | |
| 34 | 30 | | 34 | 29 | | | |
| 35 | 31 | | 35 | 30 | | | |
| 36 | 32 | | 36 | 31 | | | |
| 37 | 33 | | 37 | 32 | | | |
| | | | 38 | 33 | | | |
| | | | 39 | 34 | | | |
| | | | 40N | | | | |

**2nd Edition – 1st Edition Problem Correlation Grid**

N = New
M = 1/e problem number (modified for 2/e)
X = 2/e problem number (unchanged from 1/e)

| Chapter 8 | | | Chapter 9 | | | Chapter 10 | |
|---|---|---|---|---|---|---|---|
| 2/e | 1/e | | 2/e | 1/e | | 2/e | 1/e |
| 1 | 1 | | 1 | 1 | | 1 | 1 |
| 2 | 2 | | 2 | 2 | | 2 | 3M |
| 3 | 3 | | 3 | 3M | | 3 | 4 |
| 4 | 4 | | 4 | 4 | | 4 | 5 |
| 5 | 5 | | 5 | 5 | | 5 | 6 |
| 6 | 6 | | 6 | 6 | | 6 | 8 |
| 7 | 7 | | 7 | 7 | | 7 | 9 |
| 8 | 8 | | 8 | 8 | | 8N | |
| 9 | 9 | | 9N | | | 9 | 10 |
| 10 | 10 | | 10 | 9 | | 10 | 11M |
| 11 | 11 | | 11 | 10 | | | |
| 12 | 12 | | 12 | 11 | | | |
| 13 | 13 | | 13 | 12 | | | |
| 14 | 14 | | 14 | 13 | | | |
| 15 | 15 | | 15 | 14 | | | |
| 16N | | | 16 | 15 | | | |
| 17N | | | 17 | 16 | | | |
| | | | 18 | 17 | | | |
| | | | 19 | 21 | | | |
| | | | 20 | 19M | | | |
| | | | 21 | 20 | | | |
| | | | 22N | | | | |

# 2nd Edition – 1st Edition Problem Correlation Grid

N = New
M = 1/e problem number (modified for 2/e)
X = 2/e problem number (unchanged from 1/e)

| Chapter 11 | | | | Chapter 12 | | | | Appendix | |
|---|---|---|---|---|---|---|---|---|---|
| 2/e | 1/e | | | 2/e | 1/e | | | 2/e | 1/e |
| 1 | 1 | | | 1N | | | | 1 | 3.1 |
| 2 | 2 | | | | | | | 2 | 3.2 |
| 3 | 3 | | | | | | | 3 | 3.3 |
| 4 | 4 | | | | | | | 4 | 3.4 |
| 5N | | | | | | | | 5 | 3.5 |
| 6N | | | | | | | | 6 | 3.6 |
| 7N | | | | | | | | 7 | 3.7 |
| 8 | 5 | | | | | | | 8 | 3.9 |
| 9 | 6 | | | | | | | 9 | 3.10. |
| 10 | 7 | | | | | | | 10 | 3.11 |
| 11 | 8 | | | | | | | 11 | 3.12 |
| 12 | 9 | | | | | | | 12 | 3.16 |
| 13 | 10 | | | | | | | 13N | |
| 14 | 11 | | | | | | | 14N | |
| 15 | 12 | | | | | | | 15 | 3.13 |
| 16 | 13 | | | | | | | 16 | 3.14 |
| 17 | 14 | | | | | | | 17 | 3.15 |
| 18 | 15 | | | | | | | 18 | 3.17 |
| 19N | | | | | | | | 19 | 3.18 |
| 20N | | | | | | | | 20 | 3.19 |
| | | | | | | | | 21 | 3.20. |
| | | | | | | | | 22 | 3.40M |
| | | | | | | | | 23N | |
| | | | | | | | | 24 | 3.21M |
| | | | | | | | | 25 | 3.22 |
| | | | | | | | | 26 | 3.23 |
| | | | | | | | | 27 | 3.24 |
| | | | | | | | | 28 | 3.47 |